Earth

View of Mt. Whitney from the east side of the Sierra Nevada, a range of fault-block mountains produced by forces related to plate movements in Cenozoic time. [Photo by Robert Ishi.]

Earth

SECOND EDITION

FRANK PRESS
MASSACHUSETTS INSTITUTE OF TECHNOLOGY

RAYMOND SIEVER
HARVARD UNIVERSITY

W. H. FREEMAN AND COMPANY
San Francisco

Library of Congress Cataloging in Publication Data

Press, Frank.
 Earth.

 Bibliography: p.
 Includes index.
 1. Physical geology. I. Siever, Raymond, joint
author. II. Title.
QE28.2.P7 1978   550   77-25209
ISBN 0-7167-0289-4

Printed in the United States of America

9 8 7 6 5 4

To Billie and Doris

CONTENTS

PREFACE

TO THE STUDENT

This book is intended for beginning students who have had no previous college science courses and who may not necessarily intend to specialize in geology. For this reason, we have deliberately emphasized a broad view, one that stresses concepts and shows by many examples how science is actually done. Through the use of analogies to familiar processes, the use of "kitchen physics" and "kitchen chemistry" in explanations, and the use of many diagrammatic illustrations, we try to show the evidential bases of geological theories and the strong dependence of geology on the basic scientific disciplines of physics and chemistry. The organic world plays an important role in many geological processes, and thus we introduce some notions of biological processes where appropriate. Yet first and foremost, the book is about geological processes.

As much as possible, we have tried to impart something about what motivates contemporary geologists and about the methods they use, the old ones as well as the new. We want the student to share some of the excitement and exhilaration triggered by the many recent discoveries that have greatly increased our understanding of how this planet works and by the beginnings that have been made in obtaining direct knowledge of how our nearby sister planets compare. Both of us are active in research, but we are also teachers, and believe that the gap between what is new and what is taught to beginners should be narrowed. We take it as a challenge to integrate in a natural way the newest discoveries of plate tectonics, marine geology, geochemistry, geophysics, and lunar and Martian geology into the traditional discussions of such topics as geomorphology, sedimentation, petrology, volcanism, and structural geology.

We have not introduced the very new at the expense of eliminating the essential material, both traditional and modern, that a good course in geology should cover. We introduce the minimum vocabulary necessary to allow free discussion of the concepts involved; this is enough to serve as an introduction to any more-specialized courses that may follow. The coverage of subject matter is sufficiently complete that the book could, if used in its entirety, serve as a foundation on which to build a career in earth science. Nevertheless, our major aim is to reach the many students whose course in geology may be their sole college exposure to science and the study of the Earth. Ultimately they will participate as citizens in governmental policy decisions that pertain to geological questions.

The scientific study of the Earth has never been so important a concern for all peoples as it has become today. The energy, food, and mineral resources of the Earth are now subjects for the daily newspapers and television: the peoples and governments of the world are coming to a new awareness of their importance for the well-being of society. More than at any time in the past century, geologists are today being asked to explain how oil is distributed in the Earth, why we have no domestic supply of some valuable metals, and many other and varied questions. Many of the questions relate to difficulties we encounter in managing our environment while attempting to exploit energy and mineral resources and produce the enormous quantities of industrial and other products required to support a huge and growing population. For this reason, we have shown, in many places in the book, how *knowledge* of the science is linked to its *uses,* both in detailed practical ways and in the making of policy decisions. As geology has become the focus of more attention, it has aroused the curiosity of young people about nature in general. Enrollment in introductory geology courses has increased greatly in the past decade. Today people travel more than ever before, and as they see the diversity of the Earth, they want to understand what they see.

Geology is in a golden age as measured by the impact of the discoveries and new theories of the past ten years that have given us profound new insights into the ways this planet works. For the first time in the modern history of the discipline, an all-encompassing synthesis of much of geological knowledge has been advanced and gained acceptance across a broad spectrum of professionals in the field. That synthesis, plate-tectonic theory, born only ten years ago, has started to mature in the few years since the first edition of this book appeared. As in any major new theory, work stimulated by it has enriched the subject and at the same time introduced complexities in a once-simple idea. Applications of the theory to new areas of the oceans and continents have bred new problems that are being tackled by geologists using a framework of thinking that is still only a decade old, and not settled into a well-worn path of familiar notions.

The impact of plate-tectonic theory on almost every area of geology, geochemistry, and geophysics has been pervasive, but that theory is not the only new development in the science. The discoveries of the past few years in planetary science—in particular, the landing on Mars in 1976—have added greatly to our knowledge of how the solar system evolved and have given us better data for comparison with the planet we live on. This in turn has stimulated a resurgence of work on the earliest rocks of Earth. But these are only a few of the high spots. Every chapter of this book has had to be revised since the first edition; that is the measure of our advancing knowledge in every aspect of the subject.

The startling new developments continue to roll in and challenge our scientific powers and imaginations. That was true when the first edition of this book was published in 1974, and it is true today. Our objective is the same: to give an introduction to this broad field of knowledge that is as up-to-date as the results presented by geologists at the most recent meetings of the Geological Society of America and to present

that new material so that it is as understandable as today's newspaper, without oversimplification that would destroy the richness of the discoveries.

We hope that this book will reach many students and introduce them to geology with what we believe is a fresh approach, and impart something of the intellectual excitement, the growing relevance to societal problems, and the esthetics of the subject. If we succeed in this, the large investment we have made in time and energy will all have been worthwhile.

TO THE INSTRUCTOR

We have made each chapter as self-sufficient as possible, so that chapters may be skipped in short courses or be taken up out of sequence according to the instructor's individual taste. (Professor Roger Thomas, in his instructor's guide, has several suggestions along these lines.) We have designed *repetition, review,* and *alternative restatement* into the book with a definite purpose—to enhance learning and to increase flexibility in the way the book is used.

We make extensive use of line drawings and photographs, plus the use of boxed information and other aids to learning, for it is our feeling that these aids will be of considerable value in simplifying otherwise difficult material and will serve to motivate the student. Explanatory sketches, diagrams, and photographs are used in places as substitutes for equations, and help to make up for lack of prior knowledge of other sciences. We also use illustrations as alternative statements of concepts presented in the text and as summaries of material covered earlier. To avoid interrupting the flow of the main text, occasional bits of parenthetical material appear in smaller type in the margins. These brief notes serve as slight amplifications of the text, as interesting sidelights, and as brief comments on some of the extraordinary personalities who have been part of the quest to understand the Earth. In a few places we have used boxes to expand in a more detailed way some materials of the text. These boxes are for the student who wants to understand more deeply some of the background of the subject. They are not necessary for understanding the text; some are pitched at a slightly higher level than the rest of the book.

The introductions at the beginning of the three parts of the book and the brief abstracts at the beginnings of chapters are designed to forecast in a general way the nature of the subject matter, how it fits together, and how it relates to other chapters. Summaries in list form appear at the ends of chapters to serve as systematic reviews of major conclusions. Questions were devised to help the student test his comprehension of the materials either by essay or by solving concrete problems. The bibliographies include *Scientific American* Offprints on closely related subjects, elementary or slightly advanced paperbacks, government reports on specialized topics, and a few readily available technical articles from the geological literature.

This book is divided into three parts. Each part consists of chapters grouped together according to their relations to the major concepts of the Earth's dynamics. Part I groups topics relating to the Earth as an evolving planet and how we study it and its materials. In the first chapter we give a capsule history of the Earth and the first glimpse of the general theory about how it operates. A brief outline of plate tectonics is presented to serve as a guide to succeeding chapters, where ramifications and implications of the theory are discussed with reference to the entire range of geological subjects considered in the book. The second chapter explores time in geology, the relation of process to history, and emphasizes how field observations form the central basis of our knowledge of the geological cycle. The third chapter is concerned with the prime source of information on the Earth: rocks and minerals. The major concepts of mineralogy and petrology are introduced and linked to a brief but systematic discussion of the major rock-forming minerals and the three major rock groups.

Part II covers those aspects of the Earth that are dominated by the external solar heat ma-chine, all of the surface processes that result from the Sun's radiant energy impinging on the surface of the planet, its atmosphere, and oceans. Erosion, transportation, and deposition of chemically altered and physically fragmented rocks, and the resulting sculpture of the surface are discussed in relation to tectonics and the dynamics of the atmosphere and oceans. Part II concludes with a chapter on the interactions of the biological world and Earth's inorganic materials, and how man as a geological agent has been profoundly changing the surface environment.

Part III explores the consequences of the internal heat machine of the Earth, and how it drives major movements of the interior and determines the structure of the whole planet. Internal heat, volcanism, and the kinds of igneous and metamorphic rocks that are produced by thermal processes are the subjects of the first group of chapters. The structure of the interior as deduced from seismology, gravity, and magnetism is then explored in preparation for a detailed systematic explanation of plate tectonics. It is only after this that we come to structural geology, which then can be treated in the context of the large-scale motions of lithospheric plates. Following this is a chapter on what we know of the nature and evolution of the other planets in the solar system, with major emphasis on lunar exploration. The book concludes with a chapter on earth materials as resources, including an extended treatment of energy reserves and the central importance of energy costs in the recovery of all other resources.

October 1977

Frank Press
Raymond Siever

ACKNOWLEDGMENTS

In preparing this edition we have been helped immeasurably by the many who have pointed out corrections and given us thoughtful comments on the first edition. Among these we are especially grateful to Roger Burns (Massachusetts Institute of Technology), Adam M. Dziewonski (Harvard University), Paul Doherty (Oakland University), Rod Ewing (University of New Mexico), Bryan Gregor (Wright State University), George M. Griffin (University of Florida), C. Woodbridge Hickox (Allegheny College), M. M. Kimberly (University of Toronto), David J. Miller, Paul Richards (Columbia University), and Carl Wunsch (Massachusetts Institute of Technology). While we were planning this revision, W. H. Freeman and Company sent out a questionnaire to well-known teachers of introductory courses in geology asking for evaluation of the first edition and suggestions for the second. The well-over 100 responses, including detailed comments, were invaluable as a guide to subject matter, level, and coverage, being based as they were on actual teaching experience using the book. Of special mention are the comments made by Steven Benham (College of William and Mary), B. H. Bieler (John F. Kennedy University), John Flett Brown (Florida State University), Wolfgang E. Elston (University of New Mexico), P. G. Feiss (University of North Carolina), R. K. Frohlick (University of Rhode Island), Nicholas Greci (University of Hartford), O. T. Hayward (Baylor University), Lawrence Lackey (Memphis State University), R. Merrill (California State University, Fresno), Donald Newberg (Colgate University), Herman Pfefferkorn (University of Pennsylvania), and Robert Scholten (Pennsylvania State University). We are indebted, for new photographs, to T. Cronin, A. F. H. Goetz, H. -U. Schmincke, D. J. Stanley, and E. Winkler. Carla Montgomery helped us greatly in revising the Glossary, preparing the Index, and reading proof. Evelyn Stinchfield helped with typing and other details of manuscript preparation. As he did for the first edition, Dick Johnson of W. H. Freeman and Company gave good advice in the editing of the final manuscript.

Earth

PART ONE
THE EARTH AS AN HISTORICALLY
EVOLVED BODY AND HOW WE STUDY IT

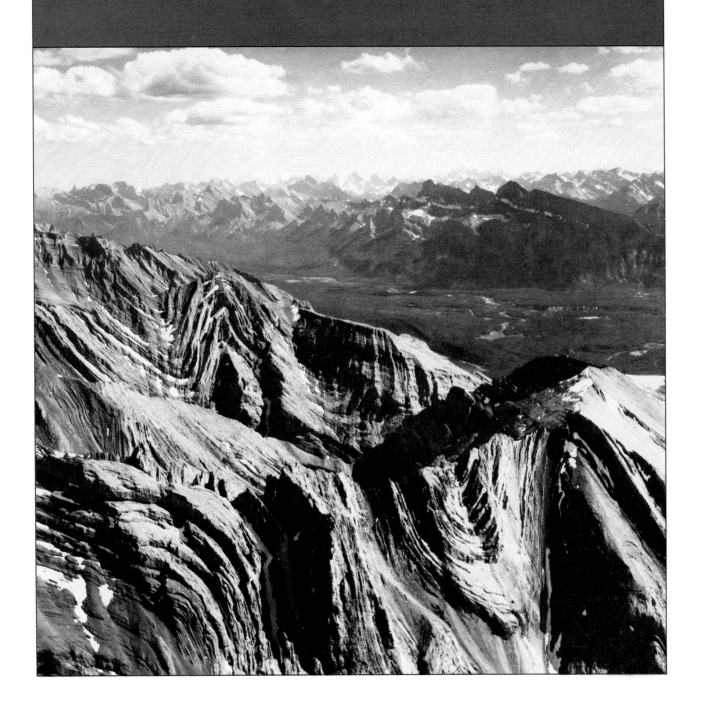

This planet on which we live has undergone constant change throughout a long history. To understand what the Earth is and how it works today, we link direct observation of processes operating at the surface with indirect measurement of forces working in the interior. The fullest knowledge comes from deducing how the planet evolved—from its beginnings to its present state.

Formed almost five billion years ago from a mass of dust rotating around the infant Sun, the Earth grew into a medium-sized planet whose history has been dominated by two driving machines. The first is the internal heat produced by radioactivity inside the Earth. The second is the external heat supplied to the surface by the Sun. The internal heat melts rocks, makes volcanoes, and thrusts mountains upward. The external heat drives the atmosphere and the oceans and causes the erosion of mountains and the reduction of rock to sediment. New methods of studying how the internal and external forces drive the Earth have generated a wealth of new information and raised many exciting new questions. In the past decade, geologists have gradually developed a new unifying theory that relates all of the dynamic Earth processes to the motions of large plates that constitute the outer shell of the planet. Called the theory of plate tectonics, it offers the most comprehensive model that geologists have ever had for explaining how the Earth works.

In the first part of this book we survey the ways in which we study this planet and what we have learned of its origin. These first chapters are a capsule of the book; in them we preview many subjects—particularly the nature of time and the materials of Earth—before they are explored in detail in later chapters.

HISTORY OF THE EARTH AND SOLAR SYSTEM

An introduction to the Earth, beginning with a cloud of dust and gas from which the solar system formed a little less than 5 billion years ago, to the birth of the Earth about 4.7 billion years ago, to the planet we know today, with its hospitable atmosphere and rich resources, a planet still active inside—as evidenced by earthquakes, volcanoes, ocean basins that open and close, and continents that drift apart.

THE UNIQUENESS OF PLANET EARTH

"Civilization exists by geological consent, subject to change without notice," said philosopher-historian Will Durant, reminding us of the remarkable circumstances that make this planet congenial to life as we know it. The Earth, after all, is a very special place—and not just because we humans inhabit it. More than a million life forms have developed on this unique spot in the solar system. *Homo sapiens,* the one species with the power of reason, is a rather recent arrival. In the study of geology, we explore not only the Earth as it exists today; we also seek answers to how it was formed, what it was like when first born, how it evolved to the planet of today, and, perhaps most exciting of all, what made it capable of supporting life.

No one knows precisely when the composition and state of the Earth's primitive atmosphere were just right for life to begin and evolve. We do know, however, that the large organic molecules that apparently preceded the evolution of the earliest forms of life could not have formed if the primitive atmosphere contained as much oxygen as the one we now enjoy.

Chemists tell us the oxygen would have destroyed them. The Earth's atmosphere and magnetic field acted as a shield against some of the biologically damaging radiation from space, just as they do today. Meteors, unbraked by the cushion of gases, would have bombarded Earth, leaving a crater-pocked, desolate surface that could never be softened by erosion. The atmosphere that exists today not only filters out the greatest part of destructive ultraviolet radiation, but together with the ocean, it stores and redistributes solar energy, thus moderating climate. Without atmosphere and oceans, there would be much more extreme temperature differences between day and night, summer and winter, and equator and pole.

The list of fortuitous conditions so propitious to life is long. Life as we know it is possible over a very narrow temperature interval—essentially within the limits set by the freezing and boiling points of water. This interval is perhaps 1 or 2 percent of the range between a temperature of absolute zero and the surface temperature of the Sun. How fortunate that Earth formed where it did in the Solar System, neither too far from the Sun nor too close to it! And Earth's size was just about right—not so small as to lose its atmos-

It is quite probable that the conditions that would allow life to flourish anywhere in the Universe would not differ much from those that have allowed life to evolve on Earth. This observation led astronomers to propose that other planets, situated about as far from their suns as we are from ours, might also have life.

Nature appreciation

Environment

Natural hazards

Natural resources

Scientific

Figure 1-1
Different aspects of geology—nature
appreciation, environmental protection,
hazard reduction, natural resources,
scientific research.

phere because its gravity was too small to prevent gases from escaping into space, and not so large that its gravity would hold on to too much atmosphere, including harmful gases.

We will see that the Earth's interior is a gigantic but delicately balanced heat engine fueled by radioactivity, which has much to do with how the surface evolved. Were it running more slowly, geological activity would have proceeded at a slower pace. The continents might not have evolved to their present form, and volcanoes might not have spewed out the water and gases that became the oceans and atmosphere. Iron might not have melted and sunk to form the liquid core, and the magnetic field would never have developed. The Earth would then have evolved as a cratered, dead planet similar to the Moon. Another scenario can be imagined: if there had been more radioactive fuel and a faster-running engine, volcanic gas and dust would have blotted out the Sun, the atmosphere would have been oppressively dense, and the surface would have been racked by daily earthquakes and volcanic explosions. Perhaps the Earth had such a fast-running era early in its history.

No wonder the Apollo astronauts were so profoundly affected by the view from the Moon of their home planet, with its inviting blue atmosphere and white clouds in contrast to the desolate terrain they could see on the Moon.

ASPECTS OF GEOLOGY

Although geology has ranked as a modern scholarly discipline for only two centuries, man has been curious about the Earth and its origins from the beginnings of pre-history. Stories of creation are invariably found in the sagas and folktales of early civilizations. In doing so, perhaps the ancients derived some feeling of security; perhaps they satisfied their own curiosity by reciting creation myths to their young, as if to put behind them the primeval chaos of an unknown creation. But a common theme was the creation, the bringing into existence, as contrasted with the idea of always having been here.

Nature's Threat. The human need to understand and to be able to explain nature in order to gain protection from her vagaries survives to this day as a major motivation toward the study of geology. Modern man seeks safeguards against nature's threats, which come in the form of earthquakes, landslides, volcanic eruptions,

floods, droughts, and the destructive sea waves known as tsunamis. Perhaps even more dangerous are man-made catastrophes, for our unique species has gained the power to trigger earthquakes, foul the atmosphere and oceans, and alter climates to the point of either initiating ice ages or melting the polar ice caps and flooding coastal cities. If man can do these things, so can he eventually predict or control most natural disasters.

Economic Geology. Were it not for the accessibility and diversity of minerals in the Earth's crust, man's cultural level would not have progressed beyond the Stone Age. The discovery of the Earth's mineral wealth is the geologist's task. If we are to extend to the many the affluence enjoyed by the few, let alone maintain our own present standard of living, new mineral deposits must be found. Prospectors have long since found the obvious deposits of iron, copper, tin, uranium, oil, and other important minerals. It is a challenge to geologists to re-explore the world, using new tools and techniques to ferret out undiscovered deposits. New and pressing concerns of geologists are conservation and environmental protection. How can we most efficiently exploit nature's wealth without waste and without devastating the landscape? Somehow we must find answers to these questions.

Scholarly Geology. Geology also has its "pure" aspects for those who work at it, in that it is interesting of and for itself. How a planet is born—the course of its evolution—and how it works today are only partially answered questions. Geologists are motivated to find answers because, like all scientists, they have unbounded curiosity and perhaps even a sense of uneasiness when important natural phenomena remain unexplained. Geologists will be hammering at outcrops, making geologic maps, exploring the sea floor, and scrutinizing Moon rocks as long as mountain-making, continental drift, sea-floor spreading, earthquakes, and other planetary features remain incompletely explained.

Geology for the Poets. Most students who enroll in geology courses have no intention of becoming professional geologists. They elect geology for many reasons. Perhaps they hope to heighten their appreciation of nature by gaining insight into her many ways. Perhaps the current crisis of the environment has induced them to learn more about a key environmental science. Perhaps Norman Mailer expressed their moti-

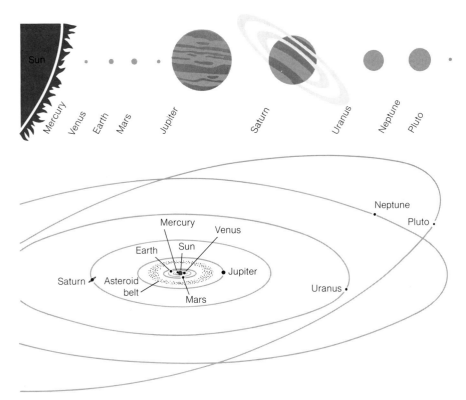

Figure 1-2
The Solar System. Diagrammatic representations of the Sun and planets.

vation when he wrote of the moon flight of the Apollo astronauts: "yes, we might have to go out into space until the mystery of new discovery would force us to regard the world once again as poets."

ORIGIN OF THE SYSTEM OF PLANETS

Let us start at the beginning with the first and most difficult problem: How did the **system of planets** originate? This question has attracted the attention of many of the great philosophers and scientists of the past two centuries. Yet it is a rare geological or astronomical congress that does not witness a fresh debate triggered by the latest experimental data or the newest theoretical advance pertaining to this question.

Explain the Observations. If anyone wishes to enter the lists with a pet hypothesis, the procedure is simple enough. On the basis of logical reasoning, develop a mechanism for the formation of the planetary system—a self-con-

sistent mechanism that will explain the mass and size distribution of the planets, the peculiarities of their orbits, the relative abundances of elements in the planets and the Sun. Useful hints can be gleaned from studies of other stars.

Whatever did happen, beginning about 4.7 billion years ago, when the planets started forming, resulted in several amazing regularities and curious groupings in the solar system:

1. The planets all revolve around the Sun in the same direction, in **elliptical,** but almost circular, **orbits** that lie in nearly the same plane; most of their moons also revolve in the same direction.

2. The planets, except for Venus and Uranus, *rotate* in the same direction as their revolution around the Sun—that is, counterclockwise as one looks from the North pole to the South pole of the Earth.

3. The distance of each planet from the Sun is roughly twice that of the next planet closer to the Sun (an ordering known as the **Titius-Bode rule**).

We will show in Chapter 2 how certain radioactive elements, uranium, potassium, and rubidium, serve as clocks that enable us to chronicle major events in the solar system, such as its beginning 4.7 billion years ago.

Light is emitted or absorbed in a characteristic way by different elements in gaseous form, as they incandesce. Analysis of light into color components (more accurately, its spectral components) reveals the composition of its source. Thus the yellow color produced when common salt (sodium chloride, NaCl) is burned (vaporized) in a natural gas flame reveals the presence of the element Na.

Kant's hypothesis, published anonymously, carried an impressive title: *Universal Natural History and Theory of the Heavens, or an Essay on the Constitution and Mechanical Origin of the Whole Universe, Treated According to Newtonian Principles.* The publisher went bankrupt and the stock was seized by the creditors, so that very few copies reached public hands.

4. Although the Sun makes up about 99.9 percent of the mass of the solar system, 99 percent of the **angular momentum** is concentrated in the large planets (see Fig. 1-3 for an explanation of angular momentum).

5. The planets form two groups: the so-called **terrestrial planets,** Mercury, Venus, Earth, and Mars, which form an inner group of small, dense bodies (densities about 4 to 5.5 times that of water); and the **giant planets,** Jupiter, Saturn, Uranus, and Neptune, which are an outer group of large bodies with low densities (between 0.7 and 1.7 times that of water). In some respects—for example, their high gas content and low density—the giant planets are more like the Sun than like the terrestrial planets.

From chemical analysis of Earth rocks, Moon rocks, and meteorites that reach the Earth from interplanetary space, we surmise that the terrestrial planets are made up mostly (± 90 percent) of four elements: iron, oxygen, silicon, and magnesium. Spectroscopic studies of the Sun show it to be composed almost entirely (99 percent) of hydrogen and helium. Presumably the high abundances of hydrogen and helium are features of the giant planets also.

The Nebular Hypotheses. There has been no dearth of theories of creation over the centuries. The modern approach to the problem, however, began in 1755 when the German philosopher Immanuel Kant hypothesized a primeval, slowly rotating cloud of gas, now called a nebula, which in some unspecified fashion condenses into a number of discrete, globular bodies. In this way Kant neatly explained the consistency of revolution and rotation directions, in that the rotation of the parent nebula is preserved in the rotation of the Sun, the revolution of the planets about the Sun, and the rotation of the planets about their axes—all in the same direction (Fig. 1-4).

The great French mathematician Laplace proposed essentially the same theory in 1796—surprisingly, without the mathematical formulation he was capable of providing. Historians of science will have to resolve the questions of whether Laplace knew of Kant's work and why he chose not to subject his own *nebular hypothesis* to mathematical examination, for had he done so he might have discovered some serious flaws.

According to Kant and Laplace, the original mass of gas cooled and began to contract. As it did, the rotational speed increased (a consequence of the **law of conservation of angular momentum,** illustrated in Figure 1-5) until successive rings of gaseous material were spun off from the central mass by centrifugal force. In the final stages the rings condensed into planets.

Not so, according to the great British physicists James Clerk Maxwell and Sir James Jeans, who showed about one-hundred years later that there was not enough mass in the rings to provide the gravitational attraction for condensation into individual planets. The coup de grâce was delivered at the close of the nineteenth century, when astronomer F. R. Moulton of Chicago showed that the nebular hypothesis violated item 4 above—namely, that the planets have most of the angular momentum. The law of conservation of angular momentum requires each part of a rotating, condensing nebula to hold onto its angular momentum; the Sun, which collected most of the mass, should have gathered up most of the angular momentum of the system. Simply stated, the Sun doesn't rotate fast enough; it should have spun faster, just as the skater in Figure 1-5 spins faster when she pulls in her arms.

Collision Hypotheses. Wanted—a theory, now that Kant and Laplace were in disfavor. Geologist T. C. Chamberlin collaborated on one theory with Moulton, his astronomer fellow professor at Chicago, and revived an early proposal (1749) of Count Buffon of France—the **collision hypothesis.** Stated simply, this hypothesis holds that giant tongues of material were torn from the pre-existing Sun by the gravitational attraction of a passing star. According to Chamberlin and Moulton, these broke into small chunks, or **planetesimals,** which went flying as cold bodies into orbits around the Sun in the plane of the passing star. By collision and gravitational attraction, the larger planetesimals swept up the smaller pieces, and those that survived became the planets. Unfortunately, the several versions of collision theories have fatal weaknesses. According to astronomers, much of the material ejected from the Sun would have come from the interior and would have been so hot, perhaps 1,000,000°C, that the gases would have been dispersed throughout space with explosive violence rather than condensed into planets. Although more angular momentum would have been imparted to the planets by a passing star than by the rotation of a nebula, the amount is still less than that observed. Finally, the vastness of space makes the probability of such a close approach of two stars extremely small.

a

b

c

d

Figure 1-3
Angular momentum, illustrated by the example of a heavy steel ball fastened to the central shaft by a very light rod. Turning the shaft causes the ball to rotate around it. The ball's angular momentum is defined as the product of the mass of the ball, its velocity, and its distance from the rotation axis. [From *New Horizons in Astronomy* by J. C. Brandt and S. P. Maran. W. H. Freeman and Company. Copyright © 1972.]

Figure 1-4
Schematic diagram of the nebular hypothesis. (a) A diffuse, roughly spherical, slowly rotating nebula begins to contract. (b) As a result of contraction and rotation, a flat, rapidly rotating disk is produced with concentration of matter in the center. (c) Contraction continues, the proto-Sun is formed, and rings of material are left behind. (d) The material in the rings condenses into planets revolving in orbit around the Sun. [After *New Horizons in Astronomy* by J. C. Brandt and S. P. Maran. W. H. Freeman and Company. Copyright © 1972.]

Figure 1-5
Illustration of conservation of angular momentum; when a skater pulls in her arms, she spins at a faster rate. Similarly, when a slowly rotating nebula contracts, its rotation speed increases.

Exciting recent discoveries of such biologically important compounds as ammonia, methane, formic acid, and formaldehyde in interstellar space and of amino acids in meteorites have profound implications for the origin of life on Earth and elsewhere in the universe. Their presence in space shows that the formation of the simple organic compounds, the building blocks of life, is an ordinary accomplishment of galactic evolution.

In June 1977, astronomers at the University of New Mexico and NASA reported a distant star in the constellation Cygnus that shows a pattern of energy radiation that indicates a young disk-shaped star. This may be the first discovery of a solar system caught in the process of birth.

Recent Theories. The thinking of the past few decades has been influenced by the discovery that space is not as empty as had been thought. Astronomical observations have detected, both in interstellar space and in nebulae, rarefied matter consisting of about 99 percent gas and 1 percent dust. The gases are mostly hydrogen and helium; the dust-size particles have compositions similar to those of terrestrial materials, such as silicon compounds, iron oxides, ice crystals, and a host of other small molecules, including organic ones. It is not surprising, then, that recent theories tend to be neo-Laplacian in that they revive the idea of a primordial, rotating cloud of gas and dust whose shape and internal motions were determined by gravitational forces and the forces of rotation. At some moment gravitational attraction became the dominant factor, contraction began, and the rotation speeded up (again, conservation of angular momentum). The cloud tended to flatten into a disk; matter began to drift toward the center, accumulating into the **proto-Sun.** The proto-Sun collapsed under its own gravitation, becoming dense and opaque as the material was compressed. Its internal temperature rose to about 1,000,000°C, at which point "nuclear burning," or fusion, began. More precisely, the Sun began to shine with the initiation of the **thermonuclear reaction** (now unfortunately duplicated on Earth by H-bombs), in which hydrogen nuclei combine under intense pressure to form helium nuclei, releasing a vast amount of energy.

What about the disk of gas and dust enveloping the primitive Sun? How did it form into planets? How did the planets pick up the necessary angular momentum, and what about the differing chemical composition of the planets? There is very little agreement among the experts about the answers to these questions.

A recent nebular-disk model, the *chemical-condensation-sequence* model, is receiving much attention lately because it seems to predict the observed variations of chemical compositions and densities of the planets (Fig. 1-6). Initially, the disk was extremely hot, so that much of its materials were in their gaseous form. As the spinning disk cooled, various solid compounds and minerals condensed out of the gas, forming grains that gradually clumped together into small chunks, or planetesimals. The planetesimals coalesced, the bigger ones with stronger gravity pulling in all the nearly condensed matter. If a planet grew at a distance close enough to the Sun so that it was too hot for certain materials to

condense, those materials would be blown away as gases by radiation and by matter streaming from the Sun. (The ejection of matter from the Sun during these early stages was also responsible for slowing its rotation.) Close to the Sun, where temperatures were highest, the first materials to condense were those with high boiling points, such as most metals and rocks. Thus Mercury, the planet closest to the Sun, is the most dense (5.4 times the density of water) because it is richest in iron. The proximity of Mercury to the Sun means that it formed at a temperature so high that iron could condense, whereas the lighter, rock-forming compounds, such as those made of magnesium, silicon, and oxygen, condensed more readily in the "cooler" environments of the terrestrial planets more distant from the Sun. Volatile (easily evaporated) materials, such as water, methane, ammonia, were mostly lost to the terrestrial planets, but could condense into ices in the cold outer reaches of the solar system, perhaps on the satellites of the giant planets. Jupiter and Saturn were big enough, and had gravitational attractions strong enough, to hold on to all of their constituents, thereby retaining the composition of the original nebula—mostly hydrogen and helium, much like that of the Sun.

The preceding should be taken for what it is—a hypothesis, a possible model. Perhaps some of these notions come close to what actually happened: we will know only after much additional work is done, some of it now underway. Nebulae at different stages of development are being studied not only with the familiar optical telescope but also with special devices that magnify x-rays and radio waves. These invisible but detectable waves provide additional information about what goes on in the remote sections of the universe. The first planetary probes have been returning data on the nature and composition of the atmospheres and surfaces of Mercury, Venus, Mars, Jupiter, and the Moon. Mathematicians are developing new tools to improve computer reproduction of the motions of rotating gas-dust clouds and growing planets. All of this activity should in time give us better answers about how it all started.

We have dwelt on the question of the origin of the solar system for several reasons. The evolutionary course followed by a planet is set by its initial state. The current state of Earth, some 4.7 billion years later, is reasonably well known to us. These two times in the course of **planetary evolution**—the beginning and now—are important constraints in developing models of how the

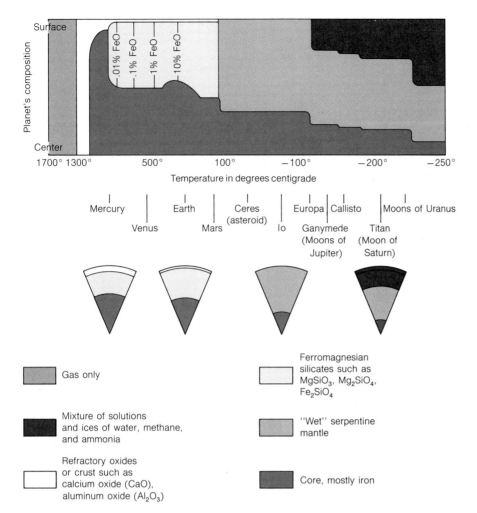

Figure 1-6
Simplified version of a chemical-condensation-sequence model proposed by John S. Lewis of M.I.T. The left edge of the diagram, at 1700°C, represents the interior of the solar nebula; the right edge, at −250°C, represents a distance from the center of the nebula near the planet Neptune, about 30 times farther out than Earth. The vertical axis predicts the object's internal composition from its center (bottom) to its surface (top), assuming that only the condensates were retained. The sequence of condensation from the hot interior to the cold edges of the nebula is shown by the decreasing iron content and by the increasing silicate and volatile content. The giant planets are not shown; their huge gravitational forces enabled them to retain the composition of the original nebula, mostly hydrogen and helium. [After "The Chemistry of the Solar System" by John S. Lewis. Copyright © 1974 by Scientific American, Inc. All rights reserved.]

Earth has changed throughout its history. The growth of ideas on the origin of the planets is an interesting story in the history of science. It illustrates how successive hypotheses are advanced, rejected, resurrected, and modified in the light of new observational data and theoretical concepts. Typical of all of science, it is especially pertinent to modern geology, where a revolution in thought and concept is currently underway.

EARTH AS AN EVOLVING PLANET

This section serves as an introduction and preview to all that pertains, in this book, to the Earth's large-scale evolution. We will sketch the transformation of the Earth from an initially homogeneous body to a differentiated planet—that is, one in which the interior is divided into layers or zones, each differing chemically and mineralogically. We will see how the process of differentiation is indirectly related to the formation of the atmosphere, oceans, continents, mountains, volcanoes, and magnetic field. The general sequence of events rather than details will be emphasized, for no other reason than that many of the details have yet to be worked out by future generations of Earth scientists.

Box 1-1 More Details on the Formation of the Planets

For the reader who wishes more examples of the kinds of reasoning used, we expand on how it is inferred that most of the gases moved to the outer part of the solar system before the planetesimals formed and grew into the terrestrial planets. Gases differ from liquids and solids in that the molecules move freely in irregular zig-zag paths as a result of repeated collisions. Physics tells us that the hotter the gas, the more rapid the movements and also that light molecules move faster than heavy ones. Unless the gas is contained by walls or held by the gravity of a planet, the rapidly moving molecules would escape. It is easy to see how a planet's atmosphere could lose light gases like hydrogen and helium. The molecules move too fast for gravity to hold them very long. But the slower-moving molecules of heavy gases like krypton and xenon should have been held selectively by the planet's gravitational field. The fact that they are deficient on Earth argues that the growth of planetesimals into planets took place in a region previously swept clear of both light and heavy gases.

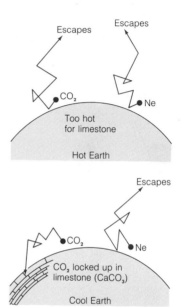

Schematic diagram showing why the rarity of such inert gases as neon and the abundance of such chemically reactive gases as water and carbon dioxide indicate that the Earth was probably cool in its beginning days.

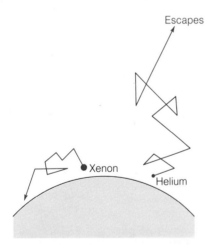

Schematic illustration of how Earth's gravity should have held on to heavy gas atoms like xenon and krypton, whereas light gases like hydrogen and helium would have escaped into space. The deficiency of both light and heavy gases suggests that planet Earth originated in a region previously swept clear of almost all gases.

Taking a chemical approach, we also infer that the Earth was probably cool when it first formed, rather than hot, because neon, the gas used in electric signs, is extremely rare in the atmosphere, but comparatively abundant in the stars. Somehow, most neon escaped from the Earth. Water molecules, however, weigh nearly as much as neon and for that reason should have escaped along with neon, yet there are oceans of water on Earth today. Water differs from neon chemically in that it reacts under "cool" conditions to form compounds that do not easily evaporate, whereas neon is chemically inert and remains a gas. Thus a cool primitive Earth would selectively retain water (and other chemically reactive gases like carbon dioxide and ammonia) by locking them up as compounds in rock, whereas inert gases like neon would gradually escape. If the Earth were initially hotter than a few hundred degrees, both the chemically reactive and inert gases would be lacking today.

Initial State—A Homogenized Conglomeration. Think of the Earth as it was before the beginning of the geologic record—that is, before the formation of the oldest rocks now known, which are nearly 4 billion years old. This period covers the first billion years in the history of the Earth, the events of which we now attempt to reconstruct, even though we lack direct evidence in the form of rocks dating back to these early times. The stage was set for the accumulation of the planet by the gathering up or accretion of planetesimals about 4.7 billion years ago. The new planet was probably an unsorted conglomeration, mostly of silicon compounds, iron and magnesium oxides, and smaller amounts of all of the natural chemical elements. Although the planetesimals were relatively cold, the growing planet soon began heating up because of three different effects.

The Initial Temperature. Each infalling planetesimal carried much energy of motion—energy that was converted to heat upon impact. Although much of the heat was radiated back into space, a significant fraction was retained by the growing planet. Just how much is uncertain, since it depended on the mass, velocity, and temperature of the planetesimals and on the rate of accretion. At a high rate of accretion, the heated impact zone would have been covered by material that arrived later before the energy could radiate back into space, and the "buried" heat would have raised the temperature of the interior.

Compression is another effect that leads to a temperature rise. A common example is the heating of the barrel of an air pump, like those we use to inflate bicycle tires. The air is compressed quickly as we push down, too quickly for the heat to be diffused away, and the barrel heats up. The inner parts of the planet were squeezed under the growing weight of the accumulating outer parts. The energy expended in compressing the interior was converted to heat, which was locally retained. The heat did not flow out because heat moves, or is conducted, very slowly in the rocks. As a result, the heat accumulated, and the temperature increased inside the Earth. Most geophysicists who have calculated the magnitude of heating think that accretion and compression resulted in an average internal temperature of about 1000°C for the newly organized planet.

Heat from Radioactive Disintegration. The heavy elements uranium and thorium, and the small fraction of potassium atoms that are heavier than ordinary potassium, are not very plentiful on Earth. Their occurrence is measured in a few parts per million (one gram in a thousand kilograms of rock). Yet these elements have had a profound effect on the evolution of the Earth because of their **radioactivity.** The atoms of these elements spontaneously disintegrate by emitting atomic particles (helium nuclei and electrons), and are thus transformed into different elements. The emitted particles are the important part of this discussion. As they are absorbed by the surrounding matter, their energy of motion is transformed into heat. At first thought, the heat generated may seem inconsequential: about 20 calories of heat is emitted by a cubic centimeter of granite in the course of a million years. This does not seem impressive when we realize that it would take some 500 million years to brew a cup of coffee using the radioactive heat released by a cubic centimeter of granite (assuming, of course, that the heat would be retained and not flow out). What *is* impressive is that the temperature would rise to the melting point of granite in several billion years—even sooner if the temperature increase due to accretion and compression were also included. Thus the disintegration of the radioactive elements provides a heat source that has persisted for billions of years. Radioactively generated heat, its outward flow slowed by the low thermal conductivity of rocks, caused the newly formed Earth to warm up, initiating the process of planetary development.

HEATING UP, OVERTURN, AND FORMATION OF A DIFFERENTIATED EARTH

The Earth Heats Up. One-hundred-fifty years ago, the French mathematician Fourier derived his heat-conduction equation, which is still used to calculate the flow of heat from one part of a body to another, together with the corresponding temperature changes. To start the computation, one needs to know the temperature at the boundaries (e.g., the Earth's surface), the beginning temperature, and the location and strength of heat sources in the body. So far as the Earth is concerned, the last two factors are uncertain. Nevertheless, one can make reasonable guesses about the starting temperature and radioactivity of the Earth and compute models of how the internal temperature may have changed in the years following the birth of the planet.

(1) Accretion

(2) Gravity compresses the original Earth into smaller volume

(3) Disintegration of radioactive elements and heat flowing away from points where particles are absorbed

Figure 1-7
Diagrammatic representation of three mechanisms that would cause the early Earth to heat up. (1) Accretion, in which impacting bodies bombard the Earth and their energy of motion is converted to heat. (2) Gravitational compression of the Earth into a smaller volume, causing its interior to heat up. (3) The disintegration of radioactive elements releases particles and radiation, which are absorbed by the surrounding rock, heating it up.

A 4000-kilogram (5-ton) planetesimal impacting with a velocity of 30 km/sec (19 miles/sec) delivers as much energy as a 1-kiloton nuclear explosion.

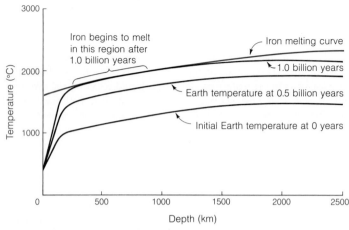

Figure 1-8
Temperature in the Earth's interior at different times in its history, according to a calculation by T. C. Hanks and D. L. Anderson. The lowest curve shows the initial temperature due to accretion and compression at 0 years. After 500 million years radioactivity caused the Earth to warm up to the temperature shown by the next curve. After 1 billion years the interior heated up and reached the melting point of iron at depths between 400 and 800 km, and iron began to melt in this region.

Figure 1-9
(a) The melting of iron leads to the formation of a heavy liquid layer. According to W. Elsasser, drops begin to develop in later stages (b,c) and sink toward the center.

Almost everyone who has done this finds the same important feature. Figure 1-8 is a graph of one of the computational results. The curves illustrate how the internal temperature increased in the years following the planet's formation. The computer verifies what we might have guessed—that radioactive heat was generated more rapidly than it could flow away (remember, rocks are poor heat conductors), so that the interior gradually warmed up. Figure 1-8 also shows the temperature at which metallic iron would melt within the Earth. The melting point increases with depth in the Earth because of the increasing pressure. The key feature of the model is that it indicates that at depths of 400 to 800 kilometers (250 to 500 miles), the temperature would have risen to the melting point of iron about one billion years after the Earth was formed. Other models show that this state of affairs may have been reached only a few hundred million years after Earth's formation.

The Iron Catastrophe. Iron is heavier than the other common elements of the Earth, and when the iron in a layer began to melt, large drops would probably have formed and fallen toward the center, displacing the lighter materials that were there. Figure 1-9 shows how this may have occurred.

Iron is an abundant element; we will see that it accounts for about one-third of the mass of the Earth. The melting and sinking of iron to form a liquid core at the center was therefore an event of catastrophic proportions. Iron "falling" toward the center would release a huge amount of gravitational energy, which would eventually have been converted to heat. The process is basically the same as the one in which the gravitational energy of a waterfall is used to turn turbines and generate electrical energy. The additional heat released during the formation of the iron core would produce an average temperature rise of some 2000°C, causing a large fraction of the Earth to melt.

Planetary Differentiation. We have seen that the Earth probably underwent a profound reorganization after it warmed to the temperature at which iron melts. Approximately one-third of the primitive planet's material sank to the center, and in the process a large part of the body was converted to a partially molten state. The molten material, which was lighter than the parent material from which it separated, floated upward to cool and form a primitive crust. Core formation was the beginning stage of the **differentiation** of the Earth, wherein it was converted from a homogeneous body, with roughly the same kind of material at all depths, to a zoned or layered or shelled body with a dense **iron core**, a **surficial crust** composed of lighter materials with lower melting points, and between them the remaining **mantle.** *Differentiation is perhaps the most significant event in the* *history of the Earth. It led to the formation of a crust and eventually the continents. Differentiation probably initiated the escape of gases from the interior, which eventually led to the formation of the atmosphere and oceans.* It is as if our planet gave a "big burp" during this violent upheaval.

But what of the other planets: did they go through the same early history? This question must remain unanswered, perhaps for a few more years, by which time we should know the extent to which other terrestrial planets have differentiated and how much radioactivity is contained in their rocks. But lack of direct information is no bar to speculation, for on the basis of what they know so far, geophysicists have made computer studies of the thermal regimes of the terrestrial planets, using reasonable guesses about conditions on these planets. They find that because of their different sizes and compositions, the planets evolve at different rates. The Moon and Mercury evolved rapidly in the first 1 to 2 billion years, then apparently became inactive and geologically "dead" (i.e., no mountain-making, volcanism, earthquakes, erosion). Earth and Venus are still quite active. Mars may be in between these extremes, perhaps 2 to 3 billion years past its peak. Data returned by U.S. and Soviet planetary probes should enable us to check these computer predictions in the next few years.

The giant planets will remain a puzzle for a long time. They are chemically so distinct from the terrestrial planets, and are so much larger, that if they have undergone differentiation the process must have followed an entirely different course. Perhaps most puzzling of all of these giants is Jupiter: through some unexplained internal process, that planet radiates two to three times as much energy as it receives from the Sun! Perhaps Jupiter and its 12 moons are akin to a small solar system whose sun never quite made it to the stage of shining.

The Earth Reborn. We take up the story of the evolution of the Earth following the catastrophic formation of the core. Early continents, if they existed, would have been engulfed and resorbed. In a sense the Earth was reborn without leaving a trace of its early history. According to the best estimates, all of this took place between 3.7 and 4.5 billion years ago. We prefer to date the event at around 4 billion years ago, near the beginning of geological time, when the oldest rocks we can now find were first formed.

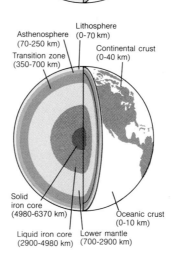

Lithosphere (0-70 km)
Asthenosphere (70-250 km)
Continental crust (0-40 km)
Transition zone (350-700 km)
Solid iron core (4980-6370 km)
Oceanic crust (0-10 km)
Liquid iron core (2900-4980 km)
Lower mantle (700-2900 km)

Figure 1-10
The early Earth (top) was probably a homogeneous mixture, with no continents or oceans. In the process of differentiation, iron sank to the center and light material floated upward to form a crust (middle). As a result, the Earth is a zoned planet (bottom), with a dense iron core, a surficial crust of light rock, and, between them, a residual mantle.

Convective Overturn. We have mentioned that the flow of heat by conduction to the surface took place so slowly in the Earth that most of the heat accumulated within the Earth, causing the internal temperature to rise. But when the interior became so hot that it became molten and material could move, a more efficient mechanism took over the transfer of internal heat to the surface—namely, overturn, or **convection.** Convection takes place in liquids and gases that are hotter at the bottom than at the top. The hotter material expands, becomes lighter than the material above it, and floats upward, carry-

14

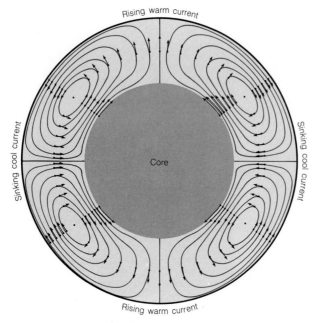

Figure 1-11
Highly schematic model of convection in the Earth's mantle, computed by C. L. Pekeris in 1935. Although the model is mathematically exact, it is too simple and regular to represent the actual Earth. Nevertheless, the warm rising currents, the cool sinking currents, and the horizontal flow at the tops and bottoms of the convection cells are features common to the recent, more realistic models, which were influenced by this early work.

Relative abundance of elements in whole Earth

Relative abundance of elements in Earth's crust

Figure 1-12
Relative abundance by weight of elements in the whole Earth and in the Earth's crust. Differentiation has resulted in a light crust depleted in iron and enriched in oxygen, silicon, aluminum, calcium, potassium, and sodium.

ing its heat to the surface, where it cools and sinks again. A schematic model of convection currents in the Earth is shown in Figure 1-11.

Once convection began in the Earth, heat was dissipated rapidly, and the planet quickly cooled. The mantle solidified, but the underlying iron core did not; it remains molten, for even 4 billion years is too short a time for it to have cooled off. Convective overturn also produced a chemically zoned Earth.

Although convection is most common in heated liquids and gases, surprisingly enough, it can also occur in solids. Under certain conditions, heated rock will slowly move upward, because its density is reduced—that is, it becomes lighter—as it expands. We will see that convective flow in the Earth's solid interior has been proposed as the driving force for such large-scale geological processes as sea-floor spreading and continental drift.

Chemical Zonation. The eight most abundant elements on Earth are listed in Figure 1-12. How we know this will become evident in later chapters. Together these elements account for more than 99 percent of the mass of the Earth. About 90 percent of the Earth is made of the four elements iron, oxygen, silicon, and magnesium. Compare the abundance of elements in the crust with the values for the Earth as a whole. Because most of the iron sank to the core, that element drops to fourth-place rank in the crust. Conversely, silicon, aluminum, calcium, potassium, and sodium move upward, with manifold increases in their concentration in the crust.

It is interesting and significant that differentiation did not lead to a vertical arrangement of elements based entirely on their relative weights, as we might have supposed. The reason is that various elements formed compounds, and it was the chemical and physical properties of those compounds—properties such as melting points, chemical affinities, and densities—that governed the distribution of elements, rather than the properties of the elements themselves. For example, certain silicates of calcium, sodium, potassium, and aluminum—notably the *feldspars* ($CaAl_2Si_2O_8$, $NaAlSi_3O_8$, $KAlSi_3O_8$)—are easily melted. They begin to melt at temperatures as low as 700 to 1000°C, and when molten they are relatively light. One might speculate that compounds like these would melt early, rise to the surface by convection, and accumulate as crust. The details are obscure, but it should be no surprise that feldspars are the most common minerals found in the Earth's crust.

The mantle, situated between the crust and the core, became the reservoir for magnesium-iron silicates, which melt less easily and are heavier than feldspars. From the abundances shown in Figure 1-12, we would expect that the dominant constituents are combinations of Fe, Mg, Si, and O. We should therefore not be surprised when we see later why most geophysicists and petrologists believe that the principal minerals in the mantle are olivine (Mg_2SiO_4—Fe_2SiO_4) and pyroxene ($MgSiO_3$—$FeSiO_3$).

Heavy elements like gold and platinum have little chemical attraction to oxygen and silicon, and most of these important metals probably sank into the Earth's core. But other heavy elements, like uranium and thorium, have strong tendencies to form oxides and silicates, which are light and could rise to accumulate in the crust. Gravity, however, is only secondarily responsible for the zonation of a planet: just as important are the relative abundance of the different elements and the way in which the electrons are grouped in their atoms, both of

Box 1-2   The Relative Abundance of the Elements

We know about the chemical composition of the universe from the spectroscopic examination of the light of the Sun and stars, from the analysis of meteorites, and from the composition of the rocks found near the surface of the Earth. The table shows our current knowledge of elemental abundances—the results of many measurements. The data support the notion that the relative abundance of elements in the universe is uniform except for local variations, such as the dissipation into space of hydrogen and helium from the terrestrial planets or the internal differentiation of a planet. It has been postulated that a large part of the Earth's

interior consists of iron. But why iron, and not some other heavy metal? We have no direct way of determining that it is iron. We do know, however, from physical calculations made on the basis of the mean density of the Earth and from seismological data that the innermost part of the Earth's interior has a high density. The choice of iron seems appropriate because among all the candidates with high atomic weight, it is by far the most plentiful. Our confidence in this choice is reinforced when we note that 58 percent of all meteorites found consist of iron.

Abundance of the principal elements in the Universe expressed as the numbers of atoms relative to a base of 10,000 atoms of silicon.

Element	Atomic number	Atomic weight	Abundance in the universe
Hydrogen	1	1	400,000,000
Helium	2	4	31,000,000
Oxygen	8	16	215,000
Neon	10	20	86,000
Nitrogen	7	14	66,000
Carbon	6	12	35,000
Silicon	14	28	10,000
Magnesium	12	24	9,100
Iron	26	56	6,000
Sulfur	16	32	3,750
Argon	18	40	1,500
Aluminum	13	27	950
Calcium	20	40	490
Sodium	11	23	440
Nickel	28	59	270
Phosphorus	15	31	100
Chlorine	17	35	90
Chromium	24	52	78
Manganese	25	55	69
Potassium	19	39	32
Titanium	22	48	24
Cobalt	27	59	18
Fluorine	9	19	16

Source: After H. Suess and H. Urey, 1956.

which determine the compounds that they form. The properties of the compounds—densities and melting points—differ from those of the pure elements and govern the distribution of the elements.

Differentiation Slows the Engine Down. One very important consequence of chemical zoning is the concentration of the heavy elements uranium and thorium in the Earth's crust as oxides and silicates. In the early stages, when these radioactive elements were evenly distributed throughout the Earth, they were probably highly effective in raising the temperature to the melting point of iron. Following the catastrophic formation of the core, however, when the interior was hot and mobile, the radioactive "fuel" began to concentrate in the outermost layers, where the heat that was generated could be conducted through much shorter distances to the surface and so be lost more easily. In this way the differentiation of a planet may act as a governor to slow down the operations of the heat engine.

Formation of Continents, Oceans, and Atmosphere. We have only the most general notion of how the first continents may have formed; the story goes like this. Lava flowing from the partially molten interior of the Earth spread over the surface and solidified to form a thin crust. This primeval crust melted and solidified repeatedly, and the lighter compounds were successively separated from the heavier ones and distributed at the top. **Weathering** by rainwater and other components of the atmosphere broke up and altered the rocks; **erosion** led to the formation of sediments—the residue of broken-down rock particles. As the sediments accumulated, they were in turn penetrated by hot gases and solutions from below, heated up and altered—or "cooked," in a sense—into new rocks, or were entirely resorbed and recycled. The end product of such processes as these was the primitive nucleus of a continent, which continued to grow by a continuation of the process. As a rough check on this theory, if we take the amount of lava ejected each year by modern volcanoes, and multiply that amount by a few billion years, the volume of rock produced corresponds fairly well with the volume of the continents.

If we start with the premise that the Earth accreted from cold planetesimals, then the oceans came from the interior as a product of the processes of heating up and differentiation.

Originally the water was locked up, chemically bound as oxygen and hydrogen in such minerals as potassium-aluminum mica ($KAl_3Si_3O_{10}(OH)_2$). As the Earth warmed up and partial melting occurred, the water was released and carried to the surface along with lava. As the lava reached the surface, much of the water escaped in the form of hot vapor clouds. Even at today's rate of volcanic activity, the lavas that reached the surface in the past would have contained enough water vapor to fill the oceans in the course of geological time, though much of that water may have been recycled by the melting of oceanic sediments containing hydrated (water-bearing) minerals.

How and when the atmosphere began to develop is a more difficult matter to determine. We can, however, give one self-consistent explanation that agrees with the known facts. There is little doubt that the earliest atmosphere was entirely different from the primarily nitrogen-oxygen one we live in now. The cold planetesimals, which aggregated to form the Earth, could have carried no atmosphere because they were too small to hold any gases by gravitation. Thus **outgassing** as part of the process of differentiation—that is, the release of gases from the interior due to internal heat and chemical reaction—is generally thought to be the primary source. From the chemical composition of lava and from studies of gases released by modern volcanoes, we can surmise that volcanic gases consisted mainly of water vapor, hydrogen, hydrogen chlorides, carbon monoxide, carbon dioxide, and nitrogen. But the light hydrogen molecules could not have been held by the Earth's gravity, and the hydrogen would have escaped into space as it does steadily today. With energy supplied by sunlight, some water vapor in the upper atmosphere may have broken down to hydrogen and oxygen by a process called **photolysis** ("breaking" by "light"). Any oxygen so formed would not have remained free (uncombined) because it is quite reactive and would have quickly combined with gases like methane and carbon monoxide to form water and carbon dioxide. It would also have combined with crustal materials—with metals like iron in olivines and pyroxenes to form iron oxides like **hematite** (Fe_2O_3).

The production of significant amounts of free oxygen and its persistence in the atmosphere probably came only after life evolved at least to the complexity of green algae, which, like all higher forms of green plants, convert sunlight to organic matter by **photosynthesis,** using car-

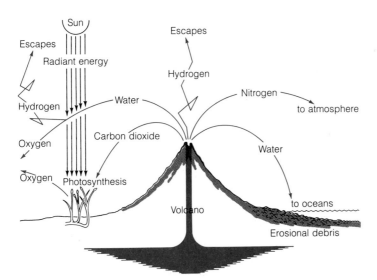

Figure 1-13
Volcanism has contributed enormous amounts of water, carbon dioxide, and
other gases to the atmosphere. Sunlight broke water molecules into its components, hydrogen and oxygen. Photosynthesis by plants removed carbon dioxide and added oxygen to the primitive atmosphere. Volcanism was an important factor in the growth of continents.

bon dioxide and water to make organic matter
and oxygen. Not until the production of oxygen
exceeded its loss by chemical combination with
other gases and metals could this by-product of
photosynthesis have begun accumulating in the
atmosphere.

The big question about the atmosphere concerns life itself. How did life develop in the
"poisonous," primitive atmosphere and evolve
the green plants that "purified" the air with free
oxygen and cleared the way for the higher forms
of life to develop? Some answers are given in
Chapter 12.

Much carbon dioxide was removed from the
atmosphere by chemical combinations with calcium, hydrogen, and oxygen, which formed
limestone, coal, and petroleum, the great bulk
lying buried in the crust. These are the great
reserves of fossil fuels that we have relied on for
energy to power our industrial societies. The
few hundredths of one percent of the atmosphere that remains as CO_2 is of course highly
important to us in that it is an essential raw
material that plants use for photosynthesis.

Earth is 140 million kilometers from the Sun.
Some calculations show that if it were only 10
million kilometers closer, the increased temperature would have prevented water vapor from
condensing into oceans, and carbon dioxide
would not have been removed from the atmos-

phere and chemically locked up in rocks. It is
doubtful if life would have formed under those
circumstances.

**The Account of the Earth's Evolution—
Fact or Fiction?** The preceding story is, of
course, speculation based on physical plausibil-
ity and extrapolation from experiment. *In all
fairness, however, it should be mentioned that we
have presented but one of several possible courses
for our planet's evolution from among the several
hypotheses currently extant. There are alternative
views for the nature of each stage, but about the
general course of events there is fair agreement.* We
are like children making a house out of a variety
of blocks: the constraint is that each block has to
fit with the ones under it and over it and that the
whole structure has to stand up. But there may
be more than one way to build the house.

Even if the details are obscure, we believe that
the general sequence of events just described
may be taken as a tentative solution (by no
means a unanimous one) to the problem of the
early history of the Earth, because it explains
several facts of paramount importance. The
Earth has an iron core and a silicate mantle. In
order for this separation to take place, the interior would have had to become hot enough for
iron to melt. The Earth has a crust that is chemically distinct from the mantle, and it contains

Figure 1-14
The outermost shell of the Earth is the strong, solid lithosphere,
riding on the weak, partially molten asthenosphere. The lithosphere
is topped by a thin crust under the oceans and a thicker continental
crust.

such high concentrations of certain elements (for example, uranium and thorium) that they must have been extracted from the whole of its body. This implies a mobility that only extensive melting could provide. Finally, there is a source of thermal energy to which we can attribute the melting—radioactivity.

In the remainder of this book, we will be concerned mainly with what happened to the Earth following the stage of primary differentiation. The mantle solidified, a primitive crust and continents developed, oceans and atmospheres were produced by outgassing, and the processes that we know today were set in motion. Differentiation slowed the internal heat engine of Earth, leaving enough heat in the interior for the planet to continue to evolve to this very day.

THE EARTH MACHINE SET IN MOTION, MUCH AS WE KNOW IT TODAY

Plate Tectonics—A Unifying Theory. Geology books written in the 1970's have a distinct advantage over their predecessors. For almost 200 years, geologists have supported various theories of mountain-building, volcanism, and other major phenomena of Earth. None had a generality sufficient to explain well the whole range of geologic processes. Now, a single, all-encompassing concept is available that interprets many of the major geologic features of the Earth. Such topics as the classification and distribution of rocks, the history of sedimentary rock sequences, the position and characteristics of volcanoes, earthquake belts, mountain sys-

tems, deep-sea trenches, and ocean basins were formerly described in more or less unrelated fashion. Today we have the advantage of being able to treat these and other topics in the context of a unifying theory, **plate tectonics,** in which the large-scale pattern, if not the underlying mechanism, is recognized. To be sure, some geologists do not now accept certain parts of the theory, and some reject it entirely. Revolutions rarely proceed by unanimous consent!

The outermost shells of our concentrically zoned planet are illustrated in Figure 1-14, a representation of what we think we know of the Earth's zoning today. Why we propose this picture will of course be justified in later chapters, rather than here. The **lithosphere** is depicted as the strong, solid, outermost shell riding on the weak, partially molten **asthenosphere.** The continents are raftlike inclusions embedded in the lithosphere. A thin crust tops the lithosphere.

The central idea of plate tectonics is remarkably simple. The lithosphere is broken into about ten large rigid plates, each plate moving as a distinct unit. The major plates and the directions in which they move are sketched inside the front cover. Many large-scale geological features are associated with the boundaries between the plates.

Plates spread apart along **divergent junctions** typified by the cracklike valley at the crest of the mid-Atlantic ridge. This particular feature is the contact between the American plate on the one hand and the Eurasian and African plates on the other. The divergent junction is characterized by earthquake activity and volcanism. The void between the receding plates is filled by melted, mobile material that rises from

Figure 1-15
Stages in the development of a divergent junction and sea-floor spreading. (Top)
The lithosphere breaks, and a rift develops under a continent. Molten basalt from
the asthenosphere spills out. (Bottom) The rift continues to open, separating the
two parts of the continent—in this example, America and Africa. A new ocean
basin, the Atlantic, is created between the separating land masses. The active rift is
marked by a mid-ocean ridge, with earthquakes and volcanism as characteristic features. [After "The Breakup of Pangaea" by R. S. Dietz and J. C. Holden. Copyright © 1970 by Scientific American, Inc. All rights reserved.]

below the lithosphere. The material solidifies in
the crack, and the plates grow as they separate.
Since new sea floor is created, this part of the
process, illustrated in Figure 1-17, has been
dubbed **sea-floor spreading.**

There seems to be little doubt that the Atlantic Ocean did not exist 150 million years ago.
Instead, the large, single hypothetical land mass
reconstructed in Figure 1-16, named **Pangaea,**
contained Eurasia, Africa, and the Americas.
Pangaea was split by a crack that subsequently
opened to form the Atlantic Ocean. The trailing
edges of the receding continents became a new
repository for erosional debris brought to the
newly formed sea from inland sources. The
sedimentary deposits were laid down in
wedge-shaped bodies along submerged continental margins. Figure 1-17 shows how thick

deposits of sediments along continental margins
can be explained by this mechanism.

If plates separate in one place, they must
converge somewhere else, and they do. Plates
grind together head-on along **convergent
junctions.** It is no surprise that crumpled
mountain ranges, deep-sea trenches, shallow and
deep earthquakes, and volcanoes are all associated with convergence. Examples are the contact
between the Nazca plate and the American plate
(see inside of front cover), where one finds the
Andes Mountains, the Chilean deep-sea trench,
and where some of the world's great earthquakes
have been recorded. Another example is the
Kuril-Kamchatka-Aleutian arc system, along
which the Pacific plate runs into the Eurasian
plate. We will see that convergent zones take on
different manifestations, depending on spread-

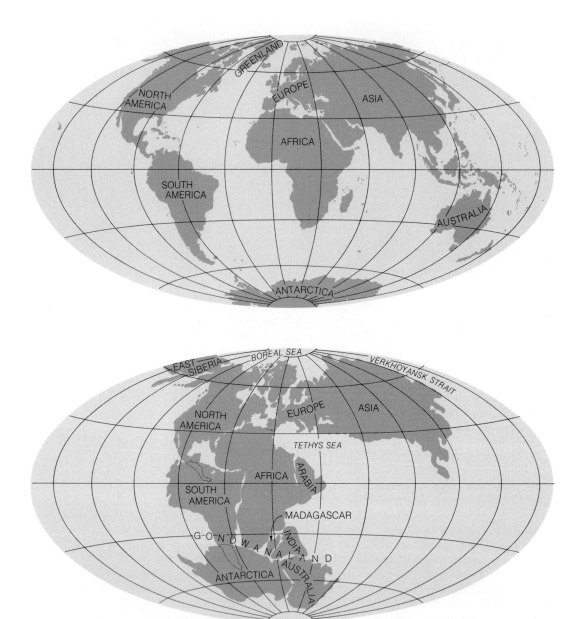

Figure 1-16
Single supercontinent of Pangaea, presumed to have existed 200 million years ago, may have appeared as shown below. Present-day map is shown at the top. [After "Continental Drift" by J. Tuzo Wilson. Copyright © 1963 by Scientific American, Inc. All rights reserved.]

Figure 1-17
As a rift widens and a new sea floor is created (a), the trailing edges of the receding continents receive erosional debris from inland, deposited as thick wedges of sediment (b). [After "Geosynclines, Mountains, and Continent-Building" by R. S. Dietz. Copyright © 1972 by Scientific American, Inc. All rights reserved.]

ing rates and whether the leading edges of plates are continental or oceanic.

It has been said that one picture is worth a thousand words. This is certainly true of Figure 1-18, which shows the profusion of geologic activity associated with but one plate-collision scenario, where the abutting edges are ocean floor and continent. The heavy, oceanic lithosphere descends into the mantle, below the lighter continental lithosphere. Downbuckling is marked by an offshore trench. Great earthquakes occur adjacent to the inclined contact between the two plates. The edge of the overriding plate is crumpled and uplifted to form a mountain chain that runs parallel to the trench. Deep-sea sediments may be scraped off the descending slab and incorporated into the adjacent mountains. What a complicated mess! As the mountains are raised, erosion by wind, ice, and water wears them down. The debris eventually ends up in the oceans to repeat the cycle of rock formation and destruction over and over again.

Such regions of convergence, where lithosphere is consumed, have been named **subduction zones.** If the divergent zones are sources of new lithosphere, then the subduction zones are sinks in which material is consumed in equal amount. Otherwise the Earth would change in size, but neither geological evidence nor physical theory support this conclusion.

Rocks caught up in a subduction zone will be squeezed and heated. A new assemblage of minerals will appear as a result of this "pressure-cooking" treatment, depending on the pressure, temperature, and deformation to which the rocks are subjected by the subduction process. **Metamorphism,** the cumulative effect of all of these processes, leads to the formation of new mineral grains and therefore new rocks. The sequence of sedimentary and metamorphic rocks in and next to convergent zones may provide the key to unraveling the history of a collision between plates.

As the oceanic plate descends into the hot mantle, parts of it may begin to melt. The rock melt, or **magma,** thus formed would float up-

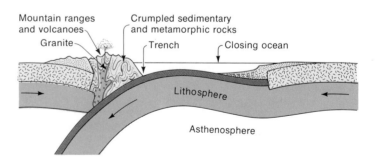

Figure 1-18
When plates collide, one plate usually buckles downward. The overriding plate is crumpled and uplifted. Deep-sea trenches (sites of the greatest of ocean depths), high mountain chains, volcanoes, and the greatest earthquakes are associated with such regions of plate convergence. [After "Geosynclines, Mountains, and Continent-Building" by R. S. Dietz. Copyright © 1972 by Scientific American, Inc. All rights reserved.]

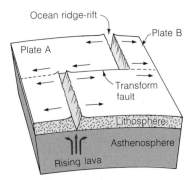

Figure 1-19
A transform fault is a plate boundary
along which two plates slide past each
other. In the example shown, Plates *A*
and *B* are separating. The ridge crest,
which marks the zone of spreading, is
offset by the transform fault. The arrows indicate the opposite plate motions on the two sides of the transform fault between the ridges.

Figure 1-20
View northwest along the San Andreas fault in the Carrizo Plains of California.
This fault is an example of a transform fault. It forms a portion of the sliding
boundary between the Pacific and American plates. [Photo by R. E. Wallace, U.S.
Geological Survey.]

ward, some of it reaching the surface as lava
erupting from volcanic vents. In a manner not
fully understood, the formation of magma in the
subduction zone may be a key element in the
creation of granitic rocks, the major rock from
which continents are formed.

Plates can separate and collide, as we have just
seen. They can also slip past one another along a
transform fault (Fig. 1-19). The famed San
Andreas fault of California is an example of
such a boundary. There the Pacific plate slides
past the American plate in a northwesterly direction. This contact is characterized by contrasting geology on both sides and by large,
shallow-focus earthquakes of the kind that destroyed San Francisco in 1906.

What we have just described is the general
pattern of the internal heat engine's work output
as we can see it today. The process probably has
been going on since the large-scale differentiation of the Earth ended some 4 billion years ago.
A description, however, is not an explanation.
We have unraveled the kinematics, or motions,
of the process, but the dynamics, or forces, that
are responsible, have yet to be understood (Fig.
1-21): so far we can do no more than make vague
reference to convection serving as an internal
heat engine. Furthermore, there is a wealth of
major geologic features that lie within the continents and whose relations to plate tectonics, if
any, have yet to be established. Nevertheless, a
grand scheme of things has been recognized, and

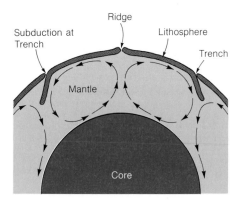

Figure 1-21
A simple model showing how convection currents in the deep interior might be the driving force of sea-floor spreading and continental drift. Hot matter rises under the ocean ridge and flows apart, carrying the plates along. Plates sink with cold matter at subduction zones.

the course of geology has undoubtedly changed.

A parallel development of the 1960's was the increasing sophistication of our awareness of the external heat engine of the Earth. That engine, powered by the Sun's energy, drives the circulation of the atmosphere and oceans, provides the rain, wind, ice, and running water that erode the mountains of the Earth. As soon as the atmosphere formed by outgassing, the external heat engine started to grind out the products of erosion and chemical decomposition; rivers began to run to the ocean, delivering sediments to beaches and deltas; ocean currents carried the finest of the sediments farther from land, where in quiet waters they accumulated on the margins of continents and in the deep sea. The external heat engine is of immediate consequence to us, for aside from its importance in most of the geological processes we see operating at the surface of the Earth, we are living in the midst of it and depend completely on its workings for our food and our energy.

The many ways in which the internal and external heat engines are linked provide exciting new territory to explore for geologists and oceanographers. As we find out more about each engine, we find out more about their interactions. Their interactions, too, can affect us drastically—as when an earthquake, which happens to occur during Peru's rainy season, triggers a massive mudflow that kills thousands of people (1970), or when a volcano like Mount Agung in Bali erupts (1963) and sends so much volcanic ash into the atmosphere that the quantity of atmospheric dust over the whole world is significantly increased.

In what follows we will deal with continents and ocean basins and interpret the information in the different kinds of rocks in the conceptual framework provided by plate tectonics. Though that concept does not explain everything, and may not even relate to some kinds of phenomena, it gives us by all odds the best framework on which to lay the story of the Earth.

SUMMARY

1. The Sun and its family of planets formed when a primeval cloud of gas and dust condensed about 5 billion years ago. The planets differ in chemical composition according to their distance from the Sun and their size.

2. Earth probably grew by accretion of small chunks of matter to reach its present size. At its birth it was probably a homogeneous and relatively cool body.

3. Because of radioactivity, Earth began heating up, and within about a billion years or less the temperatures probably reached the melting point of iron. Drops of molten iron sank to the center, and lighter matter floated up to form the outer layers that became the continents. Outgassing gave rise to the oceans and a primitive atmosphere. In this way the Earth was transformed to a differentiated planet with chemically distinct zones—an iron core, a magnesium-iron-silicate mantle, and a crust enriched in oxygen, silicon, aluminum, calcium, sodium, and radioactive elements.

4. The lithosphere, or outermost shell of the Earth, is broken into about ten large, rigid plates, which jostle each other because of their individual motions. The boundaries of these plates are zones of intense activity; associated with them are many of the large-scale geological features produced by such processes as mountain-building, volcanism, creation and destruction of the sea floor, and earthquake activity.

EXERCISES

1. What factors have made Earth a particularly congenial place for life to develop?

2. How does the chemical-condensation-sequence model explain the differences between the terrestrial planets? How and why do the terrestrial planets differ from the giant planets?

3. If you were an astronaut exploring another planet, what evidence would you look for to decide whether the planet was differentiated and whether it was still geologically active?

4. A recent hypothesis proposes that the Earth became chemically zoned not by differentiation but by accreting sequentially, first an iron core, then a rocky mantle, and finally a crust. How might this have happened? How can this idea be tested?

5. What are the advantages and disadvantages of living on a differentiated planet? On a geologically active planet?

6. Describe the central idea of plate tectonics and the large-scale geologic features associated with plate boundaries. How would you recognize an ancient plate boundary?

7. Speculate on what life would be like today if the ancient continent of Pangaea remained a single land mass instead of breaking up into Eurasia, Africa, and the Americas.

BIBLIOGRAPHY

Brandt, J. C., and S. P. Moran, *New Horizons in Astronomy*. San Francisco: W. H. Freeman and Company, 1972. (Chapters 7, 8, 15.)

Gass, I. G., P. J. Smith, and R. C. L. Wilson (editors), *Understanding the Earth*. Cambridge: M.I.T. Press, 1971.

Jastrow, Robert, and M. H. Thompson, *Astronomy: Fundamentals and Frontiers*. New York: John Wiley & Sons, 1972. (Part Three, The Planets.)

Laporte, L. F., *The Earth and Human Affairs*. San Francisco: Canfield Press, 1972.

Leveson, David, *A Sense of the Earth*. New York: Doubleday and Company, Inc., 1972.

Press, F., and R. Siever (compilers), *Planet Earth: Readings from Scientific American*. San Francisco: W. H. Freeman and Company, 1975.

Takeuchi, S., S. Uyeda, and H. Kanamori, *Debate About the Earth*. San Francisco: Freeman, Cooper & Company, 1970.

Wilson, J. Tuzo (compiler), *Continents Adrift and Continents Aground: Readings from Scientific American*. San Francisco: W. H. Freeman and Company, 1976.

2

THE GEOLOGICAL TIME SCALE
AND THE ROCK RECORD

Concepts of time are central to geology. Most geologic processes that shape the surface of the Earth and give structure to its interior operate over long times, up to millions and billions of years. The igneous, metamorphic, and sedimentary rocks exposed at the surface are the visible records of the geologic processes of the past. From the time and space relations that those rocks manifest, geologists have built the geologic time scale, which is used for placing the geologic events of Earth history in sequence according to relative age. Spontaneous decay of radioactive atoms in rocks gives absolute ages that date the geological periods and the origin of the Earth.

HOW LONG IS A LONG TIME?

The key difference between geologists (and astronomers) and most other scientists is in their attitude toward time. Though many chemical reactions and physical processes that we measure in the laboratory operate over time periods—or **time scales**—of seconds or fractions of seconds, geological processes that we can observe directly take place over a much broader time range. The time scale for earthquake tremors may range from seconds to minutes, and the times for the seismic waves generated by that earthquake to travel through the Earth and along its surface are reckoned in minutes and hours. Erosion and transportation of an immense amount of boulders, sand, silt, and clay by a major river in flood operates over a period of a few days. Sandbars move in and out from a beach in days or weeks. These are processes we can see or feel actively happening. Others cannot be observed directly; for example, the Atlantic Ocean is spreading apart at the mid-Atlantic ridge on a much longer time scale—at a rate of a few centimeters per

year. The gullying of overgrazed or carelessly farmed land by accelerated erosion takes place over a time scale of a few years. But when time scales are 50 years or more in duration, our memories start to fail us and we rely on historical records in order to measure how much a marshy tideland has filled in, how much a hillside has eroded, or how much a river has gradually changed its course.

Despite an occasional earthquake or volcanic eruption, the Earth seems to provide us with a reasonably stable foundation upon which to build a civilization. This holds true on a time scale important to organized society—namely, hundreds or thousands of years. That stability is absent on a geological time scale of millions to hundreds of millions of years, during which continents, oceans, and mountain chains have moved horizontally and vertically through large distances. Although the evidence for long-term instability is all around us, only in recent years have scientists begun to recognize a world-wide pattern in these movements. Working out that pattern requires a means of timing the move-

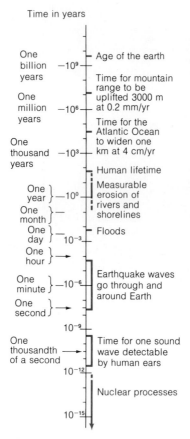

Figure 2-1
Orders of magnitude of times for some common processes and events. The scale is logarithmic, that is, it has equal divisions between all successive powers of ten.

In many geological books and journals, long time units have come into general use as abbreviations: *m.y.* for millions of years, *b.y.* for billions of years. A billion years is commonly called an *eon*.

The first holes were drilled in the deep sea in 1968 by the JOIDES (Joint Oceanographic Institutions Deep Earth Sampling) project, sponsored by the National Science Foundation and the major oceanographic institutions of the United States. This program, later called the Deep Sea Drilling Program, has continued with the drilling of many holes; in 1975 it became jointly sponsored by the United States, the Soviet Union, Great Britain, France, and Germany. It is now called IPOD (International Program of Ocean Drilling).

ments relative to each other and to a known time scale.

In Chapter 1 we discussed the time scales of millions of years, that elapsed during the formation of the Sun and the planets—times measured by radioactive clocks and inferred by reasoning from the rates of the physical and chemical processes involved. We concluded that the Earth is about 4.7 billion years old. What happened during all of the time between then and now? How long does it take geologic processes to make mountains and destroy them? What is the lifetime of a river? Time scales ranging from a few tens of years to a few billions of years are characteristic of most of the processes discussed in this book.

Why do we care about time scales? One of the most important reasons, one that comes from the heart of historical geology, the story of the evolution of the Earth as we now see it, is to be able to reconstruct just what happened when. When were the Appalachians or the Rocky Mountains formed? When did the Atlantic Ocean start spreading apart? Equally important in the value of time scales, however, is the help we get in trying to figure out *how* something happened. This comes from an old rule of physical science: if two things formed within different time scales, they are likely to have been made by different processes. Most of the time we use this rule of thumb in an unconscious way, but it is sometimes worthwhile to spell it out explicitly, as a guide to thinking about a specific problem.

How We Estimate Very Slow Rates of Earth Processes. A few simple, rough calculations give surprisingly good estimates. Rocks older than about 200 million years have not been found on the deep sea floor, even though many holes have been drilled there in the past ten years. We may therefore take the 200 million years as some sort of an upper limit to the age of an ocean basin. If 10,000 kilometers is used as a representative width of an ocean—that is, the distance the plates have spread to form the basin—the spreading rate comes out to be 10,000 kilometers/200 million years = 5 centimeters/year.

The well-known San Andreas fault in California is a transform fault along which the North Pacific plate slides past the North American plate. At some precisely located places along the fault, measurements have been made by survey for almost a century: during this period, slip along the fault, due both to earthquakes and to steady creep, has amounted to about 4 to 6

centimeters/year. On a longer time scale, the rate of movement can be determined by matching up distinctive geological formations that have been split by the fault, the separate parts moving away from each other. The average

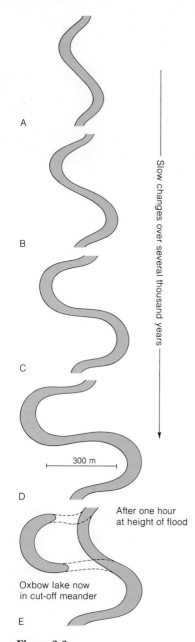

Figure 2-2
A meander loop of a river slowly accentuates its bends over hundreds or thousands of years (*a* to *d*), but in one hour's time, at the height of a flood, may break through its banks (*d* to *e*) to cut off a meander and isolate an oxbow lake.

movement over the past several million years can be inferred in this way to be about 1 centimeter/year in northern and central California. At that rate, about 25 million years ago the block containing the present San Francisco coast would have been at the latitude of the present Los Angeles! Later we will describe more precise methods for obtaining rates of plate movements in different parts of the world, including dating of magnetic patterns on the sea floor and dating of sediment samples obtained in the Deep Sea Drilling Project.

Vertical movements can be evaluated by dating marine deposits that are now above sea level. Mountains made up of rocks that are now above sea level. Mountains made up of rocks that contain marine fossils have been uplifted 3000 meters in 15 million years, giving a rate of 0.2 millimeters/year. About 40,000 years ago, during the last ice age, Fennoscandia, the area including Norway, Sweden, and Finland, was covered by 2 to 3 kilometers of ice. The tremendous weight of the ice sheet loaded and depressed that part of the lithosphere. When a warming trend set in and the ice melted away, the lithosphere there rebounded some 500 meters, as evidenced by the existence of ancient beaches at that elevation above sea level. Thus postglacial uplift of Fennoscandia took place at a rate of about 1 centimeter/year. This particular evidence gives us important data for determining the viscosity of the mantle.

Erosional processes are continuously wearing down the land surface; without mountain building and other vertical rejuvenation, such as the type just described, all land would eventually be reduced to sea level. Erosion rates can be estimated by adding up all of the disintegrated and dissolved products of erosion being carried away by rivers and wind. The rate for the North American continent has been estimated in this way to be about 0.03 millimeter/year (about 1

Figure 2-4
Photographs of Bowknot Bend on the Green River in Canyonlands National Park, Utah. The upper one was taken by E. O. Beaman in 1871 on Major John Wesley Powell's second expedition down the Green and Colorado rivers; the lower one, by H. G. Stephens in 1968. Though taken almost 100 years apart, the two photographs show little change in rocks and formations. Millions of years of erosion were required to produce the river valleys of today. [From U.S. Geological Survey.]

Figure 2-3
The North American plate has been moving south relative to the North Pacific plate along the San Andreas transform fault at a rate of about 1 cm/yr.

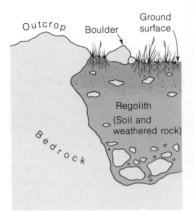

Figure 2-5
Cross section through surface of the
ground, showing relations among outcrop, boulders, and soil.

Figure 2-6
The Grand Canyon of the Colorado: a view south from the bordering Kaibab Plateau. Though the topography is rugged, the horizontal stratification of the upper
rocks in the canyon is clearly displayed. [From *Geology Illustrated* by John S.
Shelton. W. H. Freeman and Company. Copyright © 1966.]

foot per 10,000 years). Thus it takes hundreds of
millions (10^8) of years to open an ocean basin,
about 20 million (2×10^7) years to raise a
mountain, and 10^8 years to cut it down to sea
level.

Even these are relatively short periods on the
geological time scale of the history of the Earth.
The Earth has experienced many cycles of
mountain-building and erosion in the past 4
billion years. In the next sections we explore
how we can date all of the events that are parts
of those cycles.

THE ROCK RECORD

The only record we have of things that happened on Earth in the geological past is the
rocks that were preserved from erosional destruction.

**How to Use a Rock Section to Tell a Story:
The Grand Canyon.** There are a great variety
of places where the bedrock, which everywhere
underlies the surface, is exposed, not obscured
by soil or loose boulders. Such exposures, called
outcrops, range in size from small projections
of weathered rock on a hillside and ledges in the
beds of small streams to high cliffs that make the
walls of canyons in mountainous terrain. Geologists also know how to use man's engineering
works—formerly, railroad cuts, but for the past
half century, road cuts—as ideal places to study
well-exposed sections of rock. But it might take
a crew of 1000 men with bulldozers, dynamite
blasting, and heavy earth-moving machinery
more than a lifetime to even begin to excavate a
highway cut that would touch the dimensions of
a place like the Grand Canyon of the Colorado
River. And it wouldn't have any of the beauty
and grandeur of that fantastic gorge, which is
more than a mile (1.6 kilometers) deep in places,
4 to 18 miles wide (6.5 to 29 kilometers), and
280 miles (450 kilometers) long. The main part
alone is 56 miles (90 kilometers) long. It is still
an adventure to go down the Canyon of the
Colorado River in a small boat, repeating the
first trip, made in 1869. That first perilous jour-

Figure 2-7
Freshly deposited river sand and silt, showing original horizontality of sedimentary deposits. View is of a cut spaded through two layers of a sand bar in the Vermillion River, Illinois; the upper horizontal layer is made up of many inclined cross-beds and shows a ripplemarked surface. [Photo by Paul E. Potter.]

ney, 3 months long, was made by Major John W. Powell, a government geologist, and his party of nine men in four small rowboats. Powell went on to help found the U.S. Geological Survey and later became a director of the agency.

The first thing we notice about the rocks of the Grand Canyon is a pronounced horizontal **layering,** or **stratification.** This **bedding,** as it is most frequently called, is what we might expect from the settling of particles from air or water to form layers of sediment (hence the name, from the Latin *sedimentum,* meaning settled). Our expectation is supported by our experience, for we can see horizontal layers of sand being deposited on beaches or sandbars, and layers of mud and silt accumulating on floodplains of rivers.

Once we make this generalization, (which has held up for the three hundred years since it was first enunciated), we can go on to the obvious next thought: since it is absurd to think that a sedimentary layer can be deposited beneath a previously deposited bed, we conclude that any

new layer added to a series must always be added on top. Naturally we have to add the proviso that the whole series has not been deformed and completely overturned at some later time. The time sequence of stratification is the simple basis for the **stratigraphic time scale,** a clock that we can use to measure time and events.

Simple as these generalizations are, they are a beautiful example of a well-known dictum: the truly great discoveries are the ones that are perfectly obvious *after* someone has pointed them out to us. It was Nicolaus Steno, a Danish court physician living in post-Renaissance Italy who in 1669 formulated the *Principle of Original Horizontality* and the *Principle of Superposition,* which we have given above in modified form. He also stated the *Principle of Original Continuity,* which states that a sedimentary layer forms at the time of its deposition a continuous sheet that ends either by thinning to disappearance, by gradually changing to a bed of different composition, or by abutting against a wall or barrier, such as a shoreline that confines the

A glimpse of Powell's experience is given by an excerpt from his report on this survey: ". . . Now the danger is over; now the toil has ceased; now the gloom has disappeared . . . The river rolls by us in silent majesty: the quiet of the camp is sweet; our joy is almost ecstasy . . ."

depositional area. From the law of continuity we intuitively grasp the idea that the face of a bed, as we see it in the excavation for a highway cut or in the walls of the Grand Canyon, is the broken or eroded edge of a once-continuous sheet.

From these principles we get the rudiments of our stratigraphic clock; that is, we establish a total length of time necessary for all of the rocks to be laid down and a time interval within the whole span for each layer. If we had some idea of how long each bed took to be laid down, and *if* all of the time span were accounted for by the

A special kind of sediment, called *varved clay,* forms in lakes that are frozen over in the winter. The varves are layers of the clay that form couplets; one part of each couplet is a relatively thick, coarse-grained, light-gray silty clay that grades upward into a thin, fine-grained dark-gray clay. The light layers form in the summer and the dark ones in the winter, each pair marks one year. By counting the annual banding in lakes formed after the last ice age in Northern Europe, Baron G. DeGeer of Sweden was able to determine that about 8,700 years had passed since the glacial ice had retreated from all of Southern Europe. The accuracy of this method was confirmed by radioactive age determinations made much later, and only slight revision of the date had to be made.

Figure 2-8
Varved clay from Ogden, Utah. [Photo by R. M. Leggett, U.S. Geological Survey.]

time to lay down the sum of all of the beds, our clock would be constructed. But that last *if* is a big one, and the reason we suspect that a certain amount of time is not represented by rock is from the observation of river floods and other kinds of sedimentation. The silts laid down on flood plains of rivers, such as the historic ones of the Nile River in ancient Egypt, do not accumulate steadily and uniformly. We have seen that the time scale of flood deposits is about days long, but we have to remember that there is also a time scale for the times between floods, a time interval that may range from a few years to several decades. In other words, a hiatus, or interruption in sedimentation, may be two to three orders of magnitude (powers of 10) greater than the time for deposition of a layer of flood silt.

How Old is a Fossil? We have another, more powerful tool that can be used to establish the time sequence of a series of layers of sedimentary rocks, and that tool is the remains of ancient organisms found in some of those rocks. **Limestones,** one of the several kinds of sedimentary rocks, are made up of calcium carbonate ($CaCO_3$), much of it in the form of microscopic fossil animal shells. **Shales,** rocks that are hardened and compacted clays and muds, and **sandstones,** rocks made of cemented sand grains, may also contain fossil materials, such as shells and shell fragments. Some of the shells found in such rocks can easily be identified by comparison with similar kinds of shells found on beaches today. Many others can be found that look vaguely like some animals that live today but are obviously different. And others are obviously some sort of organism's shell but not like anything that we see alive today. Not all fossils are shells of invertebrates like clams, oysters, cowry shells, and periwinkles. If you dig in the hillsides of sandy rock in the badlands of South Dakota (and some other places too) you may uncover a vertebrate bone of an early piglike, cud-chewing mammal. Fish skeletons and shark teeth are found in other rocks. Plant fossils are abundant in some rocks, particularly the rocks in and above coal beds, where one can recognize fernlike and other leaves, plus twigs, branches, and even whole tree trunks.

What could be more natural than to jump to the conclusion that these fossils represent life of former times and that from them we could deduce the flow of evolution from the most primitive organisms to such a complicated one as man. The "jump" took some time to make, though. One of the people who made it first in modern times (some Greeks had known it long before) was Leonardo da Vinci. He was followed later by Nicolaus Steno, who in the seventeenth century compared teeth from modern sharks with the so-called "tongue-stones" of Malta in the Mediterranean and concluded that they must have come from the same kind of shark. Many objected to Steno's conclusion, but the similarities between the forms of modern animals, especially the hard parts, such as teeth, bones, and shells, soon piled up in such numbers that the evidence was overwhelming and could not be reasonably dismissed either as "some accident of form" or as an obscure expression of God's wisdom in creating the Earth.

But what has all this to do with making a time scale? The beginning of an answer can be found in the rocks of the Grand Canyon, for there we can find fossils in many of the exposed rocks, particularly in the limestones. Each limestone has a number of fossils of different species, but the assortment of fossils in one limestone may differ sufficiently from those in another as to be readily distinguishable. The vertical arrangement of fossils, the **faunal succession,** corresponds to the series of limestone layers that we call a **stratigraphic sequence** and has the same order. For convenience in mapping, limestones and other rocks are grouped into **formations,** which contain materials that for the most part have the same physical appearance and properties, a combination called **lithology.** Formations are a convenience for mapping. Sometimes they are all of one rock. Some formations consist of a single rock type or lithology, such as a granite or a limestone. Others may consist of interlayered thin beds of different lithologies, such as sandstone or shale. However they vary, each one comprises a distinctive group of rocks that can be recognized and thus mapped as a unit. From this stems the definition of the formation as the smallest mappable lithologic unit.

Once formations and stratigraphic sequences were mapped all over the world by nineteenth-century geologists, it became apparent that everywhere the faunal successions matched the sequences. This is the rule in fossiliferous formations of all ages since the beginning of the Cambrian Period, when shelled animals evolved. Thus fossil assemblages can be used as "fingerprints" of formations; each assemblage has slightly distinguishable characteristics, even though individual species may be present in several different formations.

It was this attribute of fossiliferous sediments

Figure 2-9
Modern and ancient cephalopods. The white shell is that of a modern chambered nautilus; the dark shell is that of a closely related form that lived about 200 million years ago. Such similarity of form was the basis for early recognition of the significance of fossils as evidence of ancient life. [Photo by R. Siever.]

Figure 2-10
Leaf-impressions of the extinct fern-like plant *Callipteris conferta* from the Hermit Shale. [From *Geology Illustrated* by John S. Shelton. W. H. Freeman and Company. Copyright © 1966.]

Figure 2-11
Fossil shark's teeth, as illustrated by Steno, 1667.

Sandy shale	No fossils
Shale	Few marine clams and other molluscs
Limestone	Abundant marine fossils of many kinds
Black shale	Small marine clams
Coal	Abundant plant fossils including tree stumps
Clay	Plant roots
Sandstone	Few land plant fossils and rare land vertebrate bones

that William Smith, an engineer and surveyor who had worked in coal mines and mapped along canals, began to see so clearly when he set about collecting fossils in southeastern England in 1793. Smith knew nothing of the idea of organic evolution that was to come from Charles Darwin some decades later. He did note, however, that different formations contain different fossils, and he was able to tell one formation from another by the differences in the fossils. As Smith extended his mapping all over southern England in the early part of the nineteenth century, he was able to draw up a stratigraphic succession of rocks that appeared in different places at different levels—a composite showing how the complete section would have looked if all of the rocks from those different places and levels were brought together in one place.

Let us see how this idea works if we forget about names of fossils and formations but simply call them by different letters and numbers. At one place, **I**, a geologist sees the following horizontal succession with its characteristic fossil assemblage.

I

Rock	Fossil assemblage
A	a
B	b
C	c

In another place, miles away, he sees another horizontal succession.

II

Rock	Fossil assemblage
B	b
C	c
D	d

Figure 2-12
Faunal succession in a sequence of lithologic units of Pennsylvanian age in the coal-bearing strata of Illinois. The assemblages of fossils are characteristic of each rock type.

Figure 2-13
Sequence of events involved in the making of an unconformity.

By simple use of the principle of superposition we infer that the composite sequence is:

A	a
B	b
C	c
D	d

But now, at place **III,** he discovers another sequence:

A	a
C	c
F	f

Here B is missing for some reason, but where does F belong—above or below D? We cannot tell from this information alone. Thus this is a problem of making an ordered sequence with respect to time from different fragments or partial records. To resolve the problem, the **stratigrapher** will have to hunt for an outcrop that shows both F and D.

The missing B at **III** may be explained by erosion. Perhaps B was once deposited after C at place **III,** but it may have been eroded away before A was laid down. Or B may never have been laid down in the first place. For example, there are places in the world today, typically in shallow marine waters, where there may be neither deposition nor erosion, but a constant balance between the two, so that no material accumulates.

The Grand Canyon Sequence Interpreted.
Let us go back again to the Grand Canyon and through the sequence from the base up. At the bottom, exposed in the inner gorge, are dark rocks that are not at all like the horizontally bedded sedimentary rocks above. They show neither bedding nor any other kind of structure, and from bodies that seem to be inserted into and cut across structures in the surrounding rocks. Some of these rocks are made up of coarse crystals; others are made up of particles so small that they cannot be seen even with a hand lens. These characteristics are interpreted by geologists to be evidence of **igneous** origin; that is, they were formed by cooling and solidification of a hot molten liquid, or **magma.** The coarsely crystalline ones are inferred to have been em-

placed in the rocks that surround them at a time when those rocks were still buried deep in the earth; these **intrusives** originated as hot magma that pushed its way into cracks and other openings in the surrounding rocks. The fine-grained rocks, **extrusives,** were formed as lava flows and ash deposits from volcanic eruptions.

Another group of rocks exposed in the inner gorge are those that have a platy or leafy texture, called **foliation,** caused by the alignment of minerals along straight or wavy planes, which can be confused with bedding. In some of these rocks true bedding can also be seen, but it is folded and crumpled. These **metamorphic** rocks (from the Greek, meaning to change form or to transform) were once sedimentary and igneous rocks, but they have been altered by the action of heat and pressure due to their deep burial in the Earth.

The lowest rocks of the inner gorge, the Vishnu formation, are a complex mixture of these igneous and metamorphic rocks. The Vishnu has no fossils, and there is no way to tell how old a rock is merely by looking at its minerals and their texture (geologists learned long ago that rocks formed by the same process at different times tend to look alike). Nevertheless, the Vishnu is at least the oldest rock we can see in the Grand Canyon inner gorge: it's at the bottom. Because of its position, it gives us our first glimpse of history there. The rocks of the Vishnu, originally formed as lava flows, ash deposits, and sediments, became deeply buried beneath the rocks that now overlie them, were metamorphosed by the resulting heat and pressure, and were later intruded by molten magma.

Above the Vishnu, and separated from it by a sharp line of discontinuity—an **angular unconformity**—is another series of rocks. An angular unconformity is a surface of erosion that separates two sets of beds whose bedding planes are not parallel. It thus signifies that the originally horizontal lower set was deformed and then eroded to a more-or-less even surface before the upper set was deposited horizontally upon it. Rocks in many places show evidence of such physical deformation. Sedimentary layers, once horizontal, are in places **folded** (bent into a wavy structure) and **faulted** (broken and displaced along fractures), as in Figure 2-15. The same structural features, sometimes less easily recognized, are found in igneous and metamorphic rocks. We can therefore add an episode of deformation and uplift to our history of sedimentation, burial, and metamorphism.

The rocks above the Vishnu are interlayered

1   "A" sediments deposited

2   "A" folded during
mountain building

3   Surface of "A" is eroded

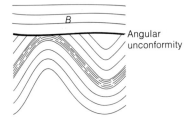

4   "B" sediments deposited
on erosion surface

Angular
unconformity

Figure 2-14
The order of geologic events involved in the making of an angular unconformity.

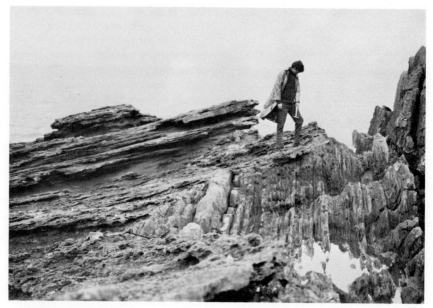

Figure 2-16
Unconformable contact of Old Red Sandstone beds on vertical Silurian rocks at Siccar Point, Berwickshire, Scotland. It was from a study of this locality that James Hutton, in 1788, first realized the meaning of unconformity. The geologist is standing just above the contact. [Photo by R. Siever.]

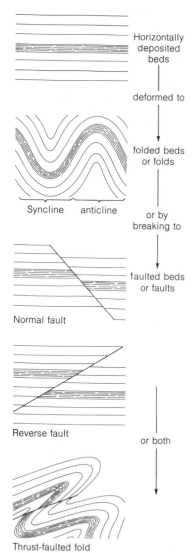

Horizontally deposited beds

deformed to

folded beds or folds

Syncline   anticline

or by breaking to

faulted beds or faults

Normal fault

Reverse fault

or both

Thrust-faulted fold

Figure 2-15
How originally horizontal beds can be deformed into folds and faults. Though easiest to see in sediments, all kinds of rocks may be folded and faulted.

sandstones, shales, and limestones. Many of them are characteristically reddish, which in combination with the varied hues of other formations in the Canyon creates a striking display of color—the extraordinary visual experience that impressed Major Powell and has awed the millions who have followed him into what is today Grand Canyon National Park.

The Grand Canyon Series, as the upper rocks of the inner gorge are called, contains no fossils, and all that we can say about it from this inspection is that it is younger than the Vishnu, older than the rocks above, and is tilted from its originally horizontal position. Sedimentary rocks like these are perfectly ordinary in every way except for two characteristics. They contain none of the fossils so typical of younger rocks, and they are typically associated with deformed and metamorphosed rocks like the Vishnu. As early as the eighteenth century, rocks of this kind were set apart from younger fossiliferous strata, and three great classes were distinguished: Primary, Secondary, and Tertiary rocks. The main difference at that time was thought to be the complexly folded and faulted nature of the Primary as contrasted with the more-or-less horizontal, overlying Secondary. The importance of fossils was to come later. What we can infer from these unfossiliferous

rocks of the Grand Canyon Series is a history subsequent to the erosion of an uplifted Vishnu terrain that includes sedimentation, moderate burial, and moderate deformation that led to tilting and gentle folding.

Another clearly discernible unconformity separates the Grand Canyon Series from the overlying, pebbly, brown Tapeats Sandstone. The Tapeats, about 70 meters (225 feet) thick, contains no fossils, but it can be dated by reference to the overlying formations that it blends into without any break, thus forming a **conformable succession.** Farther up the canyon wall, the Tapeats gradually gives way to a formation consisting dominantly of shale, a hardened equivalent of a muddy sediment, called the Bright Angel Shale. The Bright Angel Shale contains a few fossils, most of which are **trilobites,** extinct arthropods related to modern crayfish. The differences among the various trilobites of different ages can be used by paleontologists to date these rocks. By matching fossil trilobite species in different stratigraphic sequences in different parts of the world, a composite succession has been worked out. One of the consequences was the discovery that the part of the Bright Angel Shale that lies just above the nonfossiliferous Tapeats Sandstone in the western part of the Canyon is older than the part of the Shale that occupies the same stratigraphic position in the eastern part of the Canyon. This means that the sea in which the Bright Angel was deposited flooded the land in the east at a later date. This is evidence of a **transgression,** meaning that as the Bright Angel Shale was being deposited the sea was gradually moving landward, from west to east. Once again, it is simple geometric evidence that leads to this conclusion: as the sea advanced slowly from west to east, it continuously laid down sand along beaches and mud in deeper water. The reverse, the withdrawal of a sea and the inverse distribution of sediments in relation to shorelines, is called a **regression.**

The Bright Angel Shale grades upward into the overlying Muav Limestone, which is about the same thickness and contains trilobites of the same general age as those in the Bright Angel Shale. The Muav is also a part of the transgressive sequence.

Even from a great distance, most of the formations of the canyon wall can be distinguished easily. For example, the Tapeats Sandstone forms an obvious rim at the top edge of the inner gorge, called loosely the "Granite" gorge. In contrast, most of the Bright Angel Shale, just above the rim, is hidden beneath rubble, which slopes gently upward from the top of the Tapeats to the base of a higher topographic bench, or step, which is the base of the Muav Limestone.

The next formation up, the Temple Butte Limestone, is one that could easily be missed; it is thin, and in places along the Canyon wall it is missing entirely; in these places, the Redwall Limestone, which elsewhere overlies the Temple Butte, rests directly on the Muav. The Temple Butte forms the base of a steep cliff, but the important thing about it is that it contains fossil skeletons of primitive fishes, which we know from the general succession of fossil animals lived a long time after the trilobites of the Muav. Fossils of a great many marine animals that lived between the times of deposition of the Muav and the Temple Butte are known from other formations in various parts of the world—but they are all missing here. Thus there is evidence here of a great gap in the record, for there is an unconformity between the Muav and the Temple Butte. If any sediment had been laid down during the time represented by this unconformity, it was later eroded without leaving a trace. Such a sequence implies a history of Muav sedimentation and burial (but no deformation; it

Figure 2-17
A nearly complete trilobite, and the tail of another, from the Bright Angel Shale. [From *Geology Illustrated* by John S. Shelton. W. H. Freeman and Company. Copyright © 1966.]

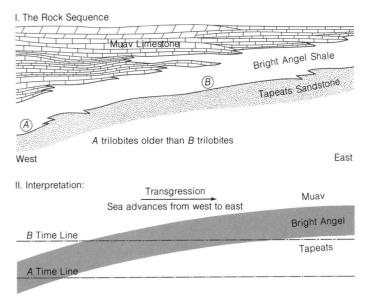

Figure 2-18
I. The stratigraphic relations of the Bright Angel Shale in the Grand Canyon region. The fact that trilobites at *A* are older than those at *B* leads to the interpretation shown in II.

Figure 2-19
Formations exposed in Diamond Creek, Grand Canyon. The Cambrian Bright
Angel Shale, which forms the rubbly slopes at the bottom, is overlain by the
Cliff-forming Muav, Temple Butte, and Redwall limestones. Above the main cliff
is the thinner Supai Formation, which crops out with gentler slopes than the cliff
formations below. [Photo by Edwin D. McKee, U.S. Geological Survey.]

Figure 2-20
Cross-bedding in the Coconino Sandstone. The cross-bedding of different layers
interferes to produce such a complex pattern that the true horizontal bedding
planes are not easily distinguished. [Photo by Edwin D. McKee, U.S. Geological
Survey.]

is still horizontal) before it was uplifted, eroded,
and later covered by sediments that formed the
Temple Butte Formation.

Another time gap is represented by an unconformity between the Temple Butte and the
overlying Redwall Limestone; still another is
represented by an unconformity between the
Redwall and the Supai Formation. The Redwall's age we know from its sparse content of
fossil marine animals. The Supai contains no
marine fossils, but it does contain fossils of land
plants. Thus it can be dated with reference to
the worldwide succession of plant fossils, a succession that has been worked out in much the
same way as the succession of animal fossils.
The fossil plant remains are similar to those of
the famous bituminous and anthracite coal beds
in the United States and the Ruhr Valley in
Europe. Of even greater interest are the fossil
footprints of primitive reptiles found in the
Supai. Thus it turns out that we can tell something of time not only from marine sediments
but from those deposited on land—the **terrestrial,** or **continental, deposits.**

Continuing up the canyon walls, we find that
there is also an unconformity at the top of the
Supai. Above the Supai is a sandy, red shale, the
Hermit Shale, which is succeeded by the Coconino Sandstone. Not only does the Coconino
contain more vertebrate animal tracks, but it has
a distinctive form of bedding, which is not
uniform and horizontal like that of many sediments, but is composed of many sets of interfering wedges of bedded material inclined at various angles up to 35° from the horizontal. This
form of bedding, called **cross-bedding,** is a
characteristic structure of sand dunes on land
though it is also characteristic of dunes formed
by currents in rivers and under the sea. On the
basis of vertebrate animal tracks and the dune
cross-bedding, most geologists believe that the
Coconino Sandstone formed by wind.

The Coconino appears to be conformable
with the underlying Hermit; that is, there is no
evidence that the beds at the top of the Hermit
have been eroded, nor do the few fossils available indicate any missing time interval. Similarly,
the Coconino is conformable with the overlying
Toroweap, a formation of limestone and red,
sandy shale, which is succeeded by a massive
formation of limestone and sandstone that forms
the top of the cliffs at the upper rim of the
Canyon—the Kaibab Formation.

If we were to inspect highlands above the
canyon rim in the general region of the Grand
Canyon, we would find formations younger than

the Kaibab; from their fragmentary successions we could build a composite that would include about 1830 to 2120 meters (6000 to 7000 feet) of red, brown, yellow, and gray sandstones, conglomerates, and shales that contain the famous petrified forest of tree trunks and, in some places, dinosaur remains.

The rocks of the Grand Canyon have many stories to tell: of the advance and retreat of the seas over the continent at this place, of the appearance and disappearance of different kinds of organisms, and of the different kinds of marine and terrestrial environments in which this remarkable variety of sediments was deposited. But one of the most important is the tale of time—the time that is represented by the rocks of the Canyon and the time that is recorded by the unconformities between so many of the formations. From the radioactive time scale, which is based upon the decay of radioactive elements in minerals, we know that the oldest formation, the Vishnu, is about 1400 to 1500 million years old, and the top of the Kaibab about 225 million years old. An enormous amount of time is represented by these rocks and unconformities.

ROCKS AS RECORDS OF EARTH MOVEMENTS

Angular unconformities not only date erosion intervals, but they also are a record of ancient earth movements. Beds below such unconformities were folded, tilted, faulted, and uplifted before erosion produced the more-or-less even, unconformable surfaces that we observe today. Erosion was, in turn, followed by additional earth movement, for only crustal subsidence could account for a change from erosion to further sedimentation. Unconformities, therefore, are records of periods of mountain-building, even though the roots of the mountains are all we can see today. **Disconformities**—time gaps between two units whose bedding planes are parallel—are less dramatic, but still imply the same general sequence of uplift, erosion, and subsidence.

There are other ways of telling a time sequence too. Though igneous rocks are not layered, as sediments are, they too have characteristics that may be used to place them in time. Igneous intrusions injected as a mobile magma may show **discordant** or **cross-cutting** contacts with surrounding rocks, typified by thin **dikes** that cut across original structures in the

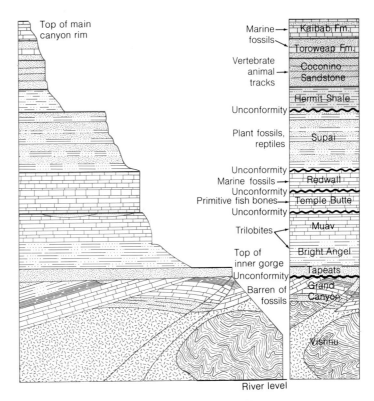

Figure 2-21
The Grand Canyon sequence. From the base up it consists of (1) the Vishnu (Precambrian), a complex group of metamorphic and igneous rocks; (2) the Grand Canyon series (Precambrian), tilted and faulted interlayered sandstones, shales, and limestones; (3) the Tapeats (Cambrian), a pebbly sandstone; (4) the Bright Angel Shale (Cambrian); (5) the Muav Limestone (Cambrian); (6) the Temple Butte Limestone (Devonian); (7) the Redwall Limestone (Mississippian); (8) the Supai Formation (Pennsylvanian), shales and sandstones; (9) the Hermit Shale (Permian); (10) the Coconino Sandstone (Permian); (11) the Toroweap Formation (Permian), mostly limestone; and (12) the Kaibab Limestone (Permian).

surrounding or **country rock;** or they may show **concordant** contacts, as in the case of **sills,** which may follow the bedding of the sediments into which they were intruded. The concordant and discordant field relations between igneous and adjacent sedimentary, metamorphic, and other igneous rocks can be used in just the same way that Steno's laws of original horizontality and superposition can be used to figure out relative ages of sediments. Similarly, folds and faults can be fitted into time sequences as well.

Why the Redwall Limestone got its name is obvious from any look at it in the Canyon. But the "red" in "Redwall" is in at least one way undeserved, for when a piece of the Redwall is cracked the fresh rock turns out to be gray. A close look at the cliff shows that the limestone is stained, as if it had been rubbed with a reddish pastel chalk. The stain is washed down by rain from the overlying sandy red shale of the Supai Formation.

Shown in Figure 2-22 is the record of a series of events that can be interpreted in only one way. Of course, once such a time-event jigsaw puzzle has been put together, as in this diagram, it looks easy. But the job of sorting out the pieces and seeing how they fit can sorely tax the imagination of a field geologist. *To sum up, the ways of ordering geologic events with respect to a relative time scale are based on interpretations of sedimentary successions, igneous field relations, such as cross-cutting, and tectonic deformation, such as folding and faulting and angular unconformity.* (The word **tectonic** refers to the deformation of the rocks of the Earth's crust and the structure of the crust in general.) By piecing together the information gleaned from the study of such field relations, geologists during the nineteenth century worked out the entire stratigraphic time scale.

Hutton and Uniformitarianism. Although the basis of the reasoning used here in interpreting the Grand Canyon sequence may seem obviously correct, it was not until the close of the eighteenth century that geologists, who were then struggling to find ways to explain the field relationships of rock formations, broke free of the static concept that the Earth was created just

as we see it today, with all of its river valleys, mountains, and plains placed where they are by God. The new way of looking at the Earth included the recognition that constant change takes place as geological forces modify the surface and the interior.

A well-known Scottish gentleman farmer, James Hutton, led the way with a book carrying the bold title *Theory of the Earth with Proof and Illustrations,* first presented to the Royal Society of Edinburgh in 1785. Hutton's greatness lies in his recognition of the cyclical nature of geological changes, and of the way in which ordinary processes, operating over long time intervals, can effect great changes. He reasoned from observation that rocks slowly decay and disintegrate under the action of water and air. This process—**weathering**—produces debris in the form of gravel, sand, and silt. Water and air also act to transport the debris, most of which ends up near or below sea level. The deposits are compacted, cemented, and ultimately become sedimentary rocks. At a later time, according to Hutton, a **plutonic** episode may occur in which subterranean heat and thermal expansion produce an intrusion of igneous rock accompanied by upheaval of the sediments and deformation into folds and faults accompanying mountain-building, called **orogeny.** Marine sediments emerge as land, bringing deposition to a halt, and then erosion of the newly emerged highlands initiates the cycle all over again.

Hutton observed and learned from the modern counterparts of each stage of his cycle: mountains being eroded, rivers carrying debris to the sea, ocean waves pounding rocks, sands and muds settling to the bottom and then being buried on the sea floor. Nature behaves in a uniform fashion throughout time, so that by studying the present one can infer the behavior of past processes. Hutton, followed by Charles Lyell (*Principles of Geology,* 1830), used and publicized this **Principle of Uniformitarianism.** Actually what remains "uniform" are the physical and chemical laws that govern geological activity. Volcanism may have been more frequent in the past than it is now. Nevertheless, ancient volcanoes should have released gases and deposited ash layers and lava flows, just as modern ones do when they erupt. Uniformitarianism, as we understand it today, does not hold that the rates of geological processes or their precise nature had to be the same.

Many of the concepts used in modern field interpretation go back to discoveries made by late eighteenth-century and nineteenth-century

Pluto was the Greek god of the lower world. Hutton's appeal to subterranean heat earned his theory the sobriquet *Plutonism.*

Figure 2-22
Relative time dating by field relations. The sequence of events shown must have been: (1) sediments *A* deposited, (2) sediments *A* deformed, (3) granite *B* intruded into *A*, (4) faulting along *C*, (5) erosion to produce unconformity at *D*, (6) sediments *E*, *F*, and *G* deposited, (7) tilting, uplift, and erosion to produce unconformity at *H*, (8) sediment *I* deposited, (9) basalt dike intruded at *J* and sill at *K*, (10) erosion to produce present land surface. Discordant contacts are illustrated by *B* and *J*, and a concordant contact by *K*.

geologists, among them: William Smith, the father of stratigraphy; George Cuvier, the great zoologist who pioneered in stratigraphy and paleontology in France; and Jean Guettard and Nicolas Desmarest, the geologists who explored the Auvergne region of France and showed that basalts were ancient lava flows. But it was Hutton who recognized that igneous bodies must be younger than the rocks they intrude. Hutton also pointed out that debris fragments in a sedimentary or igneous formation must have been derived from a parent rock older than the formation itself, and he was the first to grasp the idea that a cycle of upheaval, erosion, subsidence, and sedimentation would show as an *unconformity* in the stratigraphic record.

With these principles established, nineteenth-century geologists opened a new era. The history contained in rock formations could at last be deciphered, and man could travel backward in time to view ancient landscapes. It became possible to reconstruct the interrelations between mountains, oceans, climates, animals, and plants long since gone, as if the geologist were a magician who could conjure the past. By this time, geography and geology had their historical counterparts, *paleogeography* and *paleogeology*. Geology entered a period of discovery and glamour. It is not surprising that one of the major scientific organizations, the American Association for the Advancement of Science (A.A.A.S.), was formed in 1847 by the enlargement of the American Society of Geologists and that fifteen of the first twenty presidents of the A.A.A.S. were distinguished geologists.

EVOLUTION AND THE TIME SCALE

In 1859 Charles Darwin's *On the Origin of Species by Means of Natural Selection* was published, and the theory of organic evolution was launched. Along with it was launched one of the great controversies in the history of science: the ideas of evolution were denounced by many as monstrous and antireligious, if not at least downright silly. But geologists and biologists under the leadership of Lyell and Thomas Huxley moved in a few years to acceptance of the theory. The concept of evolution had enormous impact, for its theoretical framework gave support to the idea that the time-related changes in fossil species could be used to set up a stratigraphic time scale.

Armed with a refined science of paleontology,

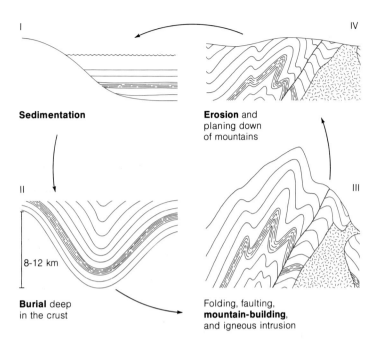

Sedimentation

Erosion and planing down of mountains

8-12 km

Burial deep in the crust

Folding, faulting, **mountain-building**, and igneous intrusion

Figure 2-23
The geologic cycle as deduced by Hutton.

based on Darwinian evolutionary theory, and with expanded opportunities for travel during the tremendous period of world exploration that accompanied European economic expansion and imperialism, geologists mapped the surface of the earth and fitted together what we now call the **Phanerozoic** (known) time scale. The names of the time periods are taken either from the geographic locality in which the formations were best displayed or first studied or from some characteristic of the formations. For example, the Jurassic is named from the Jura Mountains of France and Switzerland, and the Carboniferous is named from the coal-bearing sedimentary rocks of Europe and North America.

Each time period of the stratigraphic time scale is represented by its appropriate system of rocks, and we differentiate time units, the **periods,** from time-rock units (the rocks that represent time), the **systems.** Each major unit is divided: the period into **epochs,** and the system into **series.** Epochs and series have geographic names, except for the older names of many of the epochs, which are simply called Upper, Middle, or Lower. Thus the Upper Jurassic series comprises the rocks of the Upper Jurassic Epoch of time.

An illuminating sidelight to the enunciation of Darwin's new theory is that the discovery was actually made by both Darwin and Alfred Russell Wallace, a young, unknown naturalist working in the East Indies (Indonesia). Darwin had in 1857 explained his theory in a now-famous letter to the great American botanist Asa Gray at Harvard; Darwin's theory had been germinating in preliminary drafts for almost 20 years. In 1858 Wallace sent Darwin a manuscript that he had written in the midst of a bout with intermittent fever in the Molucca Islands. Darwin's reaction was close to panic, for Wallace's manuscript outlined his theory in essential details. On the advice of two friends, Charles Lyell, then the most famous geologist in England, and Joseph Hooker, a leading English botanist, Darwin and Wallace presented their views in a joint essay before the Linnaean Society of London on July 1, 1858. Independent simultaneous discovery of an idea whose time has come, and the rush to publish it, is not a new development in science!

40

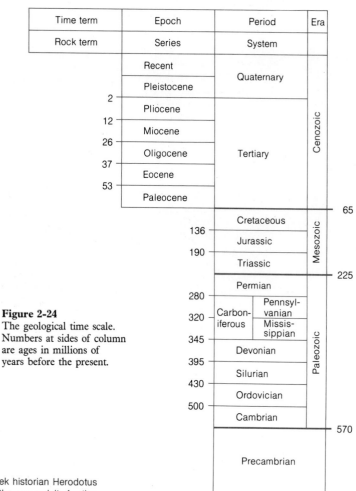

Time term	Epoch	Period	Era
Rock term	Series	System	

	Recent	Quaternary	
	Pleistocene		
2	Pliocene		Cenozoic
12	Miocene		
26	Oligocene	Tertiary	
37	Eocene		
53	Paleocene		
65	Cretaceous		Mesozoic
136	Jurassic		
190	Triassic		
225	Permian		
280	Carbon-iferous / Pennsyl-vanian		Paleozoic
320	Carbon-iferous / Missis-sippian		
345	Devonian		
395	Silurian		
430	Ordovician		
500	Cambrian		
570	Precambrian		

Figure 2-24
The geological time scale. Numbers at sides of column are ages in millions of years before the present.

It was the Greek historian Herodotus who invented the name *delta* for the large body of sand, silt, and mud that accumulates where a river empties into a lake or sea. The shape of the lower Nile floodplain valley, below Thebes, looked to him like the Greek letter delta Δ, roughly triangular in shape.

"And God said, Let the waters under the heaven be gathered together in one place, and let the dry land appear; and it was so. And God called the dry land Earth; and the gathering together of the waters called he Seas: and God saw that it was good. And God said, Let the Earth bring forth grass, the herb yielding seed, and the fruit tree yielding fruit after his kind, whose seed was in itself, after his kind, upon the Earth: and it was so. And the Earth brought forth grass, and herb yielding seed after his kind, and the tree yielding fruit, whose seed was in itself, after his kind, and God saw that it was good. And the evening and the morning were the third day." How long a day!

ABSOLUTE TIME AND THE GEOLOGICAL TIME SCALE

The question of just how many years are represented by the rocks in the stratigraphic time scale has been around for at least 2500 years. As far as we know, Xenophanes of Colophon (570–470 B.C.) was the first of the early philosophers to focus upon this problem. He recognized the significance of fossils as remnants of former life and correctly inferred that sedimentary rocks originated as sediments deposited on the sea bottom. Moreover, he concluded that such rocks and fossils must be of great age. Xenophanes was not particularly loved by some of the erudite establishment Greek philosophers, most of whom had deduced that there was no beginning and no end to the Earth. Around 450 B.C., Herodotus, the great Greek historian, traveled through the lower Nile River valley. His observations led him to reason that the Nile delta must have been made from a series of floods. It then quickly followed, by his reasoning, that if a single flood were to lay down only a thin layer of sediment, it must have taken many thousands of years to build up the Nile delta.

Aristotle and other Greek and Roman philosopher-naturalists strengthened and expanded this scholarly approach of observation combined with deduction and left a legacy to early Christian scholars, such as St. Augustine, who in all essentials continued the tradition. But the thread of that kind of thinking was temporarily lost in late medieval outgrowths of the revolution of Christian scholasticism and theological idealism, which found a solution to the problem of the antiquity of the Earth and all things on it in one book: *Genesis*. The literal interpretation of this book of The Bible gained increasing devotion by Churchmen, not in the early Middle Ages, when the teachings of the Greeks were still largely accepted in the secular world and the New Testament was still new, but in the later Middle Ages and the beginnings of modern times in a reaction to the scientific explorations of the Renaissance. Literalism, to many, was as explicit as the pronouncement by Archbishop Ussher of Ireland in 1664 that the Earth was created at 9:00 A.M., October 26, 4004 B.C. (presumably Greenwich mean time!). Other dates could be and were calculated for Noah's flood and various other Biblical events.

When modern geology started gathering momentum, through the work of James Hutton and others, no attempts were made to guess at the age of the Earth; instead, there was an obvious return to the old Greek way of looking at things. The evidence demanded that a long time was necessary for Earth processes to have had any effect in carving mountains and accumulating sediment. By looking at the time scale of processes and using the idea of uniformitarianism, geologists came to recognize that rocks are very old, and the Earth much older.

At the same time, physicists were busy making various sorts of calculations, based on the ideas of Galileo and those of Newton, who in 1687 established the basis for gravitational theory in his *Principia*. After Laplace proposed his theory of the origin of the solar system and the gravitational constant was determined, there was a sound foundation for calculating the relation between time and planetary orbits. The times necessary for the formation of the Sun and planets, and for planetary motions, seemed much too long compared with the shortness of time demanded by the Bible. Before the nineteenth century, however, physicists did not challenge religious orthodoxy: Sir Isaac Newton was a devoutly religious man—one whom we would call today a "fundamentalist." Even so, in the middle of the eighteenth century, Comte de Buffon of France analyzed rates of melting and cooling rates of iron balls and put what he learned together with his guess that the interior of the Earth had to be iron (it was so dense) and calculated how long it would take the molten earth to cool. His result, 75,000 years, made no one happy; for the fundamentalists it was much too long, and for many geologists it was much too short.

The plot thickened in 1854, when Herman von Helmholtz, one of the founders of the science of thermodynamics, seized on the problem of the Sun's luminosity. Not long before, Immanuel Kant had calculated that if the Sun's light came from ordinary combustion, it would have burned up in only 1000 years. Helmholtz realized that the way out of this bind was to infer that the Sun's light came from the heating required by the gravitational contraction of the immense mass of the Sun. His notion was that particles would literally tend to fall into the center and that the potential energy released in that fall would be converted to heat. Helmholtz came up with estimates of 20 to 40 million years.

Helmholtz's argument was taken up by another great physicist of the nineteenth century, William Thomson, better known as Lord Kelvin. In his first paper of a long career, and in many following articles, he expanded and revised Helmholtz's estimates, put them together with Buffon's cooling-rate figures and other more ingenious arguments, and pronounced that the most probable value was something like 20 to 40 million years, probably closer to 20 million.

Many geologists found themselves unable to adjust their notions of the length of geologic time to accord with Kelvin's estimate, and continued to argue vehemently that not everything was yet known about physics and that it was foolish to contradict the obvious evidence of the rocks in such composite sequences as those in the Grand Canyon, for they clearly must have taken many times 25 million years to accumulate. Others, such as Clarence King, one of the founders of the U.S. Geological Survey, who had done much of the geological exploration of the West, made his own calculations, compared them with those of Kelvin, and concluded that

Kelvin was about right. Charles Walcott, one of the most famous paleontologist-stratigraphers of the day, added up the whole known stratigraphic sequence and concluded that it could reasonably well account for as much as 75 million years, one of the figures given by Kelvin at various times. As late as the turn of the century, Lord Kelvin gave an important address to the American Association for the Advancement of Science in which he reiterated his faith in his calculations and in the physical constraints they imposed on the age of the Earth. A long answer followed from one of the geological unbelievers, T. C. Chamberlin, the head of the Department of Geology at what was then the brand new University of Chicago. Chamberlin, who held many agnostic opinions, added his speculation that there might yet be discovered new sources of energy (unknown to him then) within the particles of matter that would eliminate burning and gravitational contraction as the sole possible causes of the Sun's luminosity.

Curiously enough, the debate of 1899–1900 came four years after a discovery that was to be of world-shaking importance (both figuratively *and* literally, as it turned out!). In 1895, Henri Becquerel, a French physicist, discovered radioactivity in uranium salts, almost at the same time that the German physicist Wilhelm Röntgen discovered X-rays. Soon after, Marie Sklodowska-Curie made the crucial discovery and isola-

Helmholtz's argument that the Sun underwent gravitational collapse held unexpected implications. For example, if the Sun began to collapse some 20 million years ago, it would at that time have to have been much larger than it is today—so much larger that its radius would have extended to the Earth's present orbit around the Sun. Geologists were not prepared to accept this.

One who would not give way to Kelvin was a fellow Scotsman, Sir Archibald Geikie, who occupied the professorship of geology at Edinburgh while Kelvin was the professor of physics at Glasgow. Maybe it took an Edinburghian not to be overwhelmed by the immense forcefulness and power of the Glasgwegian Kelvin.

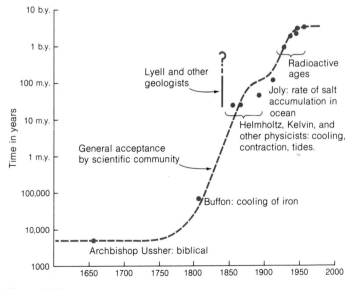

Figure 2-25
How estimates of the age of the Earth have changed in the last few centuries.

tion of radium, a radioactive element. Thus in the space of a few months, the stage was set for the use of the clocks that are built into the nuclei of radioactive atoms—the clocks that were eventually to resolve the bitter argument about the age of the Earth. Yet neither Kelvin nor Chamberlin, to say nothing of their audiences, seemed to be aware of the extraordinary implications of these discoveries, though the journals of physics and chemistry and even the Sunday newspaper supplements were popping with the news.

It was not until 1905 that Ernest Rutherford, a famous physicist who had been studying radioactive processes, suggested that radioactive minerals could be used to date rocks. He dated a uranium mineral in his laboratory at McGill University in Montreal the next year. (Though associated in nearly everyone's mind with Cambridge, England, where he became director of the Cavendish Laboratory in 1919, Rutherford was actually a New Zealander.) In the same year that Rutherford dated his first mineral, B. B. Boltwood of Yale discovered "ionium," which turned out to be an isotope of thorium—the first isotope to be isolated (see next section). Both Rutherford and Boltwood published ages of dated minerals, but it was not until F. Soddy, in 1913, clarified the nature of isotopes that the methods could be refined and made more accurate, for most of the early ages turned out to be too high. When the full series of decay products of radioactive disintegration was firmly established, it became clear that the Earth had to be not millions, but *billions,* of years old.

In a few decades all of the apparent contradictions were cleared up. In the 1920's and 1930's, astronomers and physicists recognized that the immense energies liberated by nuclear processes must be responsible for the luminosity of the sun and that the heat given off by radioactive decay was the explanation for the heat trapped in the Earth's interior.

THE CLOCKS IN ROCKS: RADIOACTIVE ATOMS

What the pioneers of nuclear physics discovered at the turn of the century was that atoms of certain elements, the radioactive ones, spontaneously disintegrate to form atoms of a different element, liberating energy in the process. The important reason why radioactive decay offers a dependable means of keeping time is that the average rate of disintegration *is fixed and does not vary* with any of the typical changes in chemical or physical conditions that affect most chemical or physical processes. This means that once a quantity of a radioactive element is made somewhere in the universe, it starts to act like the balance wheel of a clock, steadily "firing" off one atom after another at a definite rate.

To tell time, we cannot simply look at a balance wheel or listen to ticking. We need some kind of face with hands and numbers on it or the numbered counting wheels of modern digital clocks. The numbers that we use to read the radioactive clock are supplied in the form of the new atoms, the **daughter** elements, that are created from the old disintegrated ones, the **parent** elements. If we can identify and count the number of daughter element atoms, and if we know the rate of decay, we can work back to the time when there were no daughters but only parents. The idea is simple, but its practical implementation has required a major effort on the part of those geologists who combine their knowledge of nuclear physics with that of geology—the specialists in **geochronology,** which is sometimes called a subdivision of **nuclear geology** or **istotope geology.**

What Happens to a Radioactive Atom? All atoms have a dense nucleus that contains practically all of the mass of the atom. Surrounding the nucleus is a cloud of orbiting **electrons.** The nucleus contains two kinds of particles, each with mass 1: a **proton** has a positive electrical charge of +1, and a **neutron** is electrically neutral. The number of protons in the

Neutrons | Total number | + Atomic = Atomic
0 charge | of neutrons | number   weight

Protons | Total number = Atomic
+1 charge | of protons   number

Electrons | Total number = Atomic
−1 charge | of electrons   number

Figure 2-26
The structure of an atom. The nucleus of protons and neutrons is surrounded by a cloud of orbiting electrons.

nucleus, which is balanced by the same number of electrons in the cloud outside, each of which has a negative charge of -1, is unique for any element, and is called the **atomic number** (usually symbolized by Z). The sum of the masses of protons and neutrons is the **atomic weight** of the atom. All atoms of the same element—for example, carbon—have the same atomic number; the atomic number of carbon is 6. Different isotopes have different numbers of neutrons. Carbon isotopes exist with 6, 7, and 8 neutrons, giving atomic masses of 12, 13, and 14. Of these isotopes, C^{12} and C^{13} are stable; that is, they do not change or spontaneously disintegrate. But C^{14} is radioactive and spontaneously decays to the element nitrogen. Another element that decays spontaneously is rubidium 87 (Rb^{87}), which is transformed to strontium 87 (Sr^{87}). An important difference between the decay of C^{14} and Rb^{87} is the *rate* at which the

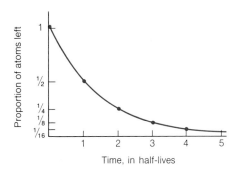

Figure 2-28
Graph showing the decrease in the number of radioactive atoms with time. In each successive half-life, no matter how long or short, the number of atoms present at the beginning of that half-life period is halved.

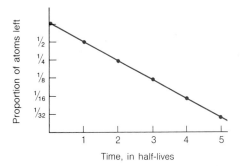

Figure 2-29
The relation between half-life and decrease in number of radioactive atoms with time is a straight line when shown with the vertical scale arranged logarithmically rather than arithmetically, as it is in Figure 2-25.

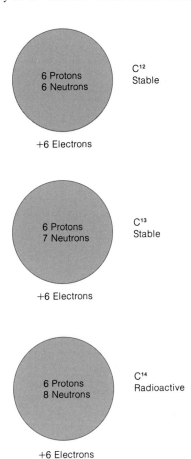

Figure 2-27
Carbon isotopes. All have the same number of protons, and thus atomic number 6, but different numbers of neutrons.

atoms decay. That rate is commonly stated in terms of the **half-life**—the time required for one-half of the original number of radioactive atoms to decay. At the end of the first half-life after a radioactive element is incorporated into a new mineral, one-half is left; at the end of a second half-life, one-quarter is left; at the end of a third half-life, an eighth is left; and so on, as shown in Figures 2-28 and 2-29.

We can now compare the rate of decay of carbon-14, which has a half-life of 5570 years, with that of Rb^{87}, which has a half-life of 47 billion years. It is the half-life that dictates that C^{14} can be used for timekeeping for only the last 30,000 years or so of Earth history, about equal to a little more than 5 half-lives (at which point all except the last $1/32$ of the original amount is gone). In contrast, 3 billion years, about the age of some very old rocks dated on earth, is only about $1/16$ of one half-life of Rb^{87}, which

Atomic weights of naturally occurring elements, which chemists spent much of their time measuring accurately in the nineteenth century and early twentieth century, turn out to be odd numbers. Thus the atomic weight of carbon given in tables is 12.01115 [relative to oxygen atomic weight as 15.999 (essentially 16)]. The reason for this is that the natural elements are mixtures of the various isotopes. The very small amount of C^{13}, and even smaller amounts of C^{14}, in most samples of carbon is enough to affect the average weight.

Box 2-1 Dating Rocks by Means of Radioactive Minerals

The decay of radioactive atoms proceeds in different ways for various elements. Carbon-14 decays by emitting β-**particles** (electrons shot from the nucleus when a neutron is split into a proton and an electron). This changes its atomic number to 7, which is characteristic of the element nitrogen, but does not change its mass (because an electron has practically no mass); the new nucleus is thus N^{14}. We show this process by the following kind of equation:

$$C^{14} - \beta \rightarrow N^{14}.$$

Rubidium-87 emits a β-particle in the same way as C^{14} to produce strontium-87:

$$Rb^{87} - \beta \rightarrow Sr^{87}.$$

Both radioactive isotopes of uranium decay by emitting α-particles, particles consisting of two protons and two neutrons (an α-particle is equivalent to the nucleus of a helium atom, He^4); the decay reactions are written

$$U^{235} \rightarrow Pb^{207} + 7He^4,$$
$$U^{238} \rightarrow Pb^{206} + 8He^4.$$

Thorium also decays to lead by α-emission:

$$Th^{232} \rightarrow Pb^{208} + 6He^4.$$

The two paths of radioactive potassium (K^{40}) decay are given by the following equations. For 11 percent of the atoms,

$$K^{40} + e \rightarrow A^{40},$$

where e is an orbital electron captured by the nucleus; for the remaining 89 percent,

$$K^{40} - \beta \rightarrow Ca^{40}.$$

The equations for calculating radioactive ages are cast in terms of the number of atoms, n, that decay in a period of time (usually per second or per year, depending on which is more convenient) relative to the total number of atoms of that element (N) in any given amount of it. The proportion n/N, which is constant no matter what N is, is called the decay or **disintegration constant,** and is usually symbolized by the Greek letter lambda, λ. The other common measure of the rate of decay, the half-life, is usually represented by T. The half-life is simply related to λ: it is always

$$T = 0.693/\lambda.$$

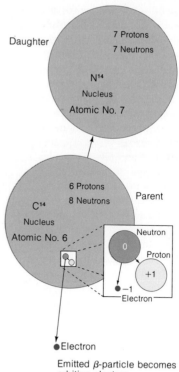

A radioactive carbon atom, C^{14}, spontaneously decays to a nitrogen atom, N^{14}, by emitting a β-particle that becomes an orbiting electron. This is the same process by which radioactive rubidium, Rb^{87}, decays to strontium, Sr^{87}.

If we choose the unit of time for λ to be the half-life, T, of the element, then $\lambda = 0.5$ by definition and

$$\log \frac{N}{N_0} = -0.3y,$$

where N_0 is the original number of radioactive atoms in a sample of the parent mineral, and y is the number of half-lives that have elapsed since the mineral was formed. The age of the rock is determined by measuring N and N_0 and solving for y; then y multiplied by T, the half-life, gives the age in years.

The solution of the radioactive decay problem is generalized and shortened to one equation by using calculus:

$$dN/dt = -\lambda N,$$

or, in integrated form (called the age equation),

$$N = N_0 e^{-\lambda t}.$$

makes it easily the choice for dating many old rocks.

The two examples we have given so far have been relatively simple decay processes. The major decay scheme that was first developed and is still used extensively is the decay of the element uranium, which has two radioactive isotopes, one that decays to lead and another to helium. In addition, another element, thorium, can also decay to lead. The half-lives of these decays amount to hundreds or thousands of millions of years, which makes them eminently suitable for dating the oldest objects in our solar system.

One other radioactive element is of great importance in dating rocks, potassium, K^{40}. It decays by a scheme that has two paths. In one path, the K^{40} decays to a calcium isotope, Ca^{40}. About 89 percent of the K^{40} atoms in any group of atoms will follow this route. The remaining 11 percent of the K^{40} atoms decay to form the inert gas argon, A^{40}. The latter decay path is the one that is used, for the daughter, A^{40}, can be easily distinguished from ordinary argon formed in other ways, whereas Ca^{40} cannot be distinguished from ordinary calcium.

Reading the Clocks. Once isotopes were discovered and instruments were invented that could make the chemical analysis for the ratios of parents to daughters, the business of dating rocks could begin. It was uranium-thorium decay that received first attention and which is, in a sense, the easiest to use, for it requires only an ordinary chemical analysis for uranium and lead. It is good enough for getting approximate dates of many uranium minerals that occur in rocks that are inferred to have had little or no original lead, but it does not distinguish between the lead that originates from the different uranium isotopes and from thorium.

The next important development came in the 1920's and 1930's, when the **mass spectrometer** was invented. That machine was designed to produce a beam of electrically charged atoms from the sample to be studied. The beam is deflected by electric and magnetic fields in such a way that the atoms are deflected by an amount proportional to their masses. Thus isotopes of elements can be separated. The precision and sensitivity of these instruments has been steadily improving, so that today even minute amounts of individual isotopes can be analyzed. The techniques of mass spectrometry and related instruments were developed during World War II by the Manhattan Project, the group assigned

to the atom bomb. A by-product of that work was a series of studies on geochronology, done right after the war by Harold Urey and many of his students. It was at that time that the potassium-argon method was first developed as an accurate dating tool by one of Urey's students, G. J. Wasserburg.

Not all radioactive decays are analyzed by mass spectrometry. Most C^{14} ages are determined from the carbon in dead plant material. During growth, plants steadily incorporate a small amount of C^{14} along with the other carbon isotopes contained in the carbon dioxide molecules in the atmosphere. When plants die, photosynthesis stops, and no new C^{14} is taken up. The relative amount of C^{14} at this point is approximately the same as the ratio in the atmosphere, but steadily decreases with age as the C^{14} radioactivity decays. The measurement of parent and daughter of C^{14}, which has a relatively short half-life, is done indirectly, by counting the decay particles being emitted by the undecayed C^{14} still present in the sample. The result is a count of what is called **C^{14} activity,** from which one can calculate the age, since the number of decay particles produced is proportional to the number of C^{14} atoms still present, and that count can be compared with the higher activity of a contemporary sample of C^{14}.

When Were the Clocks Started? Once the minerals in a rock are formed, any radioactive elements in those minerals keep ticking away all of the time. What we actually measure is the time elapsed since the radioactive parent elements became part of a rock from which their daughter elements could not escape. For example, when uranium becomes incorporated into rock-forming minerals that congeal from a molten state, there is no lead from previous decay. Once the decay process commences, however, daughter elements are trapped and quantities of lead eventually produced. The amounts of parent and daughter present in a sample of rock are a measure of the time interval between now and the time that the rock crystallized. Thus the methods based on the decay of uranium, rubidium, and potassium all give the date of crystallization of the rocks in which those minerals are found—and by geologic inference any other rocks that bear a definite age relation to the rock analyzed. Thus when we date the crystallization of a granite, we know also from geology that the absolute age of the surrounding sedimentary rocks, into which the granite was intruded when

The demand for extremely accurate ages of the Moon rocks recovered in the NASA Apollo program later led Wasserburg to devise an extraordinarily complex and sensitive mass spectrometer at Caltech that he called "Lunatic." With that instrument he can determine reliable ages of mineral grains so small that they can be seen only under a microscope.

Figure 2-30
Unequal duration of the major eras of
the geological time scale.

In the past few years, Patterson has
applied his ability to make precise
measurements of extremely small
amounts of lead isotopes to studies of
the worldwide distribution of lead in
the atmosphere. He has shown that
much of atmospheric lead comes from
the tetraethyl lead added to automobile gasoline as an antiknock agent. In
at least one way, then, the radioactive
dating of rocks has indirectly provided
what could be vital information on a
possible environmental hazard—an example of the unanticipated dividends
that the pursuit of basic science has
repeatedly shown.

it crystallized, can be no younger than the granite. If the geologic ages of those sedimentary
rocks are known by fossils and those strata in
turn overlie, and thus are younger than, other
radioactively dated rocks we can bracket the
absolute age of the sedimentary rocks, even
though they may contain no datable minerals.

There are several things that can cause dates
based directly on radiometric methods to be
incorrect. First, one must be able to show that
there has been no removal of a daughter element. For example, if groundwater solutions
had dissolved some of the lead produced by
uranium decay, the age would be underestimated. Second, one must recognize that a geological event, such as heating or partial melting
of the rock in a later metamorphic episode, may
have reset the clock to zero by allowing earlier-
formed daughter elements to escape. The interpretation of potassium-argon ages is complicated by the fact that the mass-spectrometric
analysis is for argon, a gas that can diffuse out of
the solid mineral and so give a falsely young age
for the rock. Since the argon diffusion rate depends strongly on the temperature, what is actually being dated may be interpreted as the time
when the rock cooled sufficiently to slow argon
leakage to a stop. That time has been shown to
be appreciably later than the original formation
of the rock. In this way, the difficulties in interpreting radioactive dating can be turned to our
advantage and used to learn more about the
complex history of the rocks, such as cooling
times or later metamorphic episodes.

AGES OF METEORITES

One of the triumphs of radioactive dating
emerged only gradually as more and more
workers dated meteorites by various methods.
Many problems in dating techniques came to
light as a result of this effort, but it also became
surprisingly apparent that all meteorites are of
the same age, somewhere in the vicinity of 4.5
billion years old. This is true regardless of their
composition—whether they are of the stony
kind, made up of rock-forming minerals like
those of the Earth's crust, or of the iron variety,
made up mostly of alloys of iron and nickel.
That there are no meteorites of any other age,
regardless of when they fell to Earth, suggested
strongly that they originated in other bodies of
the solar system that formed at the same time
that the Earth did. If this is true, then the
meteorites give the age of the Earth too. Though

the story is now corroborated by Rb^{87}—Sr^{87} and
K^{40}—A^{40} methods, the pioneer work was done
by Claire Patterson of Caltech, who used the
various methods based on the different paths by
which uranium and thorium decay to lead.

HOW TO SYNCHRONIZE
CLOCKS: THE STRATIGRAPHIC
AND ABSOLUTE TIME SCALES

Geologists working with fossiliferous sediments
have a fine watch by which to measure time. It is
accurate enough to enable geologists to distinguish the relative ages of formations that are
only a few meters thick and which may represent periods of time far less than a million years
in duration. A million years, we have to remember, is only about 1/5000 of the history of the
Earth. The entire world rock record of fossiliferous sediments has been mapped and subdivided into the scheme of eras, epochs, and ages
that is shown in Figure 2-24. A geologist studying fossiliferous rocks in the field needs only an
average knowledge of paleontology in order to
make a fairly accurate estimate of the epoch in
which the rocks he is studying belong. Using the
stratigraphic time scale is like reading a watch
that enables you to tell one time from another
but gives you no idea of just how long a minute
really is.

It was not surprising, then, that the discovery
of radioactive age dating was immediately seen
and welcomed by some geologists as the way to
make a combination clock that would function
as an absolute as well as a relative timekeeper.
Only ten years after the discovery of radioactivity, the first rocks were dated by the uranium-
lead method; eight years after that, Arthur
Holmes, a young British geologist who had not
yet received his doctor's degree, published the
first edition of what was to become a classic
work, *The Age of the Earth*. Holmes plotted
radioactive age dates opposite the stratigraphic
time scale by carefully figuring out as closely as
he could the age relations of the sediments,
which were dated by fossils, and of the cross-
cutting igneous rocks, which were dated by
radioactivity. His estimates were remarkable, for
most of them have held up in a general way. His
first estimate of the beginning of the Cambrian
placed it at about 600 million years before the
present. His last estimate, published in 1959, a
few years before his death, was the same as his
first—and that in the face of thousands of more
accurately determined dates made in the half

century since (see Fig. 2-24 for a more recent summary of these dates).

Authorities still differ on precise details, but the general outlines are undisputed. The Phanerozoic time scale of rocks containing fossils of higher organisms represents about 600 million years, and is divided into somewhat unequal divisions, the eras: the Paleozoic, about 350 to 400 million years long; the Mesozoic, about 150 million years long; and the Cenozoic, about 70 million years long. The epochs are similarly unequal in length. The inequalities are the result of accidents of choice. The stratigraphers of the nineteenth century divided parts of the geologic column according to what seemed convenient or appropriate to the area they were studying. If the Chinese and Indians had done most of the stratigraphic work, the column would have been far different, though the boundary between the Phanerozoic and Precambrian would still have been the same, for the evolution of shelled, higher forms of life did not take place at different times in different places; once those forms evolved, they spread rapidly (geologically speaking).

Telling Precambrian Time. Because there are no fossils to rely on, the Precambrian has always been somewhat of a mystery to stratigraphers. Although they have been able to unravel complicated sequences of sedimentary and igneous and metamorphic rocks in small areas where it was possible to correlate from one outcrop to the next (just as we could get along without fossils in correlating from one wall of the Grand Canyon to the other), sheer guesswork was required in attempting to correlate between one part of a continent and another. With the advent of radioactive dating, however, the situation has changed—so much so that well-established notions about the way the Precambrian fit together have been thoroughly upset.

There are two major differences between radioactive dating of the Precambrian and the stratigraphic dating of the Phanerozoic. First, the Precambrian "events" that can be dated are mainly episodes of igneous intrusion, or metamorphism, or mountain-building, whereas the Phanerozoic is dated by the ages of the sediments. Because of these differences in the two kinds of rock timekeepers, the Precambrian will give a much more discontinuous record, for the occurrence of intrusion, metamorphism, and mountain-building is spasmodic compared to the almost continuous record of sedimentation.

Second, the resolution, or accuracy, of radioactive dating in the Precambrian is much lower than that of stratigraphic dating. As we have noted before, stratigraphers can divide their columns into units that may be as little as a million years long, and they can usually estimate relative time to the nearest 10 million years. In contrast, the imprecision involved in sampling and analyzing Precambrian rocks for radioactive dating is such that even with the delicate and sensitive instruments now being used, old dates have to be given with a large range of probable error, expressed as plus or minus as much as 100 million years. Such a range of possible uncertainty in age—200 million years from plus to minus—is equivalent to all the time of the Cambrian, the Ordovician, the Silurian, plus part of the Devonian periods of the Paleozoic. It is therefore not surprising that Precambrian stratigraphy is still lacking in detail.

Figure 2-31 shows the kind of geologic map that has been worked out for Precambrian rocks in Canada. The provinces are drawn on the basis

Precambrian boundary
of the Canadian shield

Province boundaries

Figure 2-31
Precambrian-age map of Canada, showing provinces drawn on the basis of radioactive age determinations. [After J. A. Lowdon and others, Geological Survey of Canada, 1963.]

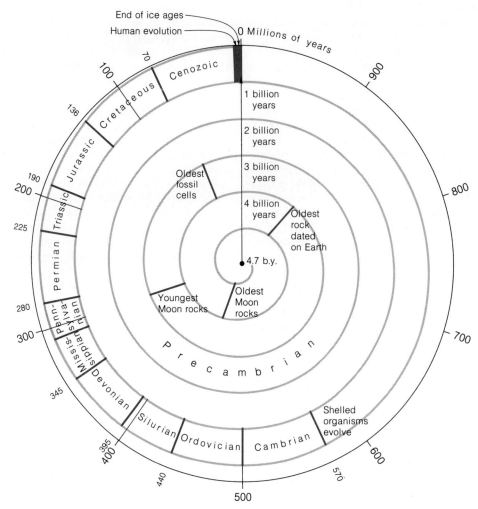

Figure 2-32
The geologic clock in time before present.

of radioactive ages. The oldest, the Superior province, is one in which most of the rocks have ages clustering about 2500 million years, corresponding to an orogeny called the Kenoran. The rocks of the Churchill province, which partly surrounds the Superior, are about 1750 million years old, corresponding to the Hudsonian orogeny; and those of the Grenville province, are about 950 to 1000 million years old, corresponding to the Grenville orogeny. The same general kind of map can be made for other Precambrian areas of the world, such as those in Scandinavia or Africa. That such maps can be made on the basis of radioactive dating alone is the triumph of the method.

We have not covered all of the ways of telling time from the rock record. Paleomagnetic stratigraphy is under steady development as a junior partner to the stratigraphic time scale (see Chapter 18). Geochemists have been using chemical reactions with known constant rates to date rocks that are too old for C^{14} and too young for the other radioactive methods. For example, many of man's early artifacts, such as arrowheads, are made of obsidian, a volcanic glass. Obsidian can be dated by the degree to which the glass, originally dry, has become hydrated, or chemically altered by absorbing water. Time is so central to the study of Earth that we continue to search for better clocks.

Figure 2-33
Relative and absolute time and history of the Earth.
[After *Geologic Time*, U.S. Geological Survey publication.]

AN OVERVIEW OF THE GEOLOGICAL CLOCK

We can now put together a clock for the whole history of the Earth. The clock is shown in the form of a spiral (Fig. 2-32); each revolution of the clock's hand corresponds to 1 billion years; each subdivision, the "hours," corresponds to 100 million years; and the "minutes" are 10 million years long. Geologists work backwards from the present as zero to the beginning at 4.7 billion years ago. From a look at this clock, we can see how short a period of the total of Earth history is taken up by the Phanerozoic eras, and what a minuscule amount of the time has elapsed since man evolved. History, as recorded by man's artifacts, his buildings, and his writings and drawings, is only the last instant of all of this time. One of the minor miracles of how people think is demonstrated by the way they can quickly shift mental gears and consider different time scales—from "Did the earth form 4.5 or 4.7 billion years ago?" to "Will this class hour never end?"

SUMMARY

1. Geologic time scales tend to be long; most are measured in thousands to millions of years. These slow rates of processes are measured by geologic change.

2. Rocks are made of minerals, which are chemical compounds, usually in crystalline form. Igneous rocks form by cooling of a magma. Sedimentary rocks show stratification and form by settling of erosional debris and chemical precipitates. Metamorphic rocks form by heat and pressure, which transforms pre-existing rocks into new ones with different mineral compositions.

3. The field relations of rocks, such as stratigraphic sequences, concordant and discordant contacts with igneous rocks, and structural deformation, can be used to deduce a history of sedimentation, uplift, deformation, igneous activity, and erosion.

4. A stratigraphic time scale can be devised from sedimentary rocks by matching the evolutionary changes in ancient life as revealed by fossils found in the strata with the stratigraphic sequence. The rocks of the Grand Canyon illustrate how field relations and fossils are used to infer a complex history of geological episodes.

5. Absolute time measurements can be made by using spontaneous decay of radioactive elements. Such dates of minerals containing radioactive substances provide an absolute age framework for the stratigraphic time scale and allow the dating of unfossiliferous Precambrian rocks. Radioactive age dating of meteorites gives the time of Earth's origin.

EXERCISES

1. What are the time scales and how might you measure the duration of the following man-made "geological" phenomena: (1) digging a hole to plant a shrub; (2) excavating a highway road cut; (3) building a large dam on a major river; (4) building a pyramid in ancient Egypt. What does this tell you about the relationship of time scale to the geometric scale, or size, of the phenomenon?

2. Make up a diagram similar to Figure 2-22 to show the following sequence of events: (1) extrusion of thick lavas; (2) erosion; (3) deposition of sediments; (4) faulting; (5) erosion; (6) deposition of sediments; and (7) intrusion of igneous dikes.

3. Many fine muds are laid down at a rate of 1 centimeter/1000 years; at this rate, how long would it take to accumulate a sequence 1 kilometer thick? If the sequence were interrupted every 10 m.y. by a disconformity, during which there was no sedimentation for 1 m.y., how long would it take to accumulate a kilometer?

4. Abraham Werner, an important figure in late eighteenth-century geology, believed that almost *all* kinds of rocks were deposited on the sea floor. What lines of evidence from the Grand Canyon or elsewhere could you use to show that this is not so?

5. Radioactive decay of which elements would be most appropriate for dating formations of the following ages? (1) early Precambrian; (2) Mesozoic; (3) Miocene; (4) late Pleistocene.

6. What different kinds of geological event are dated by flakes of mica in (1) a granite, (2) a schist, and (3) a sandstone?

7. For the past few hundred years, Man's estimates of the age of the Earth have grown longer and longer. Might the present estimate of 4.7 billion years change too? If so, what geologic theories that pertain to geologic time might have to be re-evaluated?

BIBLIOGRAPHY

Berry, W. B. N., *Growth of a Prehistoric Time Scale.* San Francisco: W. H. Freeman and Company, 1968.

Deevey, E. S., Jr., "Radiocarbon Dating." *Scientific American,* February 1952. (Offprint No. 811.)

Dott, R. H., Jr., and R. L. Batten, *Evolution of the Earth* (2nd ed.). New York: McGraw-Hill Book Company, 1971.

Eicher, D. L., *Geologic Time* (2nd ed.). Engelwood Cliffs, New Jersey: Prentice-Hall, Inc., 1976.

Eiseley, L. C., "Charles Lyell." *Scientific American,* August 1959. (Offprint No. 846.)

Hurley, P. M., *How Old is the Earth?* New York: Doubleday and Company, Inc. (Anchor Books), 1959.

Kummel, B., *History of the Earth* (2nd ed.). San Francisco: W. H. Freeman and Company, 1970.

Simpson, G. G., *The Life of the Past.* New Haven: Yale University Press, 1953.

3

ROCKS AND MINERALS

Rocks and the minerals that make them up are the tangible record of geologic processes. The varied minerals of the Earth are understood in terms of their architecture—the way in which their atoms are arranged to make crystal structures. The kinds of atoms and their type of chemical bonding determine not only the crystal structures but the chemical and physical properties of minerals, all of which are used for their identification. Rocks are divided into the three major groups, igneous, metamorphic, and sedimentary, on the basis of origin. They are further subdivided within each group according to mineral composition and texture, which provide the data that allow us to interpret details of their origin.

Picking up pretty stones and showing or wearing them must go far back into man's prehistory. The earliest records of man's practical use of stones, though, are of arrowheads and spear points made of flint (a sedimentary rock) or obsidian (volcanic glass), both of which are hard materials that break with sharp edges. From the practical use of individual stones as tools, weapons, and decorations, man moved to the wholesale mining or quarrying of rocks and minerals for building, for making clay for pottery, and then for the ores that contain metals. Today our mining is done so expertly and intensively that geologists have come to concern themselves with the exhaustion of the world's valuable mineral resources; minerals of economic significance and their reserves are covered in Chapter 22.

THE MATERIALS OF EARTH

Because of the many uses of rocks and minerals, we have a practical curiosity about where they are found and how they were formed: we want to be able to find more. Yet there are other reasons, too, for rocks, as we have seen, are the only records of how the Earth evolved, and they are an important guide to how the Earth works today. For this reason, **mineralogy** and **petrology**—studies of the nature and origin of minerals and rocks—are important subfields of geology. Finally, there is the intrinsic interest in the extraordinary range of the mineral kingdom, with its immense variety of color, form, and texture. Minerals and rocks, after all, give us the marble and alabaster of sculpture, the jade of Eastern carvings, and the pigments used by Rembrandt.

What Information Do We Want from Rocks? If the nature of rocks can give us a clue to many of the things we want to know about the Earth, how do we go about it? We need an interpretive key, just as ancient historians needed the Rosetta stone to crack the "code" of Egyptian hieroglyphics before they could read that part of man's history. First of all we want to find out just what the minerals are made up of and how the rock is put together from its constituent minerals. From its composition we

54

Figure 3-1
One of the largest copper mines in the world is an open-cut mine in Bingham Canyon, Utah, near Salt Lake City. Since operations started in 1905, the mine has produced more than 10 million tons of copper. The vertical distance between top and bottom levels of the mine is 720 m. [Courtesy Kennecott Copper Corporation.]

	Igneous	Sedimentary	Metamorphic
Mineralogy	Kind of magma How it crystallized	Source rocks eroded or chemical environment	Temperature and pressure of metamorphism
Texture	Extrusive or intrusive	Erosional history of particles	Deformational forces or nearness to intrusion
Fossils		Stratigraphic age and depositional environment	

Figure 3-2
The mineralogy and texture of a rock are the keys to inferring its origin.

should be able to say something about where the parent material came from and what it was like. What was the magma like? Or, what were the source rocks of a sediment? Or, what were the pre-existing rocks that were heated and compressed to make a metamorphic rock? From the composition and the texture of the rock we should also be able to tell something of the pressures and temperatures at which the rock was formed by comparing them with the artificial rocks and minerals made by experimental petrologists in the laboratory.

From the radioactive elements in a rock, or from the fossils in it, we can also tell its age. But the age of a rock bears little relation to its composition. Rocks of the same kind form at different times in the Earth, and age is no clue to their mode of formation.

In this chapter we cover the nature of the rocks and minerals that make up the Earth's crust and mantle. We first explore the relation of rock to mineral. Next we show how the external appearance and properties of minerals are related to the way in which their fundamental building blocks—the atoms and ions of the chemical elements—are connected with each other in the internal architecture of crystals. With that picture in mind we can then describe the mineralogy and textures of the three great classes of rocks.

Rocks Are Made of Minerals. A rock is many things. It is a collection of the particular chemical elements that make it up. Those elements are not found randomly mixed up in a rock but are distributed among an assemblage of **minerals.** A mineral is a solid chemical compound that is characterized by a definite composition or a restricted range of chemical compositions and by a specific, regular architecture of the atoms that make it up. Like all chemical compounds, minerals are homogeneous: a mineral cannot be separated mechanically into different substances. Minerals make up a rock just as bricks make up a brick wall, in a great variety of arrangements. In coarse-grained rocks the minerals are large enough to be seen with the naked eye. In some rocks the minerals can be seen to have **crystal faces,** smooth planes bounded by sharp edges; in others, such as a typical sandstone, the minerals are in the form of fragments without faces. In fine-grained rocks, the individual mineral grains are so small that they can be seen only with a powerful magnifying glass, the hand lens that the field geologist carries. Some are so small that a powerful microscope is needed to make them out.

On the basis of certain characteristics, particularly their physical and chemical properties, several thousand minerals can be distinguished, each defined by its unique set of properties. For thousands of years, people who have used minerals—whether miners looking for iron ore minerals or artists looking for minerals to grind into pigments—have employed simple physical and chemical tests to distinguish one from another. Color, an obvious characteristic, became even more diagnostic for some minerals when reduced to a powder. Differences in hardness were found to make it easy to distinguish between minerals that are similar in appearance. The way in which minerals break apart, some showing smooth cleavage planes and others rough irregular fractures, proved to be a reliable way to identify certain minerals. Simple chemical properties were found useful in the field, such as dropping acid on a mineral suspected of being calcite ($CaCO_3$) to see whether it would fizz as it dissolved, releasing carbon dioxide bubbles.

Early in the study of minerals it was realized that all grains or crystals of a mineral, like quartz, have just about the same qualities, regardless of the kind of rock in which they are found. Some minerals, particularly those that have a more complex mixture of atoms, vary slightly in their properties, depending on their precise composition. A mineral like garnet, for example, has a number of varieties, each with its own range of composition, such as the proportions of iron and other elements, and hence, properties.

Rocks are not as uniquely defined by their properties as minerals are. Because of the immense number of ways in which the thousands of minerals can be combined, the geologist is faced with a bewildering array of rock types. The only way for us to make order out of this array is to classify like with like and to sort out by general type. The major division of rocks into igneous, sedimentary, and metamorphic is just such an aid. Within each major division there are many groups and types. Using characteristic properties, we can divide the rock kingdom into several hundred general types, each with its own more-or-less distinctive earmarks.

Despite all of these numbers, it is remarkable how much can be done even if only a small number of the most common minerals and rocks are known. In most parts of the world a field geologist can make an accurate geologic map by knowing only a few dozen major minerals and even fewer common rock types. This simplification is possible because most of the thousands of known minerals are either rare or unusual on the one hand or subspecies or varieties on the other. Thus the geologist who can recognize garnet will do well, even though a mineral sophisticate who can distinguish the many varieties of garnet by their slightly different chemical compositions might do better. Naturally, the more we can

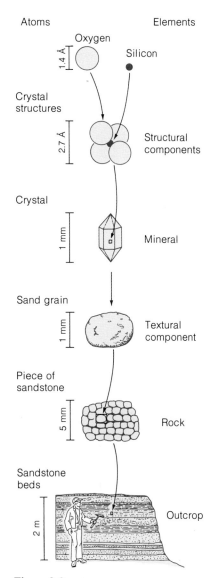

Figure 3-3
How atoms are put together to form rocks. Atoms make small structural components that combine to form minerals, which in turn combine to form rocks.

Figure 3-4
Flow chart of rock properties.

distinguish, the more the information gleaned, and the greater the power of our theories of explanation. That is why professional petrologists have to know a great deal about mineralogy.

Just how do we go about identifying minerals and explaining their origins from their characteristics? In the field we still use external form and the obvious physical properties. In the modern laboratories of mineralogists, however, advanced instruments are used to infer the basic composition and atomic architecture of minerals. These are the underlying determinants of the other properties. From analysis of crystal structure and external form, we draw the best conclusions of origin. The next sections take us from the study of crystal faces to the explanation of physical properties in terms of the atomic arrangement.

CRYSTALS: FACES AND SYMMETRY

The regularity of crystal faces is a major aspect of the external form of minerals, and for many years they were studied and identified mainly by analyzing their symmetry. In addition to his earlier contributions—enunciating the laws of stratigraphy and recognizing fossils—Steno wrote in 1669 that quartz crystals, wherever found, always showed the same angle between similar crystal faces. By the late eighteenth century, his **constancy of interfacial angles** became accepted as a generality applicable to all minerals. By 1801, René Haüy was able to summarize the laws of **crystal symmetry,** the regularities of crystal faces. That symmetry, we now know, is a manifestation of the symmetry of the internal structure of the atoms making up the crystal. As a consequence of the work of Haüy and others, the early part of the nineteenth century was a time of intense exploration of the external forms of minerals in relation to their chemical composition, a development that paralleled the great geological exploration of the Earth and the growth of the geological time scale.

How to Measure a Crystal. In the large, a crystal is a piece of matter whose boundaries are naturally formed plane surfaces. The geometry of a crystal may be relatively simple, as in the cubes of common salt, the mineral **halite,** or they may be beautifully complex, as in snowflakes, the crystals of ice. Crystals are usually formed when a liquid solidifies or when a solution becomes **supersaturated**—that is, too enriched in dissolved material to hold it any more—and the dissolved substances precipitate, or "drop," out of solution. When some liquids, such as molten silicates, congeal very quickly, the solid that forms is not crystalline but **glassy,** a condition in which crystals with plane faces do not form, but only masses with curved, irregular surfaces. This absence of crystallinity is typical of quickly cooled material in many lavas. The glassy texture is the result of a lack of regular, symmetric order to the atomic structure.

The most useful measurements that can be made on crystals are those of the angles between faces. From these measurements, an idealized drawing can be made of the geometry of all of the faces in relation to each other; such a drawing eliminates all of the imperfections of the natural faces, such as scratches or breaks. Haüy and other mineralogists discovered as a result of such work that, in addition to constancy of interfacial angles, each kind of crystal exhibits other regularities: definite symmetrical relationships exist among faces, and there are certain simple mathematical relations between the angles of all faces. The marvel of finding such simplicity in the midst of apparent complexity is what led Haüy and others to infer that there must be an underlying order to the arrangement of the atoms in crystals—an idea that could only be verified a century later when X-rays were discovered and beamed through crystals.

Another element of order appeared after hundreds of different kinds of crystals were measured. All crystals can be put into seven general systems of symmetry. A further grouping of thirty-two crystal classes can be distributed among the seven systems. Mathematical analysis

Figure 3-5
Fluorite crystals, showing cubic form. [Photo by Alfred A. Blaker.]

Figure 3-6
Photomicrographs of snowflake crystals. These were described as among the choicest specimens of crystal architecture in a 25-year search by Wilson Bentley, pioneer photographer of snow crystals. [Photos by Wilson Bentley, courtesy of Duncan Blanchard, State University of New York at Albany.]

Figure 3-7
A fragment of obsidian, a volcanic glass. The curved, sharply terminated fracture surfaces are typical of what is called *conchoidal fracture,* which characterizes glasses and a number of other materials, including many minerals. [Photo by R. Siever.]

Figure 3-8
Quartz exhibits a variety of crystalline forms ranging from groups of crystals with well-developed crystal faces, such as those on the left, to masses of crystals intergrown in such a way that no crystal faces are developed, such as in the broken pebble of vein quartz on the right. [Photo by R. Siever.]

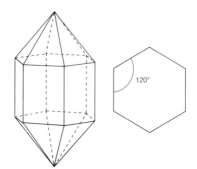

Figure 3-9
Drawing of quartz crystal. A section at right angles to the long axis, showing a regular hexagon with faces at 120° angles.

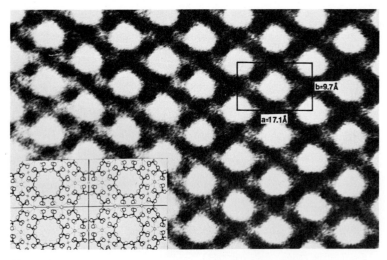

Figure 3-10
High-magnification electron micrograph of a section of the mineral cordierite, an orthorhombic magnesium-iron-aluminosilicate. This image was made perpendicular to one of the major axes of symmetry. A unit cell is outlined; the inset shows the idealized structure deduced from X-ray diffraction at the same scale as the electron micrograph. [From Peter R. Buseck and Sumio Iijima, "High Resolution Electron Microscopy of Silicates," *American Mineralogist,* vol. 59, 1974, Copyright 1973.]

has shown that there are only these thirty-two different ways of arranging atoms about a point that will allow the building of a crystal that obeys symmetry rules and fills space in three dimensions. The combined effort of measuring angles between crystal faces and analyzing the symmetry of crystals has led to a simple and orderly classification that consists of a limited number of major crystal systems and classes and which includes all crystals. The analysis of symmetry is still a part of modern mineralogy, though it is now studied by X-ray diffraction and electron microscopy rather than the observation of angles between crystal faces. Symmetry remains important because it is one of the basic clues to the pattern of regularity of the atoms in a crystal.

MINERALS AND THE MICROSCOPE

In 1858, at the end of the half century during which the modern laws of crystallography were worked out, an English geologist, Henry Sorby, published a memoir, *On the Microscopical Structure of Crystals.* Sorby's memoir was the fruit of almost ten years of work spent studying thin, transparent slices of rock with the polarizing microscope, which had been invented about thirty years earlier but hardly used. For geologists, it was the beginning of a new subject, **optical mineralogy.** That study, in turn, led to another new subject, **petrography,** the study of rocks and the crystals that make them up; the polarizing microscope, known more familiarly to most geologists as the petrographic microscope, became the major tool in both disciplines.

The inspiration of Sorby was to use the knowledge that even the darkest, most opaque-looking rocks might be made transparent if slices were thin enough, and that the way crystals affect polarized light passing through them could provide a means of identifying minerals and of studying the mineral compositions and textures of a wide variety of rocks. For the first time he could identify small grains or crystals that could be seen only with a high-power microscope.

From the various properties of minerals in polarized light, optical mineralogists have constructed detailed tables for the identification of crystals. Using these tables as he studies thin sections of rock under the microscope, the geologist can tell just what kinds of minerals are put together in a particular pattern to make up the

Box 3-1 Crystal Symmetry

One can see how a simple crystal is analyzed by taking a cube and noting, first, the obvious relation that all faces are always at 90° to each other and, second, that one can draw three mutually perpendicular imaginary planes such that each is a *plane of symmetry;* that is, each face on one side of the plane is mirrored on the other side. Or, one can hold opposite faces of the cube on an axis between thumb and forefinger and spin it around to find that there is a *fourfold axis of symmetry;* that is, in one complete rotation of 360° a

face will be repeated four times. Another axis of rotation between opposite corners is a *three-fold* axis of symmetry. The essence of symmetry is this: a simple geometrical operation can be performed that will repeat a face in another position. To put it another way, if one performs an operation such as a rotation, a new face will occupy the same position that was occupied by another face before rotation—and one cannot tell that the operation has been performed from the final appearance alone.

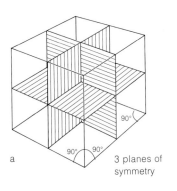

a   3 planes of symmetry

b   4-fold axis

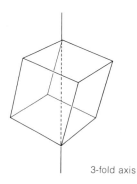

c   3-fold axis

Crystal systems.

System	Minimum symmetry	Reference axes
Isometric	4 3-fold axes	3 mutually perpendicular; all of same length
Trigonal	1 3-fold axis	4 axes, 3 horizontal with 120° intersections, 1 vertical. Horizontal axes all of same length; vertical axis any length
Hexagonal	1 6-fold axis	Same as trigonal
Tetragonal	1 4-fold axis	3 mutually perpendicular; 2 of same length, 3rd of any length
Orthorhombic	3 2-fold axes or 3 symmetry planes	3 mutually perpendicular; each of any length
Monoclinic	1 2-fold axis and/or 1 symmetry plane	2 axes at oblique angle, 3rd axis perpendicular to plane of the other 2; each axis of any length
Triclinic	1-fold axis or center of symmetry	3 axes at oblique angles; each of any length

Note: In some classifications, hexagonal and trigonal are considered to be divisions of one crystal system, the hexagonal.

60

Thin sections are made by cutting off a slice of rock about 1 mm thick with a saw containing embedded diamonds. One side is then ground smooth with silicon carbide grinding powders and cemented to a glass slide. Next, the open side is ground down until the desired thinness is reached, about 0.03 mm, the last gentle stages of polishing being monitored with a microscope. Some minerals are opaque no matter how thin they are ground. These are the metallic minerals, sometimes called the *opaque minerals.* An example is pyrite, FeS_2.

Forty years after von Laue and the Braggs opened up X-ray crystallography as a science, two young men working in the laboratories at Cambridge University in England, under the direction of the younger Bragg, who was then in his sixties, brilliantly applied their knowledge of X-rays and molecular architecture to deduce the crystal structure of the genetic substance DNA (deoxyribonucleic acid). The detective story of the search for that structure by J. D. Watson and F. M. Crick, later described by Watson in *The Double Helix,* involved a race among some of the leading figures in X-ray diffraction studies.

rock. The optical properties shown by crystals formed the basis for speculating on the atomic structure of crystals even before X-rays were discovered. Recently, these properties have come to be of interest to geophysicists, who are trying to use them to measure how thermal energy is transmitted through materials under extremely high pressures in the Earth.

THE ATOMIC STRUCTURE OF MINERALS

Though many nineteenth-century mineralogists, following the lead of earlier scientists, had speculated about how the atoms that make up all matter might be internally arranged in crystals, there was no way to confirm any relation between external form and internal structure. By the beginning of the twentieth century, many mineralogists were becoming increasingly convinced that crystal form, chemical composition, and such physical properties as color and hardness, might be explained in terms of some hypothetical atomic pattern, but they had no proof. That proof was provided in 1912 by the German physicist Max von Laue and two of his students, when they irradiated a crystal of copper sulfate with X-rays and produced an **X-ray diffrac-**

tion pattern on a film placed behind the crystal. It had already been realized that X-rays are a variety of electromagnetic radiation, like ordinary light, except that they have very short wavelengths, which give extreme penetrating power. Von Laue reasoned that if ordinary light could be **diffracted**—that is, apparently deflected around corners to give a pattern of fringes when it was directed through very tiny openings such as pinholes or slits—so could X-rays. It was known that the smaller the wavelength of the visible light—that is, the closer the wavelengths are to the blue and violet end of the spectrum—the smaller the pinhole had to be to produce diffraction patterns. Von Laue guessed that if the mineralogists were right in their speculations about crystals being orderly arrangements of atoms, the smallest "pinholes" he could use to make the very short wavelengths of X-rays diffract would be the spaces between the atoms of a crystal, which must be about one ten-millionth (10^{-7}) of a millimeter. Not only that, but the pattern of the X-rays could reveal the way the "pinholes"—and therefore the atoms—are arranged in space. It took only one year after that remarkable and crucial experiment for an English father-and-son team, William H. Bragg and William L. Bragg, to publish the first crystal-structure analysis of a mineral, halite. The Nobel Prize in physics was awarded to the Braggs for this work in 1915, when the younger, William L., was only twenty-five.

In the next dozen years a great many minerals were structurally mapped. This paved the way for the Norwegian mineralogist and petrologist V. M. Goldschmidt to outline, in 1926, all of the general principles governing the ways that the atoms of different elements are put together to form crystals. Finally, some explanation could be given for the long-known facts of the external appearance of crystals and their properties. The explanation lies in the structure of atoms, their systematic changes with increasing atomic number and atomic weight, their atomic size, and their ability to form various kinds of chemical bonds with other atoms.

The Gain and Loss of Electrons. As we noted in Chapter 2, an atom consists of a cloud of electrons orbiting the relatively small nucleus of protons and neutrons. An atom may gain or lose one or more electrons, thus forming an **ion,** charged positively or negatively depending on the relative numbers of protons in the nucleus

Figure 3-11
Microscopic view of a thin section (transparent slice) of diorite porphyry. The white crystals are feldspar; the large, dark rectangular ones are hornblende. The large crystals were all once floating in a melt, which is now represented by the fine-grained groundmass. Width of field 2.5 mm. [From *Geology of Soils* by Charles B. Hunt. W. H. Freeman and Company. Copyright © 1972.]

Table 3-1
Types of electronic structure of the elements (other than rare earths or actinides).

Type of element	Common elements	Characteristics
Noble gases	Helium, argon	Outer shells of elements have stable, filled configurations and no tendency to form chemical compounds.
Alkali metals Alkaline Earth metals	Sodium, potassium Calcium, magnesium	Outer shells have one or two valence electrons and strong tendency to lose them and form captions
Halogen group Oxygen group	Fluorine, chlorine Oxygen, sulfur	Outer shells need one or two electrons to assume stable configurations and have strong tendency to gain electrons and form anions
Boron group Carbon group Nitrogen group	Boron, aluminum Carbon, silicon Nitrogen, phosphorus	Outer shells tend to assume stable configurations by sharing electrons with other atoms and have weak tendency to gain or lose electrons
Transition elements	Iron, copper, zinc	Valence electrons tend to be gained or lost from an inner shell rather than the outer shell

and electrons surrounding the nucleus. The number of protons remains the same, even though electrons may be lost or gained. A positively charged ion, a **cation,** has lost electrons. A negatively charged ion, an **anion,** has gained electrons.

The working out of the rules that describe how electrons are tied to the nucleus was a major part of the business of atomic physics early in this century. Contemporary concepts of atomic structure view the paths of electrons around the nucleus as energy levels that vary with the shape of the orbitals (they may not be circular or even close to it), the distance from the nucleus, and the number and energy levels of the other electrons. The ease with which electrons are gained or lost is described in terms of the **electronic structure** of the elements, in which energy levels are represented as simple electron "shells"—spheres whose distance from the nucleus is proportional to their energy levels.

The elements can be divided into groups on the basis of their electronic structure (Table 3-1). One small group includes the elements whose outermost shell is populated by eight electrons. They are the inert, or noble, gases: neon, argon, krypton, xenon, and radon. Because this is a stable configuration, these elements have no tendency either to gain or to lose electrons, and so do not form any important crystalline compounds. Helium, with only two electrons, is also stable and belongs with this group.

A second group of elements is made up of those whose outermost shells may gain or lose electrons. This group includes most of the common abundant elements, such as sodium, potassium, magnesium, and calcium. These elements have a tendency either to gain or to lose electrons in order to assume the stable configuration of the inert gases. When a chlorine atom gains an electron, it becomes the chloride anion with 8 electrons in the outer shell, thus achieving the same structure as that of atomic argon. Similarly, the element potassium has a strong tendency to lose an electron and become a cation with exactly the same structure as the chloride ion. The electrons that are gained and lost, called **valence electrons,** determine the chemical behavior of the elements.

Another group includes elements with very weak tendencies to gain or lose valence electrons but strong tendencies to share them with other atoms of the same or different kind, thus achieving a stable configuration. In **electron sharing,** a shared electron cannot be considered to have been gained or lost; in a sense, both nuclei have "gained" the electron for whatever part of the time that it can be visualized as belonging to the one or the other nucleus. Carbon and silicon are two important elements in this group.

A group of elements called the transition elements consists of those whose valence electrons are in the next-to-outermost shells. These elements may form several different kinds of ions; iron, for example, forms two cations, Fe^{++} and Fe^{+++} (see pp. 95-96).

The importance of electronic structure, shells of valence electrons, and stability of the outer shell is that they all determine the nature of **chemical bonding** of one element to another in

The nucleus, containing almost the entire mass of an atom, has a diameter between 10^{-13} and 10^{-12} cm, thus having a volume only one-thousandth to one ten-thousandth of the entire atomic volume. For the convenience of using small integral numbers, the *angstrom* ($= 10^{-8}$ cm) is used as a unit of measurement for atomic diameters.

Box 3-2 Electronic Structure of the Elements

The hydrogen atom is the smallest and simplest of all atoms, having just one proton in the nucleus and just one orbiting electron (atomic number 1). Electron orbits correspond to "shells" that surround the nucleus, for electrons do not follow a simple, single path as the planets do around the Sun but can be considered to occupy, at various instants, points on a sphere, or spheres, around the nucleus. As atomic number increases, so does the number of electrons and so does the number of shells. The table lists the shells and the maximum number of electrons each can hold. The single hydrogen electron occupies the **K-shell,** the innermost of the seven shells. The element of next higher atomic number is helium, which has two electrons, both in the K-shell (atomic number 2). The K-shell can be occupied by only two electrons. The element of next higher

atomic number, lithium, has three electrons (atomic number 3), one of which occupies the next shell outward, the **L-shell.** This shell can hold eight electrons. The first two shells, K and L, fill up in order as the atomic number of the elements increases from hydrogen to neon. After that, from sodium (atomic number 11) to argon (atomic number 18), the next eight electrons start to fill up the **M-shell.** Then the regular order is interrupted and the **N-shell** starts to fill before the M-shell is completed. Then electrons are added to both M and N shells, until M is filled, whereupon with increasing atomic number, the **O-shell** starts filling and N continues being completed. This complication of shell filling helps to explain why the chemistry of the heavier elements is somewhat more varied and complex than that of the light elements, those with only two or three shells.

Electron shells of atoms.

Electron —— K-shell
Proton →

Hydrogen atom
Net charge (1+) + (1−) = 0
Atomic number 1

Hydrogen ion, a cation (K-electron lost)
Net charge (1+)
Atomic number 1

K-shell
Neutrons (Zero charge)

Helium atom
Net charge (2+) + (2−0) + 2(−) = 0
Atomic number 2

L-shell

Lithium atom
Net charge (3+) + (4−0) + (3−) = 0
Atomic number 3

Lithium ion, a cation (L-electron lost)
Net charge (3+) + (4−0) + (2−) = (1+)
Atomic number 3

As atomic number increases, electrons fill up the innermost, or K-shell, first, and then start to fill the L-shell. Ions are formed when atoms lose or gain electrons.

Shell	Maximum number of electrons possible in shell		Example
K	2		Hydrogen K-1
L	8		Carbon K-2, L-4
M	18		Silicon K-2, L-8, M-4
N	32		Iron K-2, L-8, M-14, N-2
O	50		Silver K-2, L-8, M-18 N-18, O-1
P	72		Gold K-2, L-8, M-18 N-32, O-18, P-1
Q	98		Uranium K-2, L-8, M-18, N-32, O-21, P-9 Q-2

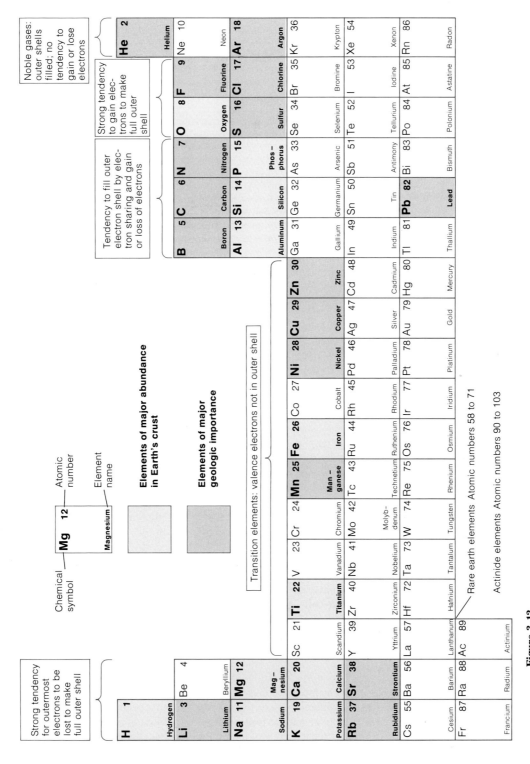

Figure 3-12
Periodic table of the elements (rare earth and actinide elements omitted), showing electronic structure and geologic importance.

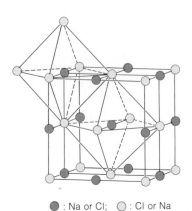

: Na or Cl; ◯ : Cl or Na

Figure 3-13
Cubic structure of sodium chloride (ions not drawn to true scale). [From R. C. Evans, *Crystal Chemistry* (2nd ed.), Cambridge Univ. Press, 1966.]

Figure 3-14
Cubic structure of sodium chloride, showing the ions in their correct relative sizes. [From R. C. Evans, *Crystal Chemistry* (2nd ed.), Cambridge Univ. Press, 1966.]

Electrostatic attraction is described by *Coulomb's Law,* which states that the attraction (or repulsion) between two charged particles is directly proportional to their product and inversely proportional to the square of the distance between them, or:

$$E = k(q_1 \times q_2)/d^2$$

where E is the attractive force, the q's the number of charges on the ions or electrons, d the distance, and k a proportionality constant associated with the medium in which the attraction takes place. The value of k is 1 in a vacuum.

Table 3-2
Ionic radii of alkali metal group of elements.

Element	Ion symbol	Atomic number $(Z) = no.\ of$ electrons	Ionic radius (angstrom units)*
Lithium	Li⁺	3	0.60
Sodium	Na⁺	11	0.95
Potassium	K⁺	19	1.33
Rubidium	Rb⁺	37	1.48
Cesium	Cs⁺	55	1.69

*One angstrom, 10^{-8} cm. See marginal note, p. 61.

crystals. There are a number of bond types, and they are not mutually exclusive. A particular bond may be largely of one type but have some characteristics of another. The simplest form of chemical bond, in some ways, is the ionic bond.

Ionic Bonds. Bonds of this type are formed by electrostatic attraction between ions of opposite charge, which is of exactly the same nature as the attraction that makes hair "stand up" when some synthetic fabrics are drawn over it. Thus ionic bonds form most strongly between elements like sodium and chlorine, which tend to gain or lose electrons and become cations or anions. In fact, the simplest of all ionically bonded crystalline substances is sodium chloride, whose crystal structure was the first to be worked out. From a look at Figure 3-13 one can see the symmetry of the ionic arrangement, that each ion of one kind is surrounded by six of the other, and that there is no "molecule" of NaCl as such. The six neighbors give rise to a new measure, the **coordination number.** Both sodium and chloride ions are in six-coordination. Or we can say that NaCl is **octahedrally** coordinated, from the regular octahedron described by lines connecting the six coordinated ions.

One can also see from Figure 3-13 that, although there is no molecule of NaCl, there is what is called a **unit cell**—the geometric form that is outlined by the minimum number of ions necessary to show the basic building block that is repeated a great number of times to form a visible crystal. X-ray diffraction studies show that there is a variation in the sizes of ions that makes it possible to deduce structures of packed spherical ions of different sizes (Fig. 3-14). When the exact size of an ion, the **ionic radius,** is calculated from such data, tables of ionic radii can be made that show certain trends (Table 3-2). The ionic radii of elements in the same chemical group, such as lithium, sodium, potas-

sium, rubidium, and cesium, increase with atomic number, in relation to the addition of electrons and electron shells.

Cations are small, most of them less than 10^{-8} centimeters in radius. But most anions are large, particularly the most common anion, oxygen. From this it is apparent that most of the space of a crystal is occupied by the anions and that the cations tend to fit into interstices between them. Figure 3-14 shows the NaCl structure with ions of approximately the correct relative size. A convenient way to measure the relative sizes of anions and cations is by **radius ratio,** the ratio of cation radius to anion radius. For some structures the radius ratio shows that the cations are too large to fit into interstices and that the anions are held slightly apart. If a slightly smaller cation were put into the space, the anions would be held less far apart and the closer packed structure would be more stable because the electrostatic attraction holding it all together would be stronger. The structure would be most stable if the cation were just small enough to fit exactly into the spaces between anions that touch each other. If a cation is smaller than the space, it will have no effect on the anions, for they cannot get any closer than contact. Detailed analyses of this sort allow crystallographers to predict what kinds of structures are possible with different elements and to explain why minerals make the kinds of crystals they do.

Covalent Bonds. Compounds that make a stable electronic configuration by sharing electrons rather than gaining or losing them are held together with **covalent bonds.** The formation of such bonds depends on the number and distribution of shared electrons in the outer shells, and so the kinds of compounds and crystal structures formed are determined by more complex factors than the simple geometric ones of dominantly ionically bonded crystals. Elements

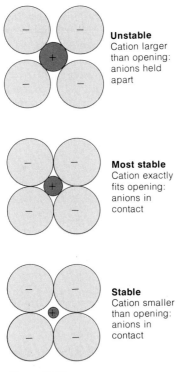

Figure 3-15
Radius ratio of cations to anions determines the stability of ionic bonds.

Unstable
Cation larger than opening: anions held apart

Most stable
Cation exactly fits opening: anions in contact

Stable
Cation smaller than opening: anions in contact

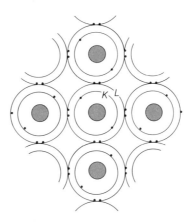

Figure 3-16
A carbon atom in diamond may share one outer electron with each of four neighbors, and so achieve the stable number of 8 electrons in the outer shell, even though each individual atom would have only 4 electrons by itself.

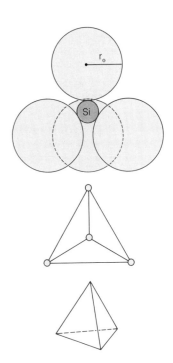

Figure 3-17
Silica (SiO$_4$) tetrahedron in three different representations.

that do not readily gain or lose electrons to form ions—for example, carbon—form bonds of this kind. The simplest covalent structure is that of diamond, in which every carbon atom (not an ion) is surrounded by four others (coordination number 4) arranged in a regular tetrahedron (Fig. 3-15). When coordinated in this way, each carbon atom shares one electron with each of its four neighbors and thus achieves a stable octet of electrons in its outer shell.

The van der Waals Bond. Weak bonds that have far less strength than ionic or covalent bonds exist between all ions and atoms in solids. They are named after the man who inferred their existence from weak attractive forces shown by atoms and molecules in gases. This form of bond is a weak electrical attraction that is related to the asymmetry of certain atoms and ions. Van der Waals bonds play a role of moderate importance in some silicate minerals, where their presence is not masked by the more powerful ionic and covalent links.

The Structure of Some Common Minerals. Though the variety of known structure types in the universe is great, geologists seldom encounter more than a relatively small number, largely because most rocks are made up of silicate minerals, which combine the two most abundant elements in the Earth's crust, oxygen (O) and silicon (Si). Silicates can be divided into a few major structure types. The basis for all silicate structures is the radius ratio of silicon to oxygen, about 0.30, which allows each silicon to be four-coordinated to four surrounding oxygens in a regular tetrahedron (Fig. 3-17). Silicate structures are made up of these tetrahedra arranged in different ways, with such cations as sodium (Na$^+$), potassium (K$^+$), calcium (Ca^{++}), magnesium (Mg^{++}), ferrous iron (Fe^{++}) and ferric iron (Fe^{+3}) in the interstices between. The bond between Si and O is about half ionic in character and half covalent, the Si sharing one of its outer electrons with each oxygen ion. Adjacent silicons may share oxygen ions, allowing networks of several kinds to be built up of tetrahedra. Many silicate minerals also contain aluminum, the third most abundant element in the Earth's crust after oxygen and silicon. The radius ratio of aluminum to oxygen is 0.36, a value sufficiently close to the silicon/oxygen ratio to allow it to take the place of silicon ion in a tetrahedral structure. The ratio is large enough, however, to allow aluminum to be octahedrally coordinated too, just like the ions in NaCl, and it may join adjacent tetrahedra by a dominantly ionic bond.

Cations that have similar coordination numbers and have similar ionic radii tend to substitute for each other and make mixed compounds that we call **solid solutions,** which are analogous in every way to common liquid solutions. Natural olivines are solid solutions of variable amounts of Fe and Mg silicates. The pure Mg olivine is Mg_2SiO_4, forsterite; the pure Fe olivine is Fe_2SiO_4, fayalite. The composition of the natural solid-solution mineral is represented by the formula $(Mg, Fe)_2SiO_4$.

Table 3-3
Major silicate structures.

Geometry of linkage of SiO_4 tetrahedra	Si/O ratio		Example mineral	Formula
Isolated tetrahedra: linked by bonds sharing oxygens only through cation	1:4		Olivine	$(Mg,Fe)_2SiO_4$
Rings of tetrahedra: joined by shared oxygens in 3-, 4- or 6-membered rings	1:3		Beryl	$BeAl_2(Si_6O_{18})$
Single chains: each tetrahedron linked to two others by shared oxygens. Chains bonded by cations	1:3		Pyroxene	$(Mg,Fe)SiO_3$
Double chains: 2 chains joined by shared oxygens as well as cations	4:11		Amphibole	$(Ca_2Mg_5)Si_8O_{22}(OH)_2$
Sheets: each tetrahedron linked to 3 others by shared oxygens. Sheets bonded by cations or alumina sheets	2:5		Kaolinite	$Al_2Si_2O_5(OH)_4$
Frameworks: each tetrahedron shares all its oxygens with other SiO_4 tetrahedra (in quartz) or AlO_4 tetrahedra	3:8		Feldspar (Albite)	$NaAlSi_3O_8$
	1:2		Quartz	SiO_2

Silicates are classified and named according to the way the tetrahedra are linked, as shown in Table 3-3. **Isolated tetrahedra** are linked by mutual bonding to a cation between. **Rings of tetrahedra** are formed by bonding of two oxygens of each tetrahedron to adjacent tetrahedra in closed rings. **Single chains** form by the same linkage. Two single chains are combined in some minerals to form **double chains,** in which the chains are linked by cations. **Sheets** are structures in which each tetrahedron shares three of its oxygens with adjacent tetrahedra to build planar lattices. In three-dimensional **frameworks,** the tetrahedra are linked by sharing oxygens with other tetrahedra. Aluminum may substitute for silicon in chains, sheets, and frameworks.

A different sort of building block is the carbonate ion. In this group of ions the carbon atom is surrounded by three oxygen atoms in a planar triangle. Groups of carbonate ions are arranged in sheets in a manner somewhat like that of the sheet silicates. The mineral calcite is made up of carbonate sheets and intervening planes of calcium ions. The mineral dolomite is made up of the same carbonate sheets separated by alternating sheets of calcium and magnesium ions.

Glasses lack the regularity of structure that is typical of the crystalline state. In silica glass, for example, the atoms are arranged in silica tetrahedra, but rather than being linked up in a regular repetitive manner, they are more or less randomly arranged, as they would be in a liquid. All natural crystal structures have a variety of defects and imperfections. These are the result of disturbances of the ordered arrangement of atoms by dislocations, which are small "faults,"

Box 3-3 Properties of Rock-forming Silicates

The major groups of silicates illustrate the influence of crystal structure and chemical composition on the properties of these important rock-forming minerals (See Table 3-3 and Appendix IV). Garnets and olivines are the two chief groups of silicates built of isolated tetrahedra linked by cations. Both groups are strongly bonded in all directions and moderately closely packed, so that they are hard and have no cleavage. The density of these minerals, relatively high, depends on both packing and chemical composition, in particular the amount of iron. Colors are also influenced by iron content. Olivines melt at very high temperatures, hence it is not surprising that they are found in high-temperature igneous rocks rich in iron and magnesium. Garnets are chemically complex; their composition reflects the bulk composition of the metamorphic rocks in which they are mainly found.

Pyroxenes (single chains of tetrahedra) and amphiboles (double chains) are much more chemically varied than the olivines or garnets. Both structures are packed moderately closely, and the common presence of iron makes these two groups fairly dense and moderately hard. But the cleavage of both is good, parallel to the silicate chains, for across these surfaces bonds are weaker than the strong silicon-oxygen bonds of the tetrahedral chains. The two differ in cleavage angle because of the varying angles made by single and double chains. Pyroxenes have high melting points, and are most likely to be found in igneous and high-temperature metamorphic rocks rich in iron and magnesium. The stability of amphiboles over large ranges of temperature and pressure is related to their chemical composition and its effect on the compactness of the structure and the bond strengths between cations of different kinds.

Micas show the most striking dependence of physical properties on structure: their perfect cleavage is due to the weak bonds between sheets, where the weakly bonded cations, such as potassium, are held. The minerals are relatively low in density and light in color, except for biotite, the iron species. The micas are found in many different igneous, metamorphic, and sedimentary rocks, a fact related to the large range of temperatures and pressures over which they can be formed.

Feldspars, the most abundant of the silicates, have relatively simple compositions; they are made up of silicon-oxygen and aluminum-oxygen tetrahedra linked in three-dimensional frameworks, with the tetrahedra bonded to potassium (orthoclase, microcline, sanidine) and/or sodium and calcium (plagioclase feldspars). Plagioclases range from albite, the pure sodium form, to anorthite, the pure calcium form. The strongly bonded silicon-oxygen and aluminum-oxygen framework gives these minerals their hardness and high melting temperatures. The cleavages are along planes of relatively weaker bonds between cations. There is sufficient variation in the way the three elements can combine to produce a wide range of melting temperatures and pressures; thus feldspars are characteristic of many kinds igneous, metamorphic, and sedimentary rocks, from the highest-temperature volcanics to the lowest-temperature sediments.

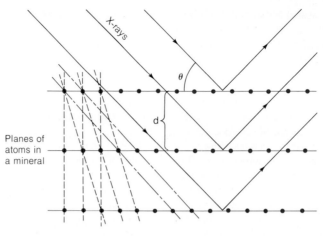

Figure 3-18
X-rays are reflected from the planes of atoms in a crystalline mineral when the
angle of incidence, θ, is in a certain proportion to the spacing between planes, d.
In addition to the horizontal planes, a few others of the many planes that could be
drawn are shown.

by holes where atoms are missing, or by places of misfit around an impurity atom or point of disorder. These defects, as well as the specific nature of crystal faces, can be related to the conditions for crystal growth and thus are clues to the environment in which the crystal grew. Since this is the petrologist's goal in understanding how rocks form, the study of the imperfections in crystal structure are becoming almost as important as the study of regularity and symmetry.

This brief tour through the world of crystal structures is intended to give some idea of the power of the principles of atomic physics, crystallography, and mineralogy, for it is from these disciplines that we have gained the extraordinary details that enable scientists to explain how crystals are put together. Now that you have some idea of what is known about structure, it is possible to show how X-ray diffraction was used to learn it all.

X-RAYS: THE DIAGNOSTIC TOOL OF MINERALOGY

Soon after Laue discovered X-ray diffraction, W. L. Bragg found out that a pattern of diffraction corresponded to one that would be formed by reflection of the X-ray beam from planes within the crystal, the reflection angles following certain mathematical requirements

that we now call Bragg's Law. Figure 3-18 shows how the planes can be visualized as made up of sheets of atoms in a regular array. As one can see from looking at any crystal structure diagrams, there are many possible planes that can be drawn. Each one reflects in accordance with Bragg's Law and so contributes its share to an X-ray pattern. The many lines of reflection that are found on X-ray patterns come from all of the planes.

The patterns of the lines can be harmonized to make a probable crystal structure. Today, sixty years after the Bragg's did their first work on NaCl, crystal structures are analyzed by automatic computers controlling X-ray diffraction equipment. The results are fed into another computer that spins out a complete structure analysis, possibly even with crystal drawings.

X-rays are being used as a rapid means of identifying minerals by their structures. That they can be so used is because no two minerals have precisely the same X-ray pattern, even though they may have the same structure type, such as the micas, muscovite and biotite, which have the same sheet structure, but whose precise patterns differ. The spacings and the intensity of the reflections depend on the kinds of atoms as well as their arrangement, so minerals are distinctive. In practice, the three most intense reflections on an X-ray pattern are compared to a list, sometimes in a card file, of minerals arranged by the spacing of their reflections. Today

The usual statement of Bragg's Law is $n\lambda = 2d \sin \theta$, where λ is the wavelength of the X-rays used, d the distance between planes of atoms (sometimes called "d-spacing"), θ the angle between the X-ray beam and the crystal planes, and n the "order" of a reflection. The order of a reflection refers to the successively higher angular positions of the crystal with respect to the X-ray beam at which for different pairs of n and θ the equation will be satisfied.

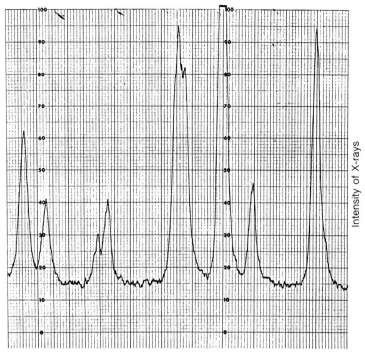

Angle of beam to crystal

Figure 3-19
An X-ray diffraction pattern of a feldspar produced by an X-ray spectrometer. The horizontal axis represents the angle of reflection of the X-ray beam from various planes of atoms in the crystal as the crystal is rotated in the X-ray beam. The vertical axis is a measure of the intensity of the reflection.

the X-ray machine is used for simple mineral identification almost as routinely as the somewhat crude physical and chemical tests were used in the last century. X-ray machines, however, are not easily carried into the field, even though some semiportable units have been invented, so it is still necessary to learn the simple diagnostic features of the common minerals (Appendix IV).

PHYSICAL AND CHEMICAL PROPERTIES OF MINERALS

A few years ago in Quincy, Massachusetts, a scratched message was discovered on the window of a house that John Hancock had owned in the eighteenth century. Speculation was that Hancock had expressed his feelings of love toward a woman by scratching their initials on the glass with his diamond ring. Whoever it was perhaps knew that a diamond is the hardest mineral known and can easily scratch glass. What makes diamond so hard was then un-

known. People also knew that mica, the sheety mineral commonly used for oven and lantern windows at that time, is especially easy to cleave into paper-thin sheets as transparent as window glass, but they did not know why. They were aware of many distinctive and useful properties of minerals. The earliest and still the simplest ways of identifying many common minerals are by testing for hardness, cleavage, and other physical properties.

Physical Properties, Bond Types, and Structures. We now know that the way atoms and ions are bound has a major effect on their physical properties, as shown in Table 3-4. Few bonds are exclusively of one type; instead, most are hybrids. For this reason, the correlation with properties can be only a weak generalization. Particular properties of a specific mineral can be explained on the basis of the kinds of atoms they are composed of and their structures, together with the bond types.

A good example is a mineral that has been used for ages as a cosmetic, talc, which has given

Table 3-4
Bond types and physical properties.

Property	Ionic	Covalent	van der Waals
Structural types	Bond strength of any ion is uniform in all directions with high coordination numbers	Interatomic or ionic bonds are strong only in a few set directions, hence coordination numbers low	Bond strength of any ion is uniform in all directions with high coordination numbers
Hardness	Strong bonds give high hardness	Stronger bonds, in general, giving higher hardness than ionic bonds	Weak bonds give low hardness
Cleavage	Ease of cleavage, poor to good, depends on distance between planes of atoms and individual bond strengths		Excellent cleavage
Melting points	Moderate to high; ions are present in the melt	Very high; molecules are present in melt	Low

Source: After R. C. Evans, *An Introduction to Crystal Chemistry,* 2nd ed., Cambridge University Press, Oxford, 1966.

us talcum powder. Talc is made up of silicate layers that are weakly bonded to each other by van der Waals forces, and so slip and break apart easily. It is that easy slippage of one layer over the other that gives talc its soapy feel and that makes it grindable to a fine, smooth, cosmetic powder. A contrary example is given by beryl, whose clear, deep-green variety is emerald. Beryl is also made up of sheets, but the bonds between them are strong, predominantly ionic; as a result, the mineral is hard and breaks with difficulty in any direction. Bonds of any character may be made weaker by imperfections of crystal structure. It is the weaker bonds in a structure that break first and so determine the hardness and other physical properties.

The various physical properties and the ways in which bonding and structure influence them are illustrated further in the next section.

Hardness. Just as a diamond scratches glass, so will a quartz crystal scratch a feldspar crystal, because one is harder than the other. Friedrich Mohs, an Austrian mineralogist, devised a scale of hardness in 1822 that spanned the spectrum from the softest to the hardest mineral known (Table 3-5). Even with all of the elegant instruments, called sclerometers, that are now available to determine hardness, the **Mohs Scale of Hardness** remains the best practical way to identify an unknown mineral. A combination of common objects and a few of the minerals on the hardness scale are all one needs to bracket an unknown mineral between two points on the scale. Hardness in more brittle materials is a variety of breakage on a small scale. The more ionic the bonding, the greater the brittleness, and most minerals tend to be somewhat brittle.

The hardness of any mineral depends on the strength of the bonds between ions or atoms; the stronger the bonds, the harder the mineral. Because bond strengths may differ along the various crystallographic axes, hardness may also vary slightly in direction. Hardness varies greatly among the silicates, from 1 in talc to 7 in quartz. The strongest bonds are those of tetrahedrally linked Si and O. In quartz they are all of that type. In other silicates the Si and O atoms are also bonded to other elements, and it is those weaker bonds that determine the lower hardness. Metallic minerals may be difficult to scratch because they deform plastically; that character gives metals their malleability or ductility, properties that allow them to be rolled into thin sheets or drawn into wires.

Cleavage. This term is used for breakage along definite planar surfaces, typified by that of mica. The number of planes of cleavage varies among minerals. The cleavage planes of a mineral have some of the same characteristics as its crystal faces, though they are not to be confused with them. They always occupy definite and constant positions with respect to the symmetry or crystallographic axes of the crystal and are parallel to a possible crystal face.

Cleavage is the expression of differing bond strengths along the various planes of a crystal. The bonds across some of those planes may be very weak, like the van der Waals bonds that are responsible for the easy breakage across the cleavage planes of mica. Calcite has three excel-

Table 3-5
Mohs scale of hardness.

Scale number	Mineral	Common objects
1	— Talc	
2	— Gypsum	
	————	Fingernail
	————	Copper wire or coin
3	— Calcite	
4	— Fluorite	
5	— Apatite	
	————	Pocket knife blade
	————	Window glass
6	— Orthoclase (feldspar)	
	————	Steel file
7	—	Quartz
8	—	Topaz
9	—	Corundum
10	—	Diamond

Mohs arranged the scale so that the hardness difference between any two adjacent minerals was about the same, except for the difference between corundum and diamond, which is much greater. Mohs could not find any mineral with an intermediate hardness, nor has anyone else.

lent cleavages parallel to the faces of a rhombohedron, the result of weak bonds. Quartz is strongly bonded in all directions and has no cleavage. Cleavage can be scaled on the basis of ease of cleaving with a chisel, from the most **perfect** cleavages of the micas to the **fair** cleavage of beryl (emerald). The most expert cleaving in the world is done in Amsterdam, where the center of the diamond "cutting" industry is; it is the excellent cleavage of diamond along many planes that makes possible the shaping of the hardest mineral known, for there is nothing harder with which to cut it!

Distinctive patterns of cleavage are identifying hallmarks of a number of common rock-forming minerals. Calcite and dolomite are easily recognized by their rhombohedral cleavage faces. Galena, lead sulfide, cleaves perfectly into cubic pieces. Two important groups of silicates that frequently look alike otherwise, pyroxenes and amphiboles, can be distinguished on the basis of their cleavage patterns. Pyroxenes, single chains of silica tetrahedra, are bonded so that two good cleavage directions are almost at right angles (93°), whereas amphiboles, double chains, bond to give two directions at 56°.

Similar to cleavage is **parting,** cleavage-like fractures resulting from bond weaknesses related to crystal imperfections that may be evident in some specimens of a mineral but not others. Some minerals reveal the character of their bonding by bending rather than breaking.

Dominantly covalent bonds are stronger in one direction than another. In mica, the bonds along the sheets of the structure maintain themselves while the weaker bonds between sheets allow bending. Micas are elastic; they spring back after bending. Other sheet silicates, like chlorite, are flexible; they remain bent.

Fracture. The way in which a mineral breaks other than along cleavage planes also serves to group them and help in identification. Fracture may be **conchoidal,** showing smooth, curved surfaces like those of a thick piece of broken glass (see Fig. 3-7); **fibrous** or **splintery, hackly,** and **uneven** or **irregular,** all of which are self-explanatory, though imprecise terms. Geometric properties of such variability and irregularity as fracture still defy the attempts of scientists to devise simple, quantitative measures to make the description objective and uniform. The type and irregularity of fracture bears a complex relation to the breaking of bonds in directions that cut across crystallographic planes. In minerals whose bond strengths are about the same in all directions, fracture patterns depend on the abundance, kind, and distribution of submicroscopic fractures and crystal defects.

Streak. The name "streak" is given to the color of the fine powder that is produced when a mineral is scraped, or rubbed, across a tile of unglazed porcelain, called a streak plate. The color is diagnostic for many minerals; for example, hematite, an iron oxide, always gives a reddish-brown streak regardless of the color of the particular mineral aggregate being streaked, which may be black, red, or brown.

Luster. The way in which the surface of a mineral reflects light gives it a characteristic luster. Mineral lusters are described by more or less self-explanatory terms (Table 3-6). The quality of light reflected from mineral surfaces is controlled by the index of refraction and the absorption of light by the elements of the mineral. Those properties, in turn, are related not only to the kinds of atoms but to their bonding. For example, covalently bonded minerals tend toward adamantine luster, whereas ionically bonded minerals are more vitreous. Other lusters are related to irregularities of the surface.

Color. In July 1976, we found out from the Viking landing on Mars that the "red planet" really is red. The surface materials are of a strong reddish hue that probably comes from hydrated ferric oxides. The same materials, thrown into the Martian atmosphere by strong winds, give the Martian sky a pinkish color. Many minerals show a characteristic color on freshly broken surfaces; others show characteristic colors on weathered or altered surfaces. We use not only the colors reflected from mineral surfaces but also the colors transmitted through minerals in microscopic thin sections. Color seen in thin sections is a good, quick guide to the identification of certain minerals. Some minerals—for example, precious opals—show a stunning play of colors on reflecting surfaces. Others will change color slightly with a change in the angle of the light shining on the surface. Minerals show a variety of other unusual optical properties, most of which are of chief interest to the gem trade, such as the cat's eye of chrysoberyl. Color may be a property of the pure substance or it may be the result of impurities. The color of pure substances is dependent on the presence of certain ions, such as iron or chromium, which are strong absorbers of certain colors of light. Most ionically bonded minerals with stable configurations of outer electron shells are colorless. Color is more characteristic of such minerals as olivine, which have bonds to transition elements (in this case iron) whose valence electrons are in an inner shell. Impurities, many too small to be seen except by the most powerful microscope, such as small dispersed flakes of

Figure 3-20
Calcite crystals. (Top) A cleavage rhombohedron whose surfaces were made by cleaving, or breaking, the crystalline material along zones of weak bonding strength in the crystal. (Bottom) Faces formed by growth of the crystal from a solution. [From *Dana's Manual of Mineralogy* (16th ed.) by C. S. Hurlbut, Jr., copyright 1952, John Wiley & Sons.]

Table 3-6
Mineral luster.

Metallic:	strong reflections produced by opaque substances.
Vitreous:	bright, as in glass.
Resinous:	characteristic of resins, such as amber.
Greasy:	surface has the appearance of being coated with an oily substance.
Pearly:	the whitish iridescence of materials like pearl.
Silky:	the sheen of fibrous materials like silk.
Adamantine:	the brilliant luster of diamond and similar minerals.

hematite in a quartz crystal, impart a general color to an otherwise colorless mineral.

Specific Gravity and Density. Though the obvious difference in weight of a piece of hematite iron ore and a piece of sulfur of the same size is easily felt by hefting the pieces in the hand, a great many common rock-forming minerals have about the same range of **density** (= mass/volume). Consequently, it became necessary to devise methods that would make it easy to measure that property of minerals accurately. The standard measure of density is **specific gravity** (= weight of the mineral in air/weight of an equal volume of water at 4°C). This is usually measured by taking the ratio of the weight of the mineral in air to the difference between the weight of the mineral in air and the mineral in water, which is the equivalent of the definition. Because density is not only useful in identifying minerals but is also a property that depends strongly on the internal structure and composition of the substance, it has been measured accurately for most minerals. Density is dependent on the atomic weight of the constituents and the tightness of packing of the atoms in the crystal structure.

Most ions have similarly sized radii, so that the major effect in density differences among minerals is the atomic weight of the constituent elements. Minerals such as hematite and magnetite have high densities because of the high atomic weight of iron. Metals tend to have close-packed structures and therefore high densities. Dominantly covalently bonded structures tend to be more open and have lower densities.

Density is also affected by pressure, and pressure-induced increases in density affect the way rocks and minerals transmit light, heat, and elastic waves, such as those associated with earthquakes (see Chapter 19). Some chemical substances form more than one kind of crystal; the different kinds of crystals are called **polymorphs.** Calcium carbonate, for example, forms both a trigonal polymorph, calcite (density 2.71), and an orthorhombic one, aragonite (density 2.93). The denser aragonite is known from experimentation to form and remain stable at high pressures, whereas calcite forms and is stable at low pressures.

Chemical properties. The distinctive chemical compositions of minerals are the basis for the major classification of the mineral kingdom. The chemical criterion used to divide the mineral kingdom into classes is the anion of the mineral. For example, halite, NaCl, is classed as a **chloride,** as is its close relative, sylvite, KCl. In this way, all minerals have been grouped into eight classes, as shown in Table 3-7.

Most of what we know about the chemical composition of minerals has been gained through the use of ordinary wet chemical methods, by which materials are dissolved, separated into their constituent elements, and their weight or volume then measured. Various other methods have been added over the past few decades as chemical instruments became more capable of measuring small quantities of elements in new ways. Most recently the **electron probe,** a device that beams electrons at a sample mineral and analyzes how the elements in the sample generate X-rays, has been used to get good chemical analyses of very small crystals.

Mineralogists have also relied for many years on quick, simple chemical tests that can be made in the field. Perhaps the best known is the "acid test," by which a dilute hydrochloric acid (HCl) solution is dropped on a mineral to see if it fizzes. If it does, it is likely to be calcite, a carbonate mineral. A full series of tests can be made with the **blowpipe,** a narrow tube through which one blows air into the flame of a gas or alchol burner to make the flame hotter. Using

Color of rocks, though sometimes spectacular and frequently useful in telling one rock or formation apart from another, is rarely of much use in deducing the details of a rock's origin. A student was once on a field trip with N. L. Bowen, a great authority on igneous rocks, and asked him to identify a particular rock specimen. He answered, with a twinkle in his eye, "That's a *black* rock."

The names "anion" for negative ion and "cation" for positive ion date back to early experiments with electrochemical cells, the ancestors of modern wet-cell automobile batteries. Because the *cat*hode, the negatively charged electrode, attracts positive ions, those ions became called *cat*ions. Similarly, the *an*ode, the positively charged electrode, attracts negative ions, hence *an*ion. Since then, hundreds of mnemonic devices (clues to memorizing) have been thought up to make it easy to remember the pair. One example: AP is not only Associated Press but anode = positive.

Table 3-7
Chemical classes of minerals*

Class	Defining anions	Example
Native elements	None: no charged ions	*Copper,* Cu
Sulfides and similar compounds	Sulfide: S^{--} and similar anions	*Pyrite,* FeS_2
Oxides and Hydroxides	O^{--} OH^{--}	*Hematite,* Fe_2O_3 *Brucite,* $Mg(OH)_2$
Halides	Cl^-, F^-, Br^-, I^-	*Halite,* NaCl
Carbonates and similar compounds	CO_3^{--}	*Calcite,* $CaCO_3$
Sulfates and similar compounds	SO_4^{--} and similar anions	*Barite,* $BaSO_4$
Phosphates and similar compounds	PO_4^{-3} and similar anions	*Apatite,* $Ca_5F(PO_4)_3$
Silicates (see Table 4-5 for details of silicates)	SiO_3	*Pyroxene,* $MgSiO_3$

* This classification, derived originally by Berzelius in the nineteenth century and used extensively by Dana, is a simplified form of the scheme used by Berry and Mason in *Elements of Mineralogy,* W. H. Freeman and Company, 1968.

An important example of the geological value of stable isotopes is the use of the ratio of O^{18} to O^{16} to determine ancient temperatures. The O^{18}/O^{16} ratio of the oxygen atoms in calcium carbonate is dependent on the temperature of the water from which it was precipitated. Thus a well-preserved fossil oyster shell can be analyzed to find the temperature of the sea in which the animal lived.

this simple instrument, minerals can be heated in various ways to perform diagnostic tests for the presence of specific elements.

There are impurities in all natural minerals, enough of them so that it is frequently hard to decide when an element is an integral part of the mineral or is merely an extraneous contaminant. Elements that make up much less than 0.1 percent of the mineral are reported in analyses by the word "trace," and many elements are called **trace elements.** But most trace elements we rarely hear about, for they are neither abundant in the earth (or the solar system) nor have they come into any important industrial use. Typical of these are lanthanum (La), one of the rare earth elements, and scandium (Sc), an element that has affinities with aluminum and boron. Trace elements are analyzed by means of an **emission spectrograph**—an instrument that vaporizes the mineral with an extremely hot electric arc and then analyzes the light emitted by the burning substance. A newer analytical method is **neutron activation:** an atomic reactor is used to bombard the mineral with the fast-moving neutrons that are formed from the radioactive decay process of uranium-235 in the reactor. The bombardment changes some of the originally nonradioactive elements in the mineral into new, radioactive elements. The abundance of the new elements can then be analyzed by counting radioactivity; one different atom among a billion others can be detected in this way. Thus we can obtain an accurate measure of

the abundance of the originally nonradioactive elements that were transmuted by bombardment. There are enough research reactors in universities all over the country that can be used by visitors to make this method practical for all those who learn how to do it.

Another part of chemical analysis is the determination of the relative proportions of different isotopes, the elements with the same atomic number (protons) but different atomic weights. In Chapter 2, we have discussed the use of radioactive isotopes in dating rocks, but there are other isotopes of some elements that are stable—that is, nonradioactive. Three of the most important are the heavy stable isotope of carbon, C^{13}, the heavy stable isotope of oxygen, O^{18}, and the heavy stable isotope of sulfur, S^{34}. The study of these isotopes in minerals, in the atmosphere, and in natural waters has contributed greatly to geology. As was discussed in Chapter 2, isotopes are analyzed by use of a mass spectrometer.

ROCKS AS MINERAL AGGREGATES

The architecture of a rock is not unlike that of a building—a design of building blocks put together in certain ways. The building blocks of a rock, of course, are minerals. Without too much difficulty, we might be able to think of all imaginable designs—all conceivable ways of putting minerals together—but the great majority of arrangements would bear little relation to any we find in nature, just as doing the same for all of the products in a building-supply warehouse would probably not bear much relation to a building like the Parthenon. The problem, then, is to find out the designs of nature and to find out why there are certain ways in which minerals are put together to form rocks and why there are many, many other ways in which they are not. Much of this book is devoted to questions such as these.

The initial subdivision of rocks is made on the basis of origin, and the three major categories are igneous, metamorphic, and sedimentary. Origin is determined by a combination of rock characters, such as bedding, the layering that indicates a sedimentary origin; foliation, the preferred orientation of crystals that indicates a metamorphic origin; and a variety of other textures and structures. Although this distinction is based partly on mineral composition, it is better to discuss such mineralogical and textural attributes within each major group and not try to make an all-inclusive definition of rock classification. For example, a pure quartz sandstone (sedimentary) and a vein of quartz (igneous) may both be 100 percent quartz, yet there are no igneous and metamorphic rocks composed of alternating bands of halite and gypsum, and there are no sedimentary rocks made up largely of pyroxene. Once the igneous, metamorphic, and sedimentary rocks have been described, it will be easier to see how the three groups can be distinguished from each other.

The Igneous Rocks. One major systematic grouping of igneous rocks is made on the basis of a combined chemical and mineralogical classification, the chemistry of the rocks being revealed largely by their dominant minerals and serving as a clue to the composition of the magmas from which they solidified. The names formerly used come from one of the first criteria used when the igneous rocks were first being studied in the last century—that is, the amount of silica, SiO_2, in the chemical analysis. During that pre-modern period of chemistry, the silica was thought to be derived from silicic acid, and so the more silica in the rock, the more "acidic" the magma. **Granite,** rich in silica, is the most abundant acidic rock. The rocks lower in silica were called basic. **Gabbro,** poor in silica, is the basic counterpart of granite. Though we now know that silica content is not a measure of acidity as that word is used in chemistry, the

terms persist even though what we really mean is "more or less **silicic.**" The amount of silica is not necessarily related to the amount of quartz, for much of the silica may be combined in other silicate minerals. In the classification by silica content, the coarse-grained igneous rock range in sequence from granite on the more silicic side, through **granodiorite** and **diorite,** to gabbro on the less silicic side.

Chemistry and mineralogic composition form the basis of the modern system of classifying the major groups, which turns out to be much the same as the classification by silica content. The two terms most commonly used come from a broad division into **light** and **dark** minerals, called, respectively, **felsic** and **mafic.** These terms were used because the dominant minerals of the light group are quartz and feldspars, both rich in silica (hence "felsic," from *fel*(*s*), feldspar, plus *ic*) and those of the dark group are pyroxenes, amphiboles, and olivines, all of which are rich in magnesium and iron (hence "mafic," from *ma*gnesium and *f* (ferrous), for iron, plus *ic*). The varieties of feldspar are most important in the classification of the igneous rocks, both because they are abundant and because the proportions of different kinds of feldspar vary systematically from felsic to mafic rocks. Granite is rich in potassium feldspar (mainly the mineral orthoclase), whereas the more mafic rocks are dominated by sodium and calcium feldspars, the plagioclases. The dark rocks are dominated by biotite mica and amphibole at the felsic end and pyroxene and olivine at the mafic end. Pyroxene and olivine are the major minerals of the **ultramafic** rocks, which are even lower in silica than the basalts and gabbros; **peridotite** is dominated by olivine and pyroxene and **dunite** by olivine.

The other major basis for classification of the igneous rocks is, as already described in Chapter 2, a textural one, whereby we differentiate between the coarse-grained granular rocks, or **phanerites** (from the Greek, *phanero-,* meaning visible), and the fine-grained **aphanites** (from the Greek *aphan-,* meaning invisible). A textural property that is in some ways a crystallographic property is the degree of **glassiness,** more commonly described by the opposite quality, the **crystallinity.** Both grain size and crystallinity are products of the speed with which a magma cools. The more rapid the cooling, the finer the grain size and the poorer the crystallinity. The slowest-cooling magmas congeal in the last stages of intrusion, when magmas become less viscous and contain more dissolved gases. These give rise to **pegmatites,** very coarse-grained rocks that may include huge crystals several meters across. The fastest-cooling magmatic materials of course, are those that are thrown high into the sky, where they instantly freeze to glass.

The granular or coarse-grained igneous rocks are subdivided on the basis of the abundance of their characteristic minerals, which are easily identifiable in coarse crystalline form in the field. The fine-grained igneous rocks, the volcanics, are more difficult to subdivide in the field because their minerals and glasses are not so easily identified. Their textures, however, are a good basis for grouping. Some volcanic rocks (covered in more detail in Chapter 15) may show the texture of **pyroclastic** rocks. These result from volcanic explosions that expel magma that quickly cools to glass. The finest fragments, which make **volcanic ash** and **dust,** are mixed with particles a few millimeters or centimeters in diameter, called **lapilli,** and larger pieces, called **blocks** and **bombs.** The resultant texture is one of an agglomeration of pieces of glass, crystals that had started to form before the explosion, and fragments of previously cooled lava. The glass may be in the form of fragments of **pumice,** a frothy mass of glass with a great number of bubbles formed by gas escaping from the melt. The sharp, spiky glass fragments are called **shards.** The bubble holes in pumice and other extrusive rocks are **vesicles,** which if they become filled with other minerals at a later time are called **amygdules.** A very vesicular rock is called **scoria.** The solidified rocks that harden from **ash falls** and **ash flows** and all of the other varieties of ejected material are lumped under the term **tuff.**

The other major textural class of volcanics includes the lavas that flow from volcanoes or large fissures in the crust. The lavas have been given Hawaiian names: **pahoehoe** for the smoother, ropy kind, and **aa** for the sharp, spiky, more jagged kind. The difference in appearance and structure are related to the ease of flowage, which depends on the lava's viscosity, which in turn is determined by the magma's composition.

The lavas and pyroclastics are named for their mineral and chemical compositions in the same way as the coarse-grained series, but fewer subdivision names are in common use. **Basalts,** the most abundant of volcanic types, are chemically the equivalents of gabbros, and **andesites** correspond to diabases and other rocks intermediate between granite and gabbro (Fig. 3-21). On the

felsic side, **rhyolite** is the aphanitic counterpart of granite, and **dacite** the aphanitic counterpart of granodiorite. Because of the glass in the volcanics, mineral compositions are not exactly the same as in corresponding granular rocks.

Mineral composition loses meaning in the entirely glassy rock **obsidian,** which is the ultimate of the fine-grained equivalents of granites and granodiorites. The glassy, sharp, broken edges of this highly silicic glass made it perfect for Indian arrowheads. The pumices, frothy glasses, are commonly silicic also.

Many igneous rocks are made up of a mixture of both large and small crystals. If some crystals are distinctively larger than the surrounding mass, or **matrix,** they are called **phenocrysts.** A rock with many phenocrysts is called a porphyry. The matrix of a **porphyry** may consist of coarse or fine crystals or, in volcanics, glass.

Putting together mineralogy and texture gives us a scheme of classification like the one shown in Figure 3-21. The mineralogical parameter measures the proportions and kinds of felsic and mafic minerals; and the textural parameter, grain size. As is true of most classifications, the rocks do not all fall neatly into pigeonholes, for composition and texture vary continuously, and we draw arbitrary dividing lines between them to preserve as nearly as possible the traditional meanings of names that have accumulated over two centuries of geological usage.

The Sedimentary Rocks. Mineralogy and texture are also useful in subdividing the sedimentary rocks. They are used in combination to set apart two main groups, the **detrital** and the **chemical.** The detrital sediments are those that carry the earmarks of the mechanical transportation and deposition of the debris of erosion, **detritus,** by currents. The minerals are fragments of rocks or minerals broken and eroded from pre-existing rocks, and so are called **clastic** (from the Greek *klastos,* to break). The rocks of ancient mountains worn down by erosion can be reconstructed from the minerals of detrital rocks. Quartz, feldspar, and the clay minerals make up the bulk of that contribution. The fragments tend to wear and abrade during transportation and so become **rounded.** During sedimentation, currents **sort** the minerals by size and weight with variable efficiency; the stronger the current, the larger the particle size carried. **Size** and **sorting** of clastic sedimentary particles are characteristic of the nature of the currents that carried them. They also form the basis for subdividing the detrital sediments into

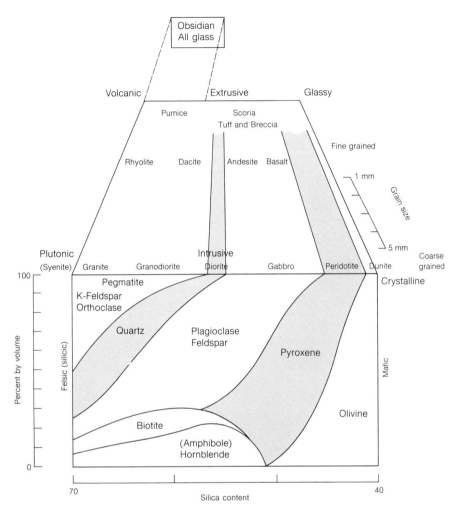

Figure 3-21
Igneous rock classification.

(1) coarse-grained, the **gravels** and their hardened, or **lithified,** equivalents, the **conglomerates;** (2) medium-grained, the **sands** and **sandstones;** and (3) fine-grained, **clays** and **muds** and their lithified equivalents, the **shales. Mudstone** is a general term for rocks composed of more than 50 percent clay and silt. Shales are characterized by **fissility,** a splitting along bedding plane surfaces. Coarse sedimentary rocks composed of sharp, angular pieces of rocks and minerals are **breccias,** which contrast with the rounded pebbles and cobbles of conglomerates.

The chemical sediments are precipitated from solution, mostly in the ocean, so that their minerals reflect the composition of the parent solution. The most abundant chemical rocks are **limestone** and **dolomite,** made up largely of calcium and magnesium carbonates, the minerals calcite and dolomite. **Limestones** may be made up in large part of calcareous fossils—shells formed by **biochemical** precipitation of calcium carbonate that animals extract from sea water. Other chemical sediments are also characterized by their chemical composition in rela-

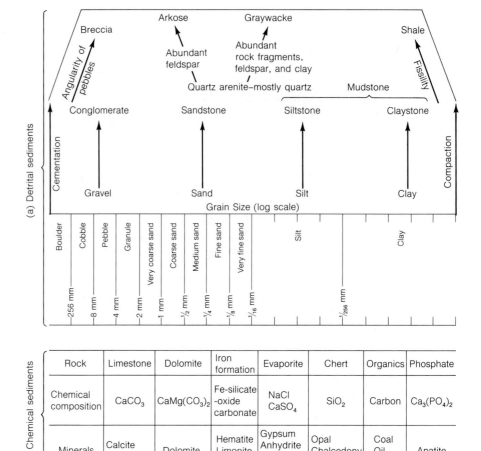

Figure 3-22
Sedimentary rock classification. (a) Detrital sediments, (b) Chemical sediments.

tion to origin. The **evaporites** are composed largely of gypsum and halite, some including a complex group of other salts crystallized from evaporated sea water. The chemical rocks show a texture of crystal intergrowths resembling that of intrusive igneous rocks, on whose surfaces crystals can be seen to fit together like a carefully constructed flagstone walk.

Mineralogy is an important criterion for distinguishing varieties of detrital rocks, particularly the sandstones. **Quartzose sandstones** or **quartz arenites** (arenite is a frequently used word for sand-sized sedimentary rocks) are mainly composed of quartz grains. This composition results from the erosional disappearance of feldspars and mafic minerals, leaving quartz, which is the most stable and resistant, as the sole residual mineral. **Arkose** is a sandstone that contains much feldspar in addition to quartz. **Graywackes** are poorly sorted dark sandstones that contain much feldspar and sand-sized rock fragments of metamorphic or volcanic rocks. Because the angular grains of graywackes are set in an abundant clay matrix, the rocks are sometimes called "dirty" sandstones, a somewhat imprecise term.

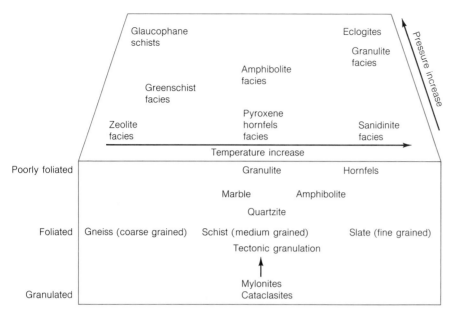

Figure 3-23
Metamorphic rock classification. The gradations in texture shown at front of diagram are not necessarily correlated with mineral facies controlled by pressure and temperature, shown on top of diagram.

Shale, sandstone, and limestone, the three most abundant sedimentary rock types, account for more than 95 percent of the total sedimentary part of the crust: shale accounts for about 70 percent, sandstone about 20 percent, and limestone about 10 percent of the total of the three.

The classification of sediments is based on mineralogy, texture, and chemical composition. The main criterion for subdivision of the detrital rocks is grain size, given as the diameter of the grain in millimeters. The boundaries are at 2 mm for gravel/sand, 1/16 mm for sand/silt, and 1/256 mm for silt/clay. The detritals are further grouped by their mineral content, mainly the relative amounts of quartz, feldspar, micas, and clay minerals. The chemical sediments are grouped by chemical composition, which is reflected in their mineralogy, into the **carbonates,** limestone and dolomite; **evaporites,** including chlorides (halite) and sulfates (gypsum); **cherts,** or **siliceous rocks,** containing much silica either as quartz or other varieties of SiO_2; **iron formations,** containing much iron in silicate, carbonate, or iron oxide minerals; **organics,** the organic carbon sediments including coal, gas, and oil; and **phosphates,** rocks containing phosphate as a variety of the mineral apatite or in clay minerals.

Many limestones and dolomites—those made up of pieces of shells and grains of carbonate minerals moved by currents—look much like detrital rocks, and they are classed according to grain size in much the same way as the sands and muds.

The Metamorphic Rocks. Just as igneous rocks are divided into intrusive and extrusive, and sediments into detrital and chemical, so are the metamorphic rocks divided into two broad genetic classes. They are either the result of **regional metamorphism** on the one hand or **contact metamorphism** on the other. Regional metamorphic rocks are produced by heat and pressure that transforms deeply buried rocks of all kinds, igneous, sedimentary and metamorphic. Contact metamorphics are made by the alteration of rocks near an igneous intrusion, largely from heat but also from pressure. The characteristic textures produced are the clues to these two modes of origin. Most regional meta-

80

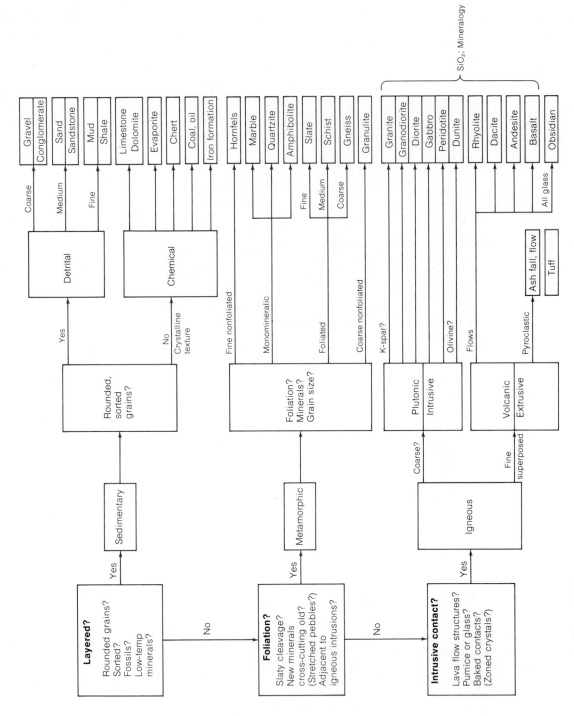

Figure 3-24
Rock identification flow chart.

morphics show **foliation**—a platy, wavy, or leafy structure imparted to the rock by the parallel alignment of minerals, particularly the sheety ones like mica. Some contact metamorphics are also foliated, but most tend to be granular, such as the **hornfelses,** which are very fine-grained silicate rocks of varied composition.

Foliation type and grain size are used, in combination, as the basis for subdividing the metamorphics into **schist, slate, gneiss, and granulite.** The schists are characterized by partings along well-defined planes of medium-grained platy micaceous minerals. The slates have more perfect planar partings and are finer grained, so that individual minerals cannot be easily seen. The gneisses are coarse grained and show much broader and less distinct foliation, and they do not split or cleave in the way schists and slates do. The planes of foliation of slates and schists are called **slaty cleavage.** Granulites are like their textural equivalents, the granular igneous rocks, in having a mosaic of interlocking, more-or-less equidimensional crystals. They show only faint foliation, if any.

Within these textural groups, mineral assemblages form the basis for further dividing the rocks into small groups, or **facies.** The metamorphic facies have a genetic basis, for the minerals are determined by the temperatures and pressures required to form them. For example, **albite-epidote-amphibole schists** are the product of moderate temperature and pressure in regional metamorphism, whereas a **pyroxene hornfels** is the result of high temperature and moderate pressure in contact metamorphism. In normal field usage, metamorphic rocks are prefixed by the name of an abundant or prominent mineral constituent—for example, **mica schist.** Others are named for a mineral constituent that is greatly predominant, such as **amphibolite. Marbles,** metamorphosed limestones, are largely made of calcite. **Quartzites,** metamorphosed quartz arenites, are mainly quartz.

Some metamorphic rocks have characteristic textures produced by the crushing and mechanical deformation of grains as the rocks are folded and faulted. The broken, pulverized grain texture is called **cataclastic,** and fine-grained rocks produced by this kind of frictional action are called **mylonites.**

The diagram of metamorphic rocks shows the relationship between the different textural groups and the facies within them. Most facies can be found in a variety of textural types, except for the highest pressure and temperature groups, in which slates and phyllites are not preserved as such.

The Information in Rocks. The characteristics of igneous, metamorphic, and sedimentary rocks can be used as a guide to identification (Fig. 3-24). Sedimentary rocks are identified as such mainly by their stratification, but also by their mineralogy and texture, as are igneous and metamorphic rocks. The identification of a metamorphic rock depends on recognition of foliation and other textures. In the same way, the earmarks of igneous rocks are their mineralogy, textures, and structures. Within the major groups, identifications are made on the same dual basis of mineralogy and texture.

From this brief summary of rock types, it should be apparent that mineralogy and texture are the major languages by which the information in rocks can be understood. The rounded quartz grains of a sandstone tell us about a history of erosion and transportation of fragments of a quartz-bearing igneous or metamorphic rock. The feldspar crystals in a granite inform us of the chemical composition of the magma and perhaps of the rate at which it cooled. The mica flakes of a schist are bits of information on the temperatures and pressures at which a shale was baked to make the schist. To get this information we need to know what the processes are by which they are made, where they operate in the Earth, and their relation to the larger architectural patterns of the Earth. It is these subjects that we move on to in the remainder of this book.

Figure 3-25
Skeleton chart of igneous rock classification.

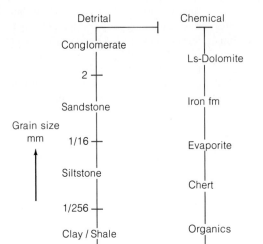

Figure 3-26
Skeleton chart of sedimentary rock classification.

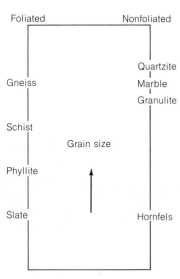

Figure 3-27
Skeleton chart of metamorphic rock classification.

SUMMARY

1. Rocks, and the minerals that make them up, are the records of the geological events of the past and contain information that is used to infer their origin.

2. Crystals exhibit external regularities of shape, constancy of interfacial angles, and symmetry relations that allow them to be divided into thirty-two crystal classes distributed among seven general symmetry groups.

3. The optical properties of minerals—the distinctive ways in which they transmit light—can be analyzed by means of a polarizing microscope to identify them.

4. The atomic structure of minerals has become known largely as a result of X-ray diffraction studies, in which X-rays are reflected by planes of atoms in the crystal.

5. The electronic structure of the elements explains the different kinds of chemical bonding of atoms in minerals. Bonding may be ionic or covalent, depending on whether valence electrons are gained, lost, or shared. A weaker type of bonding is van der Waals, which does not depend on valence electrons being gained, lost, or shared.

6. The radius of an ion in relation to those of the ions to which it is bonded determines the nature of the structures into which different ions can be organized.

7. Silicate mineral structures are made up of basic building blocks of silica tetrahedrons bonded to each other and to other ions to form isolated tetrahedrons, rings, chains, sheets, and three-dimensional frameworks.

8. Physical properties of minerals—hardness, cleavage, fracture, streak, luster, color, and density—are determined by the kinds of elements making up the minerals, their bond types, and crystal structures.

9. Chemical properties of minerals are determined by the kinds of elements present and their chemical bonding; minerals are classified on the basis of their anions.

10. Igneous rocks are divided on the basis of origin into intrusives and extrusives. The former are usually coarse grained; the latter, fine-grained or glassy. They are also classified as felsic or mafic, depending on the kinds and relative amounts of light and dark minerals. Volcanic rocks are further subdivided by texture.

11. Sedimentary rocks fall into two main groups, the detrital, those formed from particles eroded from pre-existing rocks, and the chemical, those formed by chemical precipitation of minerals from salt or fresh water. The detrital sediments are subidivided on the basis of grain size and mineralogy. The chemical sediments are subdivided primarily on the basis of chemical composition.

12. Metamorphic rocks are the products of either regional metamorphism, in which large volumes of rock are transformed by regional increases in pressure and temperature, or contact metamorphism, in which rocks close to igneous intrusions are transformed primarily by heat. Metamorphic rocks are classified by the nature of foliation or cleavage and mineral assemblages or facies.

EXERCISES

1. If a given volume of rock is made up of 1/3 magnetite (specific gravity 5.2) and 2/3 quartz (specific gravity 2.7), would it be lighter or heavier than the same volume of a rock made up of 2/3 garnet (specific gravity 3.5) and 1/3 quartz?

2. Noteworthy for their absence from the mineral kingdom are crystals with 5-fold, or pentagonal, symmetry. Describe and draw some symmetries possible in a "pentagonal system." How would you describe the reference crystal axes?

3. Draw the electronic structures of magnesium ion (Mg^{++}) and oxygen ion (O^{--}). The atomic number of magnesium is 12 and that of oxygen 8. How would these ions differ from sodium ion (Na^{+}) and fluoride ion (F^{-}), which have atomic numbers 11 and 9, respectively?

4. What property of what common mineral is the basis for sandpaper? For what kind of jobs might you prefer to use emery paper (emery is a granular variety of the mineral corundum (Al_2O_3).

5. Choose three minerals (other than diamond) from Appendix IV that you think might make good gemstones, and point out which physical properties might make them suitable for that purpose.

6. Name the properties of each of the following rocks, and describe the features that you would look for in order to identify them in outcrop: (1) a diabase dike, (2) a rhyolite flow, (3) a mica schist, (4) a conglomerate, (5) a hornfels, and (6) a marine shale.

7. In the text it was stated that no igneous rocks are composed of beds of halite and gypsum and that no sedimentary rocks are made up largely of pyroxene. Give an example of other combinations of minerals, or groups of minerals, together with their outcrop appearance, that would be incompatible with (1) igneous, (2) sedimentary, (3) metamorphic origins. Can you think of an example of a "forbidden" association of minerals and outcrop appearance—that is, a combination that could not be found in any natural rock?

BIBLIOGRAPHY

Berry, L. G., and B. Mason, *Elements of Mineralogy.* San Francisco: W. H. Freeman and Company, 1968.

Bragg, Sir Lawrence, "X-Ray Crystallography." *Scientific American,* July 1968. (Offprint No. 325.)

Ernst, W. G., *Earth Materials.* Englewood Cliffs, New Jersey: Prentice-Hall, Inc., 1969.

Hurlbut, C. S., Jr., *Minerals and Man.* New York: Random House, 1969.

Loeffler, B. M., and R. G. Burns, "Shedding Light on the Color of Minerals." *American Scientist,* November-December, 1976, vol. 64, pp. 636-647.

Pauling, L., *College Chemistry.* San Francisco: W. H. Freeman and Company, 1964.

Simpson, B., *Rocks and Minerals.* New York: Pergamon Press, 1966.

Smith, C., "Materials." *Scientific American,* September 1967.

Williams, H., F. J. Turner, and C. M. Gilbert, *Petrography.* San Francisco: W. H. Freeman and Company, 1954.

PART TWO
THE SKIN OF THE EARTH: SURFACE PROCESSES

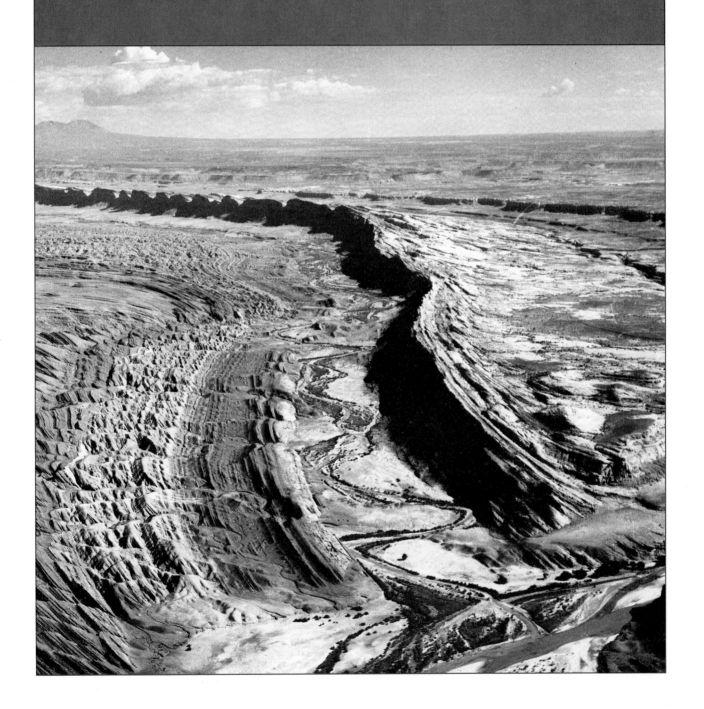

The surface of the Earth is what we explore all of our lives. It is the interface between the solid planet and the gaseous envelope of air around it. Though we may go down into mines and fly through the air, it is the surface upon which we live and upon which we depend for our existence. The interface between the solid Earth and the vast bodies of water that cover much of it is being explored too; our curiosity about the sea floor has produced a crescendo of activity over the past two decades, but in satisfying our curiosity about this interface we must rely on instruments to do our seeing and feeling.

The dominant element of the dynamics of the surface is the Sun, which irradiates it. Solar energy drives the atmosphere in a complex pattern of winds to give us our climates and weather, and it drives the ocean's circulation in a pattern that is coupled to the atmosphere. The water and gases of the oceans and atmosphere chemically react with the solid surface and physically transport material from one place to another.

The processes that operate on the surface, then, are results of interactions between phenomena caused by the external heat engine and surface manifestations of the internal heat engine: mountains, volcanoes, and rocks brought up from the interior.

4

WEATHERING: THE DECOMPOSITION OF ROCKS

The primary mechanism of erosion is weathering—chemical decay and physical fragmentation, under conditions at the Earth's surface, of minerals that formed for the most part at high pressures and temperatures in the interior of the Earth. Such minerals as feldspar partially dissolve after reacting with air and water, leaving a solid residue of clay. Other minerals, such as calcite and some mafic minerals, dissolve completely. The breakdown of rock masses to fragments ranging from boulders to clay is the result of chemical weathering combined with the forces of physical disintegration. The intensity of weathering is dependent on climate, tectonics, original rock composition, and time. Given enough time, factors other than climate are relatively unimportant. The weathering process produces the clays of the world, all soils, and the dissolved substances that are carried by rivers to the ocean. The salt water of the ocean and the chemical sediments on the sea floors are themselves end products of chemical weathering of the surface of the continents.

Mountains stand high, yet we know that they are worn away, slowly but inexorably, by erosion. Early geologists learned this by watching rivers carry sandy and muddy sediments from mountain tops to the plains below. Those sediments could have come only from the breakup of rocks. Rocks are hard, but we know they soften and disintegrate by observing the obliteration of markings on monuments and gravestones. Soils can be seen to consist partly of fine particles of rocks and minerals. Both the lowering of mountains by erosion and the origin of the raw materials of sediments can be explained in terms of weathering, which is a twofold process. It is both fragmentation, or **mechanical weathering,** and decay, or **chemical weathering,** operating together, each helping and reinforcing the other. The smaller the pieces, the greater the surface area available for chemical attack and the faster the pieces decay; the faster the decay, the more the pieces become weakened and sus-

ceptible to breakage. In this chapter we emphasize the chemical aspect, for it is in some ways the more fundamental driving force of the whole process; the effect of mechanical weathering, always important, is largely dependent on chemical decay, but it reinforces chemical action and is itself promoted by decay.

HOW LONG DOES A ROCK LAST?

The first person to make a tool of iron must have been the first to notice that it would rust, and perhaps wondered why. An old nail in soil will usually be so badly rusted that it can be snapped like a match, yet nails in wood in some of our colonial houses are still strong and covered with only a thin brownish film. A list of the kinds of places where nails rust quickly would easily show that exposure to air and moisture are im-

Figure 4-1
A weathered rock. The surface is corroded and pitted and divided by enlarged cracks and joints, in some of which plants grow, thereby helping further to weather the rock. [Photo by R. Siever.]

Figure 4-2
Two gravestones of the early nineteenth century in a cemetery in Wellfleet, Massachusetts. The lighter stone is limestone that has been ravaged by chemical weathering; the darker stone is slate, which remains practically untouched; even the delicate etching at the top of the stone is preserved. (Photo by R. Siever.]

portant factors. Rusting is a chemical process in which oxygen and water convert metallic iron to its oxidized form, ferric iron.

In contrast, some materials seem unchanged by exposure to air and water. Anyone who has hiked a trail to a lonely spot and discovered an old beer bottle knows that glass survives long exposure to the elements. Old bottles that have lain buried in moist soil do acquire a sometimes beautifully colored coating, but the main part of the glass itself seems immune from chemical attack.

We can see the same range of response to wind, rain, snow, sun, and cold in old monuments and cemeteries. Some gravestones seem to be made for the ages, but others have lost almost all of their inscriptions. In a temperate climate, limestone goes fast, but granite lasts longer. In the aridity of desert lands, everything lasts. Today we can see well-preserved details on stone monuments left by early civilizations in the Middle East; that these details still remain is directly attributable to the dry climate. Alabaster (gypsum) sculpture could never have lasted outdoors in Wisconsin as it has in North Africa.

Though we usually think of organic materials as being quick to decay or putrefy, these kinds of substances have as wide a range of responses to erosion as do inorganic minerals. Some tough resistant tissues of organisms, such as pollen grains, can survive longer than many inorganic minerals. Man, the animal that learned to synthesize thousands of new chemicals, contributes an undue share to the mass of decay-resistant organic materials by producing huge quantities of nondegradable compounds, among them being the older detergents, DDT, and the ever-present plastic products that are found scattered all over the land surface and floating in the middle of the ocean. We rely on the rapid decay of natural organic matter, which is primarily the work of bacteria, to return nutrients to soil and to produce fodder for farm animals from the fermentation of plant materials in silos. Some materials, however, just don't decay as rapidly as we would like. For example, in the past decade we have become concerned about just how long it will take natural processes to eliminate the millions of gallons of oil that get into the oceans as a result of spills of various kinds and leaks at offshore oil-drilling sites. All of that oil originated as organic matter that accumulated in sediments on the Earth's surface and was later preserved and altered by burial (see Chapter 22). The process of oil formation made the material much more resistant to decay.

Why do some inorganic materials weather so quickly and others so slowly? From everyday observations we can contrast the differences among rocks of different composition, those in different climates, and those in different surroundings, from soil to bare mountainside. Mere age of a rock is of no consequence, for we can find fresh-looking Precambrian rocks and badly weathered Pleistocene ones. How long they have been exposed to erosion is a more important matter, as anyone can testify by comparing a newly blasted road cut with one 20 or 30 years old. *Soil itself is both a factor in weathering and a result of it. The production of soil is evidently a* **positive-feedback process,** *one in which the product of the process works, by its presence, to increase the output of the process. Once soil starts to form, rock weathers more rapidly and more soil is formed.*

At the heart of the whole process are the ways in which individual kinds of minerals react with water and air. We turn now to some important examples of the major rock-forming minerals the first being the most abundant mineral in the Earth's crust, feldspar.

HOW TO DISSOLVE FELDSPAR

Feldspar is a key mineral in a great many igneous, metamorphic, and sedimentary rocks. Understanding its weathering behavior should contribute much to our grasp of the weathering process in general. The place to start is in the field, making observations that give the clue to what the natural process is; then come the laboratory experiments, which enable us to quantify and identify the intermediate and final products of decomposition under controlled conditions.

Observing Decomposition in the Field. Much as people in temperate regions are used to thinking of granite as the most permanent of rocks, those in the humid tropics know that many granite boulders in soil can easily be kicked into a heap of mineral grains. Close examination of the particles, and comparison with a fresh piece, shows that the crystals of feldspar are all punky and chalky with clay, many of them so soft that they can be gouged with a fingernail, a condition conspicuously in contrast with that of the clear unaltered quartz crystals. The rock falls apart because the original interlocking crystal network of quartz and feldspar no longer holds together when the feldspar weathers to a loosely adhering clay. The

 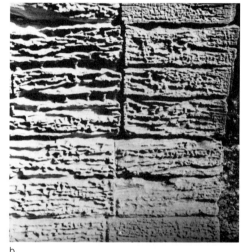

a   b

Figure 4-3
Weathered limestone blocks of a Roman aqueduct about 2000 years old, showing the pitted, etched surface caused by chemical solution. (a) One of the arches. (b) A closeup of a number of blocks. Pont du Gard, Provence, France. [Photos by R. Siever.]

Figure 4-4
Disintegrating boulder of granite partially embedded in a glacial soil, shown partly excavated by digging. The outer rim shows the original size of the boulder. [Photo by F. E. Matthes, U.S. Geological Survey.]

Drip coffee maker

Feldspar decaying
at ground surface

Hot water
drips onto
ground coffee beans,
which become spent,
producing
a pot of
coffee

Water

Partially dissolving
solid alters to a
different composition

Solution containing
some substances
dissolved from solid

Rainfall filters
into ground

Feldspar in rock
and soil alters to
kaolinite

Soil or groundwater
containing dissolved
substances from
feldspar

Figure 4-5
The process by which feldspar decays is analogous to the way in which coffee is made. In both processes water dissolves some of the substance of the solid, leaving behind an altered material and producing a solution containing the substances drawn from the original solid.

The word "kaolin" is a French modification of the Chinese "kao-ling," named for the place where the Chinese mined it for centuries before the finished product was exported as "china" to Europe. If Europeans had explored the state of Georgia before they visited China, they would have found one of the large kaolin deposits in the western hemisphere, and the name might have been different.

A *solution* is made by dissolving a relatively small amount of a substance, called the *solute,* in a much larger amount of *solvent.* Salt, NaCl, is the solute and water the solvent of a salty solution. Water, of course, isn't the only solvent. Alcohol is an excellent solvent for many organic substances. Tincture of iodine is a solution of iodine in alcohol. A solution is *saturated* when it holds all of a solute that it can; this amount is called the *solubility.* The amount of solute at saturation depends on temperature: most warmer solutions of most substances will hold more than colder ones.

The radius of the hydrogen atom is so small compared to the large oxygen atom that the hydrogens appear as small bumps on the surface of the oxygen in water. Partly as a result of this, the electrical charge is unevenly distributed and the molecule acts as a little magnet. The magnetic behavior of water is an important reason why it dissolves many solids so easily: the magnetism attracts ions of the material being dissolved, in a sense by "plucking" them out of the solid and keeping them in solution.

white to cream-colored clay is the mineral kaolinite (sometimes just called kaolin), used in pure form as raw material for pottery and china.

Decay is not nearly so rapid in temperate climates, but any outcrop of a feldspar-bearing rock will show the beginnings of the same weathering to kaolin on some grains. Only in severely arid climates typical of some deserts does feldspar stay relatively untouched. From this we infer that water is essential to the chemical reaction by which feldspar alters to kaolin. The kind of reaction can be illustrated by a useful analogy to a familiar chemical reaction of the same kind: coffee making. Freshly ground coffee beans plus hot water make a solution—the coffee—that is extracted from the solid, leaving behind spent coffee grounds as a residue. How much can be extracted from the ground coffee depends on how much water is used, how hot it is, and how long it percolates. In the same way, the feldspar-kaolinite conversion depends on the amount of rainfall, the temperature, and the length of time water stays in contact with the feldspar-containing rock, such as granite. These are the controlling factors, whether the rock is a boulder in soil or bedrock beneath a soil.

The water is of primary importance because it is such a good solvent for many natural materials. The reason is that the water molecule is polar—that is, asymmetric in charge distribution. This property gives it a weak electrical attraction for many solid surfaces, and this attraction tends to "pull" ions away from the surface of the solid minerals, thus dissolving it.

We can write an equation for the weathering of the common feldspar of granite, orthoclase, which is made up of potassium (K), aluminum (Al), silicon (Si), and oxygen (O):

feldspar + water → kaolinite

$$KAlSi_3O_8 \qquad H_2O \qquad Al_2Si_2O_5(OH)_4$$

But chemical equations are like those of algebra: they have to add up to the same on both sides. This requirement is imposed by the law of conservation of matter: the total number and kinds of atoms of the starting materials, the **reactants,** have to be the same as those of the **products** of the reaction. In what we have written, potassium appears on one side, as a component of the feldspar, but not on the other side. To make an equation of what we have written, we must add potassium to the right side. Since no potassium minerals are found in the weathered products, we presume the potassium is carried away by a water solution (like the coffee extracted from the grounds). To make the numbers come out completely right, we must also add some silicon to the right side of the equation, in addition to that bound up in the solid kaolinite newly formed by reaction. Familiarity with these kinds of equations enables the geochemist to guess intelligently what the exact form of the equation might be, but he cannot be sure until he does the experiment.

Dissolving Solids in the Laboratory. When trying to dissolve any of a great many materials rapidly, the thing to use is an acid. Strong mixtures of acids are used as cleaning solutions for laboratory glassware because of their dissolving power. The experiment of choice, then, is to immerse feldspar in a readily available acid like hydrochloric acid, HCl. The feldspar is ground to a fine powder first, to make the dissolution faster by exposing more surface area to the solution—an effect we take advantage of when we use ground coffee instead of whole coffee beans. As the feldspar dissolves, the experimenter takes small samples from the solution and analyzes them for the expected dissolved potassium ion and, he guesses, dissolved silicon in some form. At first the feldspar dissolves rapidly, as measured by the steady increase in dissolved K^+ in the solution, but then the rate of dissolution starts to level off as the feldspar reacts more and more slowly and finally undergoes no further change. If the solution continues not to change, it is presumed to be in **equilibrium** with feldspar powder. The analysis of the

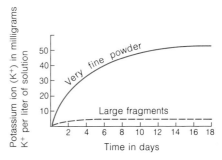

Figure 4-6

The rate at which potassium feldspar partially dissolves when put into water. The amount of feldspar that dissolves is measured by the amount of potassium ion liberated to the solution, which is measured by its concentration—that is, the number of milligrams (thousandths of a gram) of potassium per liter of solution. The feldspar dissolves at a fast rate in the first time intervals and then slows, finally until no further change can be detected. Grinding the feldspar to a fine powder makes it dissolve faster and allows more of it to dissolve.

Box 4-1   Chemical Weathering of Feldspar

The complete chemical equation for the weathering of feldspar to kaolinite is written:

$$2KAlSi_3O_8 + 2(H^+ + Cl^-) + H_2O \rightarrow$$
$$Al_2Si_2O_5(OH)_4 + 4SiO_2 + 2K^+ + 2Cl^-$$

We write the acid HCl as $H^+ + Cl^-$ to emphasize that strong acids in solution are completely ionized—that is, present as individual ions, not molecules. Similarly, we write potassium chloride as K^+ and Cl^- rather than as KCl. The dissolved silica is written as SiO_2, for in nature silicon is not present as the free metallic element. A chemically more realistic formula for dissolved silica is H_4SiO_4, silicic acid, which is simply $SiO_2 + 2H_2O$.

The equation for the weathering of feldspar can also be written with water alone considered as the acid, for it too can be a source of hydrogen ion (H^+). In that case, hydroxyl ion (OH^-) appears with the K^+ on the right side of the equation. Or one can regard carbonic acid (H_2CO_3) as the H^+ contributor, in which case bicarbonate ion (HCO_3^-) is written as the product (see Box 4-2).

It is as OH^- that water appears in the formula for kaolinite. The formula for kaolinite used to be written by some as $Al_2O_3 \cdot 2SiO_2 \cdot 2H_2O$ to show explicitly the presence of water.

The flow of material in the alteration of feldspar to kaolinite by the dissolving action of water. Some water and some hydrogen ions (H^+) are absorbed into the kaolinite structure, but all of the potassium (K^+) and some of the silica (SiO_2) ends up in solution.

Chemical formulas are written so that the number of atoms of a particular kind in the formula of a mineral or any other chemical compound is indicated by a subscript. The absence of a subscript indicates a single atom. Thus, in feldspar, $KAlSi_3O_8$, there is one atom of potassium, one of aluminum, 3 of silicon, and 8 of oxygen. In a chemical equation, a number before the formula operates as a multiplier, the number of formulas needed to balance the equation. Thus $2KAlSi_3O_8$ indicates 2 atoms of potassium, 2 of aluminum, 6 of silicon, and 16 of oxygen.

The pressure exerted by the Earth's atmosphere at sea level, one atmosphere, is equal to the pressure exerted by a 760 mm high column of mercury. For the much higher pressures characteristic of the interior of the Earth, we use the term *bar*. One bar is equal to 0.987 atmospheres. A *kilobar* is 1000 bars.

Our carbonated beverages, such as artificially carbonated soda pop or naturally fermented beer and champagne, illustrate some important properties of CO_2 dissolved in water. Part of the "bite" of such beverages is the reaction of the weak carbonic acid with the tongue. The reverse of the reaction by which CO_2 is formed from carbonic acid is the one in which bubbles of CO_2 are released from a pressurized solution of a carbonated beverage when the pressure is released by uncorking. The amount of CO_2 that can be held in solution is dependent on the temperature; the colder the liquid, the more gas it can hold—a good reason for refrigerating such drinks!

solution at this point shows the equation to be, in qualitative terms:

feldspar + hydrochloric + water →
　　　　　　　 acid

kaolinite + dissolved + dissolved + dissolved
　　　　　　 silica　　 potassium　 chloride

Three major points about this equation are important. (1) The potassium and silicon produced by dissolving the feldspar appear as dissolved material. (2) Water is used up in the reaction; it is absorbed into the kaolinite structure. (3) Hydrogen ion is used up in the reaction, and the solution becomes more basic as the reaction proceeds.

This simple experiment includes the three main chemical effects of chemical weathering on silicates: it **leaches,** or dissolves away, cations and silica; it **hydrates,** or adds water to, the minerals; and it makes the solutions less acidic—more basic. If we were to dissolve feldspar in distilled water, the reaction would still proceed, though very much more slowly, and produce a very dilute basic solution, like that of a weak caustic soda or lye solution. It is because hydrogen ion is used up that makes this reaction look to a chemist like one in which an acid mixes with a base to produce a salt, as when hydrochloric acid mixes with potassium hydroxide (KOH), a strong base, to form potassium chloride (KCl) and water. In our experiment, the feldspar acted as the base.

But nature does not pour hydrochloric acid on granite outcrops. If we think again—now with the benefit of laboratory experience—about how feldspar dissolves in nature, we are led to the most common acid on the Earth's surface, carbonic acid (H_2CO_3). This weak acid is formed by the solution in rainwater of a small amount of carbon dioxide (CO_2) gas from the atmosphere.

Carbon Dioxide and Carbonic Acid. We are familiar with everyday solutions of CO_2 in water: soft drinks made by pumping pressurized CO_2 gas into the liquid. When a carbonated beverage is left to stand until bubbling has stopped, the dissolved CO_2 has decreased to a stable value, one we usually characterize as "flat" to the taste. The remaining dissolved CO_2 is in equilibrium with the small amount of CO_2 gas in the atmosphere. We measure the amount of any gas by the pressure it exerts, using as a standard the pressure exerted by the Earth's atmosphere at sea level, called one **atmosphere** of pressure. The pressure of CO_2 in the atmosphere is about 0.0003 (or 0.03 percent) of an

atmosphere, which may seem small, but actually makes it one of the four most abundant gases, just behind argon (0.9 percent), oxygen (21 percent), and nitrogen (78 percent).

The planet Venus has an atmosphere that is almost entirely CO_2; so thick is the atmosphere at the planet's surface that the CO_2 pressure there is about 300,000 times that at the surface of the Earth. The Martian atmosphere is similarly made up mostly of CO_2, but is so thin that the CO_2 pressure is much less than that on Earth. In reading the following discussion of the role of CO_2 in weathering, you may think of the implications for weathering on those planets.

Carbon dioxide gas dissolves in water to form a new compound, carbonic acid. Carbonic acid is much weaker than hydrochloric acid. But even such a weak acid can still dissolve great quantities of rocks over a long time. When CO_2 dissolves in rainwater, the water becomes slightly acid, not enough to be noticed by plants and animals but slowly corrosive for feldspars. In areas where the air is greatly polluted with sulfurous gases from industries, rainwaters may be much more acid, for the sulfurous gases dissolve in rain in the same way as CO_2 to form sulfuric acid, a far stronger acid than carbonic acid. Although rainwater contaminated with sulfuric acid is still much too weak to sting our skins, it does damage our fabrics, paints, and metals. It also weathers our stone monuments and outdoor sculptures at such a rapid rate that public officials are beginning to take notice of their deterioration.

How Does Weathering Proceed in Nature?
Now that we have a workable model for the major chemical reaction by which rainwater weathers feldspar, we have to return to field observations to see how the process works on outcrops and in the soil. Just as a nail rusts more quickly and deeply in the soil than it does lying on a rooftop, we find that feldspars on bare rock surfaces seem much better preserved than those in pebbles buried in wet soils, which may be crumbly and coated with soft rinds of kaolinite. The chemical equation gives us a clue to this difference. First, the reaction will not proceed in the absence of water; during all of the dry periods, the bare rock is untouched. In moist soil the feldspar is constantly bathed by a corrosive acid-water solution. Second, there is more acid in the soil than in rainwater, and the stronger the acid the more extensive the decay. Some of the acids in soil are organic compounds produced by bacterial decay of plant and animal remains.

Some bacteria seem able to grow even on bare rock particles and eat away at them. The acid content of soil water gets an extra boost from plant roots and bacterial decay, which produce CO_2 by **respiration** processes similar to the one upon which we depend. They oxidize organic matter and give off CO_2; we breathe oxygen and exhale CO_2. The amount of CO_2 in soil can be as much as ten times that in rainwater, and makes soil water an efficient dissolver of feldspars.

Weathering does not proceed at the same rate in all climates. One reason is the contrast between hot and cold: the speed of chemical reactions increases as temperature rises, and, even more importantly, plants and bacteria grow and multiply much faster in warmer climates. The other reason is the contrast between wet and dry: water is needed for the weathering reaction, and vegetation grows more lushly in humid climates. It is not surprising, then, that weathering is most intense in tropical climates, which are both wet and warm.

We will see later in this chapter how mechanical erosion is related to the speed of weathering and to the topography. Just as the fresh feldspar of the laboratory experiment reacted rapidly at first and then slowed down, a fresh piece of feldspar exposed at the surface of an outcrop by mechanical breakage will chemically alter faster than one in an unbroken rock. Because the weathering products in mountains are carried away quickly by rains and melting snows, we cannot see the effects as easily as in lower, flatter

---

Box 4-2   Carbonic Acid Chemistry

We can write the following equation describing the solution of carbon dioxide in water to form carbonic acid:

$$CO_{2\,(gas)} + H_2O_{(liquid)} \rightleftharpoons H_2CO_{3\,(solution)}$$

The double arrow stresses the fact that this reaction, and the reactions given below, are reversible—that is, go both ways. The solubility of CO_2 in pure water is low, so that a liter of pure water contains only about 0.0006 gram of carbonic acid in equilibrium. Yet this is enough acid to weather rocks.

Once formed, carbonic acid spontaneously ionizes by another reversible reaction, in the same way that HCl or KCl does, to form a hydrogen ion, H^+, and a **bicarbonate** ion, HCO_3^-:

carbonic $\rightleftharpoons$	hydrogen +	bicarbonate
acid	ion	ion
H_2CO_3	H^+	HCO_3^-

This reaction is different from the ionization of the HCl and KCl because far from all of the carbonic acid molecules are ionized; only one molecule out of a thousand is ionized at equilibrium. An even smaller amount of HCO_3^-, only one ion out of 100,000, further ionizes to form another hydrogen ion and a **carbonate ion, CO_3^{2-}**

bicarbonate $\rightleftharpoons$	hydrogen +	carbonate
ion	ion	ion
HCO_3^-	H^+	CO_3^{2-}

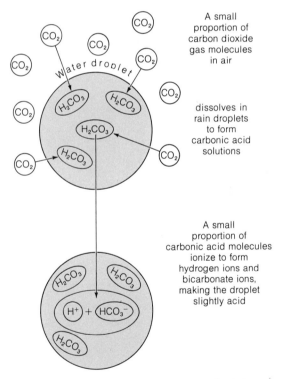

A small proportion of carbon dioxide gas molecules in air

dissolves in rain droplets to form carbonic acid solutions

A small proportion of carbonic acid molecules ionize to form hydrogen ions and bicarbonate ions, making the droplet slightly acid

The formation of slightly acid rain by the dissolution of carbon dioxide gas molecules in water droplets in the atmosphere. Once dissolved, the carbon dioxide reacts with water to form carbonic acid, which then ionizes to form hydrogen and bicarbonate ions.

areas, where much of the clays and other products accumulate on gentle slopes and in valleys to form soil.

Making the Clays of the Earth. We have given the details of how one kind of feldspar weathers to make one kind of clay. Some other silicate minerals, such as mica and volcanic glasses, weather in the same general manner, some changing to kaolinite and others to different clay minerals. Feldspar can alter to different kinds of clay minerals under different weathering conditions. **Montmorillonite** is an abundant clay formed by weathering in many warm and semiarid climates. It is also the main clay product of the weathering of volcanic ash. Yet another abundant clay mineral, **illite,** typically develops from the weathering of sediments in temperate regions. Under the extreme weathering conditions of the tropics, kaolinite can partially dissolve to give silica in solution, leaving a solid residue of the mineral **gibbsite,** aluminum hydroxide $(Al(OH)_3)$. Gibbsite makes up the deposits of **bauxite,** the earthy ore that is the major source of economically extractable aluminum in the world.

All of the clay minerals have the basic structure of sheet silicates. Each clay type owes its distinctive characters to the cations, such as sodium, potassium, magnesium, or calcium, that occupy positions in and between the sheets. Montmorillonite, for example, has a structure and cation composition that gives it the ability to soak up large quantities of water, which spreads the layers apart and makes them easily cleavable—to the point of slipperiness. If you ever drive on a montmorillonite road and get caught in a rain, which out; you may slide helplessly off the road into a ditch as your tires lose all traction on the gooey mass of watery clay. Kaolinite absorbs less water, but is just right for making pottery and ceramics.

Because feldspar and other silicates that weather to form clays compose the large bulk of the igneous and metamorphic rocks of the crust, an enormous amount of clay is produced by the weathering of those rocks. Just how large is that figure? The total amount of sediment now existing over the whole Earth is about 3×10^{25} grams. Since about one-third of all sediments (most of it in shales) is made up of clay minerals, there must be about 1×10^{25} grams of clay in the Earth! Obviously the importance of chemical weathering as a source of sedimentary materials cannot be overemphasized. Other kinds of weathering, however, result not in the formation of clay but in the complete disappearance of minerals.

DISSOLVING WITHOUT A TRACE

Whereas feldspar and other aluminosilicate minerals form clay by incomplete dissolution, minerals of other chemical compositions may dissolve completely, just like salt in water. Quantitatively, the most important of these minerals are the carbonate minerals, calcite $(CaCO_3)$ and dolomite $(CaMg(CO_3)_2)$, which together make up the limestones of the world.

Limestone, the Soluble Sediment. The fast disappearance of limestone is an obvious fact to the farmer or gardener who spreads finely ground limestone to reduce the acidity of his soil. The application has to be repeated every year or two because the limestone dissolves. Caves are characteristic of many limestone formations in humid climates. Their patterns of extensive passageways and the multitude of pits, holes, and irregular flutings on cave walls and ceilings are witness to the extensive dissolving power of groundwater. Caves and sinkholes are the indicators of abundant water acting on limestones.

Figure 4-7
Cleopatra's Needle, an obelisk of granite (left) in Egypt and (right) after being removed to Central Park, New York City. After several decades of exposure to the elements in New York, the south side of the obelisk had weathered more extensively than it had after thirty-five centuries of exposure in Egypt. [Left photo courtesy of the Metropolitan Museum of Art, New York; right photo from Erhard Winkler, *Stone, Properties, Durability in Man's Environment.* Copyright © Springer-Verlag, New York, 1973.]

The dissolution of limestone gets us back to the CO_2 system, for the carbonate ion (CO_3^{--}) found in solid form in calcite is really CO_2 in another guise. Carbonate in solution is made by dissolving CO_2 in water to form carbonic acid, as we have seen, and that acid ionizes to form bicarbonate (HCO_3^-) and carbonate ions as well as hydrogen ions. Carbonate ions are also found in solution after calcite dissolves, for that process is simply a separation of the calcium ions from the carbonate ions and of both from the solid. In the solution, the CO_3^{--} tends to combine with H^+ ions from the water to form HCO_3^-. This has the effect of making the water less acidic, which is why it is used for agricultural purposes. At the same time, if H^+ keeps on being supplied by CO_2 dissolving in the water, more and more CO_3^{--} is used up. As the CO_3^{--} converts to HCO_3^-, the solution remains undersaturated with solid calcite, which then keeps dissolving. The overall reaction by which calcite dissolves in a weak solution of carbonic acid, such as rainwater, is:

$$\text{calcite} + \text{carbonic acid} \rightarrow$$
$$CaCO_3 \qquad H_2CO_3$$
$$\text{calcium ion} + \text{bicarbonate ion}$$
$$Ca^{++} \qquad 2HCO_3^-$$

In nature, feldspar also weathers by reacting with carbonic acid. In both reactions, for feldspar and for calcite, H^+ is used up as CO_2 reacts with water, and HCO_3^- is formed as a product. In this way CO_2 is extracted from the atmosphere and put into water. The more the weathering, the more CO_2 is taken out of the atmosphere. Both reactions supply dissolved cations.

In a given quantity of water, limestone dissolves faster and in greater amounts than silicates. For both reasons, the chemical weathering of limestone accounts for more of the total chemical erosion of the land surface than any other rock, even though much larger areas are covered by silicate rocks. Some mafic silicate minerals dissolve completely, like limestone, but not as rapidly. Although they by no means rival limestone in quantity eroded from the land surface, they do account for a major fraction of the total amounts of certain elements weathered from rocks—in particular, iron and magnesium.

Mafic Minerals. The beating of ocean waves against rocky cliffs is one of nature's ways of hurling solvent at a rock. On the rocky coast of New England the chemical effects of the attack are seen when the geologist hunts for pyroxene crystals in a granodiorite. All that can be found are little cavities in the shape of pyroxene crystals. Olivine behaves the same way. Like limestone, both minerals wholly dissolve. A magnesium pyroxene, $MgSiO_3$, dissolves to give Mg^{++} and dissolved silica. An iron pyroxene ($FeSiO_3$) dissolves to give Fe^{++} and dissolved silica. The iron in pyroxene is **ferrous** (Fe^{++}), in contrast to the iron in hematite, (Fe_2O_3), which is **ferric.** When iron pyroxene weathers, not only does the silicate structure dissolve, but the ferrous iron is oxidized by oxygen to ferric iron. Ferric iron in the presence of oxygen is very insoluble in most natural surface waters, and it precipitates to form a poorly crystallized mineral that looks like rust, limonite ($FeO(OH)$), a ferric oxide that contains water (in the form of hydroxyl). The

Ferric iron is more *oxidized* than ferrous iron—that is, it has fewer electrons. Oxidation can be defined as a loss of electrons in a chemical reaction, regardless of whether the element combines with oxygen itself. Reduction is the opposite of oxidation; it is a gain of electrons. In comparison with ferric iron, ferrous iron is more reduced.

Figure 4-8
The general scheme by which calcite or other carbonate minerals dissolve in water containing dissolved carbon dioxide. The reactions are all reversible, and the system should be visualized with all reactions operating at the same time to produce the general net tendency shown by the arrows.

Figure 4-9
The general scheme by which an iron-rich silicate mineral, such as pyroxene, weathers. In the presence of oxygen and water, as at the Earth's surface, these reactions proceed sequentially and irreversibly. Limonite formed in this way is typically a poorly crystallized yellow-brown mass of the mineral geothite, sometimes mixed with another mineral, lepidocrocite, of the same composition but different crystal structure.

Limonite is actually a mixture of two minerals of the same chemical composition but different crystal structures, goethite and lepidocrocite. Goethite is far more abundant. Magnetic varieties of these iron oxide minerals give us our magnetic recording tapes.

As an experiment, some ground quartz was kept in water for three years, and at the end of that time only one part per million—one thousandth of a gram in a liter of water—had dissolved.

overall reaction, which includes oxidation and hydration of the iron and the dissolution of the silica, is:

$$\begin{array}{ccc} \text{iron} & + \text{ oxygen } + \text{ water} \rightarrow \\ \text{pyroxene} & \text{from} \\ & \text{atmosphere} \\ 4\text{FeSiO}_3 & \text{O}_2 \qquad 2\text{H}_2\text{O} \end{array}$$

$$\begin{array}{cc} \text{limonite} & + \text{ dissolved} \\ \text{(hydrated iron} & \text{silica} \\ \text{oxide)} \\ 4\text{FeO(OH)} & 4\text{SiO}_2 \end{array}$$

For every four iron atoms that are weathered after being brought to the surface of the earth by mountain-building or volcanism, two atoms of oxygen are extracted from the atmosphere. Were it not for the rapid replenishment of oxygen by the photosynthesis of plants, the weathering of mafic rocks would in the long run—millions of years—have eliminated all of the oxygen from the air. Liberated by the weathering of mafic minerals such as olivines, pyroxenes, amphiboles, and biotite mica, the iron precipitates as fine-grained, poorly crystalline limonite coatings and encrustations that color soils and stain rocks shades of red and brown. They also have served as the raw materials of artists' pigments—the ochres, siennas, and umbers. Moreover, they are the same minerals that give the "red planet," Mars, the red-brown colors of its landscape, so obvious when the first color photographs were transmitted in the summer of 1976.

One more dissolution process is important because so little of it happens. Quartz, SiO_2, dissolves completely without any residue, as does calcite, but its solubility is so extremely low and it dissolves so slowly that it is for practical purposes insoluble in water. As a result, most of the quartz in rocks remains chemically unaltered and survives as a solid residue of weathering, even though it may be mechanically modified by breakage or rounding. Quartz is thus a stable mineral under the conditions that prevail at the earth's surface. But exactly what do we mean by stability of minerals?

CONCEPTS OF STABILITY

Stability can be demonstrated rather easily by trying to balance this book on one of its corners. You may succeed temporarily, but the slightest touch will topple it. It is **unstable** in that position because the slightest change in its state—its

position in this example—will cause a larger change to another state: the book will fall flat. When it is lying flat, lift it by one edge, and as soon as you let it go it will immediately return to its flat, or **stable** position. The book can be placed in an intermediate state by standing it upright; in this position it is **metastable,** because it will return to its upright position if pushed very slightly, but will fall to its stable state if given a bigger push.

The chemical stability of minerals can be described in much the same way by reference to their tendency to go to other states. Other states of minerals are the products of reactions, simple or complex. A simple change is that shown by the different crystalline structures of calcium carbonate. Aragonite, a tightly packed structure, is stable at high pressures, but if it remains for very long at the low pressures of the Earth's surface, it will tend to change to the more open structure calcite, which is stable at low pressures. Iron pyroxene is unstable at surface conditions partly because it tends to dissolve in water. But that is not a good enough criterion, for salt dissolves even more easily in water, and it is stable. The missing criterion is that after dissolving, the stable material will reprecipitate or crystallize as the same mineral, whereas the unstable one will form something else. The dissolved salt will form new salt crystals after evaporation, but the dissolved pyroxene will form a mixture of crystals of hydrated iron oxide and silica. We can rank the stability of such minerals as salt and quartz under weathering conditions on the basis of their solubility: the less soluble, the more stable. Quartz wins hands down.

Given these criteria, we can use a combination of our knowledge of weathering in the field and chemical experimentation to deduce a ranking of minerals in the order of stability under weathering conditions, including alteration and solubility behavior, as in Table 4-1. Included in the table are the products of weathering, clays and oxides, which are among the most stable.

We can use these relative stabilities in a general way to show how drastically different surface conditions on Earth are from the environments in the Earth where the minerals were crystallized and remained stable. Muscovite, a mica, is formed at moderate temperatures and pressures, and hence has a small tendency to alter to clay minerals. Pyroxene is formed at higher temperatures and pressures, and so has a greater tendency to weather. Both the order of crystallization and the order of stability under

Table 4-1
Stability of some common minerals under weathering conditions at the Earth's surface.

Most stable	Fe-oxides
	Al-oxides
	Quartz
	Clay minerals
	Muscovite
	K-feldspar (orthoclase)
	Biotite
	Na-feldspar (albite)
	Amphibole
	Pyroxene
	Ca-feldspar (anorthite)
Least stable	Olivine

weathering conditions are related to the stabilities of chemical bonds and crystal structures under different temperatures and pressure, subjects covered in the chapters on igneous rocks (14) and metamorphism (16). The order of stability of the minerals found in igneous rocks is roughly the reverse of the order of crystallization from a granitic melt as it cools; the first to crystallize, olivine, is also the first to weather.

The instability of silicates and the solubility of carbonates and other minerals are the driving forces of chemical weathering. That chemical decay is only part of the erosional process, however. Physical breakup, the fragmentation of rocks, is the other side of the weathering coin.

FRAGMENTATION

Fragmentation, the breakup of rock masses into boulders, pebbles, sand, and silt, is a physical process that is inextricably linked to the chemical processes of rock weathering, which causes feldspars to decay to clays and causes other minerals to dissolve. Chemical decay is not always apparent when one looks at a mass of broken rock at the foot of a cliff. Pieces may look freshly broken and unaltered. But however minutely, weathering has played some role in making the rock break. Chemical weathering helps fragmentation by an interaction in which the physical breakup of the rock opens channels for water and air to penetrate the rock farther and promote chemical decay. The rate at which chemical reactions take place increases when more surface area of the solid is exposed to the gas or liquid reacting with it. For example, a single log will react with air to burn slowly, but the same log split into kindling will ignite quickly and burn rapidly. Similarly, because the ratio of surface area to volume of rocks and

Single boulder, approximately 1 meter cubed.
Volume = 1 cubic meter
Surface area = 6 square meters

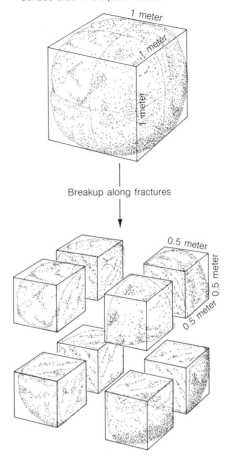

Breakup along fractures

8 cobbles, approximately 0.5 cubic meter
Volume = 1 cubic meter
Surface area = 12 square meters

Figure 4-10
As a large boulder breaks into smaller ones along fractures or joints, the surface area increases relative to volume, making more of the bulk's surface available for chemical decay.

minerals increases as the average particle size decreases, chemical weathering becomes more efficient as rocks are broken into small sand and silt particles. Chemical and physical processes are both related to the action of organisms, from bacteria to tree roots, which play their own roles in the destruction of rock.

In studying such complexly intertwined processes the geologist looks for special places where one or another effect is absent so that the others can be studied alone. Up to a few years ago, some geologists went to study mechanical fragmentation in severely cold polar regions, where there was little active plant or bacterial life and little liquid water, which it was thought would tend to minimize chemical weathering. Even in such hostile regions, however, there was enough chemical decay to be significant. The study of the moon gave a new and better opportunity to study fragmentation in the absence of ordinary chemical weathering as we understand it on Earth and so to compare and contrast mechanical erosion with and without chemical action.

Rock Fragmentation on the Moon. Even before the landing on the Moon, the shapes and slopes of surface features suggested that they were made up of piles of broken rock; with the close-up photographs of the first Surveyor, it became certain that the surface is composed of loose pieces of rock, from large boulders to fine dust (see Figs. 21-4, 21-11, 21-13). Now that we have Moon rocks to examine, we can be sure that there has been no chemical weathering of minerals in the basalts and other igneous rocks. These materials are as fresh as might be expected, having never been exposed to an atmosphere containing oxygen, carbon dioxide, and water. Fragmentation must result completely from physical mechanisms, such as the breakup of large parts of the surface rocks by the impact of meteorites, as is discussed in Chapter 21. The boulders appear to have been broken by the impact of meteorites and thrown up and showered all around the craters that have long been familiar features of the Moon's surface (see Fig. 21-7). But what about the dust? The accumulation of fine dust particles distributed so widely over the Moon's surface is only partly the product of large impacts; much of it comes from the continual spray of small meteorites ranging in size down to the finest micrometeorites. Because the rocks and dust have been dated to be billions of years old, the fragments that geologists have been able to examine have not changed in size or shape throughout most of the Moon's history.

To a minor extent there has been some rounding of the sharp edges by a sort of "sandblasting" process—the constant bombardment by micrometeorites. The effect is not unlike the smoothing of sharp edges of broken glass on a sandy dune on Earth. Rounding takes millions

of years on the Moon; a piece of glass on an Earth dune can be rounded in one year.

Other than fragmentation by these processes, Moon rocks show nothing of the jointing, cracking, spalling, and slabbing of rocks that we are so used to on Earth. Our "laboratory" investigation of another planet has ended by showing us that fragmentation on Earth has no component that does not depend in some part on chemical reaction with our atmosphere. What, then, are the Earth's particles like, and how do they form?

Kinds of Fragmentation. A look at an outcrop of a well-bedded sandstone or a schist with pronounced cleavage will show how important the original character of the rock is in determining the course of breakage. The sandstone breaks into slabs or plates along bedding planes, and the schist breaks into smaller, sometimes splintery pieces whose flat sides parallel the cleavage. The cleavage, schistosity, bedding, or other structural planes in rocks become zones of weakness, and cracks form along them.

On a larger scale, unbedded rocks—or what we call **massive** rocks, like granite—can be seen to have broken up along regularly spaced cracks, called **joints,** at intervals of a meter to a few meters apart. Joints are produced by structural deformation in the course of mountain building, and to some degree are characteristic of almost every rock type. In some igneous rocks the joints take the form of closely spaced, more-or-less plane surfaces, which in some exposures are curved. The resulting layered structure is called **sheeting.**

All these zones of weakness open as cracks when the rocks, once deeply buried in the hearts of mountain ranges, are gradually brought to the surface and the weight of tons of overlying rock is removed. The process is probably not unlike the way in which poorly glued joints in a wooden chair separate as the clamps that held them together during glueing are released. A sidelight—and confirmation—is given by the sometimes severe jointing that spontaneously occurs in deep mines as tunnels are opened up and the pressure on the rock in those passageways is released.

Once the joints, bedding planes, or other cracks are there, the infiltration of water, bacteria, and plant roots start to do their work in enlarging and wedging the openings apart (see Fig. 4-1). Plant roots play some role in this,

Some of the properties of H_2O, though they may be familiar enough to us, are actually unusual in comparison with those of many similar liquids. One characteristic whose effects are far-reaching in our lives is the response of water to heat or cold—in particular, its thermal expansion, the way it expands or contracts when the temperature is changed. As most substances do, liquid water contracts when cooled (though the amount is small). But between 4°C (about 39°F) and its freezing temperature, 0°C (32°F), it abruptly changes its course and expands. When the liquid freezes, it again behaves contrary to most other materials and expands further.

Long before power drills and saws were invented, freezing was the traditional method stonemasons used to quarry building blocks. They drilled small holes at critical points, such as at incipient cracks, filled them with water, and waited for freezing to do its work.

Figure 4-11
Joint patterns developed in several directions in metamorphic rocks.
(Photo by R. Siever.)

probably mostly by promoting chemical weathering but also by exerting physical pressure as they grow. One of the most efficient physical mechanisms is freezing and thawing of ice. Water expands as it freezes, and the expansive force exerted during freezing is strong enough to crack cast iron engine blocks—and rock too. The process has the same effect as a wedge being pounded into the crack, enlarging it and finally splitting it open. Crystallization of such minerals as salt or gypsum, which may follow the evaporation of salty solutions that infiltrated the cracks, may also wedge fractures open. During warmer periods, chemical weathering by water and organisms helps the process along by weakening the minerals holding the rock together.

If freezing is so important, maybe heating in the hot sun and cooling at night might be effective too—or so everyone thought for many years until someone tried it in the laboratory. Pieces of granite were alternately heated and cooled to

Figure 4-12
A disrupted glacial boulder in Wallace Canyon, Sequoia National Park, California. This boulder, originally one piece 2.5 m wide and 1.5 m high when it was deposited by a glacier, has been split into a series of parallel slabs by the freezing action of water that penetrated originally tight joints. [Photo by F. E. Matthes, U.S. Geological Survey.]

Figure 4-13
Exfoliation on a rocky slope, Yosemite National Park, California. The partings produced by weathering are nearly planar, and strongly resemble inclined joints. [Photo by F. E. Matthes, U.S. Geological Survey.]

Figure 4-14
Spheroidal weathering of a boulder of gabbro, Mesa Grande, San Diego County, California. [Photo by W. T. Schaller, U.S. Geological Survey.]

temperatures far more extreme than those they would be subjected to on any desert. The number of rapid alterations of hot to cold was equivalent to hundreds of years of days and nights, yet such rough treatment resulted in no visible fragmentation of the rock. Other experiments of the same kind have been tried with little success. In one experiment, water was sprayed on basalt to simulate dew at each cooling. The result was still negative, even though some chemical solution was demonstrated. Most geologists who have observed fragmentation in the desert still tend to believe that the stresses induced by thermal expansion and contraction in rocks may be significant. We know that the much more intense heat of fires can crack rocks open. Certainly the laboratory experiments so far are a poor copy of what happens in nature. We will have to wait for better experiments or observations to get a firm answer.

Perhaps thermal expansion combines with frost action and chemical weathering to produce two commonly observed kinds of mechanical disintegration, **exfoliation** and **spheroidal weathering.** Exfoliation is the peeling off of large, curved sheets or slabs of rock from the weathering surface of an outcrop. Exfoliating outcrops have the appearance of onion layers. Spheroidal weathering has the same general appearance but on a much smaller scale, in which rounded boulders spall off layers or "shells" from the surface. Large-scale exfoliation may be partly the consequence of relief of pressure. As each slab breaks off, it releases weight from the underlying mass, which then may expand enough, however slightly, to break the rock. In spheroidal weathering the pressure released by unloading is so minute that it cannot be important. Chemical weathering is thought to be of some importance in these processes, producing mechanical stresses by uneven volume changes in the surface as minerals decay. This leads to the breakage of curved plates from the rock mass.

Though people are rarely around to see such things happen, rocks can break up into smaller pieces when a boulder-size chunk falls from a rock outcrop down a cliff or talus slope. But most of fragmentation is the result of the same processes that cause chunks of rock to be split from outcrops in the first place, and the processes continue until the big pieces become small pieces. Impact of one pebble against another in the course of being carried by a rapidly flowing stream or being tossed about by waves on a shore is another cause of breakage. Less obvious than breakage as a result of impacts are the abrasion and wearing away of particles by streams and windblown sand. As we will see in Chapter 9, glaciers are effective in grinding transported rocks into a fine powder by dragging them across the surfaces of buried rock masses.

Sizes and Shapes of Fragments. The various processes that cause fragmentation produce a bewildering array of sizes and shapes. Careful study of the shapes of fragments that can be traced to their parent outcrop, even those kilometers distant, have shown that their shapes are largely inherited from the patterns of joints, bedding, cleavage, and other structures rather than being produced by the transporting medium. An experienced geologist can guess just from the shapes of pebbles on a beach what kinds of rock they came from. This inheritance extends to many sand grains, whose shapes, modified only slightly by erosion and transportation, are derived from the original crystals or grains in the eroded source rocks.

The sizes of fragments are a good clue to the intensity of mechanical erosion. A good general rule of thumb is that the higher or steeper the topography, the larger the fragments. Regardless of the rates of mechanical and chemical weathering, that govern the break-up of rocks in a particular place, the fragments will be largest close to their source. Once fragments have been gradually worked downhill from their source, they enter new domains of weathering, and they undergo further fragmentation. Moreover, once boulders and pebbles get into streams they quickly break and abrade, and the downstream decrease in size of pebbles becomes dramatic. Much of this size decrease is the result of the inability of most streams to carry large boulders very far, except in rare floods, as we will see in Chapter 7.

Sand grains, however, are not produced by mere wear—that is by the gradual abrasion of pebbles. Nor is any one sand grain the only remnant of what was once a pebble: this would require the disappearance, or wearing away, of too much material. A simple calculation shows why: if each pebble in a loaded freight car were replaced by a sand grain, the volume would be reduced to a cupful. If gradual abrasion has such results in nature, the volume of sand in the world should be much less than the volume of

Figure 4-15
A microscopic view of a thin section of the Recluse Formation (Precambrian) in Canada. The grains are angular: they retain the original shapes they had when fragmented from their source rocks. Grains are poorly sorted by size, one of the characteristics of many graywacke sandstones transported by turbidity currents. (Magnification: ×44.) [From *Sand and Sandstone* by F. J. Pettijohn, P. E. Potter, and R. Siever, copyright 1972, Springer-Verlag New York, Inc.]

pebbles. But just the opposite is true: there are enormously greater volumes of sand than there are of pebbles. The similarity in size, shape, and mineral composition of sand grains to the crystals that make granites and other coarse-grained igneous and metamorphic rocks points to the origin of most sand grains. It is the mechanical fragmentation of rocks, not their gradual wearing away, that produces most sand. As the crystals of feldspars, micas, and other weatherable minerals get eaten away at the edges, the interlocked crystals get loosened, and what was once whole rock starts to crumble into individual grains or groups of grains. In some humid regions of the tropics, small boulders can easily be kicked apart. Where weathering is slower, rocks get smaller bit by bit as grains chip off one by one.

Silt particles, smaller than sand grains, are crystals or broken fragments of crystals produced in the same way as sand grains. Clay minerals, on the other hand, are the chemical

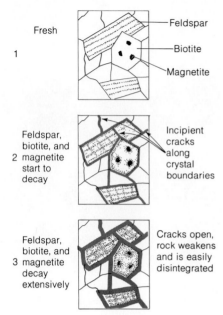

Figure 4-16
Microscopic views of stages in the disintegration of
an igneous rock, such as granite. As chemical decay
proceeds, grain boundaries weaken, and the rock
begins disintegrating into fragments.

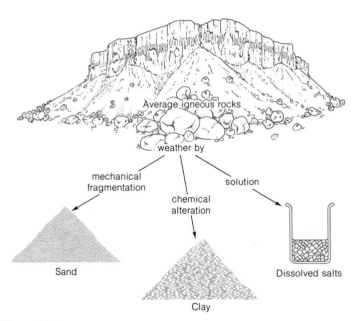

Figure 4-17
The chemical and physical processes of weathering transforms the average igneous rock into sand and clay particles and dissolved salts. The total volume of
erosional debris produced is somewhat greater than the original, depending on the
degree of chemical weathering, which adds carbon dioxide, water, and oxygen to
the original composition.

products of feldspar weathering. Clay-size particles are by definition those less than 1/256
millimeter in diameter (about 0.004 inch). Not
all particles of clay size, however, are produced
by chemical weathering; there are also some
clay-size particles of quartz, feldspar, and other
minerals that are the result of abrasion, disintegration, and physical fragmentation of larger
particles. The action of glaciers produces much
material of these sizes, sometimes called **rock
flour** (see Chapter 9).

Thus the different sizes and shapes of eroded
particles—ranging from huge boulders to microscopic clay particles—are attributable to certain characteristics of their source rocks. The
sizes and shapes of larger boulders, cobbles, and
pebbles are largely inherited from patterns of
jointing, bedding, and foliation, along which
breakage occurs. Sand grains are largely the
constituent crystals of disintegrated coarse-
grained rocks; silts are broken and abraded finer
crystals. Clays are the chemical breakdown
products of unstable minerals.

SOIL: THE RESIDUE OF WEATHERING

The Soil Profile. A good place to start with
soils is to think about them as forming a thin
layer that rests on bedrock, analogous to a coating of rust on iron. The way to see its structure,
its vertical profile, is to cut a trench through the
soil down to bedrock. The top section, or **A-
horizon,** is usually the darkest, and contains
most of the organic matter, or **humus**—tiny
particles of decayed leaves, twigs, and animal
remains. It is a zone of intense biological activity, populated by everything from worms and
insects to gophers, plant roots, and abundant
microorganisms, all living in an ecological mi-
crocosm. In a thick soil that has developed over
a long time, the minerals of the top layer are
mostly clays and residual insoluble minerals like
quartz. The soluble minerals are absent. Lower
in the soil profile, in an intermediate layer called
the **B-horizon,** there is relatively little organic
matter, and soluble minerals and iron oxides are
present. The lowest part, the **C-horizon,** is
slightly altered bedrock, broken and decayed,
mixed with clay. At its base it merges imperceptibly into solid bedrock. Soil scientists use many
different classification schemes that are much
more complex than this simple A-B-C scheme,
but the general pattern is the same for most
soils.

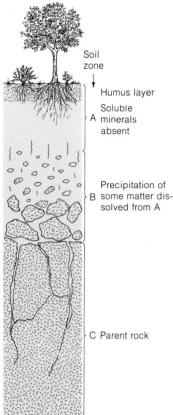

Soil
zone

Humus layer

A — Soluble minerals absent

B — Precipitation of some matter dissolved from A

C Parent rock

Figure 4-18
Typical soil profile developed in temperate regions on granite bedrock. The thickness of the soil profile depends on the age of the soil and the climate. Transitions from one zone to another are normally indistinct.

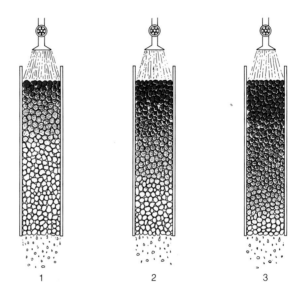

1   2   3

Figure 4-19
The extent of mineral alteration in a soil as illustrated by water flowing through a pipe packed with chemicals that react with the water. Columns 1, 2, and 3 represent successive stages in the downward progression of alteration zones under a steady flow of water. Alternatively, they can be thought to represent thè results, at the same time stages, of three different rates of flow of water, 1 the lowest; 3, the highest.

Geologists and soil scientists have put together many observations that show that the soils are thicker where they are older and where they receive warmth and moisture. These are expected conclusions from what we know about the weathering of minerals. From them we can construct a model for soil formation.

Soil Formation in Relation to Climate. We can compare a soil to a vertically oriented pipe containing fixed solid chemicals that react with water. Water runs through soils just as it would the pipe, for soils are permeable, and rainwater runs through them before infiltrating the pore spaces of the bedrock below. As rainwater passes over the solids in the pipe, it reacts chemically with them. The more fresh water that runs through the pipe, the more the solids will react with the fresh undersaturated solvent. The longer the time the water runs through, the more

the solids will be altered. The higher the temperature, the faster the reactions. All these effects combine to make the part of the solid closest to the fresh-water inflow react the most because it is there that the water is most undersaturated. The water is less efficient a solvent as it passes on through the rest of the solids, for it is starting to approach saturation. As a result, the alteration proceeds along a "front" that moves slowly along the pipe as time goes by.

This is a simplified view of what is essentially the same kind of process in soils. It explains why the tropical soils are thick and devoid of most unstable minerals and why arid soils tend to be thin and rich in unstable minerals. The complexities of clay composition also result in differences in soil mineralogy under different climates. Just as temperature speeds up mineral alteration, so does it stimulate the growth of vegetation and bacteria, which speed up the rate

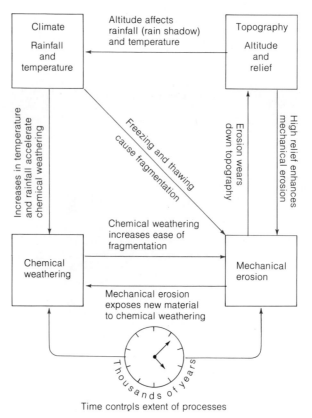

Time controls extent of processes

Figure 4-20
Interrelations among the major factors controlling
weathering and erosion.

Humus
and
leached soil

A

Some iron and
aluminum oxides
precipitated
No soluble
materials, such
as carbonate

B

C Parent rock

Figure 4-21
Pedalfer soil profile developed in a
region of high rainfall on granite. The
only mineral materials in the upper
parts of the soil profile are iron and
aluminum oxides and silicates such as
quartz and clay minerals, all of which
are very insoluble. Calcium carbonate
is absent.

of soil formation. In the extraordinarily dry, frigid environment of some bare ground areas of Antarctica, there are practically no microorganisms, much less larger organisms, and weathering is at a minimum.

A soil takes a long time to form. Many hundreds to several thousands of years may be required for an A-horizon to evolve to the point where there is a mat of altered vegetation and organic matter with altered minerals and clays. The formation of a B-layer takes even longer, from ten thousand to a hundred thousand years. It is easy to see why farmers and governments are concerned that only those agricultural methods are used that do not accelerate soil erosion, for once it is gone, a soil takes a long time to form again. A soil that has evolved to maturity is in a steady state, in dynamic equilibrium with its climate. As it is very slowly eroded from the top by natural processes—and plowing and till-

ing—it is gradually deepened by chemical reaction. If erosion is rapid, chemical decay cannot keep up, and the soil is thinned, a serious consequence for agriculture. The formation of soil can be diagrammed as a complex positive-feedback process involving the response of mineral decay and mechanical erosion to the fundamental variables of time, temperature, and rainfall and the secondarily induced variables of biological activity (Fig. 4-20). If all this is true, then we should find a fair correspondence between soil type and thickness and climatic regions—and we do.

The Major Soil Groups. At least three major kinds of soil can be classified on the basis of the minerals present in their A- and B-horizons. The expected A- and B-zones of a soil in a high-rainfall area would be leached; that is, the soluble or quickly altered materials would be carried away by the water. The resulting soil would be rich in the insolubles, quartz, clay minerals, and iron oxide alteration products. Calcium carbonate would be absent. From their abundance of aluminum and iron, the soils are called **pedalfers** (*ped* from the Greek word for soil; *al* and *fer* from the English and Latin names of aluminum and iron). Much of the eastern half of the United States and most of Canada are covered with fertile soils of this kind.

A second major group of soils are those that contain soluble minerals, indicating formation in dry, warm climates, such as those of the western United States. Since calcium carbonate is an important constituent of these soils, they are called **pedocals.** Some of the calcium carbonate may be dissolved by the occasional rainfall, but in a warm, dry climate, much of the soil water evaporates, leaving precipitated pellets and nodules of calcium carbonate, typically in the B-horizon of the soil. These nodules may form even where there is no limestone; in such soils the calcium carbonate may come from a combination of the calcium leached from silicates and bicarbonate formed by weathering reactions of carbonic acid. The pedocals contain less clay and more unaltered silicates than the pedalfers, again a result of the low rainfall. These soils are normally less fertile, as a result of the combination of mineralogy, texture of the material, and climate, which does not permit a rich population of organisms in the soil.

A third soil type is the **laterite,** a deep red soil of the tropics in which all silicates are completely altered, leaving mostly aluminum and iron oxides, with not only calcium carbonate leached, but silica as well. So much water has passed through these soils that all except the most insoluble compounds are gone. If there is little iron in the parent bedrock, then bauxite, a special variety of this kind of soil, is formed. These tropical soils, though they may support lush vegetation in places, are not very fertile soils for crop plants, because clearing and tilling cause the organic matter, the humus, to be quickly oxidized under the warm climate, so that it does not accumulate to give a rich black soil. For this reason, many lateritic soils can be used for only a few years before they become barren and have to be abandoned.

WEATHERING: SOURCE OF SEDIMENT

Weathering is not only the major process by which rocks are destroyed, but it is also the supplier of the raw material of sediment. By weakening rocks so that they are more easily fragmented, chemical weathering provides the rock and mineral particles of sedimentary detritus. The detritus bears the marks of the kind and extent of weathering in its composition. If chemical weathering is extensive, virtually the only products will be clays, iron oxides, and quartz grains. Some will remain as soil on the weathering surface; the rest will be transported by rivers and the wind to sedimentary environments where muds and quartz sands will be deposited. But such extensive weathering is an extreme, and most of the Earth's surface is not so intensely affected by the coupling of rapid chemical attack in hot, wet climates and the long time periods of crustal stability required for the process to reach an advanced stage. The intermediate stages of weathering are more common; therefore, it is more important for us to see what the sedimentary products of such weathering are.

Incomplete Weathering: Quartz and Feldspar.
If we compare the survival rates of the two most abundant rock-forming minerals, feldspar and quartz, we can get an index of weathering processes. The total amount of quartz stays relatively constant because it is so insoluble and hard, and therefore resistant to erosion. Feldspar, however, is gradually changed to clay; the longer and more intense the weathering, the less of it there will be. Conversely, if chemical weathering is slight and mechanical erosion is the major process, feldspar grains will be contributed to sediments in virtually the same proportions as they are found in the parent, or source, rock. Thus the ratio of feldspar to quartz should be a general indicator as to which of the two weathering processes is most active.

For example, the rapid mechanical erosion of granitic mountains results in the accumulation of unweathered sand and gravel river deposits that have about the same mineral composition as the original granite. Arkoses, feldspar-rich

Figure 4-22
Pedocal soil developed in a region of low rainfall on sedimentary bedrock. The A-zone is leached; the B-zone is enriched in calcium carbonate precipitated by evaporating soil waters.

A — Humus and leached soil

B — Calcium carbonate pellets and nodules precipitated

C — Parent rocks: sandstone, shale, and limestone

Thin or absent humus

Thick irregular masses of limonite and other insoluble oxides

Iron-rich clays and aluminum hydroxides

Thin leached zone

Mafic igneous rock

Figure 4-23
Laterite soil profile developed on a mafic igneous rock in a tropical region. In the upper zone, only the most insoluble precipitated iron and similar oxides remain, plus occasional quartz. All soluble materials, even including relatively insoluble silica, are leached; thus the whole soil profile may be considered to be an A-zone directly overlying a C-zone.

1   High granitic mountains: feldspar and quartz rapidly fragmented by mechanical erosion

     Transportation rounds fragments and sorts by size, producing arkose, a sandy sediment rich in feldspar

2   Low hills and plains: most feldspar weathered to clay before mechanical erosion; quartz remains intact

     Transportation rounds and sorts quartz, producing sands composed almost entirely of quartz

Figure 4-24
Two different kinds of topography on the same granitic bedrock weather to produce sandy sediments of differing feldspar content.

sandstones that form in this way, can be distinguished from their source rocks only by the nature of the sorting and other sedimentary structures, such as bedding. As the highlands are worn down, perhaps a change in climate will take place; chemical weathering will then play a dominant role, and the feldspar will be increasingly altered to clay. The sand transported and deposited by the rivers becomes dominated by quartz, with much associated clay. The rocks that are formed from such deposits are quartz-rich sandstones, or quartz arenites. In contrast with an arkose, which provides detailed information about the mineral composition of the source rock being eroded, the quartz arenite tells us mainly that the source rock contained quartz, even though an occasional grain of feldspar or some other silicate may give a bit more information on the source rocks. It is in this way that geologists working with sedimentary rocks can do detective work on the topography, climate, and rock composition of the past.

Implicit in the interpretation of climate and topography from weathering products is the control that parent rock composition has on soil composition and sedimentary detritus. It is again a matter of time and intensity. Under intense, long-continued weathering, the soils and detritus will reflect mainly climate and to-pography; the soil developed on a granite may look much like one on a shale. The shorter the time and the less intensive the weathering, the more the compositional differences of the source rocks show up in the soil and detritus. A young soil will still show some remains of unweathered minerals from which the parent rock composition can be inferred. But we gain one kind of information at the expense of another. The more we are able to deduce about the parent rock, the less likely it is that we will be able to get much information on climate, because weathering will probably have been too slight to leave a strong impression. As in our automobile junkyards, the older and rustier and more dismantled the cars are, the harder it is to tell the make, model, and year. The younger they are, the easier it is to estimate how rapidly they have rusted.

CHEMICAL WEATHERING AS THE REACTION BETWEEN ATMOSPHERE, OCEAN, AND CRUST

If chemical weathering is important as the maker of detrital sediments, it is equally important as the source of the dissolved materials that filter into the ground, that go to the oceans in

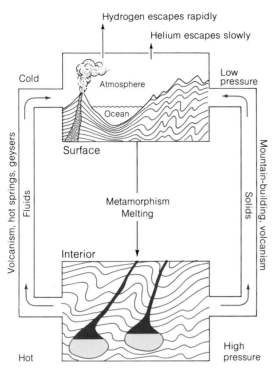

Figure 4-25
The chemical reaction system of the Earth is composed of two coupled subsystems, one in the interior, where igneous and metamorphic rocks are formed, and the other at the surface, where atmosphere, ocean, and crust react. Nothing escapes from this system except the lightest gases, hydrogen and helium, which have atoms small enough to escape the Earth's gravity field. [After R. Siever, "Sedimentological Consequences of a Steady-State Ocean Atmosphere", *Sedimentology*, vol. 11, copyright International Association Sedimentology.]

rivers, and that make sea water the complex salty solution it is. The weathering processes that produce those solutions are chemical reactions in which atmospheric gases (carbon dioxide and oxygen) combine with water to attack exposed crustal materials of the earth. Thus by describing the overall effects of weathering, we can see how the atmosphere, the waters of the continents, the oceans, and the surface of the crust are all linked in a giant chemical system.

All the gases of the atmosphere and all the water on the Earth's surface originated from within the interior of the Earth and escaped via volcanoes, hot springs, and other zones of connection between interior and surface. Probably most of this gas came out early in the Earth's history and has been added to slowly throughout geologic time. The water has accumulated primarily in the oceans, but much is stored as groundwater, and in hydrated minerals of sedi-

mentary origin. The great bulk of the carbon dioxide has not accumulated in the atmosphere, but has been transformed by dissolving in water to form bicarbonate ion and then combining with calcium to make the limestones of the crust. Another fraction of the carbon dioxide was transformed to organic carbon by photosynthesis and buried in the form of organic matter in sediments, some of it ultimately altered to coal and oil. Oxygen accumulated in the atmosphere as the by-product of the photosynthesis that produced the organic carbon. Rocks elevated to high mountains by tectonic forces and exposed to the atmosphere by erosion have also come from the interior.

All of these components, the rocks, the water, and the gases, were once together at various places deep in the Earth at high temperatures and pressures. The movements of solid lithosphere and magmas combine to allow the gases and water to separate from the rock-making materials from the interior and leak out into the atmosphere as the rocks are pushed to the surface. In the erosional processes that take place at the surface of the Earth, all those components come back into contact at much lower temperatures and pressures. A new set of low-temperature reactions—the weathering process—takes place between the rocks and gases. Water and carbon dioxide combine to form carbonic acid, which weathers silicate minerals. Oxygen oxidizes iron and other metals. Because the chemical stabilities of minerals that can be formed by these components are so different at low temperatures and pressures, an entirely new set of minerals, dominated by clays and carbonates, is formed instead of minerals like olivines and pyroxenes. Thus the earth is like a giant chemical reaction chamber made up of two subchambers, a hot one in the interior and a cold one at the exterior. The conveyor belt operating between the chambers is volcanism and tectonics.

Weathering is the reaction in the cold chamber.

The ocean basins are the receptacles for all of the dissolved products of weathering. These materials do not simply accumulate there, for in the sea they come together to precipitate sedimentary minerals. The most abundant is limestone, formed in the sea by the combination of calcium and bicarbonate ions released by weathering. In this way the calcium is precipitated—mostly in the form of shells of organisms—at the same rate that it is brought in by rivers, and the ocean stays in a steady state, unchanging in the amount of calcium, even though ions are constantly coming in and going out. So it is with all of the other elements. Because of these steady-state reactions, the oceans have probably remained at about the same composition throughout much of the history of the Earth. The ocean and its sediments are the products of the last stage in the reactions between the atmosphere and the crust.

SUMMARY

1. Chemical and mechanical weathering complement and reinforce each other in erosion.

2. Chemical reactions of weathering, such as oxidation of iron or decomposition of organic material, vary widely with climate and material.

3. Potassium feldspar weathers by partially dissolving to form solid kaolinite. Evidence for this reaction comes from field observation, its exact nature from laboratory experiment.

4. Feldspar weathers by using up water and hydrogen ion to form kaolinite, leaving potassium and silica in solution.

5. Carbon dioxide dissolves in water to form carbonic acid, an effective chemical weathering agent.

6. Chemical weathering is most active in warm humid regions and least active in cold or arid regions.

7. Clay minerals—kaolinite, montmorillonite, illite, and others—are the products of weathering of various materials under different climatic regimes.

8. Limestone is completely dissolved during chemical decay and is the rock type most rapidly attacked during weathering in humid climates.

9. Mafic minerals may dissolve completely. Iron contained in them is oxidized by the oxygen of the atmosphere and then precipitated in soils and sediments as limonite.

10. Relative chemical stabilities of various minerals at the Earth's surface are ranked on the basis of the kind and degree of solubility.

11. Fragmentation of rock into boulders, pebbles, sand, and silt is a mechanical process promoted by chemical weathering.

12. Studies of rock fragmentation on the moon show that little of the normal mechanical erosion that we observe on Earth takes place there.

13. Zones of weakness open up as cracks and joints when rocks formed in the interior are exposed at the surface. Water seeps into the openings and causes weathering: when water freezes, it wedges the rocks apart.

14. Sizes and shapes of fragmented rock particles, from boulders to sand grains, are largely inherited from such characteristics of source rocks as jointing, bedding, and crystalline texture.

15. Soils, the residues of weathering over long periods of time, form distinctive types in response to climatic regimes: pedalfers, pedocals, and laterites.

16. The quartz-feldspar ratio of a clastic sediment is a useful guide to the rate and kind of weathering in the eroding source area.

17. Chemical weathering is a reaction between the solid crust of the Earth and the atmosphere and oceans, all of which originated within the interior of the Earth.

18. The ocean keeps its chemical composition in a steady state as it precipitates chemical sediments while new dissolved substances are brought in by rivers.

EXERCISES

1. Rank the following rocks in order of their rapidity of weathering in a humid climate: granite, limestone, quartz sandstone, basalt. Give reasons for your choice.

2. Would you expect a basalt to weather more quickly than a granite in a semiarid climate? Would you expect a basalt to weather more quickly than a gabbro, its coarse-grained equivalent, in a semiarid climate? Why?

3. If you were a mountain climber and had to drive pitons (metal spikes used to hold ropes of climbers) into bare rocks at high altitudes, would you find it easier in desert mountains or mountains that receive high rainfall?

4. Describe how you might expect a calcium-iron garnet $(Ca_3Fe_2(SiO_4)_3)$ to weather chemically and what the weathering products might be.

5. If we continue to burn oil and coal at an increasing rate, we may increase the carbon dioxide in our atmosphere by 1.5 times. How might this affect weathering?

6. If you were a conservation engineer and had to design a plan for making soil form as quickly as possible on a fresh, broken rock rubble left by construction or mining operations, what would you do (without importing any soil from elsewhere)?

7. Which would you expect to fragment more rapidly into small pieces, a granite or a schist? What effects might climate have on the difference? How might the shapes of the pieces differ?

8. Of the various mechanisms of rock breakage described, which would you expect to be more important in the rainy tropics as opposed to cold polar regions?

9. What are the erosional processes that produce these three different sizes of material: blocky boulders up to several meters across, sand grains about 1 millimeter across, and clay particles a few thousandths of a millimeter in diameter? How far from the eroding outcrop might pieces of each size get in a given time period?

BIBLIOGRAPHY

Keller, W. D., *The Principles of Chemical Weathering.* Columbia, Missouri: Lucas Brothers, 1955.

Kellogg, C. E., "Soil." *Scientific American,* July, 1950. (Offprint No. 821.)

Krauskopf, K. B., *Introduction to Geochemistry.* New York: McGraw-Hill Book Company, 1967. (Chapters 4 and 7.)

Loughnan, F. C., *Chemical Weathering of the Silicate Minerals.* New York: American Elsevier Publishing Company, 1969.

McNeil, M., "Lateritic Soils." *Scientific American,* November 1964. (Offprint No. 870.)

Siever, R., "The Steady State of the Earth's Crust, Atmosphere, and Oceans." *Scientific American,* June 1974.

5

EROSION AND LANDSCAPE

Following the slow weathering that breaks down outcropping rocks to small fragments and clay, more rapid processes of active erosion and transportation take over and create the varied topography of Earth. Mass movements such as landslides erode mountainsides and together with other agents of erosion help shape the surface. The sculpture of topography is illustrated by the contrast between the Grand Canyon and the Ozark Mountains. The forms and slopes of the valleys are clues to the agents of erosion that gave them their shapes—the water, ice, and wind that act in opposition to the tectonic forces that elevate mountains. The evolution of landscape is a balance between uplift and erosion over the course of time.

Not a year passes without the appearance of headlines telling the news of a flood, a mass of mud oozing down a hillside, or a catastrophic landslide. On August 1, 1976, for example, the Big Thompson River in the Rocky Mountains of Colorado, suddenly swollen to a flood by heavy rain, swept through its narrow canyon, killing more than 60 people and washing away bridges, roads, and buildings. In 1972 Rapid City, situated at the foot of the Black Hills of South Dakota, was hit by a flash flood that shocked the country because of the suddenness with which it caused such vast destruction and tragic loss of life. Everywhere in the devastated city one could see rocks, mud, and silt brought in by the floodwaters. Disastrous as this particular event was, it should not have been unexpected. The flood, predictable enough once the rain began to fall so rapidly and continuously from a most unusual storm of long duration, was only the final transporting agent of the debris that invaded Rapid City. Much of that debris began its downhill journey a long time before, having been produced at a normal rate by chemical and mechanical weathering in the high parts of the central core of the Black Hills. The prevailing erosional process was suddenly aug-

mented by the rapid downhill movement of water-soaked soil and rock debris into the flooding tributary streams of the Cheyenne River, which rushed the masses of detritus onto the plains. Rock fragments and clay that had taken tens to hundreds of years to produce and build up on the slopes were caught up in fast downhill movements that were provoked by a storm that might occur only once in a hundred years.

This chapter is concerned with the active erosion and transportation that follow the slow, sometimes imperceptible, decay and fragmentation of chemical and mechanical weathering. The downslope transport by slow creep and rapid slides and flows makes the debris of erosion available to the major long-distance agents of transport: rivers, wind, and glaciers, all of which shape the landscape of Earth into varied forms that are diagnostic of the processes acting on the face of the planet.

MASS MOVEMENTS

Downhill movement of the debris of erosion is not an obscure process to people who suddenly find themselves the victims of a disastrous mud-

Figure 5-1
Jackson Boulevard in Rapid City, South Dakota, on June 10, 1972, after torrential rains caused a sudden flash flood that deluged the city. [Photo by Perry H. Rahn.]

A few years ago a Japanese geologist's observations of certain conditions on a hillside convinced him that a landslide would take place within a short period of time and bury a nearby village. Because he warned the people of the village, predicting the imminence of the landslide, he was instrumental in saving thousands of lives. The landslide came soon after and bore out his prediction. In gratitude, the villagers erected a shrine in his honor.

flow or landslide. Almost every year the world's television news cameras are rushed to another spot on the globe that few people had ever heard of to record the tragedy of death and destruction. Earth movements are sudden, the accompanying volumes of sliding debris often enormous, and events seem unpredictable. Yet when geologists hear some of these disastrous mass movements, many of them react strongly to the lack of foresight and poor engineering planning that are often responsible for them.

In Quebec the stage was set for a mudflow when excessively steep slopes were cut in soft formations of silt and clay in the course of widening a highway. In 1955, after a period of heavy rain, the steepened cliffs became saturated with water and suddenly gave way in a flowing mass of debris that carried away buildings, roads, and people. The deaths of three people can be traced to poor highway engineering. In 1963 more than 200 million cubic meters of rock debris roared down steep slopes into the waters of a deep reservoir impounded by a dam built in the Italian Alps. The enormous volume of debris plunged into the reservoir and created a giant spillover of water at the dam. Downstream

2600 people lost their lives in the catastrophic torrent. The dam, 265 meters (870) feet) high, was built in a steepsided valley. The engineers who designed it ignored three things: the weakness of the cracked and deformed layers of limestone and shale that walled the reservoir, an obvious geologic history of landslides, and a premonition of danger signalled by a small rockslide three years before. Though the landslide was not preventable and would have caused some damage to roads and buildings, and perhaps a few injuries, the reservoir, whose waters caused the flood and multiplied the damage enormously, might have been placed in a geologically safer place. Fortunately, mass movements like this are infrequent, and most of them do not affect many people; many are known from the geological forms they leave behind rather than from first-hand observations.

Though downhill movement of debris is obviously induced by gravity, there are other reasons why some movements are fast on some slopes and slow on others; and why some slopes are stable and why others move if disturbed. First in importance is oversteepening of slopes, illustrated best by loose sand. Sandboxes have

Figure 5-2
Air view of the landslide in Madison Canyon that slid off the mountainside in the left background after an earthquake in August, 1959. The slide dammed the Madison River, forming the lake in the foreground. [Photo by J. R. Stacy, U.S. Geological Survey.]

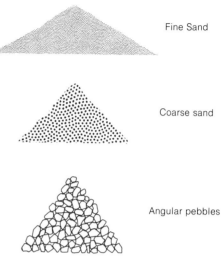

Fine Sand

Coarse sand

Angular pebbles

Figure 5-3
Angles of respose of particle mounds increase as particle sizes increase and shapes become more angular.

made nearly everyone familiar since childhood with the fact that a pile of sand will assume a characteristic slope; the angle is the same whether the pile is only a few centimeters high or three meters high. If some sand is scooped from the base of the pile very slowly and carefully, the angle of slope will steepen a little and hold. But if someone jumps on the ground near it, the slope cascades down and again assumes the original angle, which is called the **angle of repose.** That angle varies with the size and shape of the material; larger, flatter, and more angular pieces of loose material will remain stable on steeper slopes.

Next in importance is the effect of a lubricant, usually water. An extreme way to observe this effect is to try to build a sand pile with dripping wet sand: it just flows until it becomes as flat as a pancake. Another way is to try to walk down a clayey slope in the rain without sliding. Water filling the pores of permeable material allows the grains to slide past each other with little friction. The effects of slope and lubricant, of course, become more complex in other materials, depending on the nature of the mixture, the irregularities of slopes, the structurally stabilizing role of vegetation roots, and the amounts of water required to saturate the materials. Never-

theless, these effects are at the root of all downslope movements of boulders, sand, and soil, and they work in different ways to produce the variety of what we call **mass movements:** landslides, mudflows, rock slides, slumps, and creep.

Landslides. The terms **landslide** and **rockslide** refer to the rapid downhill movement of masses of rock, weathered erosional debris, soil, and anything else that may be in the way, such as houses. fences, and roads. These names are used to distinguish slides on the basis of the main material forming them. Rockslides are movements of blocks of bedrock along joints or cracks, usually along the water-lubricated bedding planes of tilted sediments. The preconditions for landslides are slopes that are too steep for the frictional forces to hold the material in place against the force of gravity. Typically, small landslides are formed in places where slopes are first steepened by erosion, either natural or artificial (such as excavations), and then soaked by rain until saturated; once saturated, the slope is in a critical stage of instability, ready to give. Once the stage of extreme instability is reached, a slide is the inevitable result. Vibrations of some kind are responsible for triggering

Figure 5-4
The scar of the Gros Ventre slide. This photo, taken in 1966, more than forty
years after the slide, shows the still-unforested slopes of the scar left by the slide.
[Photo by R. Siever.]

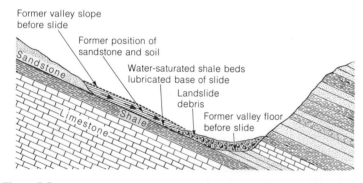

Figure 5-5
Cross section of the Gros Ventre slide, Wyoming. Arrows show the direction of
sliding of a mass of soil-covered sandstone down a water-lubricated surface of
shale underlying the sandstone. The conditions for this slide were set when the
Gros Ventre River cut its valley floor through the sandstone formation, leaving un
supported the sandstone beds higher on the valley slopes. [Modified from W. C.
Alden, 1928, *Trans. Am. Inst. Mng. Met. Eng.*, v. 76, pp. 345–361.]

many slides. The more delicately poised something is, the smaller the jar needed to knock it
over. Vibrations of strong earthquakes will trigger slides in material that might otherwise have
stayed fixed for a long time. Most of the damage
that resulted from the Alaskan earthquake of
1964 was caused by the slides it produced.

Melting snow and heavy rains made water
abundant in the valley of the Gros Ventre River
in the spring of 1925. That was the year of the
Gros Ventre slide, a classic among the landslides
of the twentieth century—perhaps because it
was witnessed by so many people and perhaps
because several geological studies were made
soon afterward. The Gros Ventre River flows
through the Jackson Hole area of Wyoming,
which is noted for its natural beauty and is
situated near Yellowstone Park. Though the
valley is sparsely settled, it is visited by many.
One eyewitness, a rancher who lived there,
barely escaped from the path of the slide on
horseback. Warned by the roar of the slide, he
looked up to see a huge mass of valleyside
hurtling toward his ranch. From the gate to his
property he watched the slide race past him at

Figure 5-6
Aerial view of slump in a hillslope underlain by weak shale. The slump is about
140 m (450 ft) wide. Stanley County, South Dakota. [Photo by D. R. Crandell,
U.S. Geological Survey.]

about 50 miles an hour and bury everything he owned.

It has been estimated that about 37 million cubic meters of rock and soil slid down one side of the valley, surged more than 30 meters (100 feet) up onto the opposite side, and then fell back to the valley floor, damming the Gros Ventre River. Most of the slide was a confused mass of blocks of sandstone, shale, and soil, but one large block, covered with soil and a forest of pine, slid down as a unit. Two years later, the large lake that formed behind the slide overflowed it, draining the lake and causing a torrential flood in the valley below.

The forces that caused the Gros Ventre slide were all natural. The stratigraphy and structure of the valley (Fig. 5-5) made it almost inevitable. On the side of the valley where the slide occurred, a permeable, erosion-resistant sandstone formation dipping about 20° toward the river rested on a soft shale. The stage was set for the event to happen, sooner or later, after the channel of the Gros Ventre River cut through most of the sandstone and left it with virtually no support where it intersected the river channel.

Only friction along the bedding planes between shale and sandstone kept it from sliding. The removal of this support by channel erosion was the equivalent of oversteepening. The heavy rains and melting snow saturated not only the sandstone but the surface of the underlying shale. Once the force of gravity overcame friction, almost all of the sandstone slid toward the bottom of the valley along the lubricated surface of the wet shale. This general pattern is characteristic of many other slides, except that some slides take place along joints or other zones of structural weakness instead of bedding planes.

In **unconsolidated** material—that is, in materials not held together by a cement or by a strong interlocking crystal structure—landslides start after a significant part of the whole mass is saturated with water and lubricated. Again, some shock, however small, can trigger the downslope movement of a whole unstable hillside of such material. Some such movements take the form of a **slump,** in which the mass travels as a unit, in most places slipping along a surface that is concave upward. Rockslides can also move as slumps. Many landslides, however,

Figure 5-7
A large mudflow that ran like a river down mountain slopes. Hinsdale County, Colorado. [Photo by W. Cross, U. S. Geological Survey.]

rather than slumping as a single unit or as several, will move as an incoherent jumbled mass flowing almost with the characteristics of a fluid. Ronald Shreve, a geomorphologist at the University of California, Los Angeles, has spent much time studying landslides. He thinks that some of them, once they start, race along on an undersurface of trapped, compressed air that provides an almost frictionless speedway.

Mudflows are particularly fluid forms of landslides that move as viscous tongues of mixed mud, soil, rock, and water. Most common in hilly and semiarid regions, mudflows are generated by infrequent, sometimes prolonged, rainstorms. The flows start down upper valley slopes and merge on valley floors. Where mudflows exit from confined valleys into broader, lower valley slopes and flats, they may splay out to cover large areas with a mixture of wet debris. Mudflows can carry large boulders, trees, and even whole houses. **Earthflows** are something like mudflows, but are less fluid and thus tend to be confined to slopes of weathered shale or clay, where they move short distances downslope. **Debris-avalanches** are another kind of flow associated with humid mountainous regions. Water-saturated soil eroded down to bedrock may move rapidly, carrying everything in its path with it. In 1962 a debris avalanche in the Peruvian Andes traveled almost 15 kilometers (9 miles) in about 7 minutes, engulfing most parts of eight towns and killing 3500 people! Mudflows and debris-avalanches are easily triggered on slopes of volcanic cinder cones as their un-

consolidated accumulations of ash and other erupted material become saturated during rains. Eruptions trigger some flows by associated earthquakes and tilting movements, cloudbursts, and sudden falls of volcanic debris. More than fifty-five such flows, many of them associated with eruptions, have occurred on the slopes of Mt. Rainier, Washington, in the past 10,000 years, according to U.S. Geological Survey geologists.

All of these rapid mass movements of mud, soil, debris, and rock are expected, though infrequent, natural occurrences—the consequences of varying combinations of processes that steepen slopes and lubricate near-surface materials with water. They cannot be eliminated, but humans can avoid provoking them by unwise engineering and can learn better ways of predicting them. We may also have to learn not to build houses in particularly dangerous places where natural movements cannot be controlled.

Rock Falls, Soil Creep, and Solifluction. **Talus slopes** are built up by the accumulation of many individual falls of talus blocks—rocks broken from the outcrop by physical and chemical forces. Though each rock falls suddenly, the accumulation of talus is slow and steady, building up blocky slopes everywhere along the base of a cliff. Some talus slopes have been accumulating for so long that they almost completely cover the bedrock. The talus slopes themselves are eroded at their lower slopes by being further broken down in size and being carried away by

Figure 5-8
A mudflow deposit on the slopes of Mt. Rainier, Washington. The mudflow consists of a mixture of volcanic ash and rock fragments, including a large volcanic bomb (above the hammer). [Photo by D. R. Crandell, U.S. Geological Survey.]

Figure 5-9
Talus produced by a rockslide at the base of a rocky valley wall in Yosemite National Park, California. The trees in the foreground were defoliated by the blast of air that accompanied the slide. [Photo by F. E. Matthes, U.S. Geological Survey.]

mudflows and other mass movements or streams.

Soil creep is a downhill movement of soil that takes place so slowly that its rate of movement is difficult to measure over short time periods, much less notice, from day to day. Yet such slow movements are the reason why trees, telephone poles, fences, and other objects apparently fixed in the soil tend to lean or be displaced slightly downslope. By comparing careful measurements of the precise positions of marked stakes fixed in bedrock with those of others in the soil, geologists have learned that most creep ranges from a few millimeters per year to a few centimeters per year, depending on the kind of soil, steepness of slope, rainfall, and vegetation. The mechanics of creep are not fully understood, but it is fairly certain that it is the result of a combination of minute movements caused by freezing and thawing, wetting and drying, thermal expansion, activities of burrowing organisms, and root movements of growing and decaying plants.

Depending on the degree of saturation, soil may move slowly or rapidly. In cold regions, where saturated ground becomes frozen, the movement of soil, called **solifluction,** takes place slowly, induced by freezing and thawing. Because ground in frigid areas may be frozen to great depths, the lower zones do not thaw. But when the surface zones of the soil thaws, the water has no place to go. The water-saturated upper layers then ooze downhill, carrying broken rocks and other debris. A related phenomenon is the movement of **rock glaciers,** which are like lobed rivers of rock that have moved down slopes and valleys in cold, mountainous regions. The pores between the rocks are partly filled with ice, and the motion is in many ways like that of true glaciers.

Though unspectacular, all of the motions of creep and related slow downslope travel of rock and soil account for a large part of the initial transportation of fragmented and weathered material from the primary sites of erosion to lower slopes, where they are further eroded and transported by streams.

Slope Wash. The prelude to organized river-channel transportation of detritus is **slope wash,** the generalized surface runoff of rainwater on the surface of the ground. Included in this category are all of the little rills and threads of water that gradually come together, ultimately to form rivulets, then streams, then river. If you have the patience and don't mind the rain, you can observe how water running down a hillside moves small particles of silt and sand, gradually undermines clayey soil from beneath pebbles, and makes them tilt and move. A rain heavy enough will produce a **sheet wash** on even slopes—a continuous sheet of flowing water. Sheet wash does not normally persist very far down a slope before it gets organized into tiny channels or rills, but a good place to see it is on sloping concrete embankments, such as those near bridges or culverts. The impact of raindrops and hailstones is sufficient to erode clay and silt and help lift it into the moving slope wash. Slope wash operates most effectively in such places as freshly graded highway shoulders and around new houses. The best way to avoid excessive erosion by slope wash is to plant grass and other vegetation. Leaves and stems shelter the surface from raindrops and retard the flow of slope wash; roots hold the soil together to resist erosion.

Though it is hard to get reliable figures on the quantity of material moved by slope wash and mass movements in general, almost all of the enormous load of erosional debris that eventually gets into the rivers of the world must have first moved downhill by various combinations of those processes. The removal of earth materials, at different rates and by different processes, creates the forms of landscape. Fragmentation, weathering, and mass movements sculpture the land in combination with rivers, the wind, and glacial ice. We now turn to the landscape to see what we can deduce from it.

THE FORM OF THE SURFACE: HIGH AND LOW

What does the surface of the land look like from an orbiting satellite? Most prominent are the mountains and the canyons, the surfaces that depart most dramatically from the more average, undulating contours of the plains or lowlands that characterize much of the Earth's surface. Lakes and rivers fleck the continents, but it is the world-encircling ocean that makes Earth the blue planet. If that ocean were siphoned off, the sea floor would show some of its own kinds of mountains, plains, and valleys. Equally prominent mountains are hidden by the South Polar ice cap on the continent of Antarctica, and by the Greenland ice cap near the opposite pole. How do we describe this varied surface of Earth?

The heights and depths that give shape to the Earth's surface are called its **topography.** The

Figure 5-10
The varied aspects of continental topography are shown by this satellite photo of the Pacific Coast of South America at Antofagasta, northern Chile, looking across Chile toward Argentina. In the foreground, an irregular coast is dominated by mountainous terrain. Inland are plains and plateaus, and in the distance are the Andes Mountains. In the middle background are large basinal depressions filled with salt flats. [From National Aeronautics and Space Administration.]

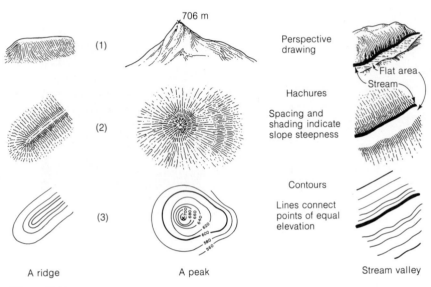

Figure 5-11
Three topographic features, a ridge, a peak, and a stream valley, as represented (1) by perspective drawings as they might look from the ground; (2) by hachures, short straight lines that indicate the degree and direction of slopes as they might look from the air; and (3) by contours, lines that connect all points of equal elevation and thus more accurately represent the configuration of the surface. The more closely spaced the contour lines, the steeper the slope. Normally, every fifth line is heavier in weight and has a number to indicate the elevation.

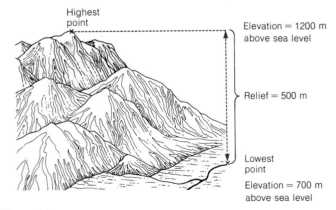

Figure 5-12
Relief is the difference between the highest and lowest elevations in a region.

standard level, or **datum plane,** to which we compare all heights or depths is usually **mean sea level,** the average between high and low tides. Vertical distances above mean sea level are called **elevations,** or **altitudes.** A **topographic map** shows the distribution of elevations in the area covered: in its two dimensions, the map gives a representation of the three-dimensional view we would get from looking down from the air. On most such maps this is done by means of **contours**—lines that connect points of equal elevation. Less commonly used in topographic maps for professional use, but often used in atlases and road maps, are **shadings. Hachures,** short lines that indicate slope, give a much more realistic but less precise idea of the land surface. Both contours and hachures bring out another measure of topography, its roughness, by illustrating the **relief**—the vertical distance between the highest and lowest points in the map area. One estimates relief on a contour map by subtracting the elevation of the lowest contour, down in a river bottom, from the highest, on a hill or mountain top. Climbing a mountain is the best way to experience what relief means. It is one matter to climb to a 3600-meter (12,000-foot) peak from a high plateau of 3000 meters (10,000 feet) but quite another to climb a 2400-meter (8000-foot) peak starting from a few hundred meters above sea level.

A CONTRAST IN TOPOGRAPHY

There is much more to landscape than the grossest features seen from the great distance of a satellite. The infinite variety of form and detail that we look upon as scenery holds much of the information we need to deduce how it was made. Again we "visit" the Grand Canyon, this time to explore the natural architecture of its surface.

The Grand Canyon Landscape. The canyon is deep, broad, rocky, and ruggedly mountainous. The Colorado River can rarely be seen from the rim, though one can make out the edge of the river gorge in which it has been cutting its way downward for the past 15 to 20 million years. Steep cliffs compete with the more gentle rubbly slopes for our attention. What we see are the effects of erosion. That word sums up the combination of chemical and physical weathering acting together with the direct erosive power of the river in its channel and the force of the wind. Although the river has removed enormous quantities of rock, we can easily trace such formations as the cliff-forming Kaibab Limestone from one rim to the other. Once a continuous sheet, as it still is under the plateau back from the canyon, it has been breached, broken up, and taken away. In this arid climate, limestone is resistant to erosion, and forms cliffs because there is so little water to dissolve it.

Merely by sampling its water, one can demonstrate the power of the Colorado River as an agent of erosion. Colorado River water, as those engineers in charge of purifying it for drinking well know, is turbid with suspended fine clay. Sand in the river channel is constantly in movement. A tremendous volume of sand, silt, and clay is being transported all the time. One measure of this volume is the amount of sediment that is dropped by the river as it enters Lake Mead, created by the building of Hoover Dam. Since the completion of the dam in 1936, many millions of tons of sediment have accumulated on the lake bottom. A close look at this sediment shows sand grains of the kind found in the Coconino and other sandstone formations, mica flakes that could have come from the Vishnu formation, and small pebbles of almost every kind of rock found in the Canyon. It is clear that the river is a prime agent of removing rock material from the Canyon.

Now focus on the topography of the canyon. In Chapter 2, in summarizing the stratigraphic sequence, we used the nature of slopes and cliffs to pick out formations. Steep cliffs are made of hard rocks that are **resistant** to erosion. In the Grand Canyon these rocks are limestones, and to a lesser extent sandstones. The gradual slopes, usually covered with talus, are underlain by shales. This differential resistance to erosion shown by the various rock types is one of the major controls on topography. Cliffs are formed as soft, less resistant, weak rocks erode and undercut overlying resistant rocks, which then break off in large blocks.

The valley of the Grand Canyon is much broader than the River itself. In the river gorge it is several times wider at the top than at the bottom, and a cut through it would show a simple **V-shaped** profile. Above the inner gorge, in the main Canyon valley, the profile is much more complex, but can be generalized to a much broader V-shaped valley. As the river cuts downward, the valley gradually widens. The metamorphic rocks of the inner gorge are much more coarsely crystalline and less porous than the rocks above and thus weather more slowly. Being much more resistant to erosion than the

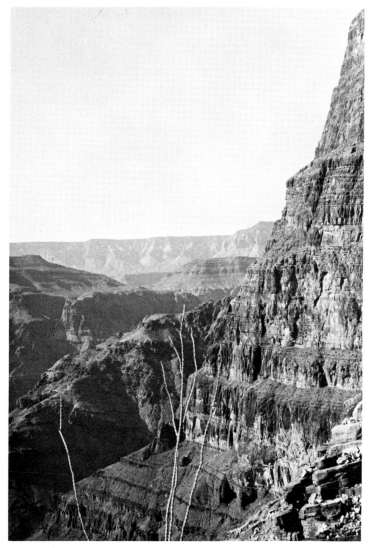

Figure 5-13
The varied nature of the slopes of the Grand Canyon are expressions of the resistance of the different kinds of rock to erosion; the steeper cliffs are formed in sandstones and limestones and the gentler, rubbley slopes formed on shale. [Photo by Edwin D. McKee, U.S. Geological Survey.]

weaker Paleozoic rocks above, the Precambrian rocks support narrower canyon walls. Above, formations like the Bright Angel erode rapidly and broaden the valley, for shales fragment easily and disintegrate in water to form silt and mud.

The Grand Canyon teaches us about the nature of erosion of a river valley in terrain where most of the formations consist of horizontal sedimentary rocks. Another part of the erosion story emerges when we contrast the Grand Canyon with an area of different topography.

One unhappy consequence of the erosional power of rivers is the silting up of reservoirs. Sediment that would normally be carried downstream is deposited in the artificial lake formed by a dam. Some reservoirs are filling with sediment at so great a rate that the useful life of the dam for flood control and irrigation purposes is shortened to a few decades, hardly enough to have made such expensive projects worthwhile.

The Ozarks. The Grand Canyon has developed rather recently. Age is always such an important factor in geology that we ought to look at old mountains. One example in the middle of the continent, nowhere near the Rockies in the West or the Appalachians in the East, is the Ozark Mountains (sometimes called a plateau). Situated in Missouri and Arkansas, the Ozarks consist of a granite core surrounded by relatively flat-lying sedimentary rocks resting on the flanks of the granite. The sedimentary lithologies are the same as many of those in the Grand Canyon. The Ozarks are not in the same league with the Rockies in height or relief, but they do include some fairly hilly topography.

Late Precambrian
High granite mountains

Sediments deposited
on flanks

Upper Cambrian
Low granite mountains

Mid-Paleozoic
Granite hills buried
by sediment

Present
Granite hills exhumed
as erosion stripped
away most sediment

Figure 5-14
Evolution of the Ozark mountains. (1) In the Precambrian, granite was intruded during a mountain-building episode and then exposed by erosion. (2) By Upper Cambrian time, the mountains were extensively eroded, and sediments were being deposited on their flanks. (3) During the Paleozoic, the granite was buried by a series of sediments. (4) From the Paleozoic to the present, erosion stripped away the sediments, exhuming the ancient topography.

The granite of the Ozarks shows the signs of moderate weathering. Outcrops are rounded and cracked, the joints enlarged by solution. The sedimentary rocks are more deeply weathered, and soils are well developed on them.

The slopes of the Ozarks are gentler and more rounded than those of the Grand Canyon. The valleys are broad V-shaped. Steep cliffs are few, and the streams meander along fairly wide valley bottoms called **floodplains,** from the frequency with which the rivers flood over their banks and occupy the entire width. The dominant aspect is one of less vigorous erosion; the streams carry much less detritus than either the Colorado or high mountain streams that carry large loads of rock debris down the steep eastern slopes of the Sierra Nevada that stand so high above the Great Basin.

The granite of the Ozarks is Precambrian. The sedimentary rocks surrounding the granite are early Paleozoic. The oldest sedimentary rock formation rests directly on the flanks of the central granite core. It is a sandstone—more specifically, an arkose, a feldspar-rich sandstone that was formed from the disintegration of the granite. The coarseness and abundance of the feldspar grains is a sign that the Ozarks were then granite hills that were being rapidly eroded when the first Paleozoic seas began lapping up around them. The Ozarks were gradually lowered further and covered by those seas, for younger sedimentary rocks cover the granite core. Still later, the mountains were exhumed, and the soft sediments were stripped away during an episode of erosion that came at the end of the Paleozoic.

Wherever we find older mountains, we see low elevations, low relief, and gentler slopes and broader river valleys. They are also all tectonically "quiet." They are rarely the sites of earthquakes or volcanoes, nor do they show any evidence of recent rock deformation or metamorphism. The conclusion: once the tectonic machine that created the mountains in a region has run down, erosion operating over a long time will wear mountains down to low hills.

THE OVERALL PATTERN

We might put it that "tectonics proposes and erosion disposes." The mechanisms that control the heights of mountains display an overall pattern that we can call a **negative-feedback** process. This kind of process is one in which the results of a first or primary action or operation

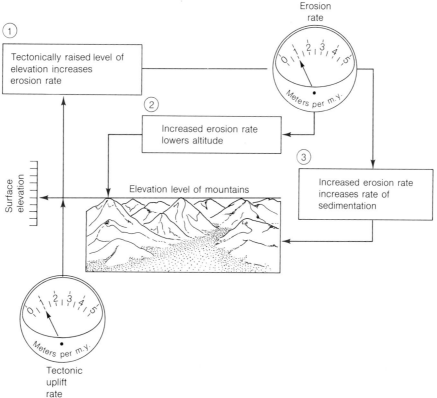

Figure 5-15
The negative-feedback loop that relates (1) uplift, erosion, (2) surface elevation, and (3) sedimentation. Tectonic uplift causes an increase in erosion rate, which in turn lowers the surface elevation and increases the sedimentation rate. The elevation is thus a balance between tectonic uplift and erosion rate.

induce a proportionate secondary action that reduces the first action. A familiar example is what happens when a thirsty person drinks a glass of water. The more thirsty the person, the faster the gulping at first. Just as the thirst induces the drinking, so the drinking acts to decrease the thirst. As the thirst decreases, the rate of drinking decreases; when thirst is satisfied, drinking stops.

The general pattern is one in which strong tectonic action elevates mountains, provoking intense erosion. The higher the mountains, the faster the rate at which erosion wears them down, but tectonics prevails and altitudes increase. As tectonic movement slows down—not because of any important effect of erosion but because its own machine starts running down—the mountains keep going up at a slower pace and for a time erosion keeps up with uplift and the mountains do not change in elevation.

Then as uplift slows, erosion becomes dominant and the elevations begin to lower. As the lowering proceeds, the erosion slows too, the whole process eventually tapering off. The relief is constantly lowered by wearing away of the mountain tops and filling in of valleys and low spots by sedimentation of the erosional debris. Sedimentation, the consequence of erosion, acts to depress relief.

The World Distribution of Elevations. The first impression from the satellite photographs was that most of the Earth's surface is flat. To check this impression we can draw from accurate maps of Earth's topography a **hypsometric diagram,** a representation of the relative proportion of the surface lying at each elevation, by plotting a graph of elevation against the total area lying at that elevation. From these diagrams we can see that the maximum height of moun-

No matter how extreme the uplift, there is a limit to mountain heights. That limit is determined by the strength of the rigid crust, which can support only so much weight before it deforms plastically and fails to support any additional load.

tains above sea level, about 8900 meters (29,000 feet), is not much different from the maximum depth of the deepest ocean trenches below sea level, about 10,800 meters (35,000 feet). In comparison to the wide areas of both land and sea floor that are relatively close to sea level, such extremes are few. The great bulk of the continental land surfaces lie within a few hundred meters of sea level, and much of the ocean floor lies at intermediate depths. Put this together with the relation of erosion to uplift, and there is a strong suggestion that on the continents the tendency is to reduce the land surface to a little above sea level. On the sea bottom the tendency is to maintain some intermediate depth below sea level; this tendency must represent some balance of forces acting on the sea floors other than erosion coupled to uplift. Another inference that comes from this diagram is that the recent tectonic activity that has caused great changes in elevation on land or in the sea, such as mountain ranges or trenches, is distributed in relatively narrow, restricted belts, a small proportion of the total surface. Those belts are the edges of lithospheric plates of the present and recent past. The face of the Earth is scarred by plate margins. The older plate boundaries of the geologic past are now healed, and largely obliterated by later erosion and sedimentation, but here and there, in places like the Appalachian Mountains, the old scars show through.

CLIMATE AND TOPOGRAPHY

If freezing, thermal expansion, and the solvent action of water are strong factors in weathering, then the overall relation between climate and erosion is clear, for all of these weathering processes are related to temperature and rainfall, the chief variables. Moreover, since erosion shapes topography, then climate also influences topography—and is affected by it as well. It is then logical to suppose that topography has some control on mechanical weathering. Here is another interesting example of the way in which the results of one process have an effect on other processes (see Fig. 4-22).

Climatic Effects. As we saw in Chapter 4, rainfall and temperature strongly affect chemical weathering and topography. Indirectly they affect mechanical weathering and erosion too, for rainfall is the source of river water, which helps break up and abrade rock and mineral particles. In addition to the obvious cooling effect of high altitudes, topography also has various effects on climate (see Chapter 8). For example, mountains cause rain shadows—dry areas on the lee slopes—because warm, moist air is cooled as it moves up the windward slopes, and the moisture is lost there as precipitation before the air reaches the lee slopes. Chemical weathering is hastened by abundant rainfall and warm temperatures, and to the extent that decay promotes mechanical weathering, these climatic factors indirectly affect mechanical weathering. In more rigorous climates, frost action and extreme daily variations in temperature are direct causes of rock disintegration. Some of the most important ways in which climate works is by its control on vegetation, which is the direct agent of much chemical alteration of rocks. Lichens—leafless, primitive plants—encrust rocks in many areas where other plants do not grow, even at high altitudes, and they contribute in their small way to chemical weathering. A dry climate promotes physical weathering relative to chemical weathering by slowing the decay produced by the solvent action of water and, equally important, by preventing the growth of much vegetation. Polar climates also inhibit the growth of plants and bacteria; in addition, chemical decay is minimized because the extreme cold prevents much moisture from remaining in the air.

Figure 5-16
Hypsometric diagram of the surface of the Earth. The curve shows the relative amounts of land and subsurface areas lying at various elevations with respect to sea level by a plot of cumulative percent of area shallower than a given depth or higher than a given altitude.

Topography, Erosion, and Tectonics. If climate influences topography, and vice versa, it is also true that topography strongly controls weathering and erosion. High altitude and relief enhance mechanical weathering, partly through the promotion of freezing and thawing, but also because the fragmented debris on mountains quickly moves downhill, exposing new fresh rock to the attack of the weather.

A climb up a typical high mountain will show the evidence of high rates of mechanical erosion. As one goes higher the soil thins. Above timber line, it becomes spotty, and much of the landscape is bare rock. Slopes of blocky talus alternate with steep cliffs and craggy points. The rocks lose the discolored, sometimes lichen-covered, rounded look that chemical weathering produces at lower elevations; instead, the angular blocks have the appearance of freshly quarried stone and quickly wear out the boots of the climber. Talus slopes here may be unstable: sometimes a small disturbance, one careless step, can set off a roar of cascading blocks that can crush almost anything in its path. In the cold, hostile environment at the top, the wind drives snow and ice across bare rock.

Field geologists have long been well acquainted with the high rates of mechanical erosion at high elevations; from the evidence of these high rates, they have concluded that if mechanical weathering is at a maximum in high, rugged mountains, then chemical weathering must be at a minimum in such places. Ronald Gibbs, one of a large group of geologists studying the Amazon River basin, decided to check this by simultaneously tracing the origins of the solid detritus from mechanical weathering and the dissolved products of chemical weathering in the river water. He traced the detritus and chemically dissolved material back to the headwaters of the Amazon in the eastern high Andes Mountains. Gibbs's findings were the cause of much surprise and some dismay among those who had not questioned "accepted wisdom." He found that the high Andes were not only the scene of accelerated mechanical weathering, but that they were the site of most of the chemical decay that took place as well—in spite of the cool, dry climate of those high altitudes. The extensive chemical decay was just not apparent in the high outcrops because the products were so quickly stripped away by mechanical erosion. The flatter lowlands of the Amazon jungle, where rotten granite cobbles and thick soils show the dominance of chemical weathering, are eroded much more slowly, both chemically and mechanically, than the uplands. In lowlands, where detritus is not removed so rapidly, the mechanical effects are masked by the chemical.

If topography is so important in weathering, a search for even more fundamental controls on weathering leads us from topographic effects to the deep-seated tectonic movements that determine the heights of mountains and depths of lowland basins. Ultimately it is those tectonic forces, which push up mountains, that influence the nature of erosion, which in turn affect the kind of debris produced. Thus we can infer historical tectonic events from the evidence of erosion provided by the rock and mineral fragments of ancient sediments. This chain of reasoning has already been touched on in Chapter 4. In the following section we explore more fully how tectonics can be deduced from sediments.

Ratio of Mechanical to Chemical Weathering. We can express the course of erosion in terms of a ratio of mechanical to chemical weathering. For example, in arid and very cold climates the ratio is high: mechanical breakup dominates. In high mountainous terrain the ratio is also high, for even though chemical weathering is active, mechanical fragmentation strongly predominates. In low plains, the ratio is low, for even though chemical decay is somewhat slower than in high mountains, mechanical erosion is so minor that chemical weathering is predominant.

We can gauge the ratio of past weathering processes by looking at the mineralogy and size of the detrital particles that make up the sedi-

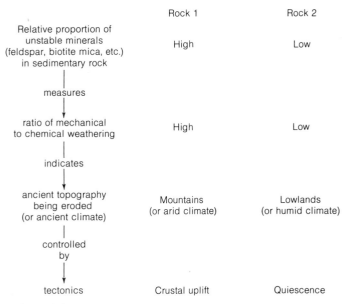

Figure 5-17
The relative proportion of stable and unstable detrital minerals in sediments can be used to infer the erosional origin of the detritus, and thus the topography and ultimately the tectonics of the source area.

mentary rocks produced by erosion of lands that have long since disappeared. The more unstable the minerals and the larger the size, the higher the ratio must have been. So a coarse sandstone with abundant feldspar, biotite, and other minerals that are easily chemically weathered speaks to us of rapid erosion in mountains. Rocks containing large angular cobbles and pebbles are even more eloquent. Fine-grained quartz sandstones, siltstones, and clay-rich shales suggest low-lying source areas where chemical alteration was dominant.

But how do we sort out the effects of climate from those of topography? A conglomeratic sandstone might have come from a low-lying arid region instead of a high mountain, and shales and siltstones might have come from wet, warm hills. The problem is one that is not yet completely settled, but most of the weight of evidence seems to support the notion that topography is more important than climate in determining the ratio of mechanical to chemical weathering. Moreover, it has become clearly recognized that topography much more strongly and directly influences climate than the other way around. Finally, because topography strongly controls the rate at which debris is removed from eroding terrain, it thus promotes both chemical and mechanical weathering. No matter how wet the climate and how great the discharge of rainwater through rivers, mechanical erosion will not have much effect on a low-lying plain.

The logic of tectonic control of erosion, and thus sedimentation, is now apparent. Tectonic movements create mountainous topography and the kind of climates that are associated with mountains. Mountains are the places where the ratio of mechanical to chemical weathering is high, producing detritus rich in course, unstable rock and mineral fragments. The ancient sedimentary rocks made up of such debris are the key to the mountains of the past. The mountains of the present, though, are the ones we can observe. They and the myriad other forms of the land can tell us even more about how landscape is shaped and why it is different in one place than another.

LANDFORMS: THE PHYSIOGNOMY OF THE EARTH

The shapes that give variety to Earth's landscape have long been subjects of interest to artists and scientists, both of whom may look with analytical eyes. In this poem "New Hampshire," Robert Frost says:

*The Vermont mountains stretch extending straight;
New Hampshire mountains curl up in a coil.*

Even though he did not use technical terms, Frost was being a **geomorphologist,** a student of the morphology (form) of the Earth. Poets, however, are free to use words in ways that scientists are not. A poet's aim is not necessarily unambiguous description, nor is a poet required to use language with precision. Those who understand poetry know this. Scientists, however, must be able to communicate with each other with as much precision as possible, hence the language of science is one of description and analysis, and much of the vocabulary is of the scientist's invention. Most of the names of landforms, however, come from the common language. There are hills and valleys, highlands and lowlands.

From Mountains to Molehills. As it turns out, even some of the most ordinary names of landforms are not easily defined with precision. We have used the word mountain many times in this book, yet we can define it no more precisely than to say that a mountain is a large mass of rock that projects well above its surroundings. A mountain can be a single peak, like the Devil's Tower, which is the preserved neck of a former volcano (see Chapter 15), or a combination of peaks, as in most high mountain ranges, where it is hard to pick out distinct separate mountains but only peaks of various heights (see the figure in Box 20-1). How do we distinguish mountains from hills, other than by size? We do not. The gamut of size is continuous, from a 5-meter (16-foot) knoll good for playing "king-of-the-hill" to Mt. Everest, elevation 9524 meters (29,028 feet); precise limits are only arbitrary. We learn to accept that the Black "Hills" are higher than some Appalachian "Mountains." In general, positive landforms more than a few hundred meters in elevation are called mountains.

A broad, flat area of appreciable elevation above its surroundings, at least on one side, is a **plateau.** Smaller plateaus are sometimes called **table lands,** and in the western part of the United States, some are called **mesas. Butte,** a French word for hill, is used, as is "mesa," for smaller elevations with flat or rounded tops surrounded by steep slopes on all sides. Few plateaus have elevations much higher than 3000

Figure 5-18
Monument Valley, Utah. Mesas and pillars of sandstone rising above shale slopes. Two structural terraces sustained by resistant sandstone beds are visible in the distance. [Photo by Tad Nichols, Tucson, Arizona.]

meters (10,000 feet), but the Altiplano of Bolivia is at an elevation of 3600 meters (12,000 feet), and the high Tibetan plateau has an average height of almost 5000 meters (16,000 feet). Something in the nature of erosion produces peaked mountains when they get higher than that. Many plateaus are relatively flat because they are floored with undeformed sediments or layers of lava flows (see Chapter 15 for a discussion of plateau basalts).

Though all hills and mountains are the result of upward tectonic or magmatic movements, their forms are dictated mainly by the erosional process, the kind of rock, and its structure. As in the Grand Canyon, shales almost always form gentle slopes, much of the bedrock being completely covered either by a rock rubble or a soil, the difference depending upon climate and vegetation. Limestones are resistant to erosion in dry climates and tend to form steep cliffs. But in the wet tropics, limestone erodes quickly, mainly by dissolving in water (see Chapter 4), and even small outcrops may be hard to find, much less steep cliffs. From these comparisons it is apparent that an important variable of land-

scape is the nature of the hillslopes. Are they steep or gradual, rock-covered or mantled with soil, convex or concave? A little further on in this chapter we will discuss how slopes can be used as important criteria for understanding landscape evolution. The relation of slopes to rock structure we discuss here.

Structural Control of Topography. The folds and faults produced by rock deformation in the course of mountain building leave their mark on the configuration of the Earth's surface. These topographic expressions of deformation are often a guide to the structures that control them. Even the shapes of features of somewhat smaller scale, such as hills, valleys, and stream courses, are controlled by a complex interaction of erosion and structural elements.

Mesas, buttes, and the complex pattern of erosion of the Grand Canyon are forms that develop in horizontal, undeformed sedimentary rocks or lava beds with alternately resistant and easily eroded layers. The resistant layers support the elevated flat-topped hills and make the cliffs; the softer layers below may erode to form gentler slopes or undercut the capping strata. In horizontal beds of uniform resistance, the topography is much more homogeneous, all the hills and valleys having about the same slope.

In a tilted and eroded series of alternating resistant and soft beds, asymmetrical ridges, or **cuestas,** tend to form. One side of a cuesta has a long, gentle slope determined by the angle of inclination of the resistant bed; the other side is a steep escarpment formed at the erosional edge of the resistant bed, where it is undercut by erosion of a weaker bed beneath. Much more steeply inclined or vertical resistant beds erode to form **hogbacks**—narrow, steep ridges of about the same shape as cuestas but more accentuated. Escarpments are also produced by near-vertical faults along which one side has been raised relative to the other. Faults can displace topography in such a way that the sides of hills appear sheared off as by a knife, river valleys show sudden detours, and ridges are offset (see Fig. 20-53).

In the early stages of folding, the upfolds, **anticlines,** form ridges; the downfolds, **synclines,** form valleys. Streams flow down the flanks of the anticlines and follow the course of the synclinal troughs. As continuing erosion bites deeper into the structure, the presence of resistant and soft beds becomes a controlling factor. For example, if the core of an anticline is soft, it may be eroded away to form an anticlinal valley. If further erosion reaches a hard layer, an anticlinal mountain may once again form. In a region that has long been eroded, a pattern of linear anticlines and synclines produces a series of ridges and valleys, such as those of the Appalachian Mountains in Pennsylvania and adjacent states. The positions of the ridges versus valleys are determined by the erosional resistance of the rocks rather than the original anticlinal highs or synclinal lows formed by structural deformation.

Figure 5-19
Cuestas formed by gently inclined beds of hard sandstone, New Mexico. [Photo by W. T. Lee, U.S. Geological Survey.]

Figure 5-20
Aerial view of the eastern edge of the Front Range of the Colorado Rockies, showing the prominent hogback of the steeply dipping Dakota Sandstone in the center and the lower hogback of the Niobrara Limestone to the right. [Photo by T. S. Lovering, U.S. Geological Survey.]

Figure 5-21
Valley and ridge topography formed on a folded terrane of sedimentary rock. The deformation is so recent (Pliocene) that erosion has not yet modified significantly the original structural forms of anticlines (ridges) and synclines (valleys). Circular dark areas in foreground are salt domes formed when deeper salt formations were squeezed upward through overlying sediments as cylindrical masses. The scene is in Zagros Mountains, Iran, looking west over the Persian Gulf. [From National Aeronautics and Space Administration.]

1 Early stage of folding:
   ridges over anticlines,
   streams in synclines

2 Later stages of erosion:
   ridges may overlie synclinal axes
   if capped by resistant beds

Figure 5-22
Two stages in the development of ridges and valleys in folded mountains. The original positions of ridges may be determined by the shape of the structure, as in (1). At later stages, however, as in (2), anticlines may be breached and eroded more rapidly through nonresistant rocks, and ridges may be held up by caps of resistant rocks.

A great valley on Mars is about ten times as long and three times as deep as the Grand Canyon. It runs from west to east along the Martian Equator, covering nearly 4000 km (2500 mi); it and the details of many other valleys that appear on photographs taken by Viking orbital satellites in the summer of 1976 provide strong geomorphic evidence that erosion by water has taken place on the planet.

The Low Spots. What is the opposite of mountain or upland? Is it a lowland plain or a valley? Those two different shapes, broad versus narrow in area, correspond to two ways that negative elevations form. A plain is a relatively flat low area that is not being pushed up by tectonic activity. We can generalize further that lowlands are broad flat areas of two kinds. They are either stable, neither moving up nor down, or they are unstable, truly the opposite of mountains. Unstable lowlands are moving down, a tectonic process we call **subsidence.** This results in **basins,** depressions of various shapes, frequently found between mountain ranges, in which case they are **intermontane basins.** Valleys, canyons, arroyos, gulches, and gullies all have the same general kind of geometry, and all are topographic lows that form in mountains and plains, highlands and lowlands. As we learned from the Grand Canyon—and as can be seen clearly by watching a stream in flood stage eroding its banks—valleys are excavated by streams; most of these excavations are made by water, some by ice. These low spots are smaller than the large land areas of plains and lowlands. A closer look at lowlands shows that much of their large area is made up of smaller, broad, flat river valleys. Thus valleys and plains are distinguished on the bases of scale as well as process.

Valleys can be steep-sided or bounded by broad, low slopes. They can be shallow, like the little gullies in a field, or as deep as the Grand Canyon. A special kind of valley—the tectonic valley—is long, narrow, relatively flat-floored, and bounded on both rims by faults. Some of these valleys are occupied by major rivers, the upper Rhine being one of the most famous. The Great Valley of California, the route of the San Joaquin and Sacramento rivers, is also a tectonic valley. A distinctive variant of the tectonic valley is the **rift valley,** formed by incipient or active spreading apart of lithospheric plates. The great African rift valleys are occupied by large lakes, such as Lake Rudolph and Lake Tanganyika. The River Jordan and the Dead Sea occupy another rift valley. Beneath the ocean, great rift valleys form the axes of mid-ocean ridges. In fact, it was the discovery of the mid-ocean rift system in the late 1950's that sparked much of the exploration of sea-floor ridges that led to the concepts of sea-floor spreading and plate tectonics. It was topography that gave the first clue.

A walk around the Mammoth Cave district in Kentucky would convince you of the existence of an entirely different kind of negative topography, for in walking across a meadow you might come upon a deep, round hole, a **sinkhole.** Some of such holes are filled with water; others quickly "drink up" all the water from a rainfall and remain open. Streams disappear into the ground at some sinkholes, and great gushing springs well up from others. This kind of land surface, called **Karst topography,** is produced in areas of plentiful rainfall where the bedrock is limestone. As in Kentucky, it is associated with caves in the limestone formations. The conclusion is inescapable that the major process of erosion in karst regions is solution of limestones by water. It is a chemical topography. The way in which Karst and caves are formed by groundwater are covered in Chapter 6.

Low areas, whether they are stable or subsiding, rarely persist for long times, because they are the natural dumping grounds for sediment. Many intermontane basins of the Rocky Mountains would be far deeper than they now appear if all of the gravels, sands, and clays eroded from the surrounding mountains were removed. The Gulf Coast country of Mississippi, Louisiana, and eastern Texas has been subsiding steadily for many millions of years, but since sedimentation there keeps pace with subsidence, the land stays above sea level. There are other forces that shape landscape into distinctive landforms. The landscapes sculpted by glacial ice are among the

Figure 5-23
Large sinkhole, about 130 by 100 by 45 m (425 × 350 × 150 ft) that formed in 1972 in central Alabama as a result of collapse of cavernous limestone below the surface. This may be the largest sinkhole to have formed in recent years. [From U.S. Geological Survey.]

most varied and complex (see Chapter 9). Desert topography owes its character in large part to wind action (Chapter 8).

The Face of North America. The landform map of North America shows the major relief patterns of the large topographic units and how clearly the erosional forms relate to tectonics and sedimentation (see Fig. 20-45). The major mountain chains are in the East and in the West; the older Appalachians are much lower and less rugged than the Rockies. Between are the prairies and plains; their gentle southward slope is well indicated by the drainage pattern. All rivers run to the Gulf of Mexico. A low **coastal plain** lies along much of the central and southern Atlantic coasts and the Gulf coast. North of the Great Lakes are the low-relief plains and lakes of Ontario and Quebec. West of the Rocky Mountains is the Basin and Range province, a region of many smaller chains of mountains alternating with elongate basins. This is the area that some see as a potential huge rift valley that may someday separate the continent into two parts. West of the Basin and Range come the Sierra Nevada, the Cascades, and, to the north, the British Columbian Rockies. The western edge of the continent is marked by the Coast Ranges on the far side of the Great Valley of California, the valley of the Willamette River in Oregon, and its northward extensions. Alaska and the Yukon of Canada are extensions of the Rockies, or, as the whole western mountain belt of the Americas is called, the **Cordillera** (from the use of the Spanish word for "rope" to describe long narrow mountain ranges).

The history of this whole continent is dimly shown by its geomorphology, each event being seen through the veil of later episodes of mountain-building, erosion, and sedimentation. If geomorphology is to be of historical value, however, it has to be based on a theory of landscape evolution. Is there some orderly sequence by which mountains are worn down to plains?

EVOLUTION OF LANDSCAPE

What is the evolution of the topography of a mountain range or a low plain? If it weren't always there, then it must have existed in some preceding state or stage, and necessarily will give way to a succeeding one. Perhaps the best way to answer the question is to study some young mountains, such as the Sierra Nevada of California (Fig. 5-24); their characteristics can then be compared with those of older mountains that have been exposed to erosion for a long time (Fig. 5-25). The youngest individual mountains are recently erupted volcanoes, but the youngest large mountainous region is the Himalayas, pushed up by the collision of the Indian subcontinental plate with the Eurasian plate. We can date the major uplift as Pleistocene because that is the age of the youngest sedimentary layers uplifted, but uplift is undoubtedly still going on. The mountains are the highest in the world, the relief is great, and the slopes and peaks are steep and rugged. Though the height of a volcano like Mt. Pelée may not be so great, it is similar in ruggedness and relief,

Figure 5-24
The eastern slope of the Sierra Nevada, a great fault escarpment nearly 2 miles (3.2 kilometers) high. The view is from the Owens Valley, Inyo County, California. These young mountains are high, steep, and rugged. [Photo by W. C. Mendenhall, U.S. Geological Survey.]

Figure 5-25
View of the Great Smoky Mountains National Park in the Appalachian Mountains
of Tennessee. The generally gentle slopes are those of a tectonically quiet mountain
belt in an advanced stage of erosion. [Photo by W. B. Hamilton, U.S. Geological
Survey.]

One way to indicate the difference between a batch process and a continuous-flow process is to contrast two ways of baking bread. In the home (or in an old-fashioned bakery), a batch of dough is prepared, formed into loaves, and then baked. In a modern, computerized bread "factory," the flour and other ingredients are continuously being mixed in complicated vessels which allow the finished dough to flow out at one end, while the raw ingredients enter at the front. The dough is on a continuous assembly line while being formed into loaves and baked.

and its slopes are as steep as can be held up by the materials (see "angle of repose" of volcanoes in Chapter 15, p. 370).

When we study old mountains, like the Appalachians, we find that their heights and relief are much lower. Although there may be many cliffs that are tricky to climb over, most slopes are more gradual, and the mountain tops have a softer, rounded appearance.

Here, then, is the germ of an idea for a time ordering of the sequence of stages in wearing down mountains. William Morris Davis, a Harvard geologist, brought this kind of study of topography to its fullest expression at the end of the nineteenth century, when he studied mountains and plains all over the world. He characterized the **geomorphic cycle** of topography as progressing from the high, rugged mountains of **youth** to the rounded forms of **maturity** to the worn down plains of **old age.** Perfect plains, the theoretical end-products, are never realized; **peneplains,** relatively flat erosion surfaces that approach being perfect plains do result from very long periods of erosion. Flat surfaces of unconformities, such as the one at the top of the Precambrian in the Grand Canyon, must repre-

sent something like a peneplain. Here and there, standing uneroded above such a plain, would be erosional remnants, perhaps of more resistant rocks. Davis believed Mt. Monadnock in Southern New Hampshire to be such a hill and named all such **monadnocks** after it.

The assumptions underlying this concept do not stand up quite so well as the geomorphic sequence itself, which has proved useful in deciphering geomorphic histories. The process is looked upon as one that a chemical engineer might describe as a "batch process," in which there is a start and stop to the operation, rather than a "continuous-flow" process, in which all parts of the operation are going on simultaneously. The mountains were thought to have been elevated over a very short time period, almost instantaneously from a geological point of view (a batch), and then to have stayed fixed tectonically as erosion slowly wore them down through the stages of the cycle. Today our knowledge of the long, drawn-out, intermittent, and uneven nature of mountain-building makes that assumption untenable. It is more of a continuous process by which mountains keep on moving up while they erode, the evolution being

Mature topography | High relief
Steep to moderate slopes
Sharp divides

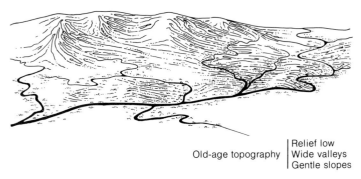

Old-age topography | Relief low
Wide valleys
Gentle slopes

Figure 5-26
Two types of topography thought by W. M. Davis to be mature and old-age stages of an evolving landscape as it is worn down by rivers.

determined by shifts in the balance between the two. Other assumptions that flawed the theory were that the sequence was characteristic of all rocks in all climates, and it is now generally agreed that progression from youth to old age can produce a variety of other forms, particularly in arid climates.

Current views of geomorphic evolution as a continuous process emphasize the **steady state,** wherein a constant balance of forces results in a topography unchanging with time, though rocks are steadily being uplifted and eroded. Such a concept tends to deny much possibility of reconstructing a geomorphic history of the region, for it says that what a region is like is the product of currently active operations, not what went before. What it will be next has little to do with what it is now. Still other models incorporate all of the operating variables: tectonics, rock

type, extent of rock weathering, and drainage in relation to climate and vegetation, together with the possibility of some randomness in the course of events. This leads to a low degree of predictability and some sense of disillusion for those who had hopes for a thoroughly orderly and predictable pattern.

Isn't it strange that the part of the Earth that we see and walk over all the time is so difficult to make a simple order of? Perhaps the very wealth of information and the complexities of all of the variables that we know have an effect on landscape are what make it so resistant to analysis. Perhaps the subject waits for those who would do as Einstein did: in describing his thought patterns about relativity, he wrote that "I had to divest myself of my intuition—then I could think clearly."

SUMMARY

1. Mass movements, including rock falls, landslides, slump, and creep are slow to rapid downhill movements induced by gravity when a slope is oversteepened by natural erosion or construction.

2. Mudflows, debris-avalanches, and earthflows are water-saturated, nearly fluid flows.

3. Slope wash is the generalized unchanneled flow of rainwater on slopes—the prelude to organized rills, streams, and rivers.

4. Topography is the areal distributions of the heights and depths of the Earth's surface, usually represented by contour maps.

5. The Grand Canyon is a landscape developed by river erosion of a series of flat-lying sediments of varying resistance to erosion. The valley is V-shaped.

6. The Ozark Mountains are a landscape of gentler forms and low relief on a very old granite uplift that has been eroded for long geologic times and partly overlapped by sediment.

7. The overall pattern of landscape development is one in which tectonic uplift, which tends to produce high altitudes, is countered by the erosional wearing down by water and ice.

8. Tectonics creates mountains, and topography strongly affects erosion. Mechanical weathering dominates in areas of high topographic relief, but is relatively less important in low-lying regions. The ratio of mechanical to chemical weathering is a function of both climate and topography, and ultimately of tectonic activity.

9. Landforms, such as hills, plateaus, and valleys, are controlled by the erosional process acting over geologic times on a variety of resistant and nonresistant rock types that are arranged in different structural patterns.

10. Karst topography is formed by chemical solution of limestones in areas of moderate to high rainfall.

11. The landform map of North America reveals the diverse effects of tectonic and erosional activity, modified by sedimentation.

12. Evolution of landscape, formerly perceived as simple erosional stages of youth, maturity, and old age following a single uplift, are understandable as series of states of balance between structural uplift and erosional wearing away.

EXERCISES

1. Which kinds of mass movements tend to follow periods of heavy rains and why?

2. What geologic conditions would you want to check on before you built or bought a house on the side of a steep, soil-covered hill?

3. What role do earthquakes play in landslides and related phenomena? Would you advise people living in areas where there are few, if any, earthquakes, to show more, less, or the same awareness of these mass movement hazards than those in areas where earthquakes are frequent?

4. In some areas the relief of the natural topography is less than that of man's architecture or construction. What kinds of topographic areas are they, and what is the magnitude of relief?

5. If you were to see the topographies of the Ozarks and the Grand Canyon 20 million years from now, assuming no great change in climate and no tectonic activity, would you expect greater or lesser differences between them than is shown now? Describe what each might look like at that time in the future.

6. Describe the changes in topography that might take place if the Ozark Mountain region were to be uplifted by 5000 meters (1) very rapidly, and (2) very slowly.

7. In flying across the country, what topographic features would you look for to tell (1) whether you were flying over structurally deformed or flat-lying sedimentary rocks, and (2) whether you were flying over beds or rock bodies of uniform resistance to erosion or varying resistance to erosion.

8. How does a mountain peak on land differ in origin from a seamount rising from the sea floor?

9. Describe three different geologic processes by which deep valleys can form on land. Which one(s) of these may also be responsible for deep valleys on the sea floor?

BIBLIOGRAPHY

Bloom, A. L., *The Surface of the Earth*. Englewood Cliffs, New Jersey: Prentice-Hall, Inc., 1969.

Crandell, D. R., and H. H. Waldron, "A Recent Volcanic Mudflow of Exceptional Dimensions from Mt. Rainier, Washington." *American Journal of Science*, 254, pp. 349–362, 1956.

Davis, W. M., *Geographical Essays*. Boston: Ginn and Company, 1909. (Reprinted 1954, Dover Publications, Inc., New York.)

Eckel, E. B. (editor), *Landslides in Engineering Practice*. Washington, D.C.: Highway Research Board Special Report 29, National Council, 1958.

Hunt, C. B., *Natural Regions of the United States and Canada*. San Francisco: W. H. Freeman and Company, 1973.

Legget, R. F., *Geology and Engineering*. New York: McGraw-Hill Book Co., 1962.

Sharpe, C. F. S., *Landslides and Related Phenomena*. New York: Columbia University Press, 1938.

Wahrhaftig, C., and A. Cox, "Rock Glaciers in the Alaska Range." *Geological Society of America Bulletin*, v. 70, pp. 383–436, 1959.

Young, A., *Slopes*. Edinburgh: Oliver & Boyd, 1972.

6

THE NATURAL WATER CYCLE AND GROUNDWATER

Water dissolves minerals during weathering, then carries the dissolved material away—into the ground or into rivers, most of which ultimately empty into the ocean. The movement of the Earth's waters from one place to another and the dissolved loads carried by them are parts of a continuous overall pattern: the hydrologic cycle. Groundwater accumulates by infiltration of water into soils and bedrock, and reappears at the surface in springs and stream beds. Groundwater levels, and thus water supplies, are a balance between the rate of infiltration and the rate of loss by springs, streams, and pumping from wells. The evolution of surface waters and the ocean are related to the escape of gases from the interior.

WATER, WATER, EVERYWHERE . . .

Since the first men rocketed to the moon, the Earth has had a new name: "the Blue Planet." Although most of us had heard or read the dry statistic that about two-thirds of the Earth's surface is covered with water, it had never been brought home as spectacularly as it was at the time of the first space flight. Given the same view of Earth, a non-Earthman space scientist might have speculated on what kind of life could possibly exist in the midst of all of the clouds of water vapor in the sky and the immense areas of the blue seas on the surface. Geologists, of course, have long wondered what other planets could possibly be like without this liquid that sustains life and takes part in almost every process on the surface of Earth. Thus it is not surprising that the study of water, the science of **hydrology,** is an important part of geology. The study of water is also a central part of oceanography and meteorology.

In this chapter we will concentrate on how water moves from one place to another on and in

the crust and, in so doing, acts as the great transporting agent of dissolved material weathered from rocks. Ice and snow, different forms of the water molecule, also play their role in hydrology; for this reason we include them in our inventory of water on the Earth, although we consider the geologic work of glaciers later, in Chapter 9.

The compound water is so well known to us that we use it to exemplify the three states of matter, solid (ice and snow), liquid (water), and gas (water vapor). We explored the solid state in Chapter 3. Matter in this state has a definite volume and is rigid; it holds its own shape, however formed. This is so because the atoms are held together strongly by chemical bonds arranged in a three-dimensional network, making the structure of a crystalline or semicrystalline solid. Ice is a crystalline mineral whose inidividual crystal forms are displayed in the enormous variety of snowflakes. A glacier is, in a sense, a "rock" body made up of an enormous

Living
Drinking
Photosynthesizing
Respiring
Metabolizing

Engineering
Cooling
Heating
Cleaning
Flushing
Irrigating

Recreation
Swimming
Fishing
Sailing
Canoeing
Diving
Skiing
Skating
Sledding
Playing

Figure 6-1
Some of the value of water.

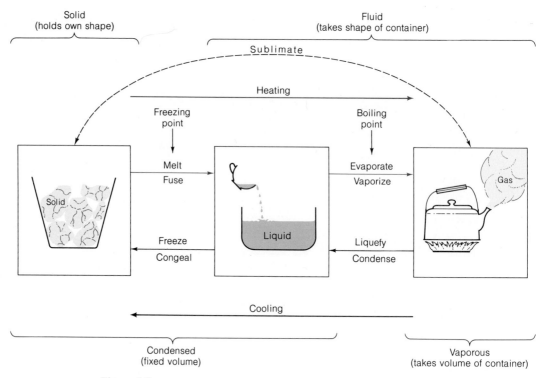

Figure 6-2
The three states of matter, as exemplified by water: ice (solid), water (liquid), and water vapor or steam (gas).

quantity of interlocking crystals of the mineral ice.

Raising the temperature of ice above 0°C causes it to turn into water, liquid H_2O. Though water has a definite volume, even though it may expand or contract with change of temperature, it is fluid; it does not hold its own shape. The molecules are loosely bound to each other and easily slip over and around each other, something like couples on a packed dance floor. It is as a liquid that water is such a good solvent and, when in motion as strongly flowing currents, able to carry mud, silt, sand, and boulders. It is at the temperatures at which H_2O is liquid that life on Earth exists, for water is the carrier of dissolved food that is vital for every form of life, from humans to bacteria.

Raising the temperature of water to 100°C (212°F) causes it to boil and form water vapor. But in contrast to the melting of ice, which takes place at only one temperature, water can slowly evaporate to form vapor at *any* temperature below boiling. Even ice can "evaporate" to vapor—a process we call **sublimation**. Pure water vapor condenses to liquid water at or below the boiling temperature. Our everyday

experience is the clue to the behavior of water vapor in air, where it is not pure but is mixed with other gases, nitrogen and oxygen. The **relative humidity** is the amount of water vapor that is in the air relative to the total amount it could hold if it were saturated—a concept similar to that of the saturated liquid solution. Because the degree of saturation changes with temperature, air saturated with water vapor at one temperature will condense some of its vapor to water droplets when it is cooled to a lower temperature, as anyone who has mowed grass on a dewy morning knows intuitively.

A gas is fluid and has no fixed volume; it expands and contracts to fill containers. Of course, the gaseous envelope that surrounds the Earth has no container; its volume and distribution are determined by the pull of gravity. Gases in general are not efficient solvents for solid substances, as are liquids, so that they cannot carry the dissolved products of weathering, as do rivers. They are not the most efficient transporter of solids, either, for the currents—the winds of our atmosphere—have to be strong to carry any particles coarser than clay or fine silt any great distance above the ground. Vapor is the

Water vapor is an invisible gas. The white clouds of the sky or the billows of steam that we associate with vapor are actually composed of tiny droplets of liquid water formed by the cooling of the vapor below the boiling point. A good way to see this is to note the spout of a boiling teakettle. At the spout, the steam of vapor is colorless, but within a short distance the white clouds appear as the vapor mixes with the cool air outside and condenses to droplets.

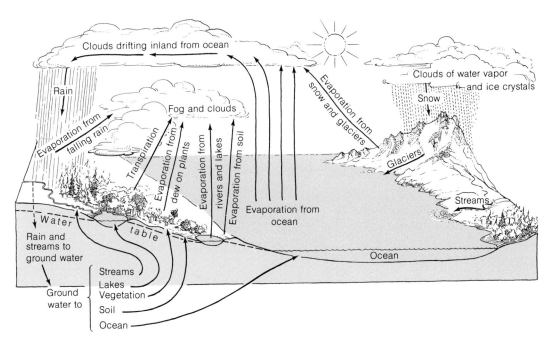

Clouds drifting inland from ocean

Rain

Evaporation from falling rain

Fog and clouds

Transpiration

Evaporation from dew on plants

Evaporation from rivers and lakes

Evaporation from soil

Evaporation from ocean

Evaporation from snow and glaciers

Clouds of water vapor and ice crystals

Snow

Glaciers

Streams

Water table

Rain and streams to ground water

Ground water to

Streams
Lakes
Vegetation
Soil
Ocean

Ocean

Figure 6-3
The hydrologic cycle. [After *Principles of Geology* (4th ed.) by J. Gilluly, A. C. Waters, and A. O. Woodford.
W. H. Freeman and Company. Copyright © 1975.]

state in which water is transported through the Earth's atmosphere—from the oceans to the continents, where it is condensed and precipitated as rain or snow.

WATER TRANSPORT: THE HYDROLOGIC CYCLE

Not only is our planet very watery, but gravity ensures that it will stay that way. Although much water is moved around from one place to another, the total is conserved. The **hydrologic cycle** is a simplified description of the ways in which waters move from one place to another and how much is transported. Knowledge of the cycle informs the judgment of water conservationists who tell us that there are limits to how much natural fresh water we can ever get to satisfy the voracious "thirst" of our industrial society. The limits are determined by the total amount of rainfall that reaches the continents.

The external heat engine of Earth, powered by the sun, is what drives the hydrologic cycle at the surface. It does so mainly by evaporating water from the surface of the warm oceans of the tropics and transporting it by winds, themselves driven by the differences between the tempera-

tures of the hot and cold parts of the globe. The water in the atmosphere condenses to clouds and eventually falls as rain or snow. Much of the rain soaks into the ground by **infiltration**—hence **groundwater.** What does not soak in collects as **runoff,** which finds its way into streams and rivers and runs back into the oceans. Some of the water in the ground may return directly to the atmosphere by evaporating through the soil surface. Another part may be absorbed by plant roots, carried up to leaves, and returned to the atmosphere by **transpiration**—the release of water vapor by plant foliage. A major fraction of the groundwater stays in the ground, most of the shallow subterranean waters slowly moving through near-surface formations and ultimately exiting into stream beds, springs, or the oceans.

Now it is clear why it is the total rainfall that determines the absolute limit of fresh water available on the continents: there is no other source. The only way man could increase the total supply would be to make artificially fresh water by modern chemical methods of desalting sea water—a different way of accomplishing what nature does by evaporation and precipitation. How the total flow from one place to another adds up—what we call a **mass bal-**

When an occasional molecule of H_2O in the upper atmosphere splits up into separate hydrogen and oxygen atoms under the effect of strong radiation from the Sun, some of the hydrogen atoms may escape permanently from Earth. Thus there is actually a tiny loss of water to outer space as a result of the steady loss of hydrogen from the atmosphere. Hydrogen is the lightest element, and some of its little atoms can move fast enough to escape from Earth's gravity—just like a rocket.

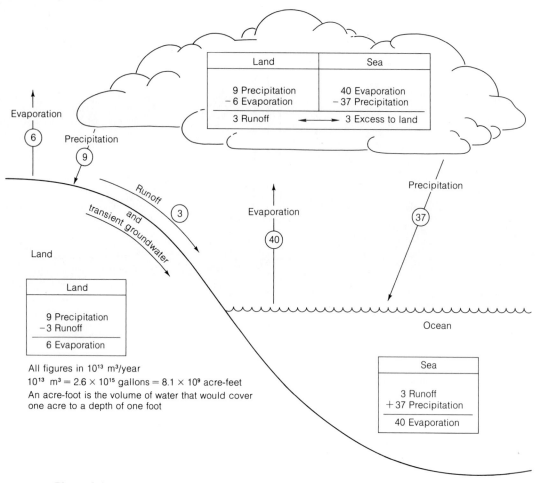

	Land	Sea
	9 Precipitation − 6 Evaporation	40 Evaporation − 37 Precipitation
	3 Runoff ←	→ 3 Excess to land

Evaporation
6

Precipitation
9

Runoff and transient groundwater
3

Evaporation
40

Precipitation
37

Land

Land	
9 Precipitation −3 Runoff	
6 Evaporation	

All figures in 10^{13} m³/year
10^{13} m³ = 2.6 × 10^{15} gallons = 8.1 × 10^9 acre-feet
An acre-foot is the volume of water that would cover
one acre to a depth of one foot

Ocean

Sea	
3 Runoff + 37 Precipitation	
40 Evaporation	

Figure 6-4
The mass balance, or water-flow budget, of land, seas, and atmosphere.

ance—is shown in Figure 6-4. From this elementary "water-flow budget" for land and sea, we can see that more water evaporates from the oceans than falls on it as rain. This is exactly balanced by the return of water via runoff from the continents, which itself exactly balances the excess of precipitation over evaporation on land.

The United States and many other developed countries of the world face the prospect of carefully planning the use of these large, but not infinite, water resources for the ever-growing demands of industry, urban population concentrations, and agriculture. A more detailed breakdown of the water budget for the United States (Fig. 6-5) gives the "road map" for the decisions that will have to be made. Though only about 7 percent of the total rainfall is used for agriculture, industry, and cities and towns,

another 71 percent is unavailable because of loss by evaporation, transpiration, and infiltration (though much of this may go to usable groundwater supplies). It is the 22 percent of untapped stream water that has one of the biggest potentials. That is why the pollution of rivers poses a much greater threat than the loss of their esthetic and recreational values. We may need all the good water we can get as the demands of our population increase. As of 1970, the United States was using 1.4 billion cubic meters of water per day (5.1×10^{11} cubic meters per year) from surface and groundwater sources. Total potential water supplies are only about three times this present use. Unfortunately, abundant river water supplies are not always near the areas of high demand, and piping water for long distances is expensive. Thus, in areas with lim-

Figure 6-5
The hydrologic cycle for the United States shows the fraction of annual precipitation used in a highly developed nation. Twenty-nine percent of the rainfall arrives at the oceans (bottom) via stream flow; 71 percent falls on various types of nonirrigated land, returning directly to the atmosphere (top) by transpiration and evaporation. Water withdrawn for irrigation, industry, and municipal use is shown at left to constitute only 7.3 percent of the total.

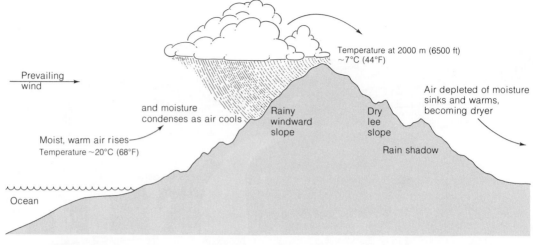

Prevailing
wind

Temperature at 2000 m (6500 ft)
~7°C (44°F)

Air depleted of moisture
sinks and warms,
becoming dryer

and moisture
condenses as air cools

Rainy
windward
slope

Dry
lee
slope

Moist, warm air rises
Temperature ~20°C (68°F)

Rain shadow

Ocean

Figure 6-6
A mountain range may produce a rain shadow on its lee slope by forcing warm, moist air to rise with a prevailing wind from the ocean. The rising air cools, causing precipitation on the windward slope and leaving the lee slope dry.

ited supplies of river water, it will become imperative to maintain—or restore—a flow of unpolluted, usable water.

Surface Runoff. The direct relation between rain and stream runoff is obvious—especially to anyone who has ever experienced a flash flood following a torrential rainstorm. The yearly amount of water flowing in streams in any region is directly related to the annual rainfall. Most of the streams in arid or semiarid regions are dry except right after the rare rains. The difference between wet and dry is particularly conspicuous when going over a mountain range into a "rain shadow"—an area of low rainfall on the leeward slope of a mountain range. Moisture-laden air rises as it crosses high mountains, cooling and precipitating much of its water vapor on the windward slope. By the time the air reaches the opposite leeward slope, it has lost much of its moisture. As it drops and warms, it becomes lower in relative humidity, and little rain falls. The Cascade Mountains of Oregon offer a striking example of the contrast. The western, windward slopes have high rainfall, the abundant water draining into the Willamette River valley with its lush natural and agricultural vegetation. But just a few tens of miles to the east, over the crest of the range, the countryside is dry and relatively barren. The Sierra Nevada, an even broader rain-shadowing mountain range, keeps the Great Basin to the east a semiarid region swept by dry winds. In this way, we arrive at a perhaps unexpected

relation between climate and tectonics—the forces that are responsible for the mountains. The Cascades, a range of extinct volcanoes that extruded enormous volumes of basalt, are the surface expression of ancient tectonic activity; they may represent a zone along which the Pacific plate was subducted beneath the western edge of the North American plate, throwing up a belt of basaltic and andesitic volcanoes above the descending oceanic plate. The Sierra Nevada is made up of granitic rocks that were thrust up

Table 6-1
Water flows of some great rivers (in m^3/sec).

Amazon, South America	113,330
La Plata, South America	79,300
Congo, Africa	39,600
Yangtze, Asia	21,800
Brahmaputra, Asia	19,800
Ganges, Asia	18,700
Mississippi, North America	17,500

as a large mass during a major orogeny of the Cenozoic (see Chapter 20).

Most of the surface runoff is dominated by the large stream networks of major river systems. Of the enormous number of streams on the continents, only about seventy major systems carry about one-half of the entire runoff from the land areas of the world. Even more dominant are a few major rivers, such as the Mississippi and the Amazon.

Rivers ebb and flow in discharge from season

In his 1967 study of the Amazon River, a member of a U.S. Geological Survey team stressed how huge the Amazon River was by using a "Mississippi" as a unit of measurement. Halfway upstream, the Amazon was only a few "Mississippis" in discharge but by the time it reached the Atlantic Ocean it was seven "Mississippi's."

Figure 6-7
A swamp or marshland acts much like a natural lake or an artificial reservoir behind a dam in storing water during times of rapid runoff and slowly releasing it during periods of little runoff.

to season, mainly as a response to seasonal precipitation patterns. In some tropical regions it rains heavily only for a few months of the year. In some maritime climates, like parts of the Pacific Northwest of this continent and most of the British Isles, the rain is abundant and more constant throughout the year. A different pattern of stream flow is shown by rivers draining snow or ice-covered country, where spring meltwaters can swell the streams to flood stage. Here the response of runoff to precipitation lags over the winter months, the precipitation that fell as snow being stored temporarily in snow and ice fields. The runoff jumps when the store is released by warming in the spring. Similarly, lakes and large areas of swamp and marshland, sometimes called "wetlands," act as storage depots for runoffs. These reservoirs, by their large volume, smooth out the big variations in discharge of rivers and release a steady outflow downstream. This is also the basis for some flood control dams. It is also the reason why some geologists have worked to stop the artificial draining of

wetlands by real estate developers, which if unchecked could wreck much of the natural flood regulation capacity in some areas.

But all of these storage areas for precipitation and runoff are minor compared to the water stored in the ground. Why do rivers continue to run day after day after several weeks of no rain—and no melting snow to feed them? How do springs continue to flow day after day to feed the rivers and lakes? Groundwater flow is the answer.

WATER IN THE GROUND

How do we know about the water in the ground? We can literally see the rain disappear into the ground in many places. Watch rain falling on a beach sometime. Some soils act like porous sand in sponging up rainwater; others have dense, tough clay layers, or "hardpans," that impede the infiltration of water and are poor absorbers of water. Poorest of all are the rocky surfaces of

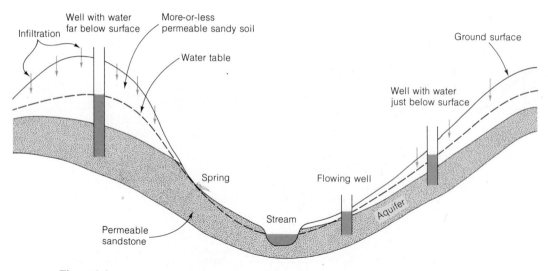

Figure 6-8
The groundwater table lies at varying depths beneath the surface, as shown by the water level in wells. The water table intersects the ground surface at springs and river beds.

mountains, which have little or no soil. There, little water runs into the ground; what does, goes through joints and cracks.

Bubbling springs show us where some of the water that soaks into the ground comes out; good places to look are on the lower slopes or the base of a hill or valley wall. If you drill a well, and have picked a good place to do it—for example, where porous sandstone beds are near the surface in a temperate climate—water will fill the bottom of the well. If you are lucky, you might even get water flowing up and out of the hole: in that event, you have drilled what is called an **artesian** well. A few more facts and you will have enough to get the general picture. After long periods of dryness, wells run dry, the ground becomes dried out well below the surface, and smaller rivers shrink and may dry up entirely. There has to be an underground connection between the water that sinks in from rain on the one hand and the rivers, springs, and wells on the other.

The underground connection has to be through soil and rock. There are no open spaces under the ground with rivers running like they do on the surface, except in cavernous limestone networks and some open lava tubes in volcanic terranes. But if you fill a short length of pipe with clean sand, put a screen at the bottom, and pour water in at the top, in a short time you will see the water dripping out at the bottom. The water travels by twisting and turning through the pore spaces between the sand grains. The smaller the pore spaces and the more tortuous

the journey, the slower the water goes through the sand. This property by which solids allow fluids to pass through them we call **permeability.** Sands are permeable; hard, compacted muds and shales are not. The permeability depends largely on the amount of pore space between the grains or crystals of the rock, the **porosity.** Rocks vary widely in porosity. Most igneous and metamorphic rocks are not very porous, only 1 or 2 percent of many of those rocks consisting of pores. Many sedimentary rocks, particularly sandstones, are very porous, rising to as much as 30–40 percent porosity. Because in some rocks the pores are all connected to give an easy path and in others the pores are disconnected and do not allow any exit, all porous rocks are not equally permeable. Clay particles obstruct paths of flow between many pore spaces in some sandstones and so may significantly decrease their permeability. This is an important factor in obtaining a good flow of oil: many such sandstone beds are saturated with oil, but the permeability is too low to allow economic pumping. Many rocks with low porosity may be fractured, and thus have some permeability.

Thus the ground acts like a sponge, soaking up rain in some places and leaking it out at other places. When we add the geological information about the structure of formations and their depth below the surface to data on the depth of water in wells dug at various places, we get the picture in Figure 6-8. The sandy or other kinds of beds that produce waters are called **aquifers.**

The Groundwater Table. If we connect the levels of water in the wells shown in Figure 6-8, we get a surface that we call the **groundwater table,** or just **water table.** That surface is the boundary between two zones of rock or soil: below the water table, the pores are completely filled with water, and the zone is called the **saturated,** or **phreatic,** zone; above the water table is an **unsaturated,** or **vadose,** zone. The unsaturated zone is also called the **zone of aeration,** because the pore spaces are partly filled with water and partly filled with air. Some of the water in this upper, unsaturated zone is at times in transit down to the water table, but much is held in smaller pore spaces in the same way that sand in a sandbox or beach stays moist long after it has been wetted. Evaporation of these little drops buried in pores is slowed almost to nothing because of the effects of surface tension. Surface tension is shown by a water surface that will support a needle or razor blade gently placed on it. This effect—whereby a skin-like surface layer of the fluid, a few molecules thick, is in a state of tension that gives it supporting strength—reduces evaporation strongly in small droplets.

Knowing the depth and shape of the water table is one of the important aims of the groundwater hydrologist and the driller of water wells. How to predict it from a combination of general understanding and detailed information on a specific area is becoming increasingly important in North America, particularly in the broad, thirsty areas of the Great Plains but also in many other parts of the West and Southwest. Even in regions of relatively abundant rainfall, it is no longer easy to put down a well almost anywhere and get water. Dowsers claim that they can somehow divine where water is underground with a forked stick or other inanimate object rather than with geological knowledge. But scientists remain firm in their conviction that there has been neither proven demonstration of success other than chance nor proposal of any verifiable mechanism that could give an objective explanation of how a forked stick could be attracted by groundwater.

Geological observation teaches us that the water table generally follows with a more subdued form the contour of the surface topography. The "outcrops" of the water table are springs and the beds of rivers; it is in these places where the water drains out of the land. That drainage gives the clue to the fact that most groundwaters near the surface are in motion. The depth of the water table is another example of the workings of a steady-state process: it is a balance between the rate of infiltration, usually called **recharge,** and the rate of discharge at rivers and springs—or pumped water wells. The water table stays at the same place when rain falls frequently enough to stay in balance with the river, spring, and well outflow. Any imbalance, typically by seasonal fluctuation of rainfall, raises or lowers the water table. A long-term imbalance results if there is either a decrease in recharge, such as from a prolonged drought, or from increase in the discharge. That is why water tables are slowly dropping in many regions where discharge has steadily climbed as a result of constantly increasing pumping of water wells. In such areas the imbalance has depleted the reservoir. For an aquifer is just as much a reservoir as any surface lake or pond that can be filled up or depleted.

The flow of groundwater and the position of the water table may be complicated by alternating permeable aquifers and relatively impermeable beds, called **aquicludes,** that hinder or prevent water movement. When aquicludes lie both over and under an aquifer, they produce a **confined** water reservoir. The water pressure in such an aquifer depends on the difference in height between it and the recharge area. If the difference is great enough, water will flow spontaneously out of a well drilled into it; such wells are called artesian wells. If enough artesian wells flow long enough to deplete the reservoir and lower the water table in the recharge area, the pressure will drop. Eventually the wells will stop flowing and have to be pumped. An aquiclude underlying a discontinuous aquifer may support a **perched water table** above the main water table, as in Figure 6-11. Some perched water tables may extend over large areas, hundreds of square kilometers.

Yet another complication is faced by the people who live at the edge of the ocean. A few summers ago, one of us had a visit from a neighbor on the seashore who wanted to know what he could do about a salty taste in the water from his well. He didn't realize that it was the extensive pumping of his and all the other wells that was causing an incursion of salt water. There is a sloping underground boundary between the fresh water under land adjacent to the sea—or under an island—and the salt water in the sea, as shown in Figure 6-12. If withdrawals by pumping are not excessive, then the recharge of the fresh water on the land is enough to keep the water table elevated above sea level and maintain a reservoir of fresh water bulged into the sea water at depth. But if withdrawals exceed recharge, the water table is lowered and the

Figure 6-9
The depth of the water table fluctuates in response to the balance between what is added by precipitation and what is lost by evaporation plus discharge from wells, springs, and streams. The changing height of the water table is a reflection of the volume of water stored in the ground, and can be analyzed as a reservoir with inputs and outputs. The flow meters indicate the relative changes typical from spring to late summer.

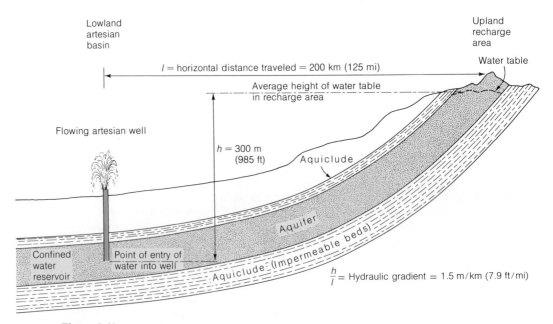

Figure 6-10
A confined water reservoir is created where water enters an aquifer situated between two confining aquicludes. The artesian well flows in response to the natural (before the well was drilled) pressure difference between the height of the water table in the recharge area and the bottom of the well, equivalent to the pressure of a water column 300 m high in this example. The actual pressure difference that governs the flow from the top of the well is the difference between the elevation of the water table and the top of the well. If the well head were as high as the water table in the recharge area, there would be no pressure difference and thus no flow.

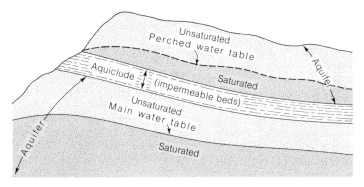

Figure 6-11
A perched water table is separated from the main water table by an aquiclude composed of shale or other impermeable beds.

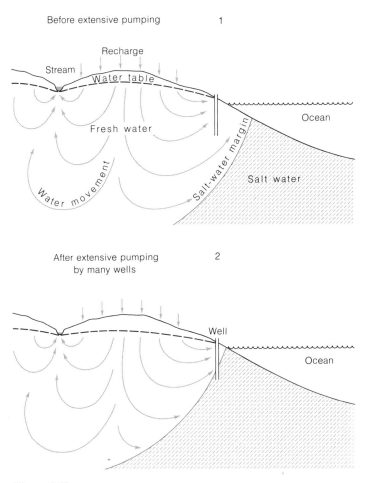

Figure 6-12
The boundary between fresh groundwater and salt water along shorelines is determined by the balance between recharge and discharge to the ocean or wells. Normally, as in (1), the pressure of fresh water keeps the salt-water margin slightly offshore. Extensive pumping, as in (2), lowers the pressure on the fresh water, allowing the salt-water margin to move inland.

Studies on the rate of groundwater movement have been confirmed and made more precise by the application of radioactive dating techniques to groundwater, using radioactive carbon, C^{14}, to date the dissolved carbon dioxide in the waters. On entering the ground the water had in its CO_2 the minute amount of C^{14} that is characteristic of rainwater, but as it slowly traveled through the ground the C^{14} decayed radioactively. The velocity is obtained by measuring the distance from the well in which the water was sampled to the recharge area and dividing this by the age as determined by C^{14}.

In a 1976 report, geologists of the U.S. Geological Survey note that there is still an estimated 5.8 billion acre feet (1.9 trillion gallons) of groundwater stored beneath the Rio Grande region of Texas, Colorado, and New Mexico. Further development of this resource will continue, for there is strong demand for water for irrigation, which uses almost 90 percent of the groundwater produced in this region.

reservoir depleted; the pressure of fresh water on the bulge decreases, and sea water moves in. Those closest to the shore are the first affected. Cape Cod, Long Island, Bermuda, and many other near-shore communities and islands have this problem to contend with. There is no solution to the inexorable incursion of seawater except to reduce the pumping or artificially increase the recharge, as will be discussed later in this chapter.

How Fast Does Groundwater Move? From studies of response of wells and springs to rainfall recharge, we have learned that the rate of movement of groundwater is fairly slow. Here is another fact of nature that is lucky for us. It is that slowness that keeps the underground reservoirs full, for fast discharge would mean that water wells would run dry after just a few days of no rain. What makes some groundwaters travel rapidly and others slowly? The details of the answer were worked out in the middle of the nineteenth century by Henry Darcy, the town engineer of Dijon, France. From observations of the heights of water in wells, the distance traveled, and the permeability of the rocks through which the water flowed came what we now call Darcy's Law.

Darcy said that, for a given aquifer, the rate of water flow from one place to another is directly proportional to the drop in vertical elevation between the two places and inversely proportional to the horizontal distance the water travels. The relation between the horizontal and vertical distances can be seen to be akin to the angle of an inclined plane; it is, in fact, the force of gravity that makes water run "downhill" underground just as a ball rolls with varying speeds down inclined planes of different slopes. Darcy also found that the greater the permeability (the ability of a porous rock to pass fluid through it), the faster the flow.

Velocities have been found by using Darcy's Law and dating groundwater by radioactivity. Velocities can also be determined by experimental observations in which dyes are introduced into groundwater at a well used as an artificial recharge point and picked up at a nearby pumping well. Movement in deeper formations is rarely faster than 100 centimeters/day or slower than 0.5 centimeters/day. In most aquifers, groundwater moves at rates of a few centimeters/day. In very permeable gravel beds near the surface, groundwater may travel as much as 15 centimeters/day.

How Far Does Water Travel Underground? The length of time that groundwater takes from recharge to discharge depends not only on its velocity but on how long its path is. Routes of travel vary widely, and in a typical flow, such as shown in Figure 6-12, some routes may be many times longer than others.

So far we have been concentrating on flow over relatively small areas, such as a hillside or valley. Flow is also demonstrable over regions the size of counties or groups of counties hundreds of square kilometers in area. Over such broad areas, flow is dominated by the geologic position of permeable formations, the aquifers. Typically the pattern is like that shown in Figure 6-10, the essential condition being a continuous aquifer with a recharge area in an upland area so that the water can run "downhill" underground. Many areas in the great plains and parts of the central midwest are underlain by sandstones of various ages that transport waters for hundreds of kilometers. Recall from Darcy's Law that the discharge and velocity are proportional to the change in height over the distance. The vertical height is rarely more than a few hundred meters (in most areas it is much less), but the horizontal distances are measured in hundreds of kilometers, hence the rates of water movement are slow and the recharge takes a long time. What are the consequences for us? If extensive water-well pumping removes the water faster than the slow recharge can fill it, the reservoir will gradually become smaller.

Mining Ground Water. A baby born when the first wells were drilled into the Ogallala, a Tertiary formation of sands (and gravels) in western Texas and New Mexico, would be about ninety years old now. He or she would have lived to see the water pressure of those wells steadily diminish and the water table drop drastically, as much as 30 meters (100 feet). The Ogallala aquifer has been the water support of a population that has gradually grown to almost half a million people in this century, providing ample water for irrigation for the agriculture that is the economic base of the region. Intensive research has been going on for the past few years by the United States Geological Survey on how to improve the recharge of this aquifer, which is very slow to recharge naturally because of evaporation and some impermeable soils. It is a hard task, for water has been pumped so extensively that at present rates of withdrawal and recharge the water table would take several thousand

Box 6-1   Darcy's Law of Groundwater Motion

The law formulated by Darcy is given in terms of the volume of water moving through any opening in a given amount of time, essentially a velocity term, and the geometry of the general flow, or the ratio of the vertical to the horizontal distance.

by multiplying the right-hand side by a proportionality factor, called K. Darcy identified K as a measure of the permeability of the rock, or in other words, how easily it transmits water.

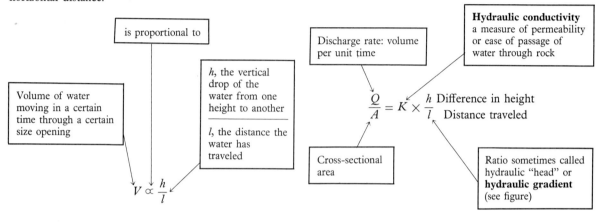

Darcy reasoned that the permeability of a rock is what more or less slowed down the flow for a given drop of height (h) in a certain distance (l) and so made this into an equation

From this equation, we can either determine the velocity of flow or, knowing the velocity, the hydraulic conductivity.

Darcy's Law.

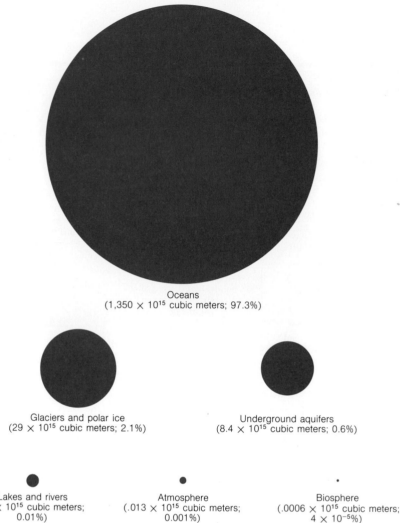

Oceans
(1,350 × 10^{15} cubic meters; 97.3%)

Glaciers and polar ice
(29 × 10^{15} cubic meters; 2.1%)

Underground aquifers
(8.4 × 10^{15} cubic meters; 0.6%)

Lakes and rivers
(.2 × 10^{15} cubic meters;
0.01%)

Atmosphere
(.013 × 10^{15} cubic meters;
0.001%)

Biosphere
(.0006 × 10^{15} cubic meters;
4 × 10^{-5}%)

Figure 6-13
Distribution of water on the earth. The amount of water present in various natural reservoirs is represented in terms of comparative spherical volumes. The number under the name of each reservoir denotes the contents of that reservoir in cubic meters. Although the atmosphere contains a mere hundred-thousandth of all the water in the hydrosphere, the influence of this small amount on the climate of the earth and on the location of hydrologic resources is far out of proportion to its mass. [From "The Control of the Water Cycle" by José P. Peixoto and M. Ali Kettani. Copyright © 1973 by Scientific American, Inc. All rights reserved.]

years to recover its original position. Other aquifers in the high plains tell the same story in varying degrees. Deeper aquifers are being explored in hopes of increasing production.

Because of the extreme slowness of recharge and the slow rates of water movement, the groundwater in such extensive areas is in every sense being mined, just like coal, so that the amount left in the ground steadily diminishes as production continues. For all practical purposes, this water is an exhaustible resource that, once gone, cannot be replenished. We are not yet in a crisis situation nationally, but certain communities, in areas where depletion is in an advanced stage, are in for tough times. The amount of usable fresh water in the ground is staggering (Fig. 6-13). Recent estimates are that it amounts to much more than 90 percent of all of the fresh water on the Earth. Rivers, lakes, reservoirs, and soil moisture account for the remainder. Glacial ice is the equivalent of seven times the groundwater supply.

The problem is to find untapped supplies and plan for the recharging of aquifers that can be replenished, particularly those that can be recharged in a short time. Long Island, in New York, offers one example of success at groundwater recharge. Five million people there depend on wells for almost half their water supply. By the early 1940's, extensive pumping had depleted the reservoir to the extent that salt water was encroaching on the aquifer, and a state-regulated program of artificial recharge was started to reverse the deterioration of the water supply. By drilling an extensive system of recharge wells so that used water could be put back into the aquifer, and by constructing large basins to help accelerate infiltration from surface waters, including storm and industrial waste drainage, the aquifer was built back up to usable levels.

The Long Island story is one of success up to now, and is an encouraging example of a stitch in time. But the situation remains precarious, for population and water demands grow daily. One of the unlooked-for results of rapid growth in urban and suburban areas such as Long Island is that natural recharge of the aquifer through seepage into soil becomes decreased as buildings increase in number and more and more paved streets, sidewalks, driveways, and parking lots appear. Our expanding urban areas not only deplete the underground reservoirs by pumping—they interfere with its natural refilling.

Karst: The Erosive Power of Groundwater. Along the northeastern shore of the Adriatic Sea, where Yugoslavia and Italy meet, lies the Karst region. An irregular terrain of hills and low mountains, with many small depressions, it has evolved on limestone bedrock that has been eroded and shaped by the dissolving power of groundwater in a humid climate. In Karst topography, sinkholes (see Fig. 5-23) are combined with underground caverns and a surface drainage of short and scarce streams that end abruptly in sinkholes.

The irregular narrowing of openings in all directions and the signs of dissolution on both ceilings and floors in many caves serve as evidence that they were formed while completely filled with water and thus below the water table. We can now walk around in these caves because the water table has since dropped as a conse-

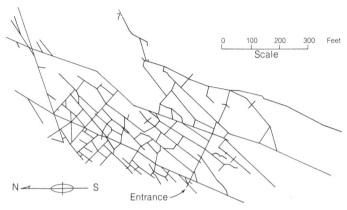

Figure 6-14
Map of Mark Twain Cave, Hannibal, Missouri. The many passageways in this complex cave dissolved along joint patterns in Paleozoic limestone. [From J. Harlen Bretz, "Vadose and Phreatic Features of Limestone Canyons," *J. Geology*, vol. 50, 1942.]

quence of regional changes in climate or topography. **Stalactites,** icicle-like forms of newly precipitated limestone hanging from the cave roof, are formed where groundwater drips as it enters the cave on its way down to the water table. In the same way, the drip builds up a **stalagmite** on the cave floor below the stalactite. All these and other forms of **dripstone** are the hallmarks of later stages of cave formation above the water table.

The groundwater in Karst regions is made "hard" by the calcium carbonate dissolved in it. Hardness and other chemical characteristic properties of water—the result of its geologic origins—are important to all of us, for the quality of the water that we drink is as vital to our well being as the quantity.

THE QUALITY OF WATER

When Portia speaks of mercy in the Shakespeare that so many have learned, she uses a common metaphor:

"The quality of mercy is not strain'd.
It droppeth as the gentle rain from heaven."
MERCHANT OF VENICE, ACT 4, SCENE I

In 1972 and 1973, after unusually wet seasons on Long Island, the water table was so high that water seeped into the basements of many homes unwisely built in low, poorly drained areas in times when the water table was low.

The amounts of limestone that have dissolved to make caverns may be huge. Mammoth Cave, Kentucky, has tens of kilometers of interconnected caves; the large room at Carlsbad Caverns, New Mexico, is more than 1200 m (4000 ft) long, 200 m (600 ft) wide, and 100 m (350 ft) high.

Possibly the most celebrated description in American literature of the maze of passageways in a limestone cave is in Mark Twain's *Tom Sawyer.* Tom and Becky Thatcher got lost in what is now known as Mark Twain cave, near Hannibal, Missouri, the scene of the novel.

Rainwater is our usual standard for purity, and in parts of the Earth where the air is still clean, so is the water. A great many, if not most, water wells produce fine water of excellent quality, just as good as rainwater to drink. Yet centuries before anyone thought of chemical contamination of our air and water, people who drank some well waters made wry faces at the taste and tended to prefer wine or beer. Some groundwaters taste of "iron"; others may have a disagreeable odor. Every few months a newspaper somewhere will feature a story about water that froths out of the faucet like detergent. What makes the difference?

Rainwater to Groundwater. One place where we can sometimes find groundwater about as pure as rainwater is under a bare dune made of pure quartz sand. Analyses of such waters show that they have about the same amount of carbon dioxide dissolved in the water as the rain—and little else. Compare this with groundwater from a Karst terrain, a **hard water**—one that contains some dissolved calcium and usually some magnesium, which makes it difficult to make a lather or soap suds. Such water may also have a slight taste given by other ions in solution.

These kinds of comparisons suggest the same conclusions that we drew from observations of rock weathering (Chapter 4): rainwater infiltrating the ground chemically alters rock and soil and in so doing becomes a groundwater containing dissolved ions and other components contributed by the plant and animal life on and in the soil. The water under the quartz sand dune is like rainwater because quartz is so insoluble that for practical purposes it is inert, and neither soil nor vegetation contribute dissolved substances to the water. In contrast to quartz sand, surface materials of soil, limestone, and shale react with rain to produce dissolved materials that contribute to the taste and hardness of the groundwater.

How Good Is the Water? The amounts of dissolved material in **potable** groundwaters—that is, waters usable for drinking—are very small, usually measured in parts per million (ppm), a unit made up in the same way as the more familiar percent, which is just parts per hundred. For example, 1 ppm is the same as 0.0001 percent, but it is much easier to use parts per million because we can almost always avoid

decimals and all those zeroes. One hundred and fifty ppm might be a typical figure for the total dissolved material in a good water, for no natural water is as pure as a carefully distilled water. The upper limit for potable water for human consumption is usually 500 to 1000 ppm; for watering livestock, it is usually 2000, though both humans and animals can get used to more in some circumstances. A water can measure in the upper range of permissible dissolved ions and yet still taste good if its dissolved materials consist largely of a mixture of calcium and bicarbonate ions. Yet a water containing only several hundred ppm of sodium and chloride ions will taste slightly salty. The worst offenders to taste are the dissolved organic compounds, many introduced by human activities. Some dissolved components have no taste but beneficial qualities. For example, the movement for fluoridation of water supplies was sparked by the discovery that in some regions small amounts of naturally occurring fluoride in groundwater are responsible for great resistance to tooth decay. Conversely, however, some toxic elements have no taste, but in more than minute quantities may be dangerous to health. Concentrations of such poisonous elements as lead and arsenic must be watched carefully. No matter how good the water may taste, it is unsafe to allow these elements to exceed a tenth to a twentieth of a part per million.

A few groundwaters are naturally **softened** as they pass through and react with formations containing zeolite minerals, which remove calcium and other ions. Zeolites, hydrous silicates, have a strong chemical tendency to absorb certain ions from water in exchange for other ions bound in the solid. If, for example, a water carrying calcium ion travels through a zeolite formation that exchanges sodium ion for the calcium, the water comes out with sodium instead of calcium, and the zeolite becomes richer in calcium and poorer in sodium. This process has been put to home and municipal use by companies that attach tanks of zeolite to the water inlet as a water softener. The commercial zeolite eventually gets used up—saturated—and has to be changed.

Groundwaters are always clear of solid materials as they come from the aquifer. The intricate passageways of the aquifer act as a fine filter and remove small particles of clay or any other solids. They even strain out bacteria. The dirtiest sewage will be clear of suspended solid mat-

Groundwater containing
dissolved calcium and magnesium

Ca⁺⁺ leaves solution
and attaches to solid,
exchanging for Na⁺,
which leaves solid
and goes into solution
(1 Ca⁺⁺ for 2 Na⁺)

Packed zeolite
water-softener
tank

Expanded view

Figure 6-15
A zeolite water softener operates by exchanging sodium (Na^+) or other ions in the solid zeolite for the ions that make the water hard, calcium (Ca^{++}) and magnesium (Mg^{++}). The exchanging ions always balance total electrical charge; thus 1 Ca^{++} will exchange for 2 Na^+.

ter once it has gone through a thick bed of sand. The dissolved matter is another story. It is not strained out.

Contamination of Water Supplies. In the past few decades the tremendous increase in the use of septic tanks for home sewage disposal has contributed a new source of dissolved material to groundwater. The septic tank waters seep into the soil and, where water-supply aquifers are shallow, will contaminate groundwater with phosphate and foaming agents from detergents and a variety of other substances that are undesirable or potentially harmful to health, such as nitrates. Water filtering into the ground through city dumps or sanitary landfill operations may introduce a number of undesirable compounds into groundwaters. Extensive salting of icy roads in the North has led to sodium chloride contamination of some aquifers. Still another source of groundwater contamination is nitrate fertilizer, which is spread over soil. The nitrate is very soluble, and although some is used by plants—the purpose of the spreading—much dissolved nitrate escapes unused into deeper parts of the soil and into groundwater. In combination, these sources (sewage and fertilizer) have increased nitrate levels in some aquifers to the worry point, for nitrate is toxic to humans even in amounts as small as 10 to 15 ppm.

It must be obvious that the faster the recharge of the aquifer, the more quickly it might become contaminated from these sources. But the fast recharge also means that the aquifer can recover in a short time, once the sources of contamination are closed off. Contamination of slow-recharge reservoirs is more serious, for by the time the results of many years of contamination start showing up, it will be too late for quick recovery. Because of the definite links between surface waters and groundwaters, we cannot afford to view the surface and the subsurface as separate entities. Integrated planning for groundwater reservoirs in relation to pollution of and from surface sources will become increasingly necessary in order to maintain the quality of our water supplies.

Deeply Buried Waters. Below the groundwater table, rocks are almost everywhere saturated with water, especially below depths of a few hundred meters. No matter how deeply oil wells are drilled, geologists always find water in permeable formations. In most places the water below the upper few hundreds of meters becomes increasingly concentrated in dissolved materials; for this reason they are frequently called **brines.** They may vary widely in chemical composition, just as surface waters do, but they are much older than the near-surface waters and presumably have had a much more complex history. These waters move very slowly, probably at speeds of less than a centimeter per year. Many are rich in ordinary salt, NaCl, particularly where a water has been steeped in buried salt beds. For example, in southern Illinois there is a series of (Paleozoic) sedimentary formations arranged in a spoon-shaped basin a few kilometers thick; the deeper one drills in this area, the more salty and concentrated the waters become. Because these deep waters are in some ways similar in composition to sea water, they used to be considered as remnants of original sea water trapped in the pores of sediments at the time of deposition. But detailed studies of the chemistry of the waters of the Illinois basin have shown that all of these waters have become salty by reacting with various rocks over a long time interval. The deeper and the older the waters, and the more time they have had to react with rocks, the greater is the content of dissolved solids.

How Deep Does Water Go? A deep well may penetrate an unconformity under a thick sequence of sedimentary formations and enter what is called "basement"—by definition, a highly complex mixture of igneous and metamorphic rocks that everywhere underlies the sedimentary rocks of the continents. Basement may range in depth from a few meters to ten kilometers or more. In the Grand Canyon, the basement is Precambrian, including the Grand Canyon Series and the Vishnu formation. Somewhere else the basement may be Paleozoic, as it is along parts of the Eastern Seaboard of the United States, where flat-lying Mesozoic and Cenozoic sedimentary rocks are separated by a widespread unconformity from deformed and metamorphosed rocks of Devonian age and older. Because igneous and metamorphic rocks have low porosities and permeabilities, the basement is relatively dry, though there are always minute amounts of water in small cracks and along boundaries between crystals. Some sedimentary sequences, notably those along the Gulf coasts of eastern Texas, Louisiana, and Mississippi, are so thick that the depth of basement is known only from seismological evidence, and it lies well beyond our present deep-drilling capabilities. Here the sedimentary formations show a decrease in permeability with depth, caused partly by compaction due to the immense weight of overlying rock. Another cause of the decrease in permeability is the

strong tendency for pore spaces to be filled up by such minerals as quartz or calcite, which are precipitated under the chemical conditions of deep burial. Though the deepest wells drilled so far—more than 9 kilometers (29,500 feet)—still penetrate permeable rocks, we can nevertheless assume that at much greater depths these sedimentary rocks will be as dense and dry as basement rocks.

The conclusion is inescapable: the accessible waters of the Earth are limited to the surface and the near-surface part of the crust. Most of it is surface water—in oceans, rivers, and lakes; the remainder is stored in rocks, to depths of not much more than 10 kilometers. The overwhelming majority of the world's *fresh* waters are in the ground rather than on the surface. Although many deeply buried waters are salty (brines), most near-surface groundwater is fresh. Rivers and lakes account for only a small fraction of the total fresh water.

Thermal Waters. In such places as Marienbad, Germany; Aix-les-Bains, France; Karlsbad, Czechoslovakia; Hot Springs, Arkansas; the restorative properties of mineral baths in hot spring pools have been known (or assumed) from the earliest days of civilization. They also are a part of our story, for the activity of these mineral waters, or **hydrothermal** waters ("hot water") is responsible for extensive deposits of travertine and other minerals that encrust rocks around the pools. Those that do not reach the surface are responsible for the formation, at great depth, of many of the richest metallic ore deposits of the world (see Chapter 22). Thermal waters are found in areas of current or recent igneous activity—deep-seated, or intrusive, activity and surface, or extrusive, activity. The water itself is mostly **meteoric** (meaning derived from rainwater, and having nothing to do with meteors except for the derivation of the name). It is mixed with water originally dissolved in the magma itself, called **magmatic** water. In areas of igneous activity, surface waters moving downward encounter hot masses of rock, become heated, and mix with the magmatic waters at depth. Return circulation takes place along fracture zones or other channels that intersect the surface at continuously fed hot springs or geysers, some of which spout intermittently like the spectacular Old Faithful in Yellowstone Park (see Fig. 15-35).

Hot water is a much more efficient dissolver of rocks than cool rainwater, and so these hy-

The deepest wells drilled are those for oil and gas exploration. Some holes have been drilled to depths of more than 9 km (29,500 ft) in Oklahoma and Texas, and it seems likely that we have sufficient knowledge about how to tackle problems of deep drilling to go at least another few km.

Figure 6-16
A typical section through continental crust, showing the distribution of water. Most is at the surface or in sedimentary rocks buried at shallow depths. Depth to basement varies greatly, but is rarely more than 10 km. Porosity and water content generally decrease with increasing depth and greater structural deformation.

drothermal solutions are more concentrated in many ions than ordinary groundwaters. As the hot solutions rise to the surface, they cool. If these hot solutions are saturated at the higher temperature, they will become supersaturated as they cool and will deposit the excess as mineral precipitates. The extensive whitish to grayish, muddy flats around some of the hot springs in

Yellowstone Park are made up of fine particles of silica precipitated from the solutions that had originally, when hotter, dissolved it from silicate rocks at depth, near the hot igneous rock. **Travertine** is a calcium carbonate deposit commonly precipitated at cooling hot springs from solutions that passed through limestone formations at depth. Other hot waters may contain large

Figure 6-17
Circulation of water over a magma that produces geysers or hot springs. Cold rainwater soaks into the soil and filters down through permeable rocks. As it approaches the magma, it heats up, therefore becoming less dense, and thus sets up a circulation system that returns it to the surface.

amounts of sulfur. Our ancestors were right when they referred to such smelly, sulfurous waters as escapes from the "hellish" interior of Earth.

In the search of new and clean sources of energy, scientists have turned their attention to hot water areas as natural sites for the development of steam turbines and other devices to convert the heat into electricity. Though this is not a generally applicable solution to the problem of our rapidly climbing energy needs, the potential for efficient harnessing this source of energy is good in areas that have hot springs or geysers. California, Iceland, Italy, and New Zealand are already exploiting their hot spring areas for power in a practical way (also see Chapter 22 and Figs. 13-1 and 15-41).

WHERE DID ALL THE WATER COME FROM?

Sooner or later after geologists began to question seriously how the Earth evolved as a planet, someone had to tackle the origin of all the water on Earth, for if it were not always here it had to come from somewhere. In the late 1940's a remarkably versatile geologist who was equally at home doing field mapping, calculating chemical equations, and studying the physics of how water currents carry sediment, found himself attracted to this problem. William W. Rubey, working for the U.S. Geological Survey on the origin of marine phosphate rocks, started wondering whether the saltiness of the ocean had ever changed much in the past. As frequently happens to people of insatiable curiosity, that question led to others. Why was the ocean salty in the first place, and where did all the water and salt come from?

Rubey compared the average chemical composition of igneous, metamorphic, and sedimentary rocks and reconfirmed what geologists had long known—that sedimentary rocks are much richer in water and carbon dioxide than the others. He followed by adding up the amounts of all of the water, carbon dioxide, chlorine, and a few other substances, such as sulfur, now present in sedimentary rocks, atmosphere, and sea waters (Table 6-2). He then compared those totals with estimates of the amounts of these substances that could have been derived by the weathering of igneous rocks. This attempt at a mass balance was reasonable; after all, we know that the process of chemical weathering of igneous rocks produces sediments and the dissolved ions in ground and surface waters that eventually end up in the oceans.

Rubey found an enormous discrepancy. There was far too much water, carbon dioxide, and chloride in the atmosphere, oceans, and sedimentary rocks to be accounted for by the weathering of igneous rocks, which contain little of these substances. The only reasonable way to make the budget balance was to revive an idea first proposed in the nineteenth century—that all of the gases released by volcanoes, hot springs, and geysers, lumped together as **volcanic emanations,** could make up the difference. A check on the composition of gases from volcanoes quickly showed that in fact their ratios of water to carbon dioxide and other elements was very crudely in proportion to the ratios calculated for the whole crust. Because these materials all tend to form gases (water vapor, carbon dioxide and other carbon gass, hydrogen chloride, chlorine, hydrogen sulfide, sulfur dioxide, and others) and were present in such abundance on or near the surface or buried in sedimentary rocks, Rubey called them **excess volatiles.** Thus he concluded that almost all of the water vapor and the other gases were released from deep in the earth by volcanism. Since chemists use the term **outgassing** to refer to the exhalation of gases from a solid or liquid as a result of heating or some other cause, it was natural to refer to release of these gases as **outgassing of the Earth.**

Outgassing does, indeed, seem to be the process responsible for the formation of the oceans and the atmosphere. But the question remains, when did it happen: did it happen all at once or over a long period of time? Rubey looked first for evidence in the geologic record that might indicate whether any change in the salinity of sea water had ever taken place. He reasoned that marine organisms are known to have little tolerance for such changes. From fossil evidence dating back to the Cambrian, he argued that marine life has never been drastically affected by variations in the salt content of the oceans. This led him to conclude that neither the oceans nor the atmosphere have changed much in composition over geologic time. Other lines of evidence led him to conclude that the volcanic gases from the interior accumulated slowly and steadily

Table 6-2
Where some volatile substances are found at or near the Earth's surface.

Compound or element	Where found
Water (H_2O)	As liquid in oceans; as vapor in atmosphere; chemically bound in hydrous minerals, such as clays, in sedimentary rocks.
Carbon dioxide (CO_2)	Dissolved in oceans; as gas in atmosphere; as carbonate minerals, such as calcite ($CaCO_3$), in limestones and other sedimentary rocks; in reduced form as organic carbon in oil, gas, coal, and other organic matter.
Chlorine (Cl)	As chloride ion (Cl^-) dissolved in oceans; as component of saline minerals, such as halite (NaCl), in evaporite deposits.
Sulfur (S)	As sulfate ion (SO_4^{--}) dissolved in oceans; as calcium sulfate ($CaSO_4$) in the form of gypsum and anhydrite in evaporite deposits; as sulfide ion (S^-) in iron sulfide (FeS_2) in the form of pyrite in sedimentary rocks.

throughout geologic time, having always been released in about the same relative compositions as they are today.

THE CONSTANCY OF SEA WATER COMPOSITION

Since Rubey's paper opened up this whole line of thought, there have been many new ideas on it. In 1959 the world's first international oceanographic congress was held in the U.N. Building in New York. For a week the delegates' lounges and bars were alive with talk about the outpouring of new information on the oceans instead of the usual diplomatic activities of ambassadors. At one session a brilliant Swedish physical chemist, the late Lars Gunnar Sillén, brought his deep knowledge of the quantitative data on inorganic chemical reactions to bear in his first essay on how the chemical composition of the oceans could be explained. Sillén started out with pure water mixed with dissolved carbon dioxide and oxygen in equilibrium with the amounts present in the atmosphere. He then calculated how that water could chemically react to equilibrium with all of the clay minerals, carbonates, and other minerals characteristic of the sediments flooring the oceans. He further calculated the same kinds of reaction between water and all of the unweathered igneous minerals that are transported to the oceans as detritus eroded from continental rocks. He concluded that the final product would be a solution much like sea water. This analysis made even more probable Rubey's estimate that sea water was always of the same composition, and emphasized even more strongly that sea water was the expectable ordinary consequence of weathering and sedimentation.

At about the same time, the work of other geochemists showed that the chemical elements dissolved in sea water were being precipitated onto the bottom as sediments at about the same rate as they were being supplied to the ocean in solution by the world's rivers. Thus we now see the oceans as the product of a steady-state process rather than the result of some early, single, cataclysmic event. Our view of Earth history has been sharply altered by the gradual recognition that steady-state processes are the rule rather than the exception.

How Long an Atom Stays in the Ocean. The steady state of the oceans leads to another concept that relates the inflow or outflow of an element to its total amount in the sea. A good example might be a crowded cocktail party, where many more people have been invited than fit comfortably in the rooms. As people come in, the rooms quickly fill up, and then as more arrive, the crush gets so much that people start to leave. At its most active, the party is in a steady-state, arrivals and departures balanced, and the rooms saturated. Now, even though some come early and stay late, and others arrive, see the crowd, and leave, there is an average length of time between each person's arrival and departure that we can call **residence time.** The length of stay at the party is determined by the number of people that can be jammed into the rooms, which we will call the capacity, and the rate of arrivals, which we will call the rate of influx (this, of course, is equal to the rate of departures, or efflux).

$$\text{Residence time} = \frac{\text{capacity}}{\text{rate of influx}}$$

A simple numerical example: if a room will hold thirty people and a new person arrives every two minutes ($\frac{1}{2}$ per minute), you can verify that the average residence time has to be one hour.

Applying all this to the oceans allows us to calculate residence times for the dissolved elements in sea water. You can visualize this as the average length of time that elapses between the entry of an atom into the sea and its removal by sedimentation. Calcium is carried in abundance by rivers, and even though it is readily taken up by many kinds of organisms that build shells composed of calcium carbonate, it has a long residence time, 8 million years. Sodium has one of the longest residence times, 260 million years. Iron, on the other hand, stays in the ocean only 140 years. Knowing the residence time of elements is important not only for working out the general scheme of things but for predicting the behavior of toxic or radioactive elements in the ocean. It is important today, for example, to determine the residence time of crude oil spilled on the sea by tankers before it is decomposed or sedimented out on the sea bottom or its beaches. Likewise, as we will discuss in Chapter 12, it is crucial that we know the residence time of carbon dioxide if we are to be able to predict the effects of excess CO_2 in the atmosphere and oceans.

Yet another way of looking at the ocean has been proposed by some geochemists, who have presented a kind of cookbook recipe for making sea water that gives much insight into the details of the process. They calculated how much and what kinds of sediment would be deposited if you took average river water, evaporated it until it contained as much chloride salt as the ocean, precipitated excess calcium carbonate, silica, clays, and other sedimentary minerals—all to make the final solution like sea water. They compared existing sedimentary rock accumulations with their results and found good agreement. This whole field of study is most active, and we are now beginning to see how plate tectonics and geochemical connections between the surface and the interior of the Earth may have a bearing on the compositions of sea water and sediments.

When All the Water Came Out. Rubey thought that the outgassing of the interior took place gradually, but information that has accumulated during the years since the late 1940's has led some scientists to believe that the great bulk of the Earth's atmosphere and oceans may have been outgassed early in its history and have been partially recycled ever since. Part of this evidence is in the isotopic composition of the gases from modern volcanoes, which indicates that they are of surface or crustal origin and are

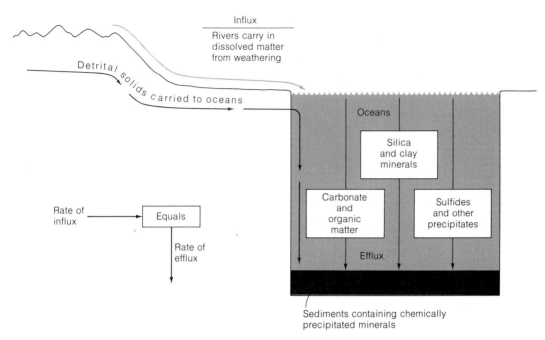

Figure 6-18
A model of the steady-state ocean. The rate of influx of dissolved substances by rivers matches the rate of efflux by chemical precipitation of sedimentary minerals. Detrital solids formed by erosion accompany the dissolved material and are deposited as sands and muds in various mixtures with the chemical precipitates.

recycled only through the outer 25 to 30 kilometers of the Earth rather than outgassed from the deep interior. Other lines of reasoning that point to early outgassing come from current ideas on the timing of the astronomical and geological events in the early history of the Earth. For instance, the Moon and the Earth were much closer during the early part of their joint history, and the Earth would have been stressed by the strong pull. Another factor is the early timing of differentiation, for the melting of iron and the formation of an iron core would have cause a profound disturbance that would also have promoted outgassing (see Chapter 1). Finally, the theory of plate tectonics holds that continuous mixing and recycling of material goes on between the crust and the mantle, and provides a rationale for the distribution and kinds of volcanic activity that contribute gases to the atmosphere and oceans. Thus we have evidence that forces promoting extensive outgassing would have been strongest in the earliest

stage of Earth history, and we have a mechanism—plate tectonics—that would allow for continuous recycling of some of the gases through the crust and mantle and also account for the gaseous volcanic emanations of today.

Putting all of these lines of evidence together, we refer again to what was called in Chapter 1 the "big burp." It is likely that there was a huge outgassing of the excess volatiles at the time when much of the earth became molten as a result of the accumulation of radioactively produced heat. At the same time, the body of the Earth would have been being distorted by large Earth tides caused by the nearby Moon. That too would have promoted the escape of gases from the interior. Since that early time of outgassing, the excess volatiles have been cycling through the crust and mantle. The temporarily dense atmosphere, the newly formed oceans, and the large volume of primitive sediments that would have formed by the condensation of water clouds and reaction of all of the gases with

Certainly not all excess volatiles came out very early in Earth history; additional outgassing of primordial material kept on at a much slower pace during geologic time. The relation of outgassing to the formation of continental landmasses early in the Precambrian is currently an active subject, with much attention being given to the oldest rocks in the world in Southwest Greenland.

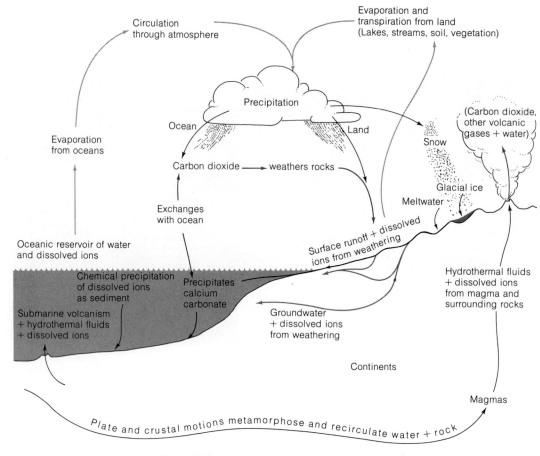

Figure 6-19
Overall hydrologic cycle. Routes of carbon dioxide
are shown in brown, water in black.

igneous rocks would long since have been deformed or subducted by plate and other tectonic movements.

Thus our concept of the history of the oceans and atmospheres includes a stage of rapid evolution early in the Earth's history, during which the steady-state "machine" was set up, followed by a second stage, almost all of geologic time, during which the "machine" has been steadily operating at more or less the same rate.

Knowing the importance of recycling of excess volatiles, we can integrate the movements of water in the hydrologic cycle with the routes of the dissolved ions and gases, such as carbon dioxide, that it carries (Fig. 6-19). The water is recycled at the surface of Earth by evaporation from land and sea, circulation as vapor and clouds in the atmosphere, and precipitation on land and sea. On land the precipitation of snow may form glaciers, whose meltwaters join ordi-

nary rainwater runoff in bringing land precipitation back to the sea. Surface runoff is connected to shallow, subsurface groundwater flow, much of which eventually returns to the surface in the beds of streams and lakes. Some surface water is incorporated into hydrous minerals and reaches the interior, where it is recycled along with solids by the tectonic, magmatic, and metamorphic processes of exchange that take place between the crust and upper mantle of the Earth. In this way the surface hydrologic cycle, powered by the external heat engine, the Sun, is linked to the Earth's internal heat engine, powered by radioactivity. Water from the interior eventually returns to the surface in volcanic emanations, which may escape at the surface or in the deep sea. Volcanism also helps recirculate carbon dioxide, one of the most abundant of the volcanic gases next to water vapor. Carbon dioxide dissolved in rain and surface waters is important in the weathering of rocks, for it releases ions from decomposed rock. Surface water and groundwater constantly carry the dissolved substances to the oceans, where they steadily recombine as the chemically precipitated fraction of sediments. Calcium carbonate forms in this way, and effectively buries some of the carbon dioxide from the atmosphere. The carbon dioxide of the oceans and atmosphere are in equilibrium with each other by exchange across the surface of the ocean. All of the operations are interrelated and combine to keep the ocean constant in composition as water evaporates from the surface and as precipitates settle to the bottom.

Thus we can visualize the operation of this great chemical processing plant as a coupling of two subunits powered by the two heat engines of Earth. In the surface subunit, water is the pipeline carrying the products of weathering to the sea, where they are removed by sedimentation. The water is purified by evaporation and recycled to continue its weathering work. In the subunit operating within the Earth, the water is recycled with solid rock as part of interior movements of crust and mantle, ultimately to reach the surface again as volcanic emanations. In the surface subunit—that is, in what geologists call the hydrologic cycle—a molecule of water may be recycled in a few years, but in the interior subunit recycling may take millions of years.

SUMMARY

1. The properties of water are unique indeed; existing as gas, liquid, and solid on the Earth's surface, water participates in all geological processes.

2. The hydrologic cycle is a description of the pathways by which water evaporates from land and sea surface and returns by precipitation as rain, ice, and snow.

3. Surface runoff is directly related to the amount of precipitation, and thus reflects the climate.

4. Groundwater forms by infiltration of precipitation through soil into permeable aquifers.

5. The groundwater table closely follows the contour of the land surface and changes in level in response to precipitation.

6. Groundwater moves at slow to moderate rates through aquifers, the rates depending on the permeability and the hydraulic gradient. Water may move for long distances underground.

7. Groundwater supplies may be depleted by excessive pumping and insufficiently rapid recharge. The water supply in some places can be replenished by increasing recharge.

8. The quality of water is dependent on the kinds of dissolved materials picked up by the water on its passage through soils and aquifers. Hard waters form when abundant calcium dissolves. Potable waters contain only small amounts of dissolved material.

9. Groundwaters may be contaminated by improper sewage disposal and by seepage of chemical nutrients applied to soils.

10. Groundwaters become more concentrated in dissolved solids at greater depths. Waters fill pore spaces of rocks down to depths where porosity decreases to the vanishing point.

11. The occurrence of thermal waters is related to the presence of igneous intrusions. Thermal waters precipitate a variety of deposits around hot springs and geysers.

12. The waters of the surface evolved from the escape of volcanic gases from the Earth's interior.

13. Sea water has stayed constant in composition throughout most of geologic time by a balance of inflow of dissolved material from rivers and precipitation of sediments. Residence time is the average length of time an atom stays in the ocean before precipitating.

14. Much of the gases and water at the surface escaped from the interior early, setting in motion the hydrologic cycle much as we know it today.

EXERCISES

1. If a thin layer of oil were to form at many places on the ocean and reduce evaporation of water from the sea surface to half of its present value, what changes might you expect in the hydrologic cycle?

2. If there were a vast increase in the number of desalination plants making fresh water out of sea water all over the world, so that a significant volume of fresh water were produced, would it affect the workings of the hydrologic cycle, and if so, how?

3. Assume that in the future, motions along the San Andreas fault, a plate boundary, were to change to divergence, separating the San Joaquin Valley from the coastal mountains to the west and changing it to a low coastal plain bordering a new arm of the Pacific. What changes in the hydrologic budget of the valley might follow?

4. Several hundred meters under the city of Chicago are permeable aquifers of sandstone, which crop out in Southern Wisconsin, 100 to 200 miles north of the city. One-hundred years ago, Chicago got much of its water from flowing wells drilled into these aquifers, but water is now difficult to pump from the wells, and the city gets its supply from Lake Michigan. What do you think might have been the history of Chicago's water supply?

5. The government of the island of Bermuda, far out in the Atlantic Ocean, does not allow private water wells, and most residents use the rainwater that collects on their roofs. Why do you think the government has this rule?

6. If, as recently happened in one State, it were discovered that radioactive waste from a nuclear processing plant had seeped into groundwater in the immediate vicinity of the plant, what kind of information would you want in order to predict the length of time before that waste might move into a groundwater aquifer many kilometers away?

7. Why do most water-well drillers not recommend drilling too deeply, many hundreds of meters, to get pure water supplies?

8. A water reservoir for a city of 50,000 people supplies 5 million cubic meters of water per year and has a capacity of 10 million cubic meters. What is the residence time for water in the reservoir if it stays full all the time?

BIBLIOGRAPHY

Bretz, J. H., "Vadose and Phreatic Features of Limestone Caverns." *Journal of Geology,* v. 50, pp. 675–811, 1942.

Davis, S. N., and R. J. M. DeWiest, *Hydrogeology.* New York: John Wiley & Sons, 1966.

Garrels, R. M., and F. T. Mackenzie, *Evolution of Sedimentary Rocks.* New York: W. W. Norton Co., 1971. (Chapter 4.)

Peixit, J. P., and M. A. Kettani, "The Control of the Water Cycle." *Scientific American,* April 1973. (Offprint No. 907.)

Revelle, R., "Water." *Scientific American,* September 1963. (Offprint No. 878.)

Sayre, A. N., "Ground Water." *Scientific American,* November 1950. (Offprint No. 818.)

7

RIVERS: CURRENTS, CHANNELS, AND NETWORKS

Most of the debris of erosion is carried downhill by running water in the streams of the Earth. Turbulent currents excavate river valleys by eroding channels and moving particles downstream. The ability of a river to transport particles in different amounts and sizes is dependent on current velocity, the total amount of water carried, and the downhill slope of the channel. Currents form ripples, dunes, and bars in the channel sediment. A river can be analyzed as a complex system of drainage patterns that form in response to the particular conditions of climate, bedrock, and particles produced by weathering.

Rivers grip our imaginations. They bring out cliches like "mighty waters" and "raging torrents" and, at more serene moments, others like "majestic flow" and "babbling brook." The variety of cliches, most of which center on the idea of constant flowing, is matched only by the variety of forms themselves. Rivers may be straight, but they may bend and loop around too. A river may flow in a broad low swale that barely has the form of a valley, but that same river in another place may rush between the nearly vertical walls of a narrow gorge. A high mountain stream in the Rockies will be a hazard to cross because of the jumble of rocks through which the water rushes, but at times of drought you can walk almost entirely across the fine sand and mud on the bed of the Missouri River at Omaha. Rivers are clear, and rivers are turbid. Some are fast, and others slow.

The factors responsible for these differences in how water moves, what it carries, and its effects on the landscape make up the subject of this chapter. We start with some notions about how water moves in currents and how the movement enables it to carry things of all sizes and shapes, from mud, sand, and pebbles to whole houses ripped from their foundations by floods.

HOW CURRENTS MOVE PARTICLES

If you slowly pour cold syrup over melting butter on pancakes, you can observe a most basic form of fluid flow: a pattern of **streamlines**—lines of flow—is formed by thin strands of melted butter flowing along with the syrup. As long as the syrup is cold, and therefore thick and sluggish, the streamlines will show the two fluids moving steadily without mixing. This is the essence of what is called **laminar flow,** in which the particles of the fluid move in parallel layers with no mixing of material across the boundaries between layers. Some, however, like their syrup hot, and that changes the picture. The property of fluids that makes them move slowly or rapidly when poured is viscosity; the viscosity of such fluids as automobile lubricating oils is usually determined by measuring the time that a certain quantity of fluid takes to flow through a small opening, like the bottom of a funnel. Viscosity is a function of temperature, so that the viscosity of most fluids is lower—that is, they flow faster—at higher temperatures. Thus hot syrup, which is less viscous than cold syrup, may not move in obvious, slow laminar flow but in a faster, more confused pattern, one of **tur-**

Flow lines do not cross
No mixing between layers

Figure 7-1
Laminar flow of a fluid between two solid channel walls. Flow lines in this type of flow do not cross, indicating that there is no mixing of fluid between layers.

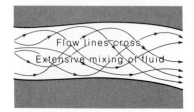

Figure 7-2
Turbulent flow of a fluid between two
solid channel walls. Flow lines in this
type of flow cross in a complex pattern; unlike laminar flow, no definite
layers of fluid can be discerned,
which indicates extensive mixing of
the entire fluid mass.

A startling development in petroleum
technology came some years ago
when chemists were able to produce
modern engine oils whose tempera-
ture-viscosity behavior is the opposite
of normal, so that the oils would be
more viscous in the summer and less
viscous in the winter—just what auto-
motive engineers had hoped for.

bulent flow. In a quiet room, tobacco smoke,
another fluid, will at first rise from a cigarette in
a straight, vertical plume of laminar flow and
then break up into a turbulent, eddying, complex flow in which the streamlines cross, interfere, and eventually become dissipated by completely mixing with air. The essence of
turbulence is in the mixing of the flow in complex patterns. The general behavior is the same
whether the fluid is a gas, like smoke in air, or a
liquid, like syrup or water.

The most important factor that determines
whether the flow of water is laminar or turbulent
is the velocity. Only very slow flows are laminar;
flow in practically all of the streams we see is
turbulent. Secondary factors are the roughness
of the stream bottom and the depth of the
stream. The shallower the stream and the
smoother the bottom, the more likely the flow
will be laminar. Laminar flow in nature can be
seen in thin sheets on nearly flat slopes, and
occasionally in very cold water in streams running over smooth bottoms. Turbulent flow varies in the intensity of eddying and swirling
movements, again mainly a matter of stream
velocity.

Strange behavior is shown by a fast-flowing,
turbulent stream where it suddenly steepens and
starts to flow even faster than before. The rush
of water smooths to what looks like straight,
uneddied movement, even though it is still basically turbulent; its surface smoothness is decep-
tive, for the flow is actually so fast that it is

commonly called **shooting flow,** as opposed to
the more **tranquil,** or **streaming flow,** at lower
velocities. Shooting flow can be seen typically in
rocky rapids or where water flows down steep
narrow chutes.

Movement of Particles. These three forms of
flow—laminar, turbulent, and shooting—differ
enough in velocity and in other characteristics
that they may be likened to fine, medium, and
coarse sandpaper in their ability to erode stream
bottoms. Laminar flows are gentle; they erode
the bottom slightly if at all and carry only the
smallest of particles—those of clay size. Turbulent flows, depending on their speed, can move
particles from clay size up to pebbles and cobbles. The fastest streams, including all shooting
flows, wear away solid rock and carry along
coarse particles at high speeds. All of the debris
of erosion that rivers deposit as sediment is
called **alluvium.** The valley floors of rivers are
covered with such sediment, and many ancient
sedimentary rocks originated in this way.

Turbulent currents move particles downstream mainly by lifting them up into the flow
or by rolling or sliding them along the bottom.
Smaller particles, clay and silt, are easily pulled
up into the flow by upward-moving eddies.
Once in the stream, the particles are carried
along in suspension; all particles so carried by a
stream at any one time are its **suspension load.**
The forward force of the moving current acts
more directly on the larger grains at the bottom,
pushing, rolling, and sliding them along. Particles moved in this way constitute the **bed load**
of a stream. Intuitively we grasp the idea that
the stronger the current, the larger the particles
it can carry in suspension or as bed load. The
measure of this ability to carry particles of different size we call **competence.** The greater a
stream's competence, the larger the particle size
it can carry; the straightforward way to measure
a stream's competence is by the largest particle
sizes it can carry.

Just as dump trucks of various sizes can all
carry sand, but some more than others, so do
streams carry similar loads, but in different
amounts depending on their size. The load of
particles of any size that a stream can transport
is called its **capacity.** Although the capacity of a
stream is related to its size, more important than
the width and depth of a stream is the amount of
water that flows in it—the **discharge,** or the
volume of water that flows past a given point in
a specified unit of time. Discharge is commonly

Figure 7-3
Streaming (tranquil) and shooting (rapid) flow are determined by slope
angle. Beyond a certain steepness of slope, slower, wavy-surfaced streaming
flows abruptly change to faster, smooth-surfaced shooting flows. Where the
slope again becomes gentle, the flow returns to streaming, the transition
being marked by a turbulent roller, or eddy.

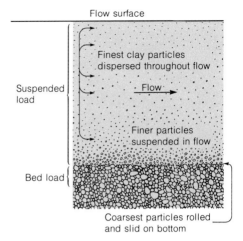

Figure 7-4
A current flowing over a bed of sand, silt, and clay particles transports particles in two ways: (1) as bed load, which moves by sliding and rolling along the bottom, and (2) as suspended load, which moves by being temporarily or permanently suspended in the flow itself. The finest clay particles remain permanently suspended in all but extremely sluggish flows.

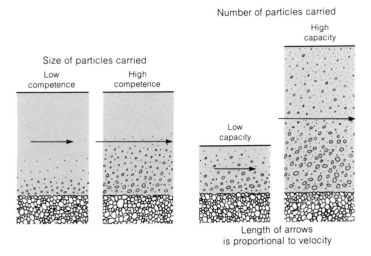

Figure 7-5
The competence of a current to carry particles is a measure of the largest sizes it can carry. The capacity of a current is a measure of the number of particles it can carry. Although both depend on velocity to some extent, competence depends much more directly on velocity, and capacity depends largely upon discharge, which is the volume of water flowing past a point in a given time.

measured in cubic meters per second or cubic feet per second. A typical small stream may vary in discharge from 10 to 10,000 cubic feet per second (0.28 to 280 cubic meters/second). The Mississippi River discharge may at times be as low as about 50,000 cubic feet/second (1400 cubic meters/second), but in flood may amount to more than 2,000,000 cubic feet/second (57,000 cubic meters/second). The Mississippi, though it can ordinarily carry only clay, silt, and sand, carries enormous quantities of those small particles; in contrast, a fast mountain stream may move boulders, but only a few of them.

A stream's competence for suspended load is a balance between the uplifting forces that turbulence exerts on particles and the force of gravity, which pulls the grains back down to the stream bed. Particles of silt and clay are so easily lifted and drop back so slowly that they tend to remain in suspension in all but the most still waters. The **settling velocity**—the speed with which particles fall through the fluid to the bed—is much greater for sand grains than for silt and clay particles. The typical movement of sand grains is an intermittent jumping, called **saltation,** in which they get sucked up by eddies into the flow, travel for a while, and then fall back to the bottom. The bigger or denser the grain, the shorter its travel time and the longer it rests on the bottom before being lifted again by a particularly strong eddy. The lighter the grain, the

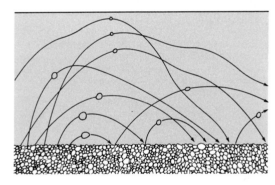

Figure 7-6
Saltation is an intermittent "jumping" motion of grains. Turbulent eddies pull grains up into the flow, where they travel with the flow for a distance and then fall back to the bed. In general, the smaller the particle, the higher it will jump and the farther it will travel. Turbulence keeps some very small particles suspended throughout a long travel path before they fall back to the bed.

more frequently it is picked up and moved along above the stream bed.

The measurement of the exact relations between current velocity and competence has been a major concern of geologists and hydraulic engineers who study transport of sediments by streams. Their objective is to use these measurements to obtain some idea of the nature of the sediment that is produced by a particular current so that they can work backwards to infer

Discharge is measured in practice at a gaging station, where the height, or *stage,* of a river is measured together with the velocity of the flow, from which the discharge can easily be calculated. There are now more than 7000 gaging stations in the United States.

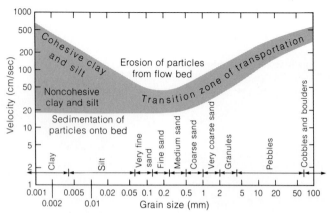

Figure 7-7
Experimental data on the relation between grain size of particles and velocity of a flow 1 m deep over a flat, granular bed. For a specific grain size, the lower line is the velocity at which all particles of that size will fall to the bed; the upper line is the velocity at which all particles of that size will continue to be picked up from the bed. The transportation zone is a transition zone in which particles already suspended will remain in the flow and in which there is no tendency for either erosion or sedimentation to take place. Cohesive behavior of most fine-grained natural materials makes them more resistant to erosion than noncohesive clays and silts. [After F. Hjulstrom, as modified by A. Sundborg, 1956, "The River Klarälven," *Geografisk Annaler.*]

Figure 7-8
Ripples in sand form in response to current action of wind or water. Their size and spacing increase as the current velocity increases. [Photo by P. E. Potter.]

the nature of ancient currents from the sizes of grains in sedimentary rocks. Engineers, for example, frequently want to predict what kind of sediment, and how much of it, will be brought in by a river to a lake behind a dam. Figure 7-7 shows the results of experimental measurements. From such a graph one can quickly read off the size of a particle that can be carried at a given velocity, or vice versa. This graph is applicable only to flows of one meter depth. The band indicates the lack of precision of the data from experiments in which it is impossible to control all factors completely and rigidly. The unexpected upturn that the curve shows for clay-size particles does not mean that they are harder to carry but that they are harder to lift from a smooth clay bottom because the particles cling together with strong cohesive forces.

Bedding and Sedimentary Structures. The movement of sand grains in current creates not only the familiar horizontal bedding planes but also ripples and dunes on the stream bed. **Ripples** in sand are the low narrow ridges that are separated by wider **troughs,** both of which can be seen on the surfaces of windswept sand dunes, on underwater sandbars in shallow streams, and under the waves at beaches. They come in an assortment of shapes, sizes, and

Figure 7-9
A ripple made by water flowing over coarse silt in a laboratory flume. The ripple, migrating from right to left, is about 10 cm (4 in.) high. Cross-bedding is clearly evident. Experiments like this help to reconstruct ancient conditions from ripple marks and cross-bedding in sedimentary rocks. [Photo by J. Southard, MIT.]

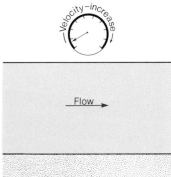

Figure 7-10
Flat bed in a flume experiment with steady flows at very low velocity over a sand bed. At this flow stage, sediment transport takes place by sliding and rolling motions of single grains. [After D. A. Simons and E. V. Richardson, 1961, "Forms of Bed Roughness in Alluvial Channels," *Am. Soc. Civil Eng. Proc.* v. 87, Hy3, pp. 87–105.]

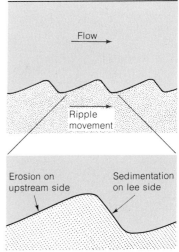

Enlarged view of ripple cross section

Figure 7-11
Rippled bed in a flume experiment. Major transport is by bed load and saltation. Ripples migrate downstream and have cross-bedded structure. [After D. A. Simons and E. V. Richardson, 1961, "Forms of Bed Roughness in Alluvial Channels," *Am. Soc. Civil Eng. Proc.* v. 87, Hy3, pp. 87–105.]

patterns that are characteristic of the currents that form them. Our main source of information is data from experiments done in laboratories where the streams of nature are simulated in flumes—long tilted channels in which the flow of sand and water can be controlled. Flumes allow careful measurement of velocity and other variables plus direct observation, through transparent side walls, of the ways in which grains move and accumulate on the bed to form ripples and stream dunes. Ripples, dunes, and a variety of other forms produced in the process of sedimentation are called **sedimentary structures.**

One of the best ways to obtain good data from a dynamic experiment is to hold all variables constant except one and to change that one variable systematically and measure the change in the result. In 1961, members of a U.S. Geological Survey group reported the results of their experiments on the mechanics of river flow with flumes. Using sensitive equipment and interpreting their results in terms of modern theory, they repeated a simple, classic experiment that was done in 1914 by one of the great geologists of that time, G. K. Gilbert. Imagine that you are redoing this experiment. Beginning with a flume containing a preformed, flat bed of sand grains, all of the same size, you start the water flowing as a very weak current by opening a faucet just a

crack. At this low velocity of flow, less than 5 centimeters per second (⅛ mile/hour), the current is too weak to move any grains, and the bed remains flat and undisturbed. Upon turning the water up a bit more to make the current a little stronger, a little more than 10 centimeters per second (¼ mile/hour), you begin to see a few grains here and there roll or slide short distances, and a rare one saltate briefly. The bed stays flat. After another increase in flow, however, you notice that many grains are saltating, and after a little while at this flow velocity, about 20 centimeters per second (½ mile/hour), small ripples a few centimeters high start to form all over the bed. Soon you notice that the ripples themselves are moving like waves almost imperceptibly downstream whereas the particles themselves move much more rapidly.

The ripples have a gentle slope upstream and a steep slope downstream: they are **asymmetrical ripples.** At the transparent sides of the flume, you can see the ripples in cross section and observe the inclined bedding that we call **cross-bedding.** Here, of course, the cross-bedding is on a very small scale compared to that seen in such rocks as the Coconino Sandstones of the Grand Canyon (Fig. 2-20). The angle of the cross-bedding is the angle of the downstream, or lee, slope of the ripple.

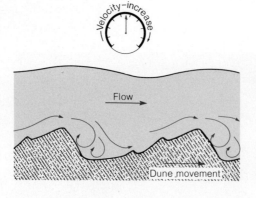

Figure 7-12
Rippled dune transport at moderate velocity in a flume experiment. Dunes have the same cross-bedded structure as ripples. Because ripples migrate downstream faster, they tend to climb over the backs of the dunes. Strong reverse eddies form in the lee of dunes. [After L. A. Simons and E. V. Richardson, 1961, "Forms of Bed Roughness in Alluvial Channels," *Am. Soc. Civil Eng. Proc.* v. 87, Hy3, pp. 87–105.]

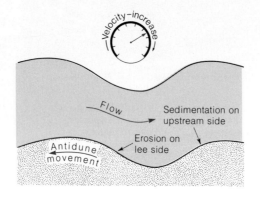

Figure 7-13
Antidune transport at high velocity in a flume experiment. Antidunes migrate upstream while there is extensive sand-grain movement downstream by suspension and bed load, almost the entire bed surface being in motion. [After D. A. Simons and E. V. Richardson, 1961, "Forms of Bed Roughness in Alluvial Channels," *Am. Soc. Civil Eng. Proc.* v. 87, Hy3, pp. 87–105.]

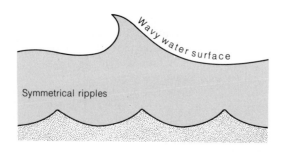

Figure 7-14
Oscillation ripples are symmetrical forms produced by waves. They commonly have much sharper crests than current ripples.

The next higher stages of velocity make the ripples move faster and grow larger, until they get many centimeters high, large enough to be called **dunes.** Dunes have the same general form and structure as ripples but are larger; they form under water as commonly as those that people more frequently observe forming under air. As the dunes grow larger in the flume, smaller ripples form and climb up their backs and disappear over the lee slope. Increasing the velocity still further, to more than 50 centimeters per second (1.25 miles/hour), changes the character of flow from streaming to shooting flow, and as it does the bed responds quickly: ripples and dunes disappear, and the bed becomes flat again.

But this time all the grains in it appear to be in rapid motion. Increasing the flow still more, to a velocity seldom met in rivers, produces a more irregular bed with some dune-like forms that move upstream and, finally, a complete washout of the whole bed of sand, which becomes suspended in the flow.

Sedimentologists—geologists who specialize in the study of sediments (there is hardly any subject that has not become a specialty by now)—have worked hard to infer from the ripples and cross-bedding preserved in rocks the kind and intensity of current that formed them. They have relied on flume studies and a knowledge of how fluids behave, coupled with obser-

Figure 7-15
Trough cross-bedding is produced on river bars as troughs are scoured and then filled with sand, building up a series of interfering structures as earlier ones are partly eroded. The open end of the trough always faces downcurrent, but the direction of crossbedding inclination may be variable, depending on the orientation of the exposure with respect to the troughs.

Figure 7-16
Potholes in granite ledges exposed at low water in the James River, Virginia. The pothole in the right foreground shows gravel at the bottom, which is the scouring agent that erodes the holes in solid rock. [Photo by C. K. Wentworth, U.S. Geological Survey.]

vations of how modern sediments, such as river sand bars and other sand accumulations are constructed. Such studies have shown us how to recognize ripples formed by wave action, for they are symmetrical and have much sharper crests than current ripples. Formed by the back-and-forth movement of waves, they are called **oscillation ripples.** Different cross-bedding forms are diagnostic of other environments. In river bars, for example, the current scoops out long, spoon-shaped troughs that get filled up by cross-beds, as in Figure 7-15, and geologists can recognize this pattern in ancient rocks.

Currents of wind act in the same way as those of water, except that wind is not confined to channels. And because air is so much less dense than water, its competence and capacity are on the average lower than those of water flows. Winds also produce a variety of kinds of sedimentary structures, which are covered in Chapter 8.

EROSION BY CURRENTS

Though it is obvious from observations of sediment transport that currents can erode a bed of soft sediment by picking up particles and carrying them downstream, one cannot so easily observe the erosion of solid rock by a stream, because it happens much more slowly. Here the analogy to the action of sandpaper (or sandblasting) is more apt, for much of the erosive power of a stream comes from the abrasion of the bottom by the sand and gravel it carries. Common on some river bottoms are pot-

holes—rounded depressions and deep holes carved into solid rock by sand grains and pebbles swirling in fast eddies. We rarely see the bedrock floor of a river except in rocky streams in mountains or where a stream crosses rapids, and even there most of it is covered by boulders of all sizes. The floors of most rivers that flow in broad valleys in plains or lowlands are covered with the sand, gravel, and mud that they carry. These rivers usually scour their bedrock bottoms only at high flood stages. The bedrock channels and walls of a river are eroded physically by a variety of other mechanisms. Just as in weathering on the outcrop, chemical decay along joints and cracks helps the breakup of bedrock, but here it is aided by the sledgehammer action of boulders slamming against solid rock. Chemical action is helped by a variety of organisms, among them the aquatic algae that attach themselves to rock surfaces (and make them slippery to cross). Once large blocks have been loosened by decay along joints, they are dislodged by strong upward eddies that literally pull them up and out by what amounts to violent, sudden suction. Channels at the bottoms of waterfalls

Figure 7-17
The Badlands of South Dakota, a region underlain by easily eroded horizontal sandstones and shales, which have been heavily gullied by slope wash, rills, and small streams. [Photo by N. H. Darton, U.S. Geological Survey.]

Niagara Falls has been carefully studied to learn the rate of its headward erosion. Historical records show that the main (horseshoe) part of the falls has been moving upstream at a rate of more than 1 m/yr,

One of the fastest eroding regions is the basin of the Eel River in Northern California, where 310 million tons of rock and soil was removed from 8000 square km (3100 square miles) in a recent 10-yr period. Some accelerated erosion may be the result of human activities, such as logging.

are eroded at an enormously rapid rate by the plunging action of the water and transported rocks, which fall with tremendous impact. Waterfalls are eroded and move upstream as the cliff that forms the falls is undercut and the upper beds collapse. This situation occurs where a nearly horizontal, erosion-resistant bed overlies more easily erodible formations.

Erosion of soft unconsolidated material by a river is much more obvious than that of bedrock channels and falls. Scouring and slumping of soft river banks is commonly seen at high water. Gullies in soils erode headward at a rapid pace. On a small scale, one can observe this kind of erosion happening during a strong rainstorm. Evidence of intense erosion of river banks, channels, and surrounding areas is widespread after a major flood.

Strong as this direct evidence is to us, it was not the only thing that convinced Hutton almost two hundred years ago that valleys—some deep and narrow, others low and broad—were eroded by the streams that flow in them. For Hutton, a key question was: where does all the sediment

carried by a stream come from? The match between the rocks and debris carried by a stream and the bedrock of the valley could be interpreted reasonably only as an indication of erosion. A clinching point was the stratigraphic matching of sedimentary beds on opposite valley walls. Because those beds were once continuous sheets, the discontinuity represented by the valley had to come later by erosion. The many lines of evidence, all supporting each other, lead to only one conclusion: valleys are cut into rock by streams. This does not always mean that the stream now in the valley is the one that cut it. As we will see in Chapter 9, mountain glaciers—rivers of ice—cut U-shaped valleys, and these are usually occupied by streams that inherited the valley after the ice melted.

THE RIVER AS A SYSTEM

Rivers have been personified as living things by various writers, who, like most of us, are affected by their constant motion and change. Rivers are dynamic systems that are some kind of balance between input and output. Overall, the inputs are all the water that reaches a river as surface runoff and groundwater plus the erosional debris from the entire area drained by it. The outputs are water and sediment, which are both ultimately carried to the ocean. In detail, any unchanging stretch of river has assumed a shape and a size in response to the input, so that output can match input. Changes in a river are the result of imbalance. Floods are obvious examples of a river channel's inability to carry off a suddenly increased input of water and sediment; the river responds by overflowing and "inventing" new channels or flow paths to carry away the water. When input decreases to normal, the river shrinks to its normal size.

As we noted earlier, the amount of water flowing past a given point per unit of time is the discharge, which is by definition equal to the cross-sectional area of the river multiplied by the velocity:

$$\begin{matrix} \text{Discharge} \\ \text{volume} \\ \text{(ft}^3 \text{ or m}^3\text{/sec)} \end{matrix} = \begin{matrix} \text{Cross-sectional} \\ \text{area of stream} \\ \text{(usually width times} \\ \text{depth in ft}^2 \text{ or m}^2\text{)} \end{matrix} \times \begin{matrix} \text{Velocity} \\ \text{(ft or m/sec)} \end{matrix}$$

Because rivers are generally wide in relation to their depth, and are fairly easily describable as simple rectangles in cross section, the width-depth relationship is more useful than cross-sectional area. Now we ask: what happens to width and depth as discharge increases—for example, as a response to increased rainfall runoff? Just looking at this relationship, one can see that the water will have to run faster, or the width or depth will have to increase, or some other combination of factors will have to change. We could think about what *might* happen for a long time, but the way to find out is to measure what actually does happen. Figure 7-18 shows some typical graphs made at a measuring station; the graphs show that there is a systematic increase in all three factors, width, depth, and velocity, as discharge increases. The proportion of increase varies from one stream to another, depending on the debris load of the river and the ease with which it erodes its banks and channel bed, for erosion is what widens and deepens a channel.

The amount of sediment that the stream carries—its transport capacity—is also related to the discharge. The higher the discharge, the larger the load of sediment, as is shown in Figure 7-19. There is also a relationship be-

Figure 7-18
Changes of width, depth, and velocity with discharge at a specific river station: Seneca Creek at Dawsonville, Maryland. The drainage area of this stream is about 260 km². Discharge is given in cubic feet per second. [After *Fluvial Processes in Geomorphology* by L. B. Leopold, M. G. Wolman, and J. P. Miller. W. H. Freeman and Company. Copyright © 1964.

tween discharge and the size of the material eroded or deposited, for the flow picks up or deposits material in accordance with the graph in Figure 7-7.

Discharge in most rivers increases downstream as more and more water is collected from tributaries. Inevitably, then, the width, depth, and velocity must change too. The progressive downstream change in these factors has been observed to follow a pattern similar to that shown by an increase in discharge at one place: width, depth, and velocity all increase systematically, width far more than depth. Velocity does not increase downstream as much as one might

Figure 7-19
Increase of suspended sediment carried by a river in relation to increased discharge at a specific river station: Rio Grande near Bernalillo, New Mexico. Discharge is given in cubic feet per second. [After *Fluvial Processes in Geomorphology* by L. B. Leopold, M. G. Wolman, and J. P. Miller. W. H. Freeman and Company, Copyright © 1964.]

expect from the increase in discharge, because the decrease in the downhill slope of a channel is accompanied by a decrease in velocity. After all, as Galileo showed the world 350 years ago, the steeper the slope, the faster the motion. The **longitudinal profile** of a river—that is, a plot of the relative elevation of its stream bed from headwaters to mouth—is concave upward, which is in accord with the steady downstream decrease in slope. Although the decrease in slope tends to slow the current, its influence may be overcome by an increase in discharge that makes the stream flow faster. In many rivers the discharge does not increase greatly downstream, and the lower downstream slope reduces the velocity. Because the slope is itself a product of the river's capability of downward erosion and the opposing capability of depositing sediment in its channel, the longitudinal profile is a response the river makes to the balance between input and output of water and sediments.

The concave upward longitudinal profile is remarkable for its generality; it evolves in small rills and large rivers, in natural streams and artificial water courses. Something so general must be bound up with some basic dynamics common to all streams. The downstream increase in discharge gives one clue. As it increases, we have seen, so in general do the width and depth of the stream. But as the width and depth increase, so does the ratio of cross-sectional area to perimeter. The effect of this increase is the same as that produced by increasing the diameter of a pipe: it allows the volume of flow to increase. The cross-sectional area, which partly governs the discharge, increases in proportion to the square of the radius (πr^2), whereas the circumference increases in proportion to the first power of the radius ($2\pi r$). The key here is that the circumference of a pipe or the perimeter of a stream is what controls the friction between the flowing water and the walls of the pipe or the banks and floor of a stream. As the volume of water increases, proportionally less of it is in contact with the sides, and so friction, which retards the flow, is relatively decreased. The less the friction, the more rapid the flow velocity. By these same kinds of analyses we can list all of the factors that change in the downstream direction that influence a river's longitudinal profile (Table 7-1). Putting all of these interrelated factors together in a single formula that would express quantitatively how a concave profile develops is a formidable task—one that has been only partially done. What is clear in a general way is that as they move downstream, rivers are

Table 7-1
Normal changes in flow properties in the downstream direction and effects on river flow.

Property of flow	Normal change in downstream direction	Effect on river downstream
Discharge	Increases	Velocity increases
Width	Increases	Ratio changes so that friction is decreased
Depth	Increases	
Velocity	Increases or decreases depending on changes in discharge and slope	Increases capacity to erode and transport
Frictional resistance to flow	Increases or decreases depending on perimeter and load	An increase causes decrease in velocity; a decrease causes increase in velocity.
Sediment load (suspension + bed load)	Increases	Increases friction
Size of sediment particles (gravel, sand, silt, clay)	Decreases	Decreases flow resistance
Slope of river bed	Decreases	Decreases velocity

able to transport more material of finer size at a higher discharge but at a lower slope. The concave upward profile seems to be another one of the steady-state equilibrium patterns that characterize so many Earth processes.

The longitudinal profile is also responsive to **base level**—the level or elevation at which the mouth of a stream enters a large standing body of water, a lake or the ocean, and so disappears as a river. Streams cannot cut below base level, for base level is "the bottom of the hill"—the lower limit of the longitudinal profile. A river may have a number of local base levels; for example, lakes or waterfalls along the watercourse form limiting levels that affect the flow of stretches immediately upstream. Changes of base level will cause a stream to change its characteristics, so that the water, sediment, and channel geometry come to a new balance. The most common adjustment to a raising of base level is predictable from the variables involved. The slope will be lowered, causing a reduction of velocity, which in turn decreases the stream's sediment-transporting ability. The stream then responds by dropping some of the sediment on the bed, which causes a change in the concavity of the profile, making it somewhat shallower than before. Lowering the base level increases the slope, the velocity, and the capacity to transport and erode the stream bed. The precise course of the change is predictable only when all of the flow-sediment relationships are known. For example, a stream greatly choked with sediment might be practically unaffected by a slight steepening of profile caused by a lowered base

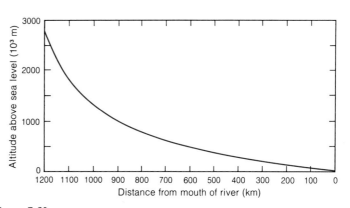

Figure 7-20
Longitudinal profile of the Platte and South Platte rivers from the mouth of the Platte at the Missouri River in Nebraska to the headwaters of the South Platte in central Colorado. This profile shows the typical concave-upward slope of rivers, much steeper at the headwaters than near the mouth. [Generalized from data of H. Gannett, in *Profiles of Rivers in the U.S.*, U.S. Geological Survey Water Supply Paper 44, 1901.]

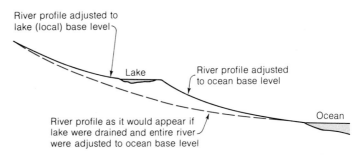

Figure 7-21
Regional and local base level as illustrated by a river flowing into a lake and from the lake into the ocean. In each river segment, the longitudinal profile adjusts to the lowest level it can reach. The lake may be a natural one or an artificial reservoir behind a dam. If the lake were drained and the river allowed to erode downward, the river bed would adjust eventually to a single concave-upward profile.

174

Figure 7-22
Change of base level and its consequences on a river profile. The original profile, adjusted to be in equilibrium with the regional base level, is altered when a dam is built. The dam impounds a lake behind it, which raises the local base level. The river responds upstream by adjusting its bed to a new profile as sediment is deposited in and in front of the lake, and it responds downstream by eroding its bed to a new profile with respect to the original regional base level.

Figure 7-23
Alluvial fans in the Mohave desert, California. Each cone-shaped fan has been deposited where the slope changes abruptly at the base of the mountains, and the fans have grown together at their feet, completely obscuring the original mountain slopes. [Photo by J. R. Balsley, U. S. Geological Survey.]

level, because the steepening would not be enough to make a significant increase in the load-carrying capacity in relation to the sediment supply.

The ways in which flow, sediment transport, and channel geometry adjust to changes in base level, so that a stream always seems to stay in balance, leads to the concept of the **graded stream.** An old idea, the concept was neatly expressed by the late J. Hoover Mackin, a leading American geomorphologist. He described a graded stream as "one in which, over a period of years, slope is delicately adjusted to provide, with available discharge and with prevailing channel characteristics, just the velocity required for the transportation of the load supplied from the drainage basin. The graded stream is a system in equilibrium; its diagnostic characteristic is that any change in any of the controlling factors will cause a displacement of the equilibrium in a direction that will tend to absorb the effect of the change." Rivers do this by forming a variety of depositional and erosional patterns and by altering the shape of the channel.

River Channels and Their Deposits. If you were to test a river severely to see how it would adjust to a change, you might pick out a place where a stream leaves a narrow valley in a mountainous area and suddenly enters a broad, relatively flat valley or plain. The change from the narrow channel of the mountain stream to the unconfined slopes of the plain is abrupt, and so is the response—a sudden slowing of velocity and an immediate dumping of sediment in a cone or fan-shaped accumulation called an **alluvial fan.** The fan itself normally shows the characteristic concave upward profile. On the steep upper slopes, alluvial fans are typically dominated by coarse materials, boulders and cobbles, gravel and sand; on their lower, gentler slopes, by finer sands, silts, and muds. Fans from many adjacent streams along a mountain will merge to form a long wedge of sediment whose external appearance may mask the outlines of the individual fans that make it up. As these compound fans grow upward and outward from a mountain front over thousands to millions of years, they build up extensive sedimentary accumulations many cubic kilometers in volume.

Channel Patterns. Streams running down alluvial fans will frequently break up into small multiple channels that branch into distributary

Figure 7-24
Formation of an alluvial fan as a stream adjusts its profile to a fault scarp.
The original fault slope is eroded above the fan as the fan is built upward
and outward from the base of the scarp in successive positions *A*, *B*, and *C*.

Figure 7-25
Braided stream choked with erosional debris, near the edge of a melting glacier. Muddy river, near junction
with McKinley River, Alaska. [Photo by B. Washburn.]

networks, and this too is a consequence of the sediment-flow relationship. Because the sediment load is large in relation to discharge, slope, and channel depth, the shallow channels tend to become filled, and the streams then break through their walls and form new channels. Many of the subsidiary channels will rejoin farther downstream, giving the stream as a whole a familiar pattern from which it gets the appropriate name **braided stream.** Braided streams are not restricted to alluvial fans by any means; they are also typical of rivers running in plains and low valleys—anywhere, in fact, where discharge is low in relation to sediment load and the stream cannot transport enough to maintain a single, deep channel. The braided pattern of multiple channels develops within the confines of a single larger channel, and there may be several scales of braiding, or braids within braids.

The word **meander** comes from the name of a river in Turkey fabled in ancient times for its twisting, winding course of looping bends. The word in geology refers to the more-or-less regular bends that may form in any river. Meanders are normal for rivers flowing on low slopes in plains or lowlands where the sediment is fine sand, silt, or mud, but in almost all kinds of terrain they are more common than long straight stretches of river. Nor are meanders restricted to rivers that carry sediment. They are common in meltwater streams on glaciers that carry no sediment. The Gulf Stream of the Atlantic Ocean meanders, and there appears to be a kind of meander pattern to jet streams in the stratosphere. Some meandering rivers have eroded deeply into bedrock. Meanders are common in streams flowing in limestone caverns, where they erode mainly by dissolving the limestone.

The three kinds of channel pattern—braided, meandering, and straight—each blend from one to the other without sharp division. Few long stretches of any river can be counted as truly straight; there are always some curves and

Figure 7-26
Meander bed and floodplain of the Animas River a few miles above Durango, Colorado. Looking northwest; river flows toward lower left. Farm buildings and roads give scale. [From *Geology Illustrated* by John S. Shelton. W. H. Freeman and Company. Copyright © 1966.]

Figure 7-27
Incised meanders of the San Juan River, San Juan County, Utah.
[Photo by E. C. La Rue, U. S. Geological Survey.]

bends. We call the measure of how straight or curved a river is its **sinuosity,** the ratio of its actual channel length to the straight-line distance down valley. A sinuosity of 1 corresponds to the perfect straight stretch. Meandering streams have sinuosities of 4 or more.

Rivers in straight channels do not flow precisely straight. The **thalweg**—the line of maximum depth of a river (usually close to the line of strongest current)—winds from one side to the other of straight stretches. Where the thalweg comes close to one bank, sand bars or mud banks tend to accumulate on the opposite bank, and a series of such bars may be found alternating from one side to the other along the channel. Straight streams also tend to have undulating beds in which shallows, called **riffles,** regularly alternate with deep spots, **pools,** usually at a repeating distance of five to seven times the channel width. Pools and riffles tend to form where there are many different sizes of sediment in the stream; the coarser sizes collect on riffles, where they may become gravel bars, and the finer sizes floor the pools. Riffles and pools, bars and mudbanks along straight rivers, and meanders all seem to show a wave-like regularity in their spacing, and seem to be different forms of the same general behavior pattern. These forms exhibit an even stronger similarity to wave-like behavior, for they all migrate downstream in much the same way that waves travel down a whipped rope. The patterns are stable. A river does not tend to meander one week and straighten the next. All of these facts support the

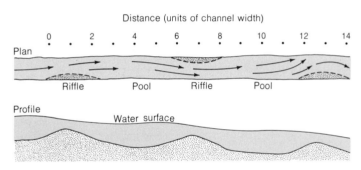

Figure 7-28
Straight reach of a river has a more or less uneven bed that consists of alternating deeps and shallows, known to trout fishermen as riffles and pools. The humps in the stream bed that give rise to the riffles tend to be situated alternately on each side of the stream at intervals roughly equal to five to seven times the local stream width. As a consequence the stream at low flow seems to follow a course that wanders from one side of the channel to the other, in a manner having an obvious similarity to meandering. [After "River Meanders" by Leopold and Langbein. Copyright © 1966 by Scientific American, Inc. All rights reserved.]

idea proposed by Luna B. Leopold and W. B. Langbein, two of our most acute analysts of streams, that a river tends to take the course of least resistance—to minimize the work it must do in running downhill with a certain sediment load along a certain slope. The characteristic channel patterns are appropriate "solutions" that rivers find for different sets of prevailing conditions.

Meanders, because they are so easily seen, have been studied the most. They move both downstream and to the side, and we have the

"Channelization" is a new word used to describe the artificial straightening of a sinuous channel to one with uniform gradient and cross section. This is done in an attempt to improve drainage and flood control and to reclaim wetlands of the floodplain for farming or urban development. Many channelization projects have led to adverse environmental effects, such as deterioration of aquatic life, accelerated erosion and silt deposition, and even poorer flood control.

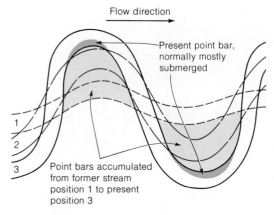

Figure 7-29
Lateral movement of river meanders gradually enlarges point bars: 1, 2, and 3 are three stages in the meander movement.

Figure 7-30
Formation of river-valley deposits by a meandering channel. As the meanders swing from one side of the valley to the other, they leave a train of point bar and channel deposits from former channel positions, overlain by finer-grained silts, clays, and occasional sands deposited by floods. Point bars are usually cross-bedded, and floodplain deposits are horizontally bedded and ripplemarked.

In *Life on the Mississippi,* Mark Twain humorously expressed his version of a common misunderstanding of scientific extrapolation: "In the space of one hundred and seventy-six years the Lower Mississippi has shortened itself two hundred and forty-two miles. That is an average of a trifle over one mile and a third per year. Therefore, any calm person, who is not blind or idiotic, can see that in the Old Oolitic Silurian Period, just a million years ago next November, the Lowest Mississippi River was upward of one million three hundred thousand miles long, and stuck out over the Gulf of Mexico like a fishing rod. And by the same token any person can see that seven hundred and forty-two years from now the Lower Mississippi will be only a mile and three-quarters long, and Cairo and New Orleans will have joined their streets together and be plodding comfortably along under a single mayor and a mutual board of aldermen. There is something fascinating about science. One gets such wholesale returns of conjecture out of such a trifling investment of fact."

results of numerous river surveys to show just how they do. The sideways movement is accomplished by erosion along the outside of the bend, where the current is strongest, and by deposition of a curved bar on the inside of the bend, called a **point bar,** where the current is weakest. Some meanders on the Mississippi shift as much as 20 meters per year. As the meanders move sideways and downstream, so do the point bars, building up an accumulation of sand and silt that covers the part of the valley floor over which the channel has migrated. Characteristic patterns of cross-bedding in these deposits have been recognized to be the same as those in ancient sandstones, in which the down-current direction of cross-bedding has proved to be a major clue to the direction of flow of river systems that date back hundreds of millions of years.

As meanders move, they may progress unevenly, so that the relatively straight parts between bends get closer and closer to one another. When they get close enough, the river may cut across to the next loop, shortening its course and leaving behind the abandoned bend as an **oxbow lake** (Fig. 2-2). These lakes soon fill up with mud and silt, which support the growth of reeds and other vegetation. The cut-off may take place anytime, but it is most likely to happen during a flood stage, when the stress on the

banks is high. The shortening is only temporary in comparison with the many thousands or millions of years of a river's lifetime, for new meanders are constantly evolving and enlarging, lengthening the course. Over a long time period on a given slope, the average length of the channel tends to remain constant. This is another way of stating that the river tends to maintain the same concave longitudinal profile.

The River Floodplain. As meanders migrate back and forth across a river valley, laying down deposits of gravel, sand, and silt in the channels as they go, they create a wide belt of almost flat plain (Fig. 7-30), called a **floodplain.** The name is appropriate, for it is this part of the stream valley that is covered with water when a river overflows its banks at flood stages. The areal extent of a floodplain may be large in proportion to that of the river channel itself. For example, the part of the floodplain of the Mississippi River that stretches from the junction of the Ohio and Mississippi rivers at Cairo, Illinois, south to New Orleans at the delta, embraces about 80,000 square kilometers (about 30,000 square miles). Floodplains of the Nile, the Tigris, and the Euphrates were important in history and prehistory for their rich agriculture on fertile silt and clay deposited at times of flooding. Floodplain deposits are of two kinds, coarse and fine. The coarse material, usually gravel and coarse sand, is deposited as channel beds or bars, which tend to be smeared out by lateral migration of the river. The fine material, silt and clay, may be deposited partly by settling action as flood waters spread over the floodplain, but much of it may be from the lateral migration of muddy banks and bars of the river channel. Some of the fine material comes from the fill of oxbow lakes. Some of the coarse material is channel sand and gravel that flows through breaches in the banks during floods, forming fans or linear accumulations that extend away from the channel, called **splay** deposits.

During floods, when a river overflows its banks, the flow of sediment-laden water rapidly decreases as it spreads out over the floodplain. Along the strip bordering the river banks, where the decrease is particularly rapid, much coarse sediment is deposited; lesser amounts of finer sediment are distributed more widely over the floodplain. In this way, successive floods build up ridges on both sides of a river channel, to form **natural levees** that confine the river within its banks between flood stages. Some levees have been built up many meters above the surrounding plain, so that the plain may be lower than the river surface. Rivers that carry mostly fine-grained sediment in suspension do not build natural levees, or at most deposit very low ones.

Rivers regularly overflow onto their floodplains, as any river-bottom native can tell you. Rivers reach the **bankfull** stage, that level in which the water completely fills the channel, every year or two on the average. They break their banks and flood every 2 or 3 years, again on the average. Most of these frequent floods are small. The larger ones come much less frequently. We speak of a "ten-year flood" as a flood of a certain discharge that has a probability of recurring every ten years. A fifty-year flood might be twice as big as the ten-year flood, but will recur on the average only once every fifty years. These are probability statements, not predictions, and the people who live in river towns have learned not to relax after one large flood in the false security that the next one will not recur for another so many years. The U.S. Geological Survey has published maps of the potential for recurrence of floods of given discharges in the United States.

A ten-year flood is a moderate event, normally only one and a half to two times the low flood that recurs on the average every year, the "mean annual flood." The fifty-year flood is more likely

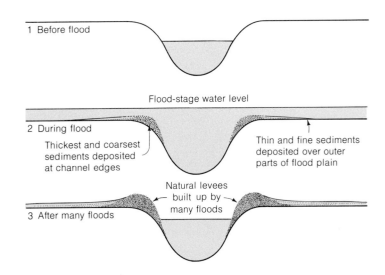

Figure 7-31
The formation of natural levees by river floods. As a river flood stage overflows its banks, it rapidly decreases in velocity away from the channel and drops most of its sediment, the coarser fraction near the channel and the finer fraction as a thinner layer of silt and clay over most of the floodplain. Successive floods build up the natural levees to ridges many meters high.

Figure 7-32
Floodwaters of the Feather River at Nicolaus, Sutter County, California, after a break in the river's levee during a flood in December 1955. The river channel is to the left (note broken bridge), and the break in the levee is in the left foreground. [Photo by W. Hofmann, U.S. Geological Survey.]

Figure 7-33
River drainage basins of central and southern Illinois,
showing divides between the rivers discussed in the text
and the hierarchical nature of drainage networks.

the few rivers studied is carried by floods that recur at least every five years—events of moderate intensity that happen often. Though the most infrequent events are very intense, they do not recur often enough to add much to the total. The amount transported by rivers in their everyday stages is too small to contribute significantly.

DRAINAGE NETWORKS

About fifty miles west of Denver, U.S. Highway 40 crosses Berthoud Pass at an altitude of 3450 meters (11,314 feet) above sea level. At the crest of this pass is the **continental divide,** the line west of which all water flows eventually to the Pacific Ocean and east of which to the Atlantic. The continental divide is a continuous line that runs north and south the length of North America, dividing the continent into two enormous areas that contribute water to the major river systems on either side. In northern Wisconsin, about 50 miles southeast of Duluth, on Lake Superior, near the town of Cable, U.S. Highway 63 crosses a fairly low east-west rise at an elevation only a few hundred meters above sea level. This rise is another continental divide, separating all of the water that flows to the north, to the Great Lakes and the St. Lawrence River, from the water that flows to the south via the Mississippi and its tributaries. These **divides** and all of the smaller ones, down to the ridges that separate small ravines, separate **drainage basins,** the areas that funnel all their water into the streams draining them.

A good example of the hierarchy of drainage basins and divides can be found at Springfield, Illinois, in the drainage basin of the Sangamon River (Fig. 7-33). To the south is the divide between it and the smaller drainage basin of Macoupin Creek. The rivers of both drainage basins empty into the Illinois River, and so Springfield is also in the larger Illinois River drainage basin, separated by a divide some sixty miles east of Springfield from the drainage basin of the Wabash River, which drains eastern Illinois and western Indiana to the Ohio River near Shawneetown, Illinois. And so it goes. The Ohio and Illinois both drain to the Mississippi, which is the master river of the whole drainage basin east of the north-south continental divide and south of the east-west continental divide. Figure 7-34 shows the Colorado River basin, a large region of the Southwestern United States that is drained by a single river system.

to be a catastrophic event, and may be as much as three times the mean annual flood. The floodplain is overflowed by a depth of water proportional to the magnitude of the flood. The fifty-year flood, for example, may cover the floodplain with a depth of water equal to about eight-tenths the bankfull depth, whereas the ten-year flood will be only about half the bankfull depth. The depths vary widely with the width of the floodplain and the details of its topography.

Does a river do most of its work of erosion and transport during everyday stages, during small or moderate floods, or during the major events that come only once in a generation? It appears that the great bulk of the sediment in

Figure 7-34
The natural drainage basin of the Colorado River Basin covers about 630,000 km^2 (243,000 mi^2), a large part of the Southwestern United States. [Modified from U.S. Geological Survey.]

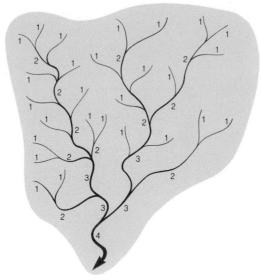

Figure 7-35
Order numbers of streams are designated by their position in the hierarchical network pattern. Streams of order 1 have no tributaries; those of order 2 have tributaries of order 1; those of order 3 have tributaries of order 2; and so on. The number of streams of a given order in a drainage basin decreases strongly as order number increases. Thus, in the illustration above, there are 27 streams of order 1, seven of order 2, two of order 3, and one of order 4.

Divides are not immune from change. By virtue of discharge, slope, or other factors, the stream on one side of a divide may be able to erode and transport much more rapidly than the stream on the opposite side. It may, as a result, break down the divide between the two at some place along it and take part or all of the drainage of the slower stream. Victorian geologists of the last century used a moralistic word for this kind of "capture" and called it **stream piracy.** The breaching of divides and capture of streams is common in small rills, becomes less common as streams grow larger, and is rare in large rivers. Piracy explains such oddities as narrow valleys or gorges that have no active streams running in them: the part of the stream that cut the valley was drained away, its course having been changed by the pirate stream.

The streams in all drainage basins follow certain rules. They all are connected by a one-way network by which smaller tributaries drain into larger ones with a definite pattern. The number of streams and their distance apart both follow a fairly orderly distribution. Most tributaries of about the same size are about the same length, and the intervals between the mouths of tributaries are fairly uniform. The larger the drainage area, the longer the stream, the ratio between the two being constant for similar terrains. Robert Horton, an American hydraulic engineer, used as a basic measure of the hierarchy of streams their **order**—that is, their position in the tributary network. A stream of order 1 has no tributaries; a stream of order 2 has tributaries of order 1; a stream of order 3 has tributaries of order 2; and so on. Thus the order is defined by the order of tributaries: we count up as we move downstream. As the order of streams increases, the following changes are systematic (see Fig. 7-36): the length of main streams increases, the number of main streams decreases, and the drainage area increases. These general characteristics of drainage networks seem to be exhibited by many kinds of systems. For example even the blood circulatory systems of mammals seem to have some of the same characteristics. Here, as in the meander story, there are some underlying laws that govern a wide range of phenomena that at first sight seem unrelated. Some believe these general patterns reflect the presence of a random element in the geometrical arrangement of all these networks.

Though all drainage networks branch in the same way, the shape of their patterns varies greatly from one kind of terrain to another, mainly as a response to the rock type or structural pattern of folds and faults. The most common is **dendritic** drainage, named for the characteristic pattern shown by most branching deciduous trees. This fairly random pattern is typical of terrain floored by uniform rock types, such as horizontal sedimentary rocks or massive igneous or metamorphic rocks. Differential weathering of fractures or joint systems in bedrock localizes stream flow, producing a more ordered and geometrical **rectangular** drainage pattern. A special variety of rectangular drainage, the **trellis** pattern, is formed where bands of rock resistant to weathering alternate with bands that erode more rapidly, typically in a region where rocks have been deformed into a series of parallel folds. Drainage from a central high point, such as a volcano or a domal uplift is **radial.** From this series of examples, one can see that drainage patterns reflect mainly the underlying structure of the rocks and their varying resistance to erosion, though the density of drainage depends more on climate. Areas of high rainfall tend to have many more streams

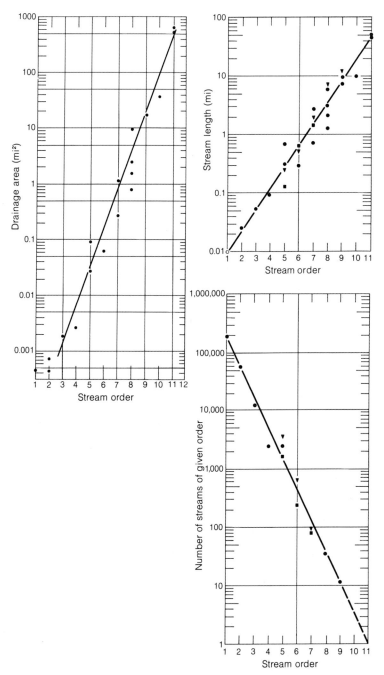

Figure 7-36
Relation of stream characteristics to stream order in drainage network of arroyos near Santa Fe, New Mexico. (Upper right) Relation of stream length to stream order. (Lower right) Relation of number of streams to stream order. (Left) Relation of drainage area to stream order. [After *Fluvial Processes in Geomorphology* by L. B. Leopold, M. G. Wolman, and J. P. Miller. W. H. Freeman and Company. Copyright © 1964.]

Figure 7-37
Typical dendritic drainage pattern, characterized by a branching pattern similar to that of the limbs or roots of trees.

Figure 7-38
Typical rectangular drainage pattern developed on a strongly jointed rocky terrain. Drainage tends to follow the joint pattern.

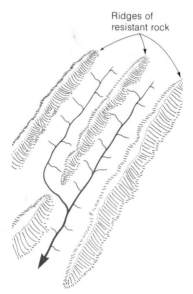

Figure 7-39
Typical trellis drainage developed in valley and ridge terrain, in which rocks of varying resistance to erosion are folded into anticlines and synclines.

Figure 7-41
The development of a superposed stream by erosion of horizontal beds unconformably overlying folded beds of varying resistance to erosion. As the downcutting stream encounters the buried anticline, it erodes a narrow gorge, or water gap, in the resistant beds of the anticline.

Figure 7-40
Typical radial drainage pattern developed on a large single peak, such as a large dormant volcano or a domal uplift.

than arid regions. One rock type, limestone, may virtually eliminate surface drainage in areas of high rainfall, because it dissolves to form caves and underground drainage. The northern part of the humid, rainy Yucatan Peninsula of Mexico has no streams because all of the water sinks into porous, cavernous limestone.

Geologic events may strongly control the course of a river. Streams flowing in a dendritic pattern on flat-lying sediments may erode through the sediments to expose underlying, strongly folded and faulted rocks of varying resistance to erosion. Because these **superposed** streams, preordained in their courses by their former bed of sediments, cannot break out easily to form a wholly new drainage pattern appropriate to the new bedrock, they adjust by cutting relatively narrow valleys or gorges through ridges of resistant rock, and elsewhere meandering through broad valleys in softer rock.

Drainage networks can be used for geological detective work. Near the mouth of one major river, pollution by a toxic chemical was discovered. The problem: to find the polluting source in a large drainage basin. By a statistical analysis of the branching of the different order streams, geochemists were able with a minimum of time-consuming sampling and analysis to eliminate quickly large sections of the basin and concentrate on the stream segment from which the pollution came. Better consideration of how drainage networks behave might have persuaded engineers and government leaders to avoid the environmental disasters caused by the building of the Aswan Dam on the Nile River in Egypt. The lower discharge and current velocity below the dam has promoted the spread of aquatic plants that choke watercourses and harbor parasitic disease organisms causing malaria and Bilharzia.

Sooner or later, the end comes to all rivers. But why? If a stream runs downhill on land, why doesn't it continue downslope under the waters of a lake or ocean until it hits the lowest spot? That rivers do stop when they empty into large standing bodies of water is so well known as to appear intuitively obvious. The answer comes from watching the behavior of a river as it enters the sea and mixes turbulently with the surrounding water. The mixing gradually transfers the powerful forward momentum of the flowing river to the surrounding water and dissipates the current. It does so in much the same way that a billiard ball shot into a large cluster of balls on a small pool table will lose its forward motion and transfer it to more or less random movements of all of the balls as they break apart and rebound from the cushions and from each other, gradually coming to a stop as friction overcomes their motion.

The current decays more or less gradually, depending on its volume and velocity. The discharge of the Amazon River, the world's largest, was recently measured at 4 billion gallons per minute (15 million cubic meters/second) by a team of U.S. and Brazilian hydrologists. The flow from the river maintains its integrity many kilometers out to sea. In contrast, small streams entering a turbulent, wave-swept coast may mix so rapidly that the current disappears almost immediately.

Delta Sedimentation. The dissipation of the river currents sets in motion a train of events that accounts for some major sedimentary deposits: deltas. The dying current loses its competence for transporting particles and so deposits the series of sedimentary layers that make up the delta. The simplest deltas are formed by modest streams entering fresh-water lakes. Because the density of the entering river water is the same as that of the surrounding lake water, the current mixes in all directions in a cone-like pattern and rapidly slows to a halt. The coarsest material is dropped first, followed by medium and fine materials farther out. In the usual situation, where the lake bed slopes away from the floor of the river channel, the coarse material builds up a depositional platform like that shown in Figure 7-43. **Foreset** beds, inclined downcurrent from the delta front in every way analogous to cross-bedding, are covered by thin, horizontal **topset** beds and preceded on the lake

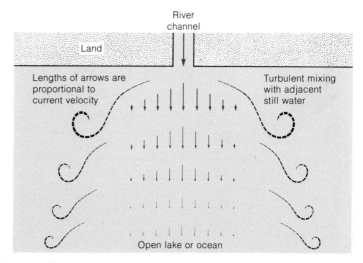

Figure 7-42
Decrease in the velocity of flow as a river enters an open body of water, such as a lake or an ocean. The current persists for the longest distance along the main line of flow and drastically decreases to either side. The current mixes with still water around the edges of the flow, losing momentum as it does so. [Data in part from C. C. Bates, "Rational Theory of Delta Formation," *Bull. A.A.P.G.,* v. 37, pp. 2119–2162, 1953.]

Figure 7-43
A typical fresh-water delta, characterized by well-defined topset, foreset, and bottomset beds. The slope of the delta front is fairly steep, up to 25°. The main river channel may or may not break up into distributaries, depending on the stream discharge and the sediment load: the greater the load in relation to discharge, the greater the tendency to form distributaries.

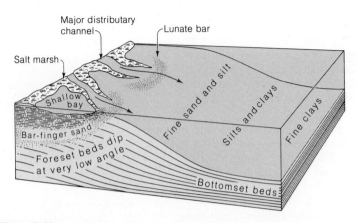

Figure 7-44
A typical marine delta, in which the foreset beds are fine-grained and deposited at a very low angle, normally only 4 to 5° or less. Lunate bars—crescent-shaped sand accumulations—form at the distributary mouths, where the current velocity suddenly decreases. As the delta builds forward, the bar-finger sand is built up by the advance of the lunate bar and the distributary channel. Between channels, shallow bays fill with fine-grained sediment and become salt marshes. This general structure is found on the Mississippi River delta.

bottom by thin, horizontal **bottomset** beds. This sequence has been reproduced, on a small scale, in laboratory flumes.

Deltas formed in the sea are generally the same in form but tend to be stretched out more in the horizontal dimension. The reason for this is that the fresh water of the river, (density about 1 gram/cubic centimeter) enters sea water (density 1.02 grams/cubic centimeter). The lighter fresh water tends to "float" on the sea water and consequently mixes with it only in two dimensions—horizontally but not vertically as in a fresh-water lake. A lower mixing rate means that the current dissipates more slowly, so that coarse, medium, and fine material spreads out along a much longer path. The slope of foreset beds on large marine deltas may be only a few degrees.

Major rivers, such as the Mississippi and the Nile, form large deltas thousands of square kilometers in area with complex structures. The Mississippi has been studied intensively for generations by hydraulic engineers responsible for the operations of the waterway and more recently by geologists trying to work out the relations between river, sediment, and sea that make it like it is. The Mississippi delta, like most others, reverses the normal dendritic drainage pattern in which smaller tributaries join to form bigger ones. As it approaches the

sea and lowers its slope, the river branches to form **distributaries** that funnel off the water in various paths to the sea, many small ones and three large ones near the mouth. At the mouth of main distributaries the coarsest sediment, sand, is dropped at crescentic bars, and silt and mud are carried farther out. The sediments at these distributaries grow seaward as long sand fingers, **bar finger sands,** whereas the finer muds and silts get washed by shore currents and waves into the bays between, gradually filling them up with mud and swamp deposits. In this way the whole delta is built out into the sea.

The delta of the Mississippi has been growing for many millions of years. It started out around Cairo, Illinois, in Cretaceous times and has advanced about 1600 kilometers since then. The pattern of its growth for the past few thousand years has been mapped by C^{14} dating of wood found by drilling into the different kinds of deposits at various depths (Fig. 7-45). Deltas grow in one direction for a while and then shift to another, seeking a shorter path to the sea. The individual subdeltas interfinger and partially pile up on top of each other to form a rather complex mass of sediment. Because of this complexity, recognition in the rock record of major ancient deltas formed hundreds of millions of years ago is no mean task, but the geologist has one good clue: the close juxtaposition of coarse

Figure 7-45
The Mississippi delta complexes of the past 6000 years are a series of major distributary centers that shifted with time as the river built its delta first in one direction and then in another. The oldest complex that has been mapped underlies the present area of Atchafalaya Bay and the mouth of the Atchafalaya River. It was succeeded by a series of deltas deposited to the east and west of the modern birdfoot delta. For more than a decade before 1955, the Mississippi River was diverting an increasing amount of its discharge to the Atchafalaya, an indication that the river was again about to shift its major site of delta building. At that time, the Army Corps of Engineers began construction to prevent major diversion into the Atchafalaya. [Map compiled from various sources, including C. R. Kolb, and J. R. Van Lopik, 1966, *in* M. L. Shirley (ed.) *Deltas in their Geological Framework,* Houston Geol. Soc.; D. E. Frazier, "Recent Deltaic Deposits of the Mississippi River: Their Development and Chronology," *Gulf Coast Assn. Geol. Soc. Trans.,* v. 17, pp. 287-315, 1967.]

sandy beds containing land plant or animal fossils with finer beds of the same age containing marine fossils. Parts of the Catskill Mountains of New York State have been deduced to be just such an ancient delta, formed in Devonian times. Coarse, land-deposited sandstone and conglomerate in the east, near the Hudson River, interfinger with finer marine sandstones and shales farther west. The river forming that delta came from a belt of high mountains roughly paralleling the Taconic and Green Mountains and ancestral to them.

Rivers Without Deltas. Not all rivers, even those that carry large loads of sediment, deposit deltas. Some enter the sea at places where a combination of waves, shore currents, and tides work together to move the sediment along the shore as rapidly as it is dropped by the river. In this way, the river's detritus is spread out along the coast, sometimes for hundreds of kilometers. A delta is formed only when the sediment load is great enough and the waves and ocean currents weak enough to permit it to form. Some rivers form small deltas of coarse material, the finer material—the bulk of the load—being swept away by waves and currents.

However rivers end their journey, they drop two kinds of load, the solid particles of rock detritus and the dissolved salts coming from weathering. The rivers of the Earth constitute the major transport system for the products of weathering, most of which end up in the sea. The sediment load of the world's rivers that is discharged to the oceans is estimated to be about 18 trillion tons per year. The material carried in solution in river water adds another 4 trillion tons per year. Water, however, is not the only agent that erodes, transports, and deposits. In the next chapter, we discuss another, the wind.

SUMMARY

1. Water flows in laminar and turbulent currents. Most natural streams flow turbulently and erode, transport, and deposit solid materials. Depending on turbulence, velocity, and slope, streams have competence to carry particles of a certain size and a certain capacity of total sediment load. Particles move by suspension, saltation, and rolling.

2. The sandy sediment deposited by stream currents typically shows crossbedding and ripples. Ripples, dunes, and flat surfaces form in an orderly sequence on sand beds as the velocity is increased.

3. Currents effectively erode unconsolidated material and hard rock by undercutting, scouring, sandblasting, and plucking.

4. The river is a dynamic system characterized by discharge, velocity, and slope. Changes in one are accompanied by mutual changes in the others as the river adjusts its longitudinal profile.

5. Longitudinal profiles tend to be graded in adjustment to base level.

6. River deposits are alluvial fans formed in response to a sudden change in slope. Channels form meanders and pools and riffles with regular patterns of point bars and other channel deposits.

7. Most of the buildup on floodplains happens during the moderately frequent, moderately high floods that come every few years.

8. Drainage networks show hierarchical branching patterns that follow rules of distribution. The pattern of drainage may be dendritic, rectangular, trellis, or radial, depending on topography, rock type, and structure.

9. Deltas are the major sites of deposition of sediment by rivers. They show a structure of topset, foreset, and bottomset beds that differs from lake delta to ocean delta. Not all rivers have deltas; the sediment of these rivers is dispersed by strong shoreline currents or tides.

EXERCISES

1. Predict the probable sequence of events that would follow the building of a dam on a river that has an ample supply of sediment and that is graded in equilibrium.

2. What could you infer about the changing current conditions that produced a series of sand beds in which the lowest beds are cross-bedded in a series of large interfering troughs, the middle beds finely rippled, and the highest beds horizontal with no ripples or any other structures?

3. Would you think that the ratio of first- to second-order streams in a trellis drainage system would be much greater than, about the same, or much less than the ratio of first- to second-order streams in a radial drainage system? Why?

4. In the middle part of its length, a major stream runs through a belt of cavernous limestone with Karst topography. How would its discharge-velocity relations be affected, and how might the drainage network pattern change?

5. You are the city engineer of a city of 100,000 population, built partly on the floodplain of a major river. Two years ago the city suffered the most disastrous flood in its 200-year history, and the city council now says that you need not worry about contingency planning for another major flood for the next few years. What would be your response to the council?

6. One popular engineering project used to control rivers is channelization—the artificial straightening and widening of the river channel. What natural changes might you expect to take place over a number of years after the river is left free to adjust its course naturally after channelization?

7. Both alluvial fans and deltas have drainage patterns in which a channel breaks up into a number of distributaries. Is there a common cause for this behavior? If so, what is it? If not, what are the causes in each case?

8. Given a simple drainage network of four first-order streams, each with a discharge of 100 cubic meters per second, that drain into two second-order streams and finally into a single third-order stream, what will the discharge become in the second- and third-order streams?

BIBLIOGRAPHY

Leopold, L. B., and W. B. Langbein, "River Meanders." *Scientific American,* June 1966. (Offprint No. 869.)

Leopold, L. B., M. G. Wolman, and J. P. Miller, *Fluvial Processes in Geomorphology.* San Francisco: W. H. Freeman and Company, 1964.

Matthes, G. H., "Paradoxes of the Mississippi." *Scientific American,* April 1951. (Offprint No. 836.)

Morisawa, M., *Streams—Their Dynamics and Morphology.* New York: McGraw-Hill Boook Company, 1968.

Morgan, J. P. (editor), *Deltaic Sedimentation, Modern and Ancient.* Tulsa, Oklahoma: Society of Economic Paleontologists and Mineralogists Special Paper 15, 1970.

Sundborg, Ake, "The River Klarälven. A study of Fluvial Processes." *Geografiska Annaler,* Uppsala University, vol. 38, pp. 125-316, 1956.

8

WIND, DUST, AND DESERTS

Wind, though less powerful than water currents, can erode sand and silt effectively, particularly in arid regions. The deserts of the world, sites of intensive wind action, display special varieties of topography and erosional and depositional processes that are intenser than those of humid regions. Sand dunes, depositional landforms created by wind, are heaps of sand that accumulate in different shapes and move in response to the abundance of the sand supply, the strength and direction of the wind, and the nature of the bedrock surface.

All of us have been caught, at one time or another, in a high wind so strong that it could have blown us over if we hadn't leaned into it or held on to something solid. A wind strong enough to move a body weighing more than 50 kilograms (110 pounds) is easily capable of blowing sand grains into the air, as anyone who has ever been in a sandstorm can attest. Wind is a turbulent stream of air, and its ability to erode, transport, and deposit sediment is much like that of water, for the same general laws of fluid motion that govern liquids govern gases as well. There are differences, of course, and they are traceable to two properties of wind: its low density and the fact that its flow is unconfined, not restricted to channels. The low density of air limits its competence to move larger particles, and the fact that its flow need not be confined enables it to spread over wide areas and high into the atmosphere. In contrast to rivers, whose discharge is dependent upon rainfall, it is the lack of rain that allows wind to work most effectively. Most rivers flow uninterruptedly for long periods of time; winds, on the other hand, can spring up and die down in a short time. In this chapter, we will discuss arid environments,

the deserts of the Earth, because so many of the geologic processes of the desert are related to the work of the wind. Winds are also important because they are coupled to the waters of the ocean as they blow waves into being and influence the general circulation of the oceans. A common term used to describe the activity and deposits of the wind is **eolian,** from "Aeolus," Greek god of the winds.

HOW MUCH CAN THE WIND CARRY?

Winds are highly variable in direction and power (see Table 8-1). Though the average wind on a breezy day might be about 15 kilometers (9 miles) per hour, gusts up to twice that speed occur intermittently and may spawn momentary dust or sand clouds. Most people in temperate climates are used to winds that come mainly from one direction, the prevailing westerlies. Those in the tropics are familiar with the equatorial easterlies. Yet within these belts the winds will be variable in direction and power, depending on the movement of air masses and storms.

Many of us live with wind fluctuations during the day, such as the sea breeze that blows during warm summer days and dies down in the evening, or the daytime valley breeze and nighttime mountain breeze in high-relief terrain. More constant are the steady, strong winds that blow for days without letup, like the dry Chinook winds of the eastern slopes of the Rocky Mountains and the Mistral that howls down the Rhone Valley of France in the winter.

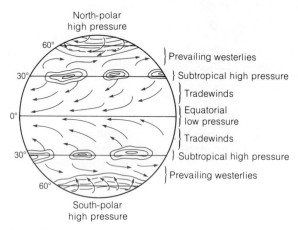

Figure 8-1
The global pattern of belts of surface winds and barometric-pressure cells. The subtropical high-pressure cells move somewhat and change size from summer to winter. Arrows show generalized wind directions.

The distribution and intensity of winds in combination with climate has much to do with the location of wind erosion and windblown deposits on Earth. The prevalence of sea breezes, for example, is responsible for the sand dunes blown back from sandy beaches along coasts. Most of the geologic work of the wind is done by the moderately infrequent strong winds of long duration, just as the major part of a river's geologic work is done by floods. Everyday mild winds and the rare tornado, whose winds may exceed 160 kilometers (100 miles) per hour but which covers only a narrow strip on the Earth's surface for a short time, are responsible for relatively little geologic change. Hurricanes and typhoons are important agents because of their frequency in certain maritime regions, but, because of the rain they bring, they do their work by causing floods and stirring up waves rather than by blowing sand or dust: their rain washes dust particles out of the air and wets down the ground surface, which prevents pickup of further particles. This points to dryness of the wind as a crucial prerequisite for erosion and transport.

Sand Transport. The wind exerts the same kind of force on particles on the land surface as a river current exerts on its bed, the turbulence and forward motion combining to lift particles into the windstream at least temporarily. **Saltation,** the bounding and jumping movement of

Table 8-1
Terminology of wind speeds, according to 1939 international agreement and U.S. Weather Bureau, with the effects of winds on the sea.

Beaufort number*	Wind speed (km/hr)†	International description	U.S. Weather Bureau description	Effect of wind on the sea
0	<1	Calm		
1	1–5	Light air	Light wind	Mirror surface to small wavelets
2	6–11	Light breeze		
3	12–19	Gentle breeze		
4	20–28	Moderate breeze	Gentle–moderate	Large wavelets to small waves
5	29–38	Fresh breeze	Fresh wind	Moderate waves, many whitecaps
6	39–49	Strong breeze		
7	50–61	Moderate gale	Strong wind	Large waves, many whitecaps, foamy sea
8	62–74	Fresh gale		
9	75–88	Strong gale	Gale	High waves, foam streaks, and spray
10	89–102	Whole gale		
11	103–117	Storm	Whole gale	Very high waves, rolling sea, reduced visibility
12–17	>117	Hurricane	Hurricane	Sea white with spray and foam, low visibility

Source: Based in part on N. Bowditch, 1958, "American Practical Navigator," U.S. Navy Hydrographic Office Publ. 9.
* The Beaufort scale was devised near the beginning of the nineteenth century as a way of measuring winds at sea by noting types and heights of waves, spray, and visibility.
† Today, wind speed is usually measured in knots (nautical miles per hour; 1 nautical mile = 1.15 statute miles or 1.85 kilometers).

grains that we explored in the previous chapter, operates in the air in the same way that it does under water, but in the air it is much more effective: partly as a result of the lower frictional and retarding force of the air, saltating grains will frequently rise to heights of 50 centimeters over a sand bed and up to 2 meters over a pebbly surface. In a strong wind, there can be so many saltating grains that there will be a cloudy layer near the ground dense with blowing particles and capable of sandblasting any object in its path. The saltating grains falling back to the ground hit the surface with all the force of the wind combined with gravity, hardly cushioned at all by the air. This strong impact induces saltation of some of the grains on the surface as they are struck. Its much wider effect is the pushing forward of struck grains, not enough to throw them up into the air but enough to cause a general forward creep of sand particles along the surface as the rain of saltating grains falls on it. A sand grain striking the surface can move another grain up to six times its own diameter. Because saltation blows smaller grains more quickly and surface creep moves larger particles more slowly, the two will sometimes separate: the fine sand blows away, leaving behind a pavement of coarser sand and gravel. The fine sand, up to 0.1 millimeter in diameter, accumulates in dunes and sheets downwind.

The amount of sand that can be moved by winds of various strengths is shown in Figure 8-4, taken from a famous book on sand and sand dunes by R. A. Bagnold, a British officer in the desert forces in Egypt and Libya. Before and during World War II, Bagnold pioneered the study of the forms and movements of desert sand. As can be seen from the graph, half a ton of sand per day can be moved over a meter-wide strip of ground by a strong wind of 48 kilometers (30 miles) per hour. As wind increases to gale force, about 80 kilometers (50 miles) per hour, the rate of sand movement increases more rapidly. No wonder that a whole house can be buried in a long sandstorm driven by strong winds.

Dust Transport. Turbulent winds can easily sweep small dust particles high into the atmosphere, once they are lifted off the ground surface. But it is not so easy for the wind to pick up small particles of clay or dust from the ground, mainly because, in a thin layer less than one millimeter thick right next to the ground surface, the air is practically still. Sand grains protrude through this layer into the windstream

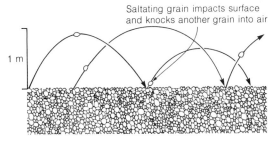

Figure 8-2
Saltation transport of sand grains in wind. As a saltating grain falls to the ground, it may strike another grain lying on the surface with sufficient force to throw the struck grain into a saltation trajectory.

Figure 8-3
Saltation layers formed during many windstorms will be so dense that the ground cannot be seen, yet the top of the layer may be sharp and the air above it clear.

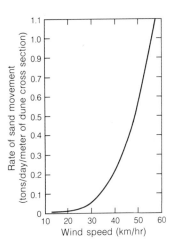

Figure 8-4
The amount of sand moved across each meter of width of a dune cross section in relation to wind speed. High-speed winds blowing for several days can move enormous quantities of sand and change dune positions markedly. [After R. A. Bagnold, *The Physics of Blown Sand and Desert Dunes*, London, Methuen, 1941.]

**The Skin of the
Earth: Surface Processes**

Edward Goldberg of the Scripps Institution of Oceanography has recently detected charcoal fragments in sediments of the oceans. They serve as guides to the extent of forest fires in the ancient ages during which these sediments were deposited.

above, and thus are caused to roll or saltate; smaller particles, however, are directly affected only at high wind speeds. But once a saltating sand grain or other particle hits the ground and kicks up a bit of dust, the wind catches it. Smaller dust particles, many of which are only a few thousandths of a millimeter in diameter, settle so slowly that the slightest air currents keep them suspended. Violent volcanic explosions can inject pyroclastic dust high into the stratosphere, and such dust may take years to settle.

The capacity of air to hold dust is enormous. In large dust storms, one cubic kilometer of air may carry up to 1000 tons; if such a storm covers hundreds of square kilometers, it may carry more than 100 million tons of dust. In the worst dust storms of the 1930s in the "dust bowl," the western plains of the United States, whole farmhouses were buried in the dust. The entombment of the Roman city of Pompeii was largely caused by a torrential fall of volcanic dust from Mt. Vesuvius. Wind erosion of dry plains plays an important role in denuding arable soils, a major reason why soil conservationists are worried about the preservation of our agricultural lands.

Detritus Carried by the Wind. Sand grains carried by the wind may be of almost any mineral, but most are quartz, which reflects the dominance of that mineral in most sands and

Figure 8-5
Dust storm raised by a northeast wind over the vineyard district of southern California. [From *Geology Illustrated* by John S. Shelton. W. H. Freeman and Company. Copyright © 1966.]

sandstones. The grains are typically frosted in appearance, like the ground-glass focusing screens of many cameras. It has been shown by experiment that much of this frosting results from the long-continued action of dew. This moisture, even the tiny amount that is found in arid climates, is enough to dissolve away little pits and holes on the grain, creating a matte surface. The frosting, which is limited to the grains lying on the surface of the ground, is quickly smoothed and polished when the grains are blown into a river and transported by water. This experimental and observational evidence, which includes studies showing that wind alone could not produce the frosted surface, contradicts a long-held inference that the matte appearance is the result of sandblasting, which is known to produce frosting on large glass objects. "Common sense," here based only on one kind of observation, doesn't always give the right answer in science.

Give the wind enough sand-sized rock or mineral fragments of any variety and it will blow them to form dunes. In Bermuda, for example, winds from the ocean have produced dunes made up of the calcium carbonate fragments of shells and coral. The White Sands National Monument area in New Mexico is largely covered by dunes of gypsum grains eroded from evaporite bedrock in a dry climate. In some places, clay and silt particles will clump together to form sand-size grains that are blown into dunes.

Dust, the fine-grained particles carried by the wind, is of every conceivable origin. It includes microscopic rock and mineral fragments of all kinds, but most common are the silicate minerals, as might be expected from their abundance as rock-forming minerals. Among these, two types are most important: clays from soils and volcanic dust. Pollen, hair, bacteria, and a great variety of fragments of plants and animals are also components of dust. Fragments of charcoal can be seen in dust blown from areas with forest fires. Since the industrial revolution, civilization has been producing a rapidly multiplying dust component consisting of particles of ash from burning coal and many solid chemical compounds from manufacturing processes. The burning in automobile motors of the tetraethyl lead that is added to gasoline causes the accumulation of large quantities of tiny lead particles in the atmosphere. Lead from that source may be a hazard to health in areas densely congested with automobiles.

WIND EROSION

Winds need chemical and mechanical weathering coupled to dryness to assist them in eroding and transporting materials. Wet materials are cohesive, the water binding the particles together enough to resist the wind's tendency to pull them apart. By themselves, winds can do little to erode most solid rock exposed at the surface; but once given some fragmentation of mineral particles, the wind can act.

Deflation. As dry, loose particles of dust and silt are lifted and blown away, the surface of the ground is gradually eroded and lowered, or **deflated.** This occurs on dry plains and deserts, on temporarily dried-up floodplains of rivers, on tidal flats, or on lake beds. Deflation is characteristic, too, of cold dry periods on the plains of mud, silt, and sand formed by melting glaciers. Where vegetation is firmly established, the effect of wind is small, both because the roots bind soil together and because stems and leaves break up the wind and shelter the ground. But where the vegetation cover is breached naturally by drought, or artificially by construction or deep tracks made by motorcyclists, deflation may attack and scoop out shallow depressions or hollows. Once started, the hollows grow as wind stress on the surface becomes more efficient, usually helped by rapid water erosion during storms.

Deflation can attack rock surfaces, detaching small fragments, especially from sandstones that weather to form loose grains, but formation of depressions in rock surfaces is slow from this cause alone, except in some desert areas underlain by soft, easily disaggregated sandstones. Deflation, by removing the fines from a heterogeneous mixture of gravel, sand, and silt, can produce a remnant surface of gravel too large for transport. Over thousands of years, the gravel accumulates as a layer of **desert pavement,** which protects the soil or beds below from further erosions. Deflation may be only part of the process that forms such pavements, for there is some evidence that pebbles just below the surface work their way up to the top in some manner, leaving behind a thin substrate of sand and silt.

Sandblasting. Armed with blown sand, a wind can effectively wear away and shape solid rock surfaces by the constant impact of grains. Such sandblasting accounts for some erosion

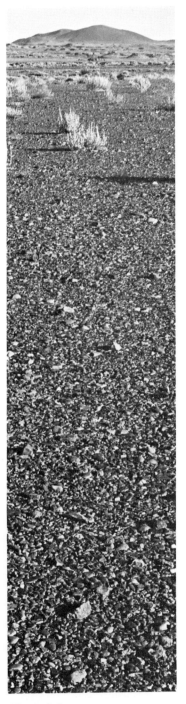

Figure 8-6
Desert pavement in the valley of the Little Colorado River, Arizona. [Photo by Tad Nichols, Tucson, Arizona.]

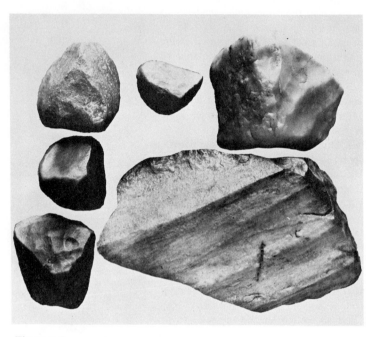

Figure 8-7
Ventifacts—pebbles and cobbles pitted and faceted by windblown sand. From Sweetwater County, Wyoming. [Photo by M. R. Campbell, U.S. Geological Survey.]

Figure 8-8
A Libyan desert landscape. In the foreground, a rocky pavement; in the background, sand dunes are gradually covering a rocky ridge. [Photo by G. H. Goudarzi, U.S. Geological Survey.]

and rounding of the parts of rock outcrops close to the ground, the frosting of smooth rock surfaces (and glass bottles), and the shaping of **ventifacts,** or wind-faceted pebbles. Such pebbles, which show several curved or almost planar faces that meet at sharp ridges, are almost invariably composed of a fine-grained rock, such as chert or quartzite. The pebbles are faceted by erosion of their windward side. Storms occasionally roll or rotate pebbles, thus exposing a new windward side to be sandblasted to a plane. As with frosted surfaces, ventifacts buried in deposits give us clues to strong wind action at the time of their formation. The main finds of ventifacts in most parts of the world have been in relatively recent glacial deposits; they are also common in deserts. Ventifacts are rare in older deposits, possibly because the combination of strong winds, sand for sandblasting, and pebbles to be shaped is a rare association that has been limited to regions affected by the few glaciations of the earth's history and to rarely preserved pebbly desert deposits.

DESERTS: MUCH WIND AND RARE WATER

The hot, dry deserts of the world are among the most hostile environments to humans, yet, with their strange forms of animal and plant life, and their barren forms of bare rock and sand dune, they exert a strong fascination for many people. If you get out into the desert, away from automobiles and trailbikes, you may find one of the stillest, quietest places on earth. You may also find yourself in a sudden windstorm, with sand stinging and penetrating everywhere. The desert is where the wind is best able to do its work of eroding and depositing. It does so in partnership with river action that, however infrequent, still does the major part of the work.

Where Deserts Are and How They Evolve. Maps that show average rainfall throughout the world show the great tropical deserts, such as the Sahara and Kalahari of Africa and the Great Australian Desert, all lying at about the Tropics of Cancer and Capricorn (latitudes 23°30′N and 23°30′S, respectively). These deserts are under virtually stationary areas of high atmospheric pressure. The stable high-pressure areas are characterized by continuously subsiding air that is warmed up as it sinks, producing low humidity. Tropical deserts normally receive less than 25 millimeters (1 inch) of rainfall each year, in some places less than 5 millimeters (0.2 inch). They are all on the westward sides of continents.

Another belt of deserts and semiarid lands are those of the middle latitudes—between 30° and 50° in each hemisphere—such as the deserts of central Asia and the Great Basin and Mohave deserts of the western United States. Here, dryness is a result either of distance from the great reservoir of moisture, the ocean, or of being in the rain shadow of a mountain range. The mountain ranges of the western coastal states of the United States and Canada cause moist air coming east from the Pacific to rise and cool, precipitating rain on their western slopes. When the air descends again on the eastern side, it warms and dries, carrying less total moisture than before. Thus rainfall is limited in the large arid and semiarid regions of the western interior intermontane basins. So the deserts, in a sense, are a matter of tectonics, for the rain-shadow deserts of middle latitudes are there by virtue of mountains produced by forces within the Earth, and tropical deserts are there because continen-

tal drift has placed the continents on which they occur astride the Tropics of Capricorn and Cancer. We may now see another way in which the external and internal heat machines of the Earth are linked. Deserts may evolve in areas that previously have been moist regions. A rising mountain range on the edge of a continent may interact with wind patterns to make deserts in their lee, where before there had been a more humid coastal plain. A large part of a continent, such as the Sahara, may be moved by plate motions into an equatorial arid belt, where before there had been a moister temperate zone. Indeed, there is good evidence that long ago, during the Ordovician Period, the northwestern Sahara was covered by glaciers.

In 1973, millions of people living in the Sahel, the semiarid southern borderland of the Sahara, were devastated by a drought unprecedented in historic times. This resulted in a real encroachment of the Sahara into these borderlands and an expansion of the desert. The reason for that expansion is under intense debate. In addition to natural climatic fluctuations, poor grazing and agricultural practices may have had

There is another kind of desert on Earth—cold, dry areas of the polar regions in which the frigid air is extremely low in water vapor. A special example is the dry valley region of southern Victoria Land in Antarctica, where extreme drought and cold make it the one environment on Earth that most closely resembles a Martian terrain.

Figure 8-9
Major desert areas of the world in relation to prevailing wind directions and major topographic elevations. Sand dune areas are only a small proportion of the total desert areas. [After K. W. Glennie, *Desert Sedimentary Environments,* Elsevier, 1970.]

Figure 8-10
Desert mountain slopes, partly covered with alluvium, looking down into Death Valley, California. In the distance is the Panamint Range. [Photo by H. Drewes, U.S. Geological Survey.]

The land area of the world is about 145,000,000 km². Desert and near desert areas are about 27,500,000 km² (about 19 percent) and semiarid regions about 21,200,000 km² (about 14.6 percent).

Great quantities of even the shallow groundwaters of arid regions are of marginal quality or too saline to drink because of evaporation in the unsaturated zone. Improvement of economic desaliniation techniques could greatly increase desert resources.

an important climatic effect, working to make what was merely a bad situation into a catastrophe.

All told, arid regions amount to one-fifth of all the land area of the Earth. Semiarid steppe and plains regions account for an additional one-seventh. Because the dynamics of the Earth that produce deserts have been operating through known geologic time, we must infer that deserts have always been present, though we cannot be sure that they always covered areas as extensive as those covered today. At certain times in the past, perhaps the Earth was even more extensively covered by deserts.

Erosion and Deposition in the Desert. As different as deserts are, there are no geologic processes that are unique to them. Weathering, downslope movements, and transportation operate in basically the same way in deserts as they do elsewhere on Earth, but with a different balance. Soils are thin or absent because of the lack of abundant vegetation and slowness of chemical decay of rocks, both of which are traceable to the lack of moisture. Organic-rich layers in desert soils are to be found only directly beneath the widely separated shrubs. What little fine soil is formed is likely to be blown away by the strong winds. Sand, gravel, rock rubble of many different sizes, and bare rock are characteristic of much desert surface.

The coarser, more heterogeneously sized fragments produced by desert weathering form steeper slopes than do the products of weathering in more humid regions covered by soil and vegetation. Desert slopes look, in some way, more like mountainous terrain above the timber line. Everywhere, the landscape is without the softening effects of vegetation and chemical weathering, which produce the characteristic rounded slopes and rounded rock edges. Instead, one sees steep cliffs and valley walls with masses of angular talus blocks at their bases. Yet chemical weathering is not completely absent. Many iron silicate minerals, such as pyroxene, will weather slowly in desert climates, producing the oxidized rusty-iron color of some desert detritus. Clays and soils do form, but slowly. The iron oxides that form from weathering may build up to a hard crust, called **duricrust.** Crusts of calcium carbonate, silica, and other minerals may also form.

Even the driest desert gets occasional rain. Rain falling on most desert areas may infiltrate permeable rock and surface debris to become groundwater. Some eventually reaches the groundwater table far below—as much as hundreds of meters below, in extreme cases—but most stays in the unsaturated zone, some of it very slowly evaporating. An oasis in the desert generally owes its existence to the groundwater table coming close enough to the surface for roots of palms and other plants to reach it. Some oases are fed by intermittent streams; being dependent on rainfall and runoff, they are seasonal.

Infiltration can be relatively slow; it may be virtually absent in areas with much impermeable rock. The rare heavy rain storm produces so much water in so short a time that it cannot all soak in; thus is born the desert intermittent stream. The runoff is rapid, being unhindered by vegetation, and may cause flash floods along valley floors that have been dry for years. Because the loose debris on the surface is not held by vegetation, the erosive power of such streams is great, and the streams become choked with sediment, sometimes so much so that they look more like mudflows than rivers. Because such a high proportion of stream flows in the desert are floods or nearly so, they are efficient eroders of valleys in bedrock. Valleys in the deserts have the same range of shapes, depending on the rock type, as those found elsewhere, but far more of them have steep valley walls caused by the rapid erosion. A normally dry valley, called a **dry wash** (in the Middle East, a **wadi**), is floored with a flat alluvial fill of coarse debris left from the last water flow; the ordinary features of levees and floodplains are absent. Alluvial fans (see Chapter 7) play a significant role in runoff in mountainous deserts because of the high sediment load of the streams coupled with the fast infiltration and loss of water in the normally permeable fan itself. Mudflows contribute much to alluvial fans of arid regions.

The drainage systems of deserts are widely spaced because of the relatively infrequent rainfall, but their patterns may be similar to those of other terrains—with one difference: because of water losses by evaporation and infiltration, many of the streams die out, never reaching across the desert to join larger master streams or the ocean. Because many deserts are associated with mountains, this discontinuous or **interior drainage** is compounded by dead-ended intermontane basins called **bolsons.** Such basins—whose drainage exits are blocked by faults in combination with alluvial fans or landslides—may be the sites of temporary lakes, **playa lakes,** formed by storm runoff. Playa lakes may last days, weeks, or longer before complete evaporation leaves a **playa,** a flat lake bed of clay, sometimes encrusted with salts precipitated during evaporation. Playa lakes that are highly alkaline may precipitate sodium bicarbonate or sodium carbonate. Others contain a variety of unusual precipitated salt deposits, such as borax,

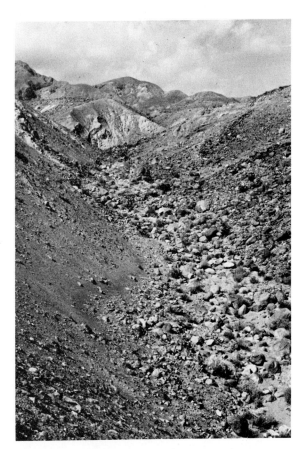

Figure 8-11
A desert dry wash. Such valleys are river channels only briefly during infrequent desert rainfalls. [Photo by F. Press.]

a sodium borate, $(Na_2B_4O_7 \cdot 10H_2O)$, which is quarried in California from ancient playa-lake deposits. Desert streams tend to contain a higher concentration of dissolved salts than those in humid regions because they redissolve salts deposited by evaporation from earlier runoff. The playas may start out fairly fresh and then become saturated with salts, the particular variety depending on the kinds of rocks from which they were weathered. Because of the unusual nature and great variety of minerals they contain, playa lakes are natural hunting grounds for geochemists interested in the ways in which salts are formed.

Deserts do not necessarily respect shorelines. Along the coast of the Persian Gulf, for example, on the shores of Saudi Arabia, the desert marches right up to the water's edge. There, the interplay of the tides, winds from the water, and sediment produces large flat areas just above the high-water mark that are crusted with a layer of

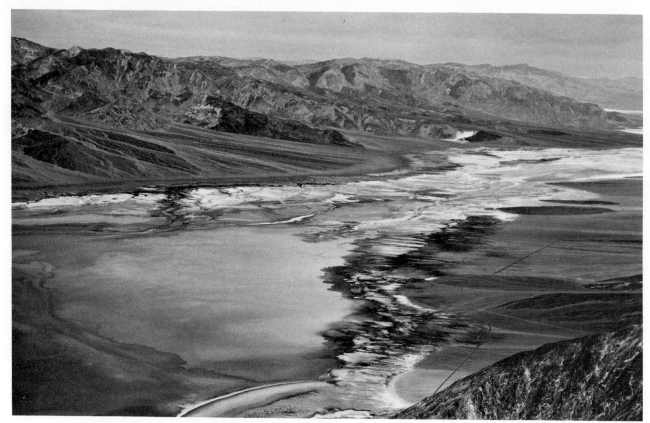

Figure 8-12
View of Death Valley, California, a desert playa, northwest of Dante's View. Surrounded by mountains and filled with debris from them, playas are intermittently occupied by lakes. Light-colored areas are salts, deposited by a Pleistocene lake. [Photo by Harold E. Malde, U.S. Geological Survey. Courtesy of Charles B. Hunt.]

Isolated erosional remnants elevated above pediments (similar to monadnocks) take a variety of forms. Some are spectacular pinnacles; others are rounded knobby masses or isolated rocky mountains called inselbergs (from the German, meaning "island mountains").

sandy detritus cemented with salt, gypsum, and calcium carbonate. This kind of flat, called by the Arabic word **sabkha,** is formed by the evaporation of salt water that has seeped upward by a wicklike action from a shallow sea-water table below, augmented by the drying of sea spray blown inland.

Erosion and sedimentation patterns are responsible for **pediments,** one of the characteristic landforms of the desert. These are broad, gently sloping areas of bedrock, spread as aprons around the bases of mountains. A cross section of a typical pediment and its mountain would show a fairly steep mountain slope abruptly changing to the gentle slope of the pediment. A pediment is an erosional surface covered with scattered detritus, which is normally more plentiful downslope, the lower surface of the pediment being covered with compound alluvial-fan deposits merging with the sedimentary fill of the lower valley or basin. The pediment is formed

by running water that builds up an apron of alluvium below as it continues to cut back an erosional platform above. As such, it is an evolutionary product of long-continued headward erosion of rock types (such as sandstones, shales, and volcanic tuffs) that are easily eroded in the desert environment. The precise way in which pediments evolve has been a subject of argument for most of this century, and there is as yet no widely accepted explanation.

For generations, Hollywood and TV westerns made in southern California and Nevada have shown us the kind of arid-land topography that is formed in regions of flat-lying sedimentary rocks: Tablelike uplands capped by flat erosion-resistant beds and bounded by steep-sided—sometimes vertical—erosional cliffs rise up prominently above pediments and desert flats. A mesa is a large upland of this kind, ranging from a few to many square kilometers in area; a butte is a small version of a mesa, being

Figure 8-13
A variety of sabkha flat (salt flat) formed in depressions in the desert interior. The white is a crust of salt formed by evaporation. Similar sabkhas form at desert sea margins where sea water laps onto tidal flats. [From G. H. Goudarzi, U.S. Geological Survey; photo by Harry F. Thomas.]

Figure 8-14
Stages in the evolution of a typical pediment, an erosional form produced in arid climates. The surface of the pediment is covered by thin deposits of alluvial sands and gravels, which merge downslope with the depositional surface of the intermontane basin sediments. The mountain slopes retreat steadily but keep about the same slope angle, in contrast to the rounded slopes in humid climates.

Figure 8-15
The evolution of a mesa is controlled by an erosion-resistant bed overlying weak, easily erodible rocks. The border of the mesa retreats as the lower beds are eroded, undercutting the resistant beds, which then break off as large talus blocks.

Figure 8-16
Desert sand "mountains" in the Saudi Arabian desert may reach heights of as much as 250 m
(820 ft). [From Arabian American Oil Co.]

only a few acres in area. The capping bed of a
mesa tends to maintain the upland level. If it is
breached, however, erosion cuts down rapidly
and creates the cliffs. As the cliffs retreat, the
upland area shrinks, finally leaving only a few
small, isolated mesas above the surrounding
lowland.

Large, small, or in between, the valleys and
uplands of the dry regions of the world, like
those of humid regions, are forms produced by
the eroding action of rivers. Even where water is
scarce, it is running water—however infrequent—that does most of the basic work of
erosion. The wind helps, but it rarely controls.
What the wind does control is the transport and
deposition of sand, shaping all the mounds,
ridges, and swirling forms of dunes.

DEPOSITIONAL LANDFORMS
OF THE WIND: DUNES

Erosion sculptures the rocks of the desert into
crags, angles, cracks, and blocks, but sand dunes
provide the soft forms of undulating slopes and
rounded lows, sometimes framed by sinuous,
sharp crestlines. The overwhelming impression
one gets standing in the middle of a dune field is
one of an incomprehensible mass of forms with
no order, all merging together. Yet, as with
everything else, there are patterns, but sometimes they can be seen clearly only from the air.
The patterns are not accidental: they depend
upon the kind and amount of sand available to
the wind, upon the underlying rocks, and, most
of all, upon the direction, duration, and strength
of the wind. The same factors determine where
dunes form.

Where Do Dunes Form? Though we may
think of deserts as being unending expanses of
sand dunes, only a small fraction of most desert
land is covered by sand. Only a little more than
one-tenth of the Sahara is sand-covered, and
sand dunes are far less common in many of the
arid lands of the southwestern United States.
Most people are more familiar with the dunes
that form behind beaches, such as the dunes of
Provincetown on Cape Cod, the Indiana dunes
on the south shore of Lake Michigan, and the

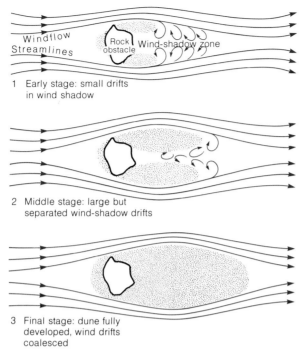

1 Early stage: small drifts
in wind shadow

2 Middle stage: large but
separated wind-shadow drifts

3 Final stage: dune fully
developed, wind drifts
coalesced

Figure 8-17
Formation of sand drift in the lee of an obstacle, such as a rock.
The obstacle, by separating the flow streamlines, creates a wind
shadow in which the eddies are weaker than the main windflow,
thus allowing saltating grains to settle and build up a drift. The
drift is a streamlined body built in response to the nonstreamlined
obstacle. [After R. A. Bagnold, *The Physics of Blown Sand and
Desert Dunes,* Methuen, 1941.]

coastal dunes of Oregon. Dunes may also form along the banks of some large rivers.

These places all have in common a ready supply of loose sand. Beach sand deposited by waves is the source of coastal dunes; in river valleys, it comes from the sandy channels and floodplain deposits of rivers at low water. In the desert, sand is produced by the weathering of sandy bedrock formations. Linked with the supply of sand is wind power. Shorelines are likely places for dunes to form because strong sea or lake winds tend to blow sand inshore away from the beaches. As we have noted, strong winds, sometimes of long duration, are common in deserts.

Dynamics of Dunes. Given adequate sand and wind, how does a dune start? Any obstacle to the wind can be enough to start the formation of a dune, be it a large rock, a clump of vegetation, or even a slightly humped-up pile of peb-

bles. Wind streams, just like water streamlines, separate around obstacles and continue slightly deflected, creating a wind-shadow zone in which the wind velocity is much less than in the deflected streams. Blowing sand grains are deflected with the wind stream. Many will, as they saltate, come to rest by chance in the wind shadow, as in Figure 8-17. There they stay, unable to continue their travels because of the lower wind velocity, piling up to form a sand **drift.** In a strong wind, you can perform this experiment yourself to see exactly how it happens.

If an obstacle is big enough to get a sand drift started, the drift soon becomes an obstacle itself. This is another example of positive feedback, in which the result of an action continues to enhance that action. If there is enough sand, and if the wind continues to blow in the same direction for a sufficient time, the drift grows into a larger mound of sand—a dune. Dunes may also form

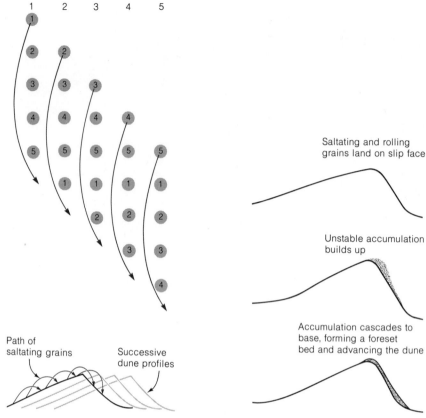

Figure 8-18
The movement of a column of people by sequential movements of individuals from rear to front (above) is roughly analogous to the movement of a ripple or dune by individual grain movements, though all the sand grains do not move sequentially in as simple a pattern.

Figure 8-19
The formation of the slip face of a dune. The slip face accumulates an unstable slope as a result of the deposition of saltating, rolling, and sliding grains. Intermittently, this accumulation becomes so unstable that it spontaneously slips—that is, cascades—to the base, and a new, lower-angle, stable slope is formed.

by growth from sand ripples, much as underwater dunes form in flumes and streams. Desert and coastal dunes are normally covered by ripples moving over them, just like the ripples that form on the surface of large underwater dunes.

As a dune grows, the whole mound starts moving downwind. The sand grains constantly saltate up the low-angle windward slope to the top, then fall over into the wind shadow on the lee slope, as in Figure 8-18. As grains accumulate on the lee slope, they spontaneously cascade down in little groups to keep a more or less constant angle of repose, which is the hallmark of this **slip face** of the dune (Fig. 8-19). The slip face, deposited at the angle of repose, creates the cross-bedding of the dunes.

As dunes accumulate, interfere with each other, and then become buried in a sedimentary sequence, the shapes of the dunes as they appeared under the wind are lost, but the cross-bedded structure remains. Cross-bedded ancient sandstone units many meters thick are evidence of high dunes that were most likely windblown, because underwater dunes are rarely that high. From the direction of the cross-beds, we can get the average direction of the ancient winds, or **paleowinds.** From this and other kinds of information, we can start to reconstruct ancient climates—**paleoclimates**—that can be harmonized with former positions of continental plates relative to the poles.

The height of dunes is determined by a switchover from positive to negative feedback. Positive feedback makes the little ones grow bigger by more rapid pileup of saltating grains on the windward slope than on the slip face, but only to a point. When the dune reaches a certain height, the windstream lines become "squeezed"

Figure 8-20
Dunes in the Arabian desert, showing the slip face of a large dune advancing on a sand-rippled surface. The grooved appearance of the slip face is formed by cascades of sand grains assuming the stable angle of repose. [From Arabian American Oil Co.]

upward and together by the mound of sand (Fig. 8-22). As more air has to rush through a smaller space, the wind velocity increases, ultimately to the point at which sand grains blow off the top to the advancing slip face as fast as they are brought up, and a steady state is reached. Exactly what that steady-state height is, of course, depends on the wind speed and the size of the sand grains. Dune heights of 30 meters (100 feet) are not uncommon, and some huge dunes in the Sahara may reach 100 meters (330 feet).

Dune Types. In an attempt to make some order out of immense diversity, dunes have been lumped into several major types, though there are gradations among them and many irregular shapes that are hard to fit into the scheme. The solitary crescent-shaped dune, the **barchan**, which moves over a flat surface of pebbles or bedrock, is a product of limited sand supply. Where sand is abundant, vegetation is absent, and sand dominates the landscape, dunes form in long, wavy ridges that lie transverse to the prevailing wind—hence, **transverse dunes.** These dunes have the same easily distinguishable slip faces as barchans, and they may grade into them at the edges of the dune field, where

Figure 8-21
Cross section of a sand dune, showing interfering sets of cross-beds, a response to variable wind directions. The appearance can be similar to the interfering trough cross-bedding of Figure 7-15.

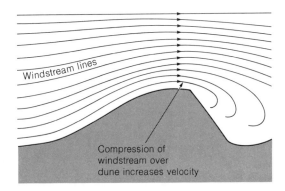

Figure 8-22
Limitation of the height of a sand dune by a compressed windstream. As the dune grows higher, the windstream (shown by streamlines) becomes more compressed and thus travels at a greater velocity, which makes it more competent to transport sand grains. Eventually, a height is reached at which the wind speed is so great that all of the sand is transported, and the dune stops growing vertically.

Figure 8-23
Aerial photo of transverse dunes on the Saudi Arabian desert, aligned in a general direction
at right angles to the prevailing wind direction. [From Arabian American Oil Co.]

the sand supply is more limited. Typical sandy-beach dunes are transverse dunes; in some places, a series of them may form back from the shore. The sand is supplied by the beach. In more humid regions, there is a balance between the rate of sand movement and the growth of vegetation, which binds the sand and stabilizes it, preventing further movement. If the vegetation of such stabilized dunes is overwhelmed by sand at some point along the shore, the dune migrates inland, forming a **blowout,** a dune shaped like a parabola. Blowouts may be natural, but these days, when beachfront vegetation is sometimes bulldozed away by home or road builders, blowouts are often the result of a crude upsetting of the sometimes fragile balance between vegetation and sand. Those who have tried it can speak with feeling of the difficulty of planting vegetation and getting it to grow and stabilize the dune once a blowout is on the move. Over many years, vegetation gets a chance

to stabilize the dunes as they move inland, farther from their source of sand on the beach. The hilly wooded or shrub-covered topography of shorelands in many places is one of overgrown, older, stabilized dunes.

Wind can blow sand into long, straight ridges more or less parallel to the prevailing wind—**longitudinal dunes,** or, as Bagnold called them, **seif dunes.** These dunes may reach heights of 100 meters and may extend many kilometers. Moderate sand supply, a rough pavement, and winds of several directions (but all of them in the same general quadrant of the compass) combine to form the long ridges.

DUST FALLS

No one had to teach the geology of dust deposits to western dust-bowl farmers in the 1930s. Their houses and croplands were buried by

Figure 8-24
Longitudinal dunes parallel to the prevailing wind direction in the Saudi Arabian desert. The upper photo is a view of the dunes as seen from the great height of a satellite (Gemini IV); the lower is a low-altitude airplane photograph. [From Arabian American Oil Co.]

dust. The extent of those dust falls was dramatic, but geologists had years earlier deduced such falls from thick deposits of unstratified fine-grained silt and clay called **loess.** Loess is composed of angular particles of quartz, feldspar, mica, and mafic minerals, mixed with abundant clay minerals. In North America, the origin of Pleistocene loess as windblown material was originally demonstrated by its pattern of distribution in the upper Mississippi Valley as a blanket of more or less uniform thickness on hills and valleys alike, all in or near formerly glaciated areas. Even more conclusive was the much greater thickness of loess on the eastern

Figure 8-25
Pleistocene loess, showing prismatic jointing, in Colorado.
[Photo by H. E. Malde, U.S. Geological Survey.]

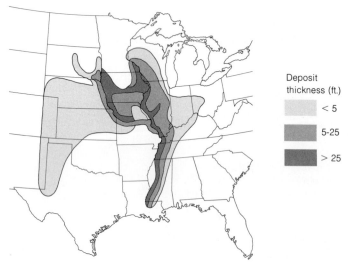

Deposit
thickness (ft.)

< 5

5-25

> 25

Figure 8-26
Loess and other eolian deposits in the central United States. The loess thins lee-ward from its sources along the major river valleys that discharged outwash in Pleistocene time. Westward, toward the Rocky Mountains, the eolian deposits on the Great Plains are sandy. [From *Geology of Soils* by C. B. Hunt. W. H. Freeman and Company. Copyright © 1972.]

sides of major river floodplains than on the western sides and the rapid fall-off in thickness and grain size farther east of the valley. The facts were consistent with deposition from prevailing westerly winds blowing over stream valleys carrying abundant silt and clay from the outwash of melting glaciers.

Loess is a distinctive sediment. It tends to form vertical cracks and walls when pieces break off during erosion, and it is frequently filled with thin tubes and nodules of calcite, most of them oriented vertically. The vertical cracking may be caused by a combination of vertical root penetration and uniform downward percolation of groundwater, but the details still await a good explanation. Loess is sometimes picked up and redeposited in river deposits, which, if not too well stratified, may easily be confused with the original windblown material. The correlation of the distribution of thin loess over parts of Illinois, Iowa, and adjacent states and the crop-producing capacity of those areas is not accidental. Soils formed on loess are some of the most fertile. They are also easily eroded into gullies by small streams and deflated by the wind when poorly cultivated. Ultimately, after the tragedy of the dust bowl, the fertility of the land was increased—no consolation to the thousands who had been driven from their farms, like the Joads of John Steinbeck's *Grapes of Wrath.*

Loess is found in deserts or downwind of deserts, as in China, where loess was deposited to thicknesses of 30 to 100 meters over wide areas by winds blowing over the arid lands of central Asia. Measurements of airborne dust far out to sea have been made by oceanographic research vessels and the mineral composition compared with the sediment at the sea bottom. Thus, dust has been discovered to be an important constituent of deep-sea sediments, perhaps accounting for as much as twenty percent. Much of the dust is traceable to volcanic activity and, as we noted before, volcanic dust falls are important eolian deposits. Volcanic dust may be the most important source of particulate matter in the atmosphere. Since particulate matter increases the power of Earth's atmosphere to reflect sunlight, it can affect our worldwide climate. There has been some speculation that modern civilization's pollution of the atmosphere by tiny particles of lead, soot, and thousands of other materials might raise the level of dust in the atmosphere enough that the Earth might cool by a small amount. People then envision the catastrophe of a new ice age. A sober look at the data, however, has convinced most scientists who have looked into the question that natural volcanic dust is far more important, and that the amount of it in the atmosphere has probably been fluctuating a good deal for much of geologic time. If doom befalls us in the form of a new ice age, at least it won't be the fault of the dust of modern civilization.

Last but not least, dust in the atmosphere provides us with some marvelous red sunsets.

SUMMARY

1. Winds are important agents of erosion and transportation, particularly in deserts.

2. The distribution of the wind belts of the Earth and the relation of winds to mountain ranges and shorelines are closely related to the locations of such windblown deposits as sand dunes.

3. Wind transports dust by suspension and sand grains by saltation. Air can hold enormous quantities of dust extending high into the atmosphere, but sand is transported in smaller quantities near the ground. Wind-deposited sand grains are frosted by the dissolving action of dew.

4. Wind erosion deflates arid regions and may produce desert pavements. Sandblasting facets and polishes rocks into ventifacts.

5. Deserts are located in a few tropic regions of stable high pressure and in the rain shadows of mountain ranges.

6. Erosion and deposition operate in much the same way in deserts as they do elsewhere but with different intensity, as a result of dryness, lack of vegetation to bind soil, and rate of river flows. Much of desert erosion is caused by rivers.

7. Drainage of deserts is widely spaced and normally interior, and may include playas and bolsons. Shoreline deserts form sabkha flats, in which carbonate and evaporite deposits may form.

8. Pediments are characteristic erosional forms of arid lands.

9. Dunes, the constructional products of wind deposition, form by wind action in deserts, behind beaches, and along some sandy river valleys. All dunes are crossbedded, and they fall into a few general types: barchans, transverse dunes, and longitudinal or seif dunes.

10. Loess is a deposit of windblown dust in deserts and in regions that were glaciated during the Pleistocene.

EXERCISES

1. Do you think a study of the shorelines of continents would show a tendency for coastal sand dune belts to be more abundant and wider on the eastern than on the western coasts or vice versa. Why?

2. In terms of visibility and sandblast, which vehicle would be more affected by a sandstorm—a low slung sports car or a high freight truck? Do you think the same would hold true in a dust storm?

3. You are asked to estimate requirements for hauling away windblown sand from a two-lane highway over which a dune is advancing in a region where the wind blows an average of 40 km/hr all day. What tonnage trucks would you provide, and how many trips would you make each week?

4. Describe a set of conditions that might again produce widespread dust storms similar to those of the 1930's in the western plains.

5. Describe the possible changes in the Sahara desert if the African continent were to move toward the north pole approximately 2000 km.

BIBLIOGRAPHY

Bagnold, R. A., *The Physics of Blown Sand and Desert Dunes.* London: Methuen Publishing Company, 1941.

Glennie, K. W., *Desert Sedimentary Environments.* New York: Elsevier Publishing Company, 1970.

Hadley, R. F., "Pediments and Pediment-Forming Processes." *J. Geol. Education,* v. 15, pp. 83–89, 1967.

Idso, S. B., "Dust Storms." *Scientific American,* October 1976.

Starr, V. P., "The General Circulation of the Atmosphere." *Scientific American,* December 1956. (Offprint No. 841.)

9

THE FLOW OF ICE: GLACIERS

Low temperatures and precipitation of snow contribute to the formation of glaciers and snow fields in cold polar regions and in high mountains. As snow accumulates, it becomes compacted, gradually changing from snowflakes to granules to solid, massive ice. As glacial ice moves down valleys, it sculptures the topography by eroding rock and transporting the debris to the terminus, where melting takes place. Glaciers of continental size, like those in Greenland and Antarctica, produce a variety of erosional and sedimentary landforms. The glacial landforms of the recent past are evidence of the Pleistocene glacial epoch, during which huge areas of North America and Eurasia were covered by ice. Advances and retreats of the ice fronts caused large fluctuations in sea level, alternately flooding and exposing shallow ocean margins of the continents. The causes of past ice ages and any predictions of future ones are equally uncertain.

Ice is a rock, a mass of crystalline grains of the mineral ice. That idea should not seem surprising; after all, it is a solid substance that occurs naturally on the Earth. It is hard like most rocks, but its composition makes it much less dense. It shares with igneous rocks an origin as a frozen fluid. Like sediments, it is deposited in layers at the surface of the Earth, and can accumulate to great thicknesses. Like metamorphic rocks, it is transformed by recrystallization under pressure. Masses of ice may creep, flow, or slide downhill, and just like other masses, they may be folded and faulted. A large mass of ice that is on land and shows evidence of being in motion or of once having moved is called a glacier. The motion of glaciers is the clue to the effective work they do in eroding the surface of the Earth into distinctive sculptural forms and in transporting rock debris and depositing it in various ways and forms. The movement of glaciers is now invested with a new and practical interest for humans: early warning of global climatic changes may be indicated by advances or retreats of glaciers. Glaciers are abundant on to-day's Earth. It is estimated that there are probably between 70,000 and 200,000 glaciers of all kinds and sizes in the world.

THE FORMATION OF GLACIERS

High altitudes and high latitudes have something in common, for they are both cold. High altitudes are cold because the lowest 10 kilometers of the atomsphere steadily cools with distance from the Earth, and high latitudes are cold because the angle of inclination of the Sun's rays increases toward the poles. In parts of the Earth that are high enough, or north or south enough, not all of the snow that falls in a year melts. It accumulates in **snow fields** and becomes transformed into ice. In the warm regions of the Earth near the equator, glaciers form only above about 4500 meters (about 15,000 feet). The altitude necessary for glacier formation decreases toward the polar regions, where ice is stable the year round at sea level. Because moisture-containing winds tend to drop most of their

Figure 9-1
Thrust faulting in glacial ice, showing its rock-like characteristics. The slanting
lines are a series of thrust faults along which the ice on the right was pushed to
the left and upward. Jointing and fracturing are also prominent in this photograph
of Susitna glacier, Alaska. [Photo by B. Washburn.]

The dry valleys of South Victoria Land
have been investigated by many kinds
of scientists in the past decade. The
Dry Valley Drilling Project sponsored
by Japan, New Zealand, and the
United States has drilled a number of
holes to find out the history of the
bedrock and glacial deposits of the
area.

Many of the terms used in glacial geology come from words used by the
Swiss and French people of the Alps.
The word "glacier" itself comes from
the old French of the Alpine province
of Savoy. *Firn* is a German-Swiss
word used for "last year's snow." The
word *névé* means the same as "firn,"
but comes from a French-Swiss dia-
lect word derived from the Latin word
for "snow."

snow on the windward side of a coastal mountain range, the lee side is likely to be cold but
desert-like, and lacking in glaciers. For example,
glaciers in the high Andes Mountains are limited to the western slopes; the dry eastern slopes
are barren of ice. Inland mountains far from
sources of moisture are not likely to have glaciers unless, as in Antarctica, it is so cold all year
round that there is no melting and all snow is
preserved. Thus, even arid climates, if cold
enough, will promote the formation of glaciers.
A few places along the coast of Antarctica,
however, are so devoid of moisture that no snow
falls, and the ground, though frozen hard, remains relatively dry and free of ice.

Most of us are familiar with ice-making from
the common experience of putting water into an
ice-cube tray and then freezing it in a refrigera-
tor. Those of us who live in northern regions
know that rivers and lakes freeze over in water.
Glaciers, however, do not just freeze; they grow
by a different process—the gradual transformation of snow into glacier ice. A fresh snow fall is
a fluffy mass of loosely packed snowflakes,
which are small, delicate ice crystals, grown in
the atmosphere. As the snow ages on the ground
for weeks or months, the crystals shrink and
become more compact, and the whole mass
becomes squeezed together into a more dense

form, **granular** snow. As new snow falls and
buries the older snow, the layers of granular
snow further compact to **firn,** a much denser
kind of snow, usually a year or more old, with
little pore space. Further burial and slow cementation—a process by which crystals become

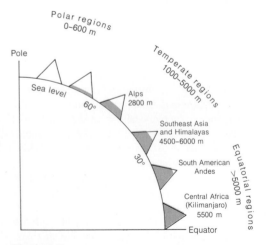

Figure 9-2
The height of the snow line, the altitude above
which snow does not completely melt in summer,
varies with latitude from at or near sea level in
polar regions to heights of more than 6000 m at the
equator. The exact height of the snow line varies
with local and regional climate.

bound together in a mosaic of intergrown ice crystals—finally produce solid glacial ice. One can think of snow as a sediment that becomes transformed by burial into the metamorphic rock ice by a process of **recrystallization,** the growth of new crystals at the expense of old ones. The whole process may take as little as a few years but more likely ten or twenty years or longer. The snow is usually many meters deep by the time the lower layers are converted to ice.

The formation of a glacier is complete when ice has accumulated to a thickness (and thus weight) sufficient to make the ice move slowly under pressure, in much the same way that rock deforms plastically deep in the Earth. Once that point is reached, the ice flows downhill, either as a tongue of ice filling a valley or a thick ice cap that flows out in all directions from the highest central area where most snow accumulates. The trip down leads to the eventual melting of ice. In medium and low latitudes, ice melts and evaporates as it flows to lower elevations. In polar climates the ice breaks off in huge chunks at the ocean's edge, and the chunks float out to sea as icebergs, which finally melt.

The Budget of a Glacier. During winter, the typical glacier grows slightly as snow falls everywhere on the ice surface. In summer, the glacier shrinks, mainly as the snow on the surface of the lowermost reaches melts and evaporates to uncover solid ice, while the upper reaches stay snow-covered. The annual growth budget of a glacier is the amount of solid water added by snow, the **accumulation,** minus the amount lost, called **ablation.** In temperate climates ablation takes place primarily by melting and in polar climates mainly by evaporation and sublimation—the transformation from solid to vapor without melting—as well as by breaking off of icebergs. The difference between accumulation and ablation is a measure of either growth or shrinkage of the glacier. When accumulation minus ablation, the net budget, is zero over a long time period, the glacier is in a steady state, accumulating new snow in its upper reaches and constantly moving downslope to the lower reaches, where ablation takes place. Glaciers' budgets fluctuate from year to year, and many show long-term trends of growth or shinkage in response to climatic variation over periods of many decades. Geologic evidence suggests that many glaciers have tended to stay very roughly in a steady state over the past several thousand years.

Because snow and ice vary so much in inter-

90% air

50% air

20–30% air

<20% air as bubbles

Figure 9-3
Stages in the transformation of snow crystals to granular ice as snow changes to nevé and glacial ice. Accompanying the change of individual crystals is an increase in density by elimination of air. [After H. Bader and others, "Der Schnee und seine Metamorphose," *Beiträge zur Geologie der Schweiz,* 1939.]

Figure 9-4
Icebergs calving from the Miles glacier, Alaska. As the ice meets the sea, it breaks into large irregular masses, many as big as a small island, to become icebergs. [Photo by B. Washburn.]

Figure 9-5
Melting of ice at the terminus of a glacier, showing the dark accumulation of debris at the wasting ice front and the formation of meltwater streams (lower left). [Photo by B. Washburn.]

nal air space, accumulations are measured by the height of a column of liquid water equivalent to the total amount of precipitation falling over each square centimeter per year. In the cold, dry interior regions of Antarctica, the accumulation may be only 5 centimeters; in the wet maritime climate of Iceland, however, a glacier may accumulate more than 300 centimeters each year.

In most temperate climates, ablation occurs primarily by melting under the Sun's rays and less by evaporation. Warm air may blow over the lower reaches of the glacier and speed melting further. The air becomes chilled in the process. If the air is humid, it may precipitate rain over the lower glacial slopes, causing even more ablation. The meltwaters of glaciers in some areas have assumed increasing importance as a possible source of fresh water for irrigation and other purposes. The city of Tacoma, Washington, gets hydroelectric power from a meltwater-fed river that originates in the Nisqually Glacier. In the cold of the Antarctic, where melting is minor, ice ablates more by the breaking off of icebergs and sublimation.

HOW ICE MOVES

Once the ice on a slope builds to a great enough thickness, it begins to flow downhill. The effect of thickness on flow can be demonstrated with a viscous fluid like honey. A thin layer of honey on a slightly tilted piece of bread will flow very slowly, but if more honey is poured on to increase the thickness, it flows much more rapidly. The speed of the flow can also be increased by tilting the bread more. The greater the thickness of glacial ice, and the greater its slope, the faster the movement of the glacier. The difference between the way ice flows and the way a brick slides down an inclined board is that the brick slides only along its base, whereas the ice moves throughout its bulk by internal sliding or flowing movements, as well as along its base.

Some glacial geologists think it is feasible to tow icebergs south from Alaska to provide fresh meltwater for water-poor areas along the West Coast.

Figure 9-6
Photomicrograph of typical crystalline mosaic of glacier ice. Sample is from the Antarctic Ice Sheet, depth 193 m, Byrd Station, Antarctica. Each grid measures 1.0 cm. Each small area of uniform white, gray, or black is a single crystal as seen in polarized light. The tiny circular and tubular spots are bubbles of air. [From A. J. Gow, U.S. Army Cold Regions Research and Engineering Laboratory.]

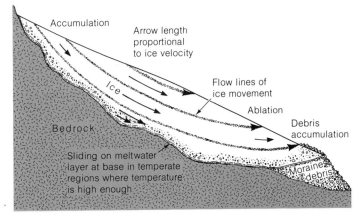

Figure 9-7
How ice flows in a typical valley glacier of temperate regions. The rate of movement decreases toward the base. In temperate climates, where temperatures at the base of the glacier are sufficiently high that the ice pressure will cause melting, the entire thickness of the glacier will move by sliding along the liquid layer next to the ground.

This internal flow throughout the ice accounts for much of its motion. Under the stress of weight, individual crystals of ice slip tiny amounts over distances of about a ten-millionth (10^{-7}) of a millimeter in short time intervals, but the sum total of all those small movements in the enormous number of ice crystals over longer time periods amounts to much larger movements of the whole mass. It could be visualized as a large bulk made up of many randomly arranged packs of playing cards, each pack held together by rubber bands, the whole thing moving as the sum of many small slips between cards in the individual packs. This kind of movement is similar to the movement shown by metals, which slowly creep when subjected to a stress—or to the movement of hard rocks at high temperatures and pressures when buried deep in the Earth. This movement is not the whole story. Other processes are at work also. Ice crystals tend to melt and recrystallize a microscopic amount farther downslope, and other crystal distortions result in movement.

The sliding of a glacier along its base accounts for an important part of the total movement; the ice at the base of some glaciers is near the melting temperature, and much of the movement takes place there. Some of the sliding is caused by melting and refreezing of the ice at the base. The melting results from some

combination of the pressure of the overlying ice and the flow of heat upward from the interior of the Earth. If enough melting takes place, a layer of liquid water forms at the bottom; such a layer was found when the bottom of the Antarctic ice sheet was penetrated by a drill at a depth of more than 2 kilometers below the surface.

In the deeper layers of ice, the solid material that might otherwise tend to be pulled apart by the forces of movement is held together by the compressive force of the overlying mass of ice. But the upper layers of a glacier have little pressure on them, and so the surface ice behaves as a rigid, brittle solid, becoming cracked as it is dragged along by the movement of the plastic ice below. These cracks are the **crevasses** that break up the surface ice into many small blocks near bedrock walls and at places where the ice surface steepens sharply in the direction of flow. The movement of the surface at these parts of a glacier is a "flow" resulting from slipping movements between these irregular blocks.

Well over a century ago, the first measurements were made of the speed of Alpine glaciers by placing stakes in the ice and noting the changes in their position over a few years. The stakes showed clearly that the center of the tongue of ice moved much faster than the edges, where friction of the ice against rock walls hindered the flow. The most rapid movement was

Figure 9-8
Crevasses in a valley glacier are deep cracks in the ice. They typically form along the sides of the glacier or, as in right foreground, across the glacier at a bedrock hump in the valley floor. Upper basin of Muldrow glacier, Alaska. [Photo by B. Washburn.]

One of the pioneers in the measurement of glacier flow was *Louis Agassiz,* a Swiss zoologist and geologist. As a young professor, not yet thirty, he built a hut on a glacier and, with the help of his students, mapped its movements. Twelve years later, he emigrated to the United States and became instrumental in founding glacial geology here.

about 75 meters (250 feet) in one year. Since then, a wide range of ice speeds have been measured, ranging from a few centimeters to a meter per day. It has also been shown that the base of a glacier moves more slowly than the upper parts, as shown in Figure 9-9. This was done by sinking a straight tube vertically into the ice and measuring its bending as the upper parts moved faster than the lower.

Sudden movements of glaciers, called **surges,** sometimes occur after long periods of little movement. Surges last more than two or three years and may travel at rates of more than 6 kilometers (3.7 miles) in one year. The movement comes largely from a sudden redistribution of ice from upper to lower parts of the glacier with little change in accumulation rate or in the total size of the ice mass. Debate goes on about whether surges are caused by periodic melting of the base of the glacier, allowing it to slide rapidly for a while until freezing slows it, or whether they are caused by intermittent releases of ice that gradually piles up in middle parts of

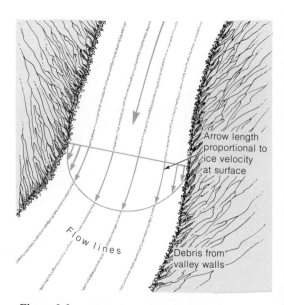

Arrow length proportional to ice velocity at surface

Flow lines

Debris from valley walls

Figure 9-9
A valley glacier moves most rapidly at its center, and with greatly reduced velocity along the valley walls.

Figure 9-10
Valley glaciers showing high snowfields and cirques in the background, tributary glaciers flowing down steep valleys, and their junction with the master glacier in the foreground. Harvard glacier, Alaska. [Photo by B. Washburn.]

the glacier while the lowest parts are melting. A few geologists think that the large number of surges that have been observed in recent years herald an era of glacial advance, a new ice age, but most glacial specialists think that these movements are peculiar to a particular variety of glacier that we have come to know better in recent years and whose movements have no global climatic significance.

SHAPES AND SIZES OF GLACIERS

On the basis of size and shape, we can easily divide glaciers into two general types: the **valley glacier** and the much larger **continental glacier**.

Valley Glaciers. The glaciers best known to skiers are valley glaciers, rivers of ice flowing downhill in narrow ribbons. They start as snow fields in the high slopes in amphitheatre-like hollows, **cirques**. As the ice forms from firn in the cirque, it flows down the course of the

valley, in some places passing over uneven slopes where the smooth surface of the ice may break up into crevasses. As the glacier moves down its valley, it may be joined by tributary valley glaciers. Unlike the waters of tributary rivers, however, the ice of tributary glaciers does not mix with that of the main glacier but runs along in separate streams, side by side. Another difference between rivers and glaciers is that although the ice surface is at the same level at the junction of glacier tributaries, the floors of the valleys at that place may be at very different depths below the ice surface, which is why there are **hanging valleys** where former glacial tributaries entered a main glacial valley, as in the Yosemite Valley of California, where Bridal Veil Falls plunges over the edge of the steep-walled valley.

Where valley glaciers terminate on land, streams of meltwater flowing on and under the glacier coalesce downstream to form a single river. Sometimes melting at the ice margin is uneven, and larger blocks of ice may be left isolated as the main part of the glacier melts back in warm weather. Glaciers ending at the

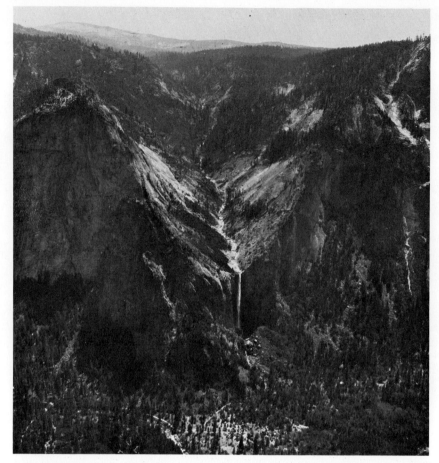

Figure 9-11
The hanging valley of Bridal Veil Creek, which empties into the main Yosemite
Valley by Bridal Veil Falls. The valley of the creek has not been strongly affected
by glacial erosion and retains much of its original V-shape. [Photo by F. E.
Matthes, U.S. Geological Survey.]

water's edge form cliffs of ice, many of them
standing from 30 to 60 meters or even more
above the lake or sea level. Because ice is less
dense than water, it floats; the buoyant force
exerted upon it, combined with the melting
action of sea water and tidal movements, breaks
off icebergs from the edge of the ice. The icebergs then drift with ocean currents (a hazard to
ships), many ending up in warmer waters where
they gradually melt.

The position of the terminus of a glacier,
which is a response to the balance between
accumulation and ablation, can be a sensitive
indicator of climate. In the 1930's, for example,
many glaciers were observed to shrink fairly
steadily by retreat of the ice margin up the
valley. This was just a part of a general warming
trend that had gone on since the middle of the

nineteenth century. Since 1940 there has been
evidence in glacial advances of a slight cooling
trend confirmed by world weather records.

Continental Glaciers. Enormous, thick
sheets of glacial ice cover nearly all of Greenland and the continent of Antarctica. These
glaciers are not confined to valleys, but cover all
the land surface. The 2,800,000 cubic kilometers
(672,000 cubic miles) of Greenland ice covers an
area of 1,726,400 square kilometers (666,560
square miles), about 80 percent of the total area
of the land. In cross section, the ice has the
shape of an extremely wide lens, convex on both
the smooth upper surface and the rough lower
boundary with the ground. At the center of the
ice sheet, in the middle of the island, the ice is
more than 3200 meters (10,500 feet) thick.

Figure 9-12
The evolution of hanging valleys and their waterfalls by tributary valley glaciers. (Top) During glaciation, tributary ice enters a major glacier at different levels. (Bottom) The region after deglaciation.

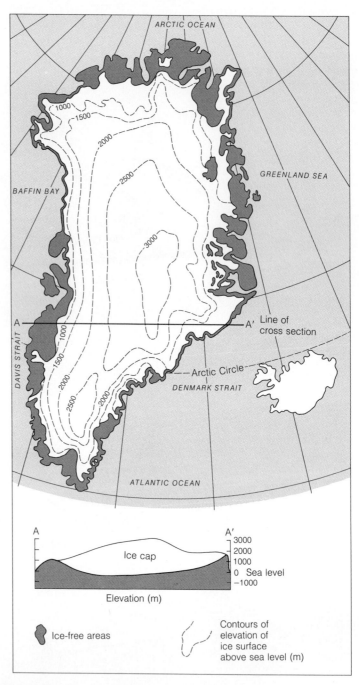

Figure 9-13
(Top) Map of Greenland, showing the extent of the glacial ice cap and the elevation of the ice surface. (Bottom) A generalized cross section of south-central
Greenland, showing the central depression of the rock floor and the lens-like shape
of the ice cap. The ice moves down and out from the thickest section. [Information
from J. Haller, *Geology of the East Greenland Caledonides*, Figure 2. Copyright
1971 by John Wiley & Sons.]

It is in the central area that the snow accumulates in a huge field of firn that gradually transforms to glacial ice. The ice surface is thus built up at the center and slopes to the sea on all sides. The glacier moves down and out in all directions. At the edge of the sea, where much of the coast is rimmed by high mountain ranges, the ice sheet breaks up into narrow tongues resembling valley glaciers that wind through the mountains to the sea. This glacier is the major source of icebergs in the North Atlantic.

As large as the Greenland glacier is, it is dwarfed by the Antarctic glacier, which covers more than 90 percent of the entire continent. The area covered by ice is about 12,500,000 square kilometers (4,830,000 square miles), and ice thicknesses exceed 3000 meters (10,000 feet) in much of the central area. In some ice-buried valleys, the rock floor of the ice is more than 2500 meters (8200 feet) below sea level. The ground beneath the ice is mountainous over much of the continent; in many places along the margins of the continent, mountains rise up through the surrounding ice. A conspicuous body of ice in the Antarctic, the Ross Ice Shelf, is a thick layer of ice about the size of Texas. The ice shelf floats on the water of the Ross Sea, but is attached to the main part of the glacier on land. In Antarctica, as in Greenland, the ice domes in the center and flows out to the margins, where it ends in much the same way as the Greenland glacier.

GLACIAL LANDFORMS

As both valley and continental glaciers move over their bedrock floors, they erode large quantities of material and transport it downstream. There it is deposited as the ice melts. An accumulation of rock, sand, and clay riding on the ice or left on the ground after the ice melts is a **moraine.** Glacial erosion and deposition produce a variety of distinctive topographic landforms made up of sedimentary debris, which are left behind as clues when the ice melts. From the study of those forms and materials and their comparison with those of modern glaciers came the suggestion that great polar ice caps may have extended far south into Europe and North America during a former epoch.

Abrasion and Sediment Transport by Ice. To anyone who has been in an alpine valley near the end of a glacier, the evidence is plain. As the ice melts, rock material of all sizes is dropped,

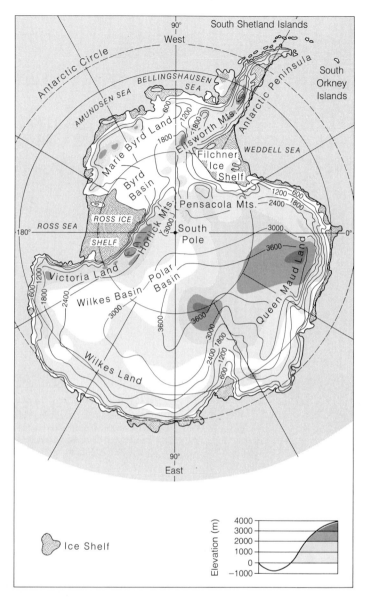

Figure 9-14
Contour map of Antarctica, showing the relief of the continental ice and the land beneath it. The relief of the ice is indicated by the black contour lines, and the height of the land is indicated by various shades of brown. The continental land that lies below sea level is shown in white. The black stippled areas are ice shelves. The black circle around the south pole is at 80° latitude; the next circle out is at 70° latitude. [From "The Antarctic," by A. P. Crary. Copyright © 1962 by Scientific American, Inc. All rights reserved.]

Scientists working in the Antarctic have drilled through the Ross Ice Shelf so that they could sample the water beneath it in the Ross Sea, a part of the Antarctic Ocean that had hitherto been inaccessible.

Figure 9-15
Moraines of the Northern Iliamna glacier, Alaska. In the middle background is the
present ice margin, and in the foreground a series of semicircular terminal moraines, called recessional moraines, deposited as the ice melted back from its farthest extent. [Photo by B. Washburn.]

Figure 9-16
A huge erratic boulder carried to Cape Cod during the
Pleistocene glaciation. The boulder is a metamorphic rock
type typical of areas in southern New Hampshire. Doan Rock,
Eastham, Massachusetts. [Photo by R. Siever.]

from the finest clay to huge boulders. The ice
itself can be seen to contain all of these materials, with by far the greatest part of the load
being near the base and along the valley walls.
As the ice melts back from the bare rock pavements over which it moved, it reveals parallel
scratches and grooves aligned in the direction of
ice movement. In many valleys of the Alps,
granitic rocks crop out high in the mountains,
and sedimentary rocks make up the lower
stretches of the valley. Yet in the lower stretches,
many of the boulders at the melting ice edge are
granitic blocks, some of them as big as a house.
All signs point to the conclusion that the ice is
the scraper that plucks, grinds, and tears rock
particles from the walls and floor of the valley
and drags them downslope.

Flowing ice does just as much work as running water does, only much better. The capacity
of ice to erode is great because it engulfs jointed,
cracked blocks in its solid mass and breaks them
against the rock pavement below, grinding both
into small grains, much into a fine pulverized

Figure 9-17
Glacial polish, striations, and grooves formed on a fine-grained granite surface. Sequoia National Park, California. The direction of ice movement was diagonally toward the right and away from the camera. Since the glaciation, the rock has been disrupted into angular blocks by repeated frost action. [Photo by F. E. Matthes, U.S. Geological Survey.]

rock flour. The scratches, or **striations,** are the relic of that action. Striations are clues to the direction the ice moved at that point. By mapping striations over wide areas, we can reconstruct the flow patterns of glaciers. Small hills of bedrock are smoothed on the up-current side and plucked to a rough shape on the down-current side. They too give us an indication of the direction of ice movement.

As a transporter of debris, ice is most effective because once the material is picked up by the ice, it does not settle out like the load carried by a river. Thus ice can carry huge blocks that no other transporting agent can budge. The carrying capacity of ice is tremendous: some ice is loaded with so much rock material that it looks more like a sediment cemented together with a little ice. Just how far the material will be carried depends on the length of the glacier.

Ice erodes and transports material from the sides of its valley with a special efficiency. Not only does it scrape the sides below the ice level, but the ice acts as a conveyor belt for any debris that happens to fall or slide from higher up on the valley walls onto the surface of the glacier. **Lateral moraines,** strips of dirt and rock that flow with the ice along the sides of valley glaciers, are remarkable tracers of the flow of individual tributaries. The lateral moraines of joining ice streams merge and form a single **medial moraine** in the middle of larger flows. The ice arrives at the end of the glacier carrying its load, some of it as clearly marked segregations of lateral and medial moraines, much of it in the basal layers, and the rest dispersed throughout the bulk of the ice.

Sculpture of Topography. Much of the kind of rugged mountainous terrain that has been celebrated for its scenic beauty is the product of glacial erosion. The Sierra Nevada, the Cascades, the Rockies, and the Alps all have high valleys that were filled with glaciers just a little more than ten thousand years ago, as evidenced by the signs we have learned to recognize: striations, large blocks carried from high in the mountains, moraines, and cirques. In the mountains of northern California, Oregon, and Washington, there are now only small relic glaciers left in the few places that receive enough snow and stay cold enough to preserve ice all year round. The rest of the terrain is exposed, and we can see the effects of Pleistocene glaciation. Farther north, in Canada and Alaska, glaciers become more numerous, but some of the ice-sculptured topography is still exposed.

Photographs of the surface of Mars suggest the possibility that glaciers may once have been active near its South Pole. Deep grooves may have been gouged by glaciers, and step-like terraces of rocky debris may be moraines.

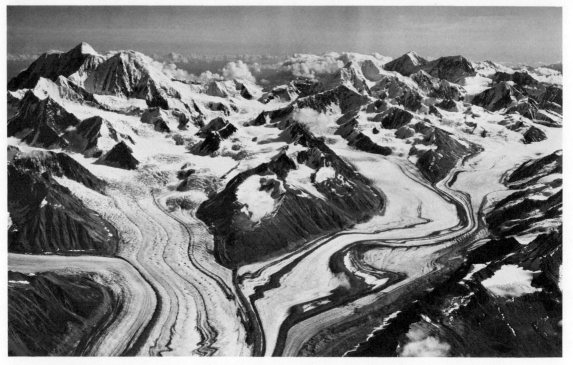

Figure 9-18
Forks of Susitna glacier, Alaska, showing how lateral moraines (dark bands), formed at the valley walls of the tributaries, coalesce to become medial moraines in the merged stream of ice. Irregular distortion and folding of bands reflects differential deformation of ice as it flows. [Photo by B. Washburn.]

Figure 9-19
Alpine sculpture of mountainous terrain by glaciers on the approaches to Mt. McKinley, looking up Ruth glacier. This region was completely glaciated in the Pleistocene; since that time the shrinkage of the ice has revealed the sharp, knife-like divides between adjacent valleys and the generally rugged topography. [Photo by B. Washburn.]

As glaciers ate away at the mountains, the topography acquired a distinctive appearance. Cirques were formed at the heads of glaciers as the ice plucked and undercut the highest peaks and ridges, and adjacent cirques gradually met to form knife-sharp divides. The result is a jagged, serrated, linear crest. The valleys were excavated to a characteristic **U-shape,** with steep walls and a flat floor, as the glacier scraped and rounded off irregularities. As the ice retreated, hanging valleys of glacial tributaries were exposed. Lakes formed in depressions in cirques. Most spectacular are the **fiords,** arms of the sea that occupy U-shaped valleys that were cut below sea level by valley glaciers descending from coastal mountains.

Depositional Landforms. If glacial erosion is accountable for rugged alpine topography, deposition of glacial debris is responsible for some of the most tried and true country scenes that decorate calendars: rolling hills, small lakes, and fertile fields. Plains in the Dakotas, rolling hills in Iowa and Wisconsin, Finger Lakes in New York, rocky fields in New England are all depositional products of a large continental glacier of a past so recent that its depositional landforms have not been obliterated by erosion. The many different elements that compose such varied landscapes, both in North America and in Europe, led Louis Agassiz and others of the nineteenth century to the hypothesis, now fully accepted as theory, that these parts of the Earth had recently gone through a great ice age.

In many of their characteristics, glacial deposits differ greatly from river, wind, or ocean deposits. In regions formerly covered by ice, the general topography tends to lack organized drainage networks, as though rivers had not had a chance to shape divides and valleys into a systematic, branching tributary pattern. Instead there are hollows with no outlets, some of which are filled with lakes. In some places there are isolated hills, in others long and sinuously winding ridges, none of which seem to have much relation to the underlying bedrock.

The bedrock is rarely seen in some of these regions. It is deeply buried, sometimes 50 meters (160 feet) or more. The ground over the bedrock is mostly a heterogeneous mixture of sand, clay, pebbles, and boulders rather than ordinary soil. Many of the pebbles and boulders differ entirely in composition from the bedrock. Some rare fossils in this material turn out to be the bones of extinct, large, arctic-dwelling elephants, the woolly mammoths. But mostly there are no signs of life at all.

Figure 9-20
View down Yosemite Valley from Glacier Point Trail above Union Point. At right is El Capitan. The U-shape of the valley is typical of glacially eroded terrain. [Photo by F. E. Matthes, U.S. Geological Survey.]

There was no way in which the geologists of Agassiz's time could relate all of these characteristics to erosion, transportation, and deposition by water or wind. It was this and the striking similarity of some landforms to the moraines and other products of modern valley glaciers that led to Agassiz's conclusion: glacial ice was responsible, but the areal extent of the various landforms is so great that the ice that produced them must have been a continental glacier like those of Greenland and Antarctica. Once the idea of a former continental glaciation gained acceptance, the many geologists who lived and worked in the northern provinces of Europe and North America began to realize that many of the landforms around them fitted the new concept of continental glaciation.

Glacial moraines proved to be important pieces of the puzzle. The hilly ridges composed of heterogeneous rock fragments, sand, and clay were recognized as **terminal moraines,** similar

Figure 9-21
Generalized geographic map of North America showing the maximum extent of glaciation in Pleistocene time. Arrows indicate direction of ice movement. [After U.S. Geological Survey.]

to those of valley glaciers, marking the farthest advance of the ice. Long before there was a glacial theory, the heterogeneous materials that make up moraines were thought to have "drifted in" somehow from other areas. The name applied then is still in use: **drift** is the name for *all* material of glacial origin found anywhere on land or at sea. The drift of moraines, heterogeneous and unstratified, was inferred to be the direct deposit of melting ice and was given the name **till,** a Scottish word for much of the rocky soil of Scotland. Mapping an ice front then becomes a matter of finding the limit of till, usually marked by a hilly ridge. Because a terminal moraine consists of till built up at the melting front of the ice, its height is a rough measure of how long the ice front remained in a certain position, its rate of ablation exactly balancing the rate of advance.

Terminal moraines may be deposited in the relatively shallow waters of continental shelves wherever ice pushes out from land at a level below that of the sea, as does the Antarctic Ice Sheet today. Cape Cod and Long Island are two of the best known of these moraines. Built up many meters from the sea floor by debris dropped from melting ice, such moraines are left as islands or capes when the ice melts. Because the areas behind some of these moraines are built up less by glacial deposition than the terminal moraine, they become flooded by the sea. Long Island Sound and Cape Cod Bay are two such areas.

In front of terminal moraines, no till is found. Instead, drift of another kind may be found— stratified deposits made up of the same kinds of materials as the till of the moraine, but well sorted by size into distinct layers of gravel, sand, or finer materials. The gravels are rounded and the sands are cross-bedded. This stratified material is glacial **outwash,** the drift caught up and modified, sorted, and distributed by streams of

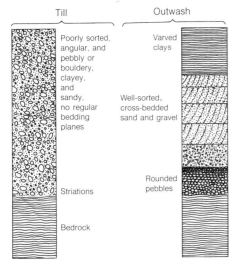

Figure 9-22
Comparison of generalized sections of glacial till and outwash. Till is a mixed, poorly sorted accumulation of material of all sizes left behind by melting ice. Outwash is a sorted, stratified deposit of water-transported drift.

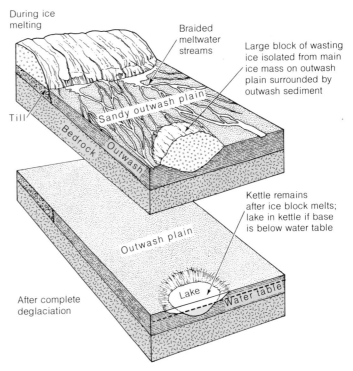

Figure 9-23
Evolution of an outwash kettle. As a glacier retreats, it may leave behind large blocks of wasting ice that are gradually buried by outwash from the receding ice front. After the front has retreated far enough from the region, outwash sedimentation stops, the ice block melts, and a depression remains, filled with water if it is deep enough to intersect the groundwater table.

meltwater running away from the glacier. Some of the outwash forms small hills, **kames,** where sand and gravel accumulated by meltwater streams were dumped near or at the edge of the retreating ice. Other accumulations show the structure and shape of deltas built out into lakes. These deltas, called **delta kames,** are left behind as flat-topped hills that are frequently exploited as commercial sand and gravel pits.

The gravelly kames grade into the silts and clays that are characteristic of lake-bottom sediments. The silts and clays typically show the alternating coarse and fine layers that we call **varves** (see Fig. 2-8). Putting all of this together, we infer that a stream of glacial meltwater once discharged into a lake near the ice front, building a delta of sand and gravel. The varved sediments of the lake are the finer materials that were carried in suspension beyond the delta. In summer, only the coarser silt was laid down on the lake floor. In winter, when the lake froze over, the water became still, and even the finest clay settled out. This concept of an annual cycle of deposition, by which pairs of mud layers of different lithology were laid down, was used to tell how long a lake had been in existence while the ice melted. By matching the varves of many lakes of different ages in a glaciated region, geologists were able to construct a chronology that revealed the total time elapsed

since the last glaciation. Some glacial lakes became very large. When the till dams that created them were breached, they may have drained rapidly, creating huge floods. The great dry channels of the "Scablands" of Eastern Washington are relics of a great flood caused by the draining of glacial Lake Missoula. From giant current ripples and other channel characteristics, geologists have estimated flow velocities as high as 30 meters per second and a discharge of 21 million cubic meters per second.

What of the hollows, the undrained depressions, or **kettles,** found in so many areas of both till and outwash? Many kettles in outwash are steep-sided and occupied by lakes or ponds. Again the clue came from observing the ablation of modern glaciers, many of which melt back unevenly, sometimes leaving behind immense, isolated blocks of ice, around which course streams of meltwater carrying glacial sediment. Imagine what would happen if a block of ice about a kilometer in diameter were left behind by a retreating glacier. A mass of ice that big

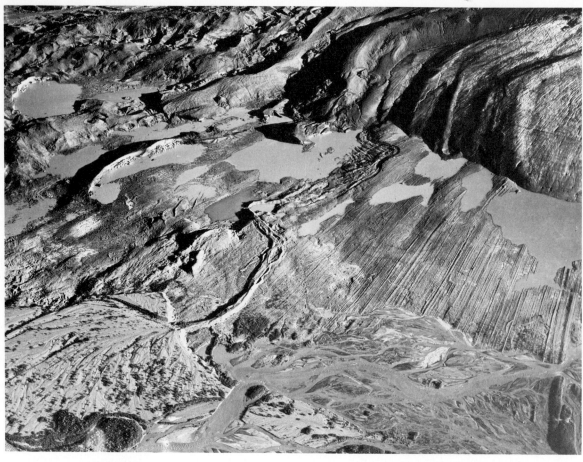

Figure 9-24
Retreat of the ice margin has revealed an esker formed by a stream that ran under the glacier. The esker is the winding ridge of sand and gravel running from upper right to lower left. The grooves at right are in soft glacial sediment and are not bedrock striations. [Photo by B. Washburn.]

would take a long time to melt—thirty years or more—and it might become partly buried by outwash sand and gravel. By the time it could melt completely, the main ice margin might have retreated so far that little outwash would reach the hole left by the ice block. If the hole were deep enough so that its bottom lay below the groundwater table, a lake would form.

The territory behind a terminal moraine has its own kettles and is rich in other forms created by ice movement and by meltwater. **Ground moraine** is a mantle of till deposited underneath the ice. It may be so thick that it completely buries bedrock everywhere, or it may be a relatively thin cover that exposes bedrock knobs and pavements in many places. **Eskers** are long, narrow ridges of sand and gravel situated in the middle of ground moraine. Varying

in height and width from a few meters to tens of meters, they wind for kilometers in a direction roughly parallel to the direction in which the ice moved. The well-sorted materials of eskers look like water-transported outwash, and the eskers themselves have the shape of stream channels; some even show "tributary" eskers. The deduction made from this geologic evidence is that eskers form from meltwater streams flowing in tunnels along the bottom of a melting glacier. The water seeps through crevasses and cracks in the ice and gradually opens tunnels that run downhill to the end of the glacier. Eskers, like kames, are favorite sources of sand and gravel for road construction and other uses.

Drumlins are streamlined hills of till and bedrock that parallel the direction of ice movement. The shape of a drumlin is like that of an upside-down elongate spoon with the gentle slope in the down slope direction. They may be 25 to 50 meters (75 to 150 feet) high and a kilometer long. Some drumlins are all till; others are largely bedrock with a cover of till. They may be formed either by ice erosion of an earlier till accumulation or by a subglacial shaping of accumulated till into streamlined forms. Knobs, drumlins, and irregular elongate hills of ground moraine are some of the different shapes taken by materials of different strength and resistance to erosion when overridden by an ice sheet.

Identification of a glacial landform is a matter of perceiving its shape, which is best done from a hilltop or a good topographic map, and matching the form with the nature of the material making it up. The contrast between the heterogeneous mixture of sizes and shapes of till and the rounded, evenly sorted gravel or sand of waterlaid, stratified drift is a good first guide. Just the presence of many lakes, swamps, and other undrained depressions is sufficient evidence to put one on the watch for other characteristic glacial landforms.

Permafrost. In cold regions where the summer temperature never gets high enough to melt more than the surface, the ground remains perennially frozen below the surface. Permafrost today covers as much as 25 percent of the total land area of the Earth. In Alaska and northern Canada it may be as much as 300–500 meters thick. Permafrost includes various proportions of ice and soil and contains aggregates of ice crystals in layers, wedges, and irregular masses. Permafrost is a difficult material to handle in engineering projects, such as roads, foundations, and the Alaska pipeline, because when the surface melts, the water cannot infiltrate the still-frozen ground below and the wet soil may creep, slide, and slump.

Glacial Topography and Culture. Three-quarters of a century ago, a geologist in Illinois said that he could predict voting habits by where people lived with respect to glacial drift. The northern part of the state is covered with fertile black soil formed on relatively unweathered glacial till deposited during the most recent glaciation, which ended about 10,000 years ago. There lay the voting strength of the prosperous Republican farmers. South of the terminal moraine that records that glaciation, the land is far less productive; gray clayey soil was formed on a till of an older glaciation. The much greater time elapsed since the older glaciation, more

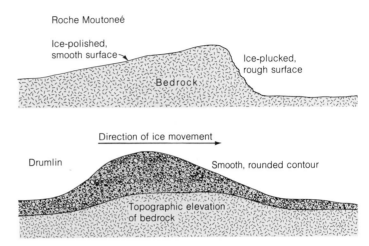

Figure 9-25
Two similarly shaped glacial landforms. (Top) Roche Moutoneé, a polished rock knob, is formed as the ice rides over a bedrock protuberance, smoothing the side facing the direction from which the ice moved and roughening the downflow side by plucking cracked and jointed rock. (Bottom) Drumlins are composed of till; some have a bedrock base with a streamlined shape formed by ice movement. The steep side commonly faces the direction from which the ice came, but the reverse is also found.

than 60,000 years, allowed deep weathering that reduced its fertility. Farmers were Democrats on that soil. Their voting habits have changed since then, but the effects of the glacial epoch cannot be underestimated as an influence on our lives. Much of the richest farmland in America is on glacial drift. Much of the abundant good water supply of the glaciated terrain is from aquifers of sand and gravel in the drift. Sand and gravel deposits are abundant. Lakes, one of our best recreational resources, are another of the gifts of the glacial epoch. But there are liabilities too. Any New England farmer can speak with feeling about all of the rocks in his fields of bouldery till, and geologists are sometimes frustrated by the drift that covers bedrock and prevents them from mapping geologic formations and mineral resources.

THE PLEISTOCENE EPOCH AND INDIRECT EFFECTS OF GLACIATION

From an intensive study of landforms, geologists deduced that a great continental glaciation

Some deposits of the early Pleistocene, too old for C[14] dating, have been dated in the same way as the more ancient rocks—that is, on the basis of the fossils they contain. Land deposits have been dated on the basis of snails, and marine sediments have been dated on the basis of foraminifera, small single-celled organisms that secrete shells of calcite.

Pleistocene foraminifera, the tiny calcareous animals that live in the ocean, bear testimony to the coldness of the water by the special ratio of the isotopes of oxygen in the calcium carbonate of their shells. The proportion of ordinary oxygen, O[16], and the heavy oxygen isotope, O[18], depends on the temperature of the water, and the shells from different layers of sediment show a warming and cooling of the sea that correlates with expansion and contraction of glaciers on land.

had effectively extended both polar ice caps far into what are now temperate climates. They also reasoned that the glaciation was recent, for everywhere the drift is soft, like freshly deposited sediment. It also lies at the surface everywhere and so was one of the last sediments to be deposited, covered only here and there by recent river and other deposits. Then, early in this century, matching of varved clays from glacial lakes gave a good absolute date: the most recent retreat of ice had taken place between 8000 and 15,000 years ago. In the 1940's, the decay of radioactive carbon, C[14], was applied to the dating of materials younger than about 30,000 years, and the youngest glacial deposits of the Pleistocene Epoch, the ice ages, were opened to accurate dating.

In the course of mapping the glacial deposits, geologists found that there were actually several different layers of drift. Furthermore, the older layers had well-developed soils, including fragments of plants that botanists said were characteristic of warm climates. As the evidence grew, a new conclusion became inescapable: during the ice age, the great continental glaciers alternately advanced and retreated. Between glaciations, there were long interglacial periods, during which warm climates returned to a large part of the formerly glaciated lands. At least four major periods of advance and retreat could be deduced on the basis of landforms and stratigraphy of moraines. These were named Wisconsinan, Illinoian, Kansan, and Nebraskan in order of increasing age. Some of the interglacial periods lasted longer than the glacial ones. In the past decade, we have learned from the study of deep-sea deposits, which give us some measure of ancient ocean temperatures, that there have been many shorter, more regular cycles of glaciation and deglaciation. This has been confirmed by more accurate dating of glacial sediments by radioactive decay of C[14] and other elements. Moreover, in recent years, volcanic materials that are found in some regions between older glacial layers on land have been dated by the potassium-argon method. Even on now-tropical Hawaii, Pleistocene glacial drift, deposited by small ice caps on the tops of volcanoes, has been correlated with worldwide glacial periods in this way.

Some of the indirect effects of glaciation were explored as this picture emerged. The origin of the Pleistocene loess deposits, the thick layers of windblown dust, was traced to extensive floodplain and outwash plain deposits of fine muds that came from rock flour ground up by the glacier (see Chapter 8 and Fig. 8-26). Many river valleys that carried the meltwaters of receding glaciers became choked and filled with that sediment. As the exploration of the seas started, oceanographic research vessels brought up samples of marine sediment of the glacial epoch. In the northern and southern parts of the oceans, much of the Pleistocene sediment was like stratified drift, the product of melting icebergs.

Sea-level Changes. We know from the enormous volume of ice that occupied land during the Pleistocene and from the way the hydrologic cycle works that the sea is the likely source of the ice. Most of the water that precipitated as snow did evaporate from the ocean. The more water that was tied up in ice, the less the ocean could be replenished by river runoff to keep its steady level. As the ice accumulated, the level of the sea lowered everywhere in the world's oceans.

The total volume of ice on Earth today is a little more than 25 million cubic kilometers. Total ice volume during the height of the ice age can be estimated from the area covered by the ice sheets combined with calculations of the thickness of ice necessary to keep the glaciers moving so many hundreds of miles from their areas of accumulation. Startling as it may seem, the volume must have been about 70 million cubic kilometers. The extra 55 million cubic kilometers that came from the sea to make the additional ice lowered sea level by about 130 meters (425 feet)! Imagine the series of changes caused by that great a reduction in sea level. Much of the shallow sea areas adjacent to the shorelines of continents were left above sea level. In glaciated regions, the ice sheets extended far beyond present shorelines. Some of the newly emerged coastal plains in nonglaciated areas were more than 100 kilometers (62 miles) wide. Rivers extended new channels across them and created new deltas at the water's edge. Wide strips of beaches were formed. Mammoths, huge Pleistocene elephants, roamed those low coastal plains, and no doubt Pleistocene Man did too, for early prehistoric cultures were evolving in the land beyond the ice sheets. The relics of all of these happenings have been found by oceanographic research vessels exploring the shallow areas that became reflooded by the sea as the ice melted.

The figures for ice and sea-level changes can be looked at in another way. What if the 25 million cubic kilometers of water now tied up as

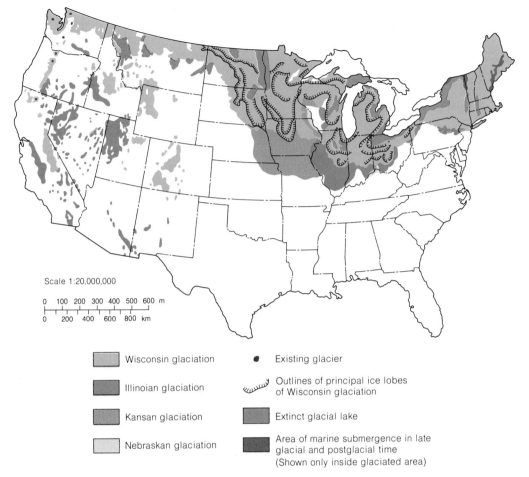

Scale 1:20,000,000

Wisconsin glaciation	Existing glacier
Illinoian glaciation	Outlines of principal ice lobes of Wisconsin glaciation
Kansan glaciation	Extinct glacial lake
Nebraskan glaciation	Area of marine submergence in late glacial and postglacial time (Shown only inside glaciated area)

Figure 9-26
Glacial geology of the conterminous United States.
[Compiled by C. S. Denny, U.S. Geological Survey.]

ice were to melt? The change in sea level would be catastrophic, for the melting of all existing ice would raise the oceans by about 65 meters (210 feet). This would inundate many major cities of the world, such as London, New York, and Tokyo, plus the great bulk of the low-lying areas of the continents, where much of the world's population lives. Those who would tinker with the Earth's climate in ways that might cause the ice to melt are well advised to remember this simple calculation.

But what if it should happen naturally? What if we are really just living in an interglacial period like those during which the Pleistocene ice sheets withdrew? On the other hand, since the 25 million cubic kilometers of ice on Earth today is vastly more than existed during most times in the history of the planet, the Earth could be considered to be in a glacial age. It has

been only 10,000 years since the last retreat of huge continental glaciers, and we have no reason to suppose that the ice will not advance again. It appears that there are some very real and possibly practical reasons, in addition to our natural scientific curiosity, why we ought to think about the causes of ice ages.

Causes of Ice Ages. For many years geologists have speculated, calculated, and theorized, but no complete agreement yet exists as to the causes of ice ages. The theories themselves have two different parts. One is an explanation of a gradual cooling of the Earth's atmosphere over tens of millions of year that finally led to the glacial epoch of two million years ago. There is evidence that polar ice caps began forming long ago in the Cenozoic and grew throughout the last part of that era. The other part of the theo-

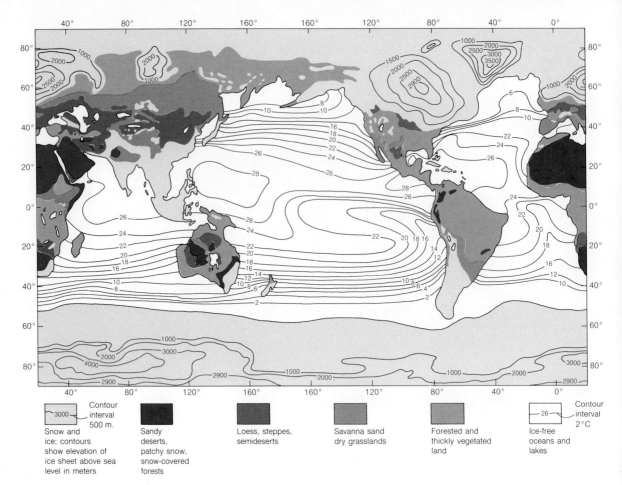

Snow and ice; contours show elevation of ice sheet above sea level in meters.

Sandy deserts, patchy snow, snow-covered forests

Loess, steppes, semideserts

Savanna sand dry grasslands

Forested and thickly vegetated land

Ice-free oceans and lakes

Figure 9-27
Sea surface temperatures (°C), ice extent, and ice elevation for August, 18,000 years ago. Continental outlines represent sea-level lowering of 85 m. [Modified from CLIMAP, "The Surface of the Ice-Age Earth," *Science,* vol. 191, 1976.]

ries is an accounting for the oscillations during the Pleistocene—the growth and advance of ice during glaciations, and the shrinkage and retreat during the interglacial periods. The Earth retained its polar ice caps, just as it does now, even during those interglacials. We will cover just a few of the major ideas to give some notion of the kind of thinking that has gone on.

Most theories have concentrated on reasons why the Earth would cool, causing the onset of glaciation. Perhaps most naturally, some have sought an explanation in a possible variation in the heat radiated from the Sun. It has been suggested that there may be periodic changes in the rate at which the Sun burns its nuclear fuel, but no firm evidence has been found. It remains

a speculation. According to another theory, injections of great quantities of volcanic ash into the atmosphere would block a portion of the Sun's rays and so cool the Earth. Though some cooling could be expected from this mechanism, no one has produced strong evidence of a period of volcanic activity in the late Cenozoic that was significantly greater than at other times. Recently an inventory of volcanic ash layers in many cores obtained by the Deep Sea Drilling Program showed no pronounced change in volcanic activity throughout the Cenozoic.

A more attractive theory for general cooling relates to the positions of the continents relative to each other and to the poles. Today there are large land areas in the broad, cold regions surrounding both north and south poles. At certain times in the geologic past, one or the other pole was in the middle of the oceans, where currents and general movement of ocean waters allowed a sufficient exchange of heat with the atmosphere to make the distribution of temperature relatively uniform from poles to equator. Once the land areas were near or at the poles, the heat difference between poles and equator was increased and the polar regions became very cold. If this theory is correct, the events leading to ice ages must have been set in motion about 20 million years ago, for that was when the continents approached their present positions relative to the poles. Indeed, there is now some evidence of small high-latitude glaciers that started well before the main, or Pleistocene, ice ages. But the main glacial ages had to wait until relative positions of the continents interacted with ocean currents in such a way as to inhibit further the transfer of heat across the globe. How this happened is a problem of joint concern to historical geologists, glaciologists, physical oceanographers, and meteorologists.

The alternation between glacial and interglacial epochs has been explained as the result of astronomical cycles. The shape of the Earth's orbit around the Sun changes periodically, putting us sometimes slightly closer and sometimes slightly farther from the Sun. In addition, the Earth wobbles slightly on its axis of rotation, and this wobble also affects very slightly the heat received by the Earth at different latitudes. These motions were first worked out carefully by Milutin Milankovitch, a Yugoslavian geophysicist, and seem to fit with the durations of the glacial and interglacial periods. Milankovitch worked out these ideas in the 1920's and 1930's, but it was not until the past few years that there was a sufficiently long and detailed chronology of the Pleistocene to match with his predictions. That chronology and the verifica-

tion of the theory, announced in late 1976, has been the work of an international project, partly sponsored by the National Science Foundation, called CLIMAP ("Climate: Long-range Investigation, Mapping and Prediction"). The astronomical theory of oscillations has to be superimposed on a theory of Earth cooling in order to arrive at a reasonable explanation as to why these oscillations took place during the Pleistocene.

The Pleistocene is not the only epoch for which there is a record of glaciation. Ancient glaciations are recorded by rocks that are the lithified equivalents of till, **tillites.** Such rocks are recognized by their poorly sorted mixture of sand, pebbles, and clay and the association with striated bedrock pavements. The Dwyka, a late Paleozoic tillite of South Africa, preserves a record of a glacial epoch affecting the southern continents, at that time coming together to form the supercontinent of Pangaea. Tillites record Ordovician and Precambrian glaciations as well. Why glacial periods come every so often in the history of the Earth remains uncertain. Nor is there any certainty about the effects that future glaciations may have on our existence on Earth. If there is another glacial episode, it will happen on a time scale of thousands of years, slow enough for all of us to ignore, but with implications of yet another change for the continuous record of human culture. Primitive society was well advanced when early humans were living in caves in southern France during the last ice age and changed greatly after deglaciation. Our first sensitive indicators would be the advance of mountain glaciers in Alaska and elsewhere. But we would have no way of knowing whether such an advance indicated any more than a temporary period of slight cooling that might last only a few years or tens of years and then be followed by another warm period.

SUMMARY

1. Glaciers are masses of ice formed by the gradual transformation of snow by recrystallization and pressure.

2. The size of a glacier is determined by the rate at which snow accumulates and the rate of ablation by melting, evaporation, and iceberg calving.

3. Ice moves downhill partly by internal plastic flow, which is mainly the result of many small slips along planes of individual ice crystals, and partly by sliding along its base.

4. Surface ice breaks into crevasses as a result of the movement of ice masses over steep changes in slope and along valley walls. Glaciers move with a wide range of speeds; some glaciers move in fast surges.

5. Valley glaciers form in alpine mountains and erode U-shaped valleys, hanging valleys, and cirques.

6. Continental glaciers are of great size and exist today only in polar regions, where melting is almost nonexistent, as in Greenland and Antarctica.

7. Glaciers produce many erosional and depositional landforms. Ice abrades material from the walls and floors of valleys and transports it to ice fronts, where it accumulates as moraines.

8. Landforms of Pleistocene continental glaciers include moraines and various forms of till and drift, such as kettles, kames, varves, eskers, and drumlins.

9. There were several glaciations during the Pleistocene, each recorded by a till of a different age and by temperature fluctuations of the oceans. Sea level changed extensively as the ice sheets waxed and waned, at times leaving large areas of the continental shelves of the world exposed as land.

10. Causes of glaciation have been sought in astronomical theories to explain oscillations during colder periods and general cooling as a result of movements of continents with respect to the poles.

EXERCISES

1. List the ways in which snow and sand are similar and glacial ice and marble are similar.

2. Mt. Washington is the highest peak of the White Mountains of New Hampshire, at 1920 meters (6293 feet), and official weather records show winter temperatures as low as 60°C below zero. Discuss the reasons why it has no glacier and what changes in the current conditions might produce one.

3. One of the dangers of exploring glaciers is the possibility of falling into a crevasse. What topographic features of a valley glacier or its surrounding rocky terrain would you use to indicate that you are on a part of the glacier that might be badly crevassed?

4. What differences in the composition and texture of the glacial till would you expect between two glaciated areas, one on a geologically young series of coastal plain soft shales and loosely cemented sands, the other on an old granitic-metamorphic rock terrain.

5. A number of ancient rock formations have been the subject of controversy concerning their possible glacial origin. What characteristics of glacial till or glacial landforms might you expect to use to establish that a rock 270 million years old is a tillite?

6. You are assigned the job of mapping a terminal moraine of a late Pleistocene glaciation. What characteristics of topography or till composition would you use to distinguish it from ground moraine on the one hand and outwash on the other? How might you distinguish it from an esker?

7. If you were in charge of a global watch to monitor any indications of a resumption of extensive continental glaciations like those of 15,000 years ago, what kinds of observations would you direct your teams to make? How much warning in centuries, years, days, or hours might you expect to give the city of Chicago that another glaciation was imminent?

BIBLIOGRAPHY

Field, W. O., "Glaciers." *Scientific American,* September 1955. (Offprint No. 809.)
Flint, R. F., *Glacial and Quaternary Geology.* New York: John Wiley & Sons, 1971.
Knight, C. and N. Knight "Snow Crystals." *Scientific American,* January 1973.
Paterson, W. J. B., *The Physics of Glaciers.* London: Pergamon Press, 1969.
Price, R. J., *Glacial and Fluvioglacial Landforms.* New York: Hafner Pub. Co., 1973.
Robin, G., "Ice of the Antarctic." *Scientific American,* September 1962. (Offprint No. 861.)

10

OCEAN PROCESSES

The sea is the end of the line for the weathered debris of continental erosion. The material brought to the ocean by rivers and worn away from its coasts by wave erosion is distributed along its shores as beaches or transported by currents to the continental shelf and deeper parts of the ocean. Beaches are the expression of a balance between the supply of sand provided by erosion of the shore and the transport of sand by rivers, wave erosion, and longshore currents. The continental slopes, continental rises, and abyssal plains are shaped by turbidity currents that transport much material from the shallower to the deeper parts of the sea. The current patterns of the general circulation of the oceans influence the distribution of fine-grained pelagic sediment that mantles the topography of the deep oceans.

About 100 years ago, in 1872, H.M.S. *Challenger,* a small wooden warship converted and fitted out for scientific study of the seas, set out from England on a four-year voyage over the world's oceans. From that first systematic study eventually flowed fifty thick volumes on the currents, the underwater topography, the bottom sediments, and the life of the deep sea, which opened the eyes of land-bound geologists. What had been the realm of groundless speculation had suddenly been transformed into a matter of serious interest: the acquisition of observations about the ocean and the building of theories to explain them. Early musings on "featureless plains" beneath the water were abandoned as the discoveries rolled in: the mid-Atlantic ridge and other high ranges of submarine mountains, deep troughs and trenches, vast areas of hilly topography, and, to be sure, some great flat plains. The rocks and sediments of the sea floor were found to be as diverse as the topography: fine-grained brownish clays, blue clays, sands, silts, and, in some places, even pebbles and cobbles.

H.M.S. Challenger.

Figure 10-1
H.M.S. *Challenger,* as depicted in the official *Challenger* report. [Courtesy Science and Technology Division, The New York Public Library, Astor, Lenox and Tilden Foundations.]

Figure 10-2
A modern oceanographic research vessel, the R/V *Knorr* of the Woods Hole Oceanographic Institution. This ship is equipped for a wide variety of marine geological, geochemical, and geophysical research. [Courtesy Woods Hole Oceanographic Institution.]

Figure 10-3
A rocky headland on Mt. Desert Island off the coast of Maine. To the extreme right is a small sandy pocket beach formed in a recess between headlands. [Photo by R. Siever.]

In many parts of the deep sea, the *Challenger* scientists found "oozes," sandy or muddy sediments dominated by the shells of tiny organisms, some of calcium carbonate, some of silica. Perhaps as surprising was the discovery of igneous rocks and unusual cobble-shaped lumps of heavy rocks: manganese nodules.

The broad outlines of the problems of marine geology were laid out by the voyage of the *Challenger*. What was the origin of the varied topography? What explained the different arrays of sediment and other rock types on the bottom? What role did ocean currents, tides, and waves play in forming the sea floor? Today, a hundred years after these questions first came to be asked, hundreds of oceanographic research vessels from different countries are exploring the sea, providing some answers to those questions and discovering new facts that raise new problems. More than any other endeavor, it was oceanographic research that has led to our current ideas of the dynamics of the Earth. Plate tectonics, the conceptual framework of this book, could not have been substantiated without oceanographic expeditions. Some 80 percent of the Earth's surface is covered by water, so that the 20 percent available for direct observation is in a real sense atypical. A hundred years ago, the study of the sea was primarily either pure science (science for its own sake) or applied science in the service of the shipping trade. In the decades after World War II, much oceanographic research was financially supported by nations interested in the military advantages that might accrue to them from a knowledge of the sea, which was soon to become the home of the nuclear missile-launching submarine. Now oceanographic research is made more urgent, both by the possibility that the resources of the sea can be used to support the world's growing population and by the companion danger of pollution of the seas.

The study of the oceans—oceanography—has united geology, geophysics, and geochemistry with biology, physics, and meteorology to become a field of knowledge much too broad to cover in this book. In this chapter, we will discuss those aspects of oceanography that continue the story of the erosional, transportational, and sedimentational processes that shape the surface of the Earth's crust beneath the sea as well as on land. We will start with the most familiar part, the edge of the sea.

The coast, the broad region that is the meeting place of land and sea, can be carved into many kinds of shapes: steep rocky cliffs, broad low beaches, crescents of small beaches in small bays alternating with rocky headlands, or wide, sweeping, sandy tidal flats. The forces that shape coasts are essentially the same as those that form other topographies: the destructive processes of erosion operating in conjunction with currents that transport and deposit debris and the tectonic forces that cause uplift or subsidence of the Earth's crust.

Wave Erosion. At the **shoreline,** the line along which the water meets the land, the major erosive agent is wave action. The force of high waves breaking against a rocky cliff during a storm can be awesome in its violence; you can feel the ground shake with the shock. Nearby sensitive seismometers, used to detect far-distant earthquakes, will register the small tremors of the solid earth caused by the sudden impact of tons of water on solid rock. Moderately high waves, about 3 meters (10 feet) high at the breaking point, have been measured to produce a force of more than 70 grams per square centimeter (30 pounds per square inch). So when you see waves break against a concrete seawall and throw water 5 meters (16 feet) into the air, you can estimate an impact force equivalent to dashing about 175 grams (0.4 pounds) against each square centimeter of rock surface. It is not surprising that such seawalls, built to protect homes just back of the shore, quickly start to crack and constantly have to be kept in repair.

The waves are even more destructive than the force of the water alone, for the waves catapult pebbles, cobbles, and, in intense storms, boulders against the shoreline rocks. The physical destructiveness of the waves is further enhanced by the chemical weathering action of sea water that is forced by wave pressure into every tiny crack and crevice. The chemical decay extends and widens the cracks, preparing them for the disintegrating physical beating by the waves.

Where waves break against bluffs of softer unconsolidated material, such as soils or recent glacial deposits, the rate of erosion may be extraordinary. The high sea cliffs of glacial materials facing the open Atlantic along the Cape Cod National Seashore are retreating at a rate of

Figure 10-4
Waves splashing against a rocky shore. Big Sur, Monterey County, California. [Photo by Cole Weston. Reprinted with permission of the publisher, Sierra Club Books. From *Not Man Apart*.]

Figure 10-5
Sandy Cliffs of glacial deposits at Wellfleet, Cape Cod. Composed of easily erodible, unlithified clays and sands, these cliffs retreat about a meter per year under the attack of waves. [Photo by R. Siever.]

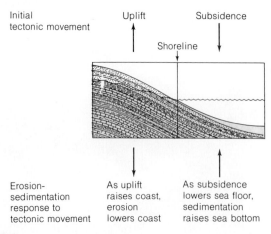

Initial
tectonic movement

Uplift

Subsidence

Shoreline

Erosion-
sedimentation
response to
tectonic movement

As uplift
raises coast,
erosion
lowers coast

As subsidence
lowers sea floor,
sedimentation
raises sea bottom

Figure 10-6
Shoreline profiles are a balance between tectonic forces and erosional
and sedimentational processes that counter them. The greater the uplift of the land, the greater the erosion; the greater the subsidence of
sea floor, the greater the tendency for sedimentation to build up the
bottom. Similarly, subsidence of coastal lands decreases erosion, and
uplift of sea floor inhibits sedimentation.

Henry David Thoreau visited Cape
Cod four times between 1849 and
1857 and kept a record of his observations that was published as *Cape
Cod.* His description of the beach and
other parts of the Cape remains one
of the great examples of the combination of natural history with conversa-
tions with and observations of people
that was common in the nineteenth
century. One good edition is the one
put out by W. W. Norton & Co. with
an introduction by Henry Beston.

uplifted, erosion, principally the work of waves,
will attack it by the same kind of negative-feedback process explored in Chapter 5 for landscape evolution: the more the uplift, the more
intense the erosion that counters it. If the land
subsides with respect to sea level, a different
negative-feedback process operates: the low spot
tends to get filled in by sedimentation. Uplift
and subsidence may operate simultaneously in
different parts of the same region. For example,
some coasts are broken up by tectonic forces
into a pattern of large blocks bounded by faults,
which allows some blocks to be raised while
others are depressed.

Tectonically uplifted coasts, where erosion is
active, have a topography of prominent cliffs
and headlands jutting out into the sea alternating with narrow inlets and irregular bays, some
filled with small rocky beaches. Jagged, irregular
shapes dominate in hard, rocky terrain. In softer
sediments, the topography is characterized by
the gentler slopes of straight bluffs, marked with
occasional landslide and slump scars. The waves
undercut the cliffs, causing huge blocks to fall
into the water, where they gradually become
worn away. Along such coasts, the retreat of the
sea cliff may leave isolated remnants standing in
the sea far from the shore. As the waves erode,
they plane the surface just below sea level and
create a **wave-cut terrace.**

Once the uplift stops, erosion wears away the
land, making the shoreline move back from the
sea while the land surface is lowered. Given a
very long period of complete stability, the
coastline would be reduced to a low coastal
plain. This hypothetical state is not reached in
nature, for the shoreline, not far from the junction of oceanic and continental crust, is normally

about a meter each year. Since Henry Thoreau
first walked the length of those cliffs in the
middle of the nineteenth century, about 6 square
kilometers (2.3 square miles) of land area has
been eaten by the ocean. At that rate, real estate
land (or "sea") values on Cape Cod will be
worth little in a few thousand years!

The Forces that Shape Shorelines. Just as
the surface of the land is the product of interplay of tectonic forces lifting up the land, erosion wearing it down, and sedimentation filling
in the low spots, a shoreline is a result of the
same kinds of forces. The shore may be uplifted
or it may subside with respect to sea level. If it is

Figure 10-7
Uplifted marine terraces, Palos Verdes Hills, California. [Photo by John S. Shelton
and R. C. Frampton. From *Geology Illustrated* by John S. Shelton. W. H. Freeman
and Company. Copyright © 1966.]

involved in upward or downward tectonic movements, in many places in relation to convergences or divergences of lithospheric plates. The shorelines of virtually the entire Pacific Ocean are notably unstable, as are those of the Mediterranean Sea.

Much of the eastern shore of North America has been a subsiding coast over the past 100 million years, as has much of the shore of the Gulf of Mexico. The long-term sinking of the crust is thought by some to be characteristic of a continental margin when it coincides with the trailing edge of a lithospheric plate. Where the land sinks, sediment tends to build up. These coasts have long, wide beaches and wide, low-lying plains of relatively recently deposited sediment behind the shoreline. Typical shoreline landforms along such coasts are sandbars (shallow, narrow ridges of sand parallel to the beach just offshore); low-lying sandy islands; and wide tidal flats that are either sandy or muddy. There is a balance here between the subsidence that creates depressions and the sedimentation of debris eroded from the land that tends to fill up the low places. The relative intensity of the two processes determines the result. A plentiful supply of sediment from the land combined with only slight subsidence produces a shoreline that is built up and advances seaward. Small amounts of sediment combined with deep subsidence results in deep basins, bays, and other indentations of the coast.

Pleistocene Sea-level Changes. Thus far, we have covered long-term local or regional movements of the solid crust with respect to sea level, assuming that the general level of the oceans remains constant. Studies of the Pleistocene glacial epoch have revealed that there have been short-term rises and falls of sea level, some more than 130 meters (425 feet), caused by the removal of water from the sea to form huge continental glaciers (see Chapter 9). These world-wide changes in sea level, called **eustatic** changes, affected all coasts. During periods of lowered sea level, erosion dominated in a situation equivalent to tectonic uplift of the land. Valleys were deepened, and formerly submerged rocky terrains were attacked by waves. As sea level rose again when the ice melted, the deepened valleys were flooded far inland. Today, many of the rivers of the central Atlantic coast gradually widen and become mixed with sea water long before they reach the main shoreline. These long fingers of sea indenting the land are called **drowned valleys.** A drowned valley is one major type of **estuary**—any coastal body of

Figure 10-8
Drowned river valleys are greatly elongated estuaries formed either by general subsidence of the coastal region or by a general rise in sea level that floods the river valleys. The photograph shows such a valley, locally called "calanque," in limestone terrain on the Mediterranean coast east of Marseilles, France. [Photo by R. Siever.]

Initial condition

After subsidence or sea-level rise: retreat of shoreline and drowning of river valley

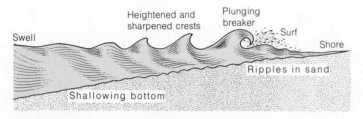

Figure 10-9
Formation of a plunging breaker as swell approaches a gently sloping beach. As low regular swell meets a shallowing bottom, wave crests become higher and steeper until the breaker plunges.

Figure 10-10
Vertical air photo showing waves approaching a point of land and being bent (refracted) around it. In the lee of the offshore rocks, the waves form an interference pattern. [Photo from U.S. Hydrographic Office Publication 234.]

water that is open to the ocean and is diluted by fresh water from the land. To some extent, all of the shores of the world were slightly drowned by the sea-level rise that accompanied the melting of glaciers 10,000 years ago. The shores of northern Europe and North America are now rising tectonically because the Earth's crust is still rebounding as a result of being unburdened of the great weight of glacial ice. This, of course, works counter to the sea-level rise. Recent studies show that the sea level from Maine to Virginia has been rising at a rate of 0.25–0.35 centimeters per year; the rate has been much faster than that for some short periods.

With this additional complexity, we now have four major forces shaping shorelines: tectonics, erosion, sedimentation, and eustatic changes in sea level. How erosion and sedimentation interact is most clearly shown by beaches.

BEACHES

Beaches change constantly, and their dynamics can teach us much about the processes that operate at shorelines. The most obvious things about a beach are the materials of which it is made—sand and pebbles—and the action of the waves. Perceptive observation of these two gives a picture of the beach as a dynamic environment, not a fixed, static landform: the waves, in constant motion, move the material of the beach, acting sometimes to destroy the beach and sometimes to broaden and extend it. If we stop to consider the waves, we can begin to see how they work.

Waves. The best place to start looking at waves is from the rise in elevation that is behind every beach. Best is a high bluff, but a low sand dune will do. Once the first sensation of the whole sweep of the shore starts to fade, you can notice some of the elements of regularity about the waves. Waves appear to form some distance from the shore, build up, and break into splashing **breakers,** or **surf,** near the shore. The breakers, separated by troughs, succeed one another in an orderly way. Some distance from the shore, the waves can be distinguished only as low, broad, regular, rounded ridges, called **swell.** The swell becomes higher as it approaches the shore and assumes the familiar sharp-crested wave shape. The crest builds up even more as the wave rolls closer to the shore, finally to a steep high wall of water that then breaks forward in a collapse of splashing surf. The time interval between waves, the **period,**

may be as short as a few seconds or as long as 15 or 20 seconds. A closer watch on the wave period may reveal more complex regularities, such as a few small waves with short periods alternating with larger waves from long periods. An experienced surfer learns the particular sequence of waves on a beach on any given day and knows that it changes from day to day.

Still looking at the shore from some height, you can distinguish a regular horizontal pattern to the crests of waves as they approach the shore. Far from shore, the lines of swell are parallel to each other but usually at some angle to the beach. As the waves approach the beach, no matter what the direction or angle, the parallel rows of waves start to bend gradually, so that they are approaching the shore in a direction that is more nearly at right angles to the shoreline; then they finally break into surf and sweep up on shore almost, but rarely exactly, at right angles (that is, the waves themselves lie nearly parallel to the shore when they break.

How do these observations fit together to give an explanation for wave patterns? First we must consider the movement of a piece of wood or other light material floating on the water. The piece moves a little forward on a wave crest and then a little backward as a trough between waves passes. The wave form moves steadily toward the beach, but the water itself just moves back and forth. Experiments in large laboratory tanks in which artificial waves are generated show that small floats at different depths in the water all move with a characteristic motion: approximately circular vertical orbits. The orbits have large radii at the top of the water, but they gradually decrease to zero at some depth below. Careful experiments of this kind show a relation between the **wavelength** of the wave pattern, which is the distance from crest to crest, and the orbital motion. At a depth of about one-half the wavelength, orbital motion essentially stops.

Now we can infer what happens as waves approach the shore across a shallowing bottom. At the distance from shore at which the bottom is only one-half the wavelength from the surface, the orbital motions of the lowest levels of the water start being restricted because the water can no longer move vertically: right next to the bottom, the water can only move back and forth horizontally. In the next higher level, the water can move vertically just a little, this motion combining with the horizontal motion to give a flat elliptical orbit. Higher in the water, the orbits become more circular the farther they are from the bottom.

It is the flattening of the orbits that makes

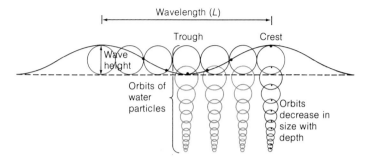

Figure 10-11
Wave forms are produced by orbital motions of water particles; each water particle continues orbiting about the same position while the wave form travels.

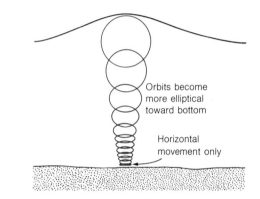

Figure 10-12
Orbits of water particles become elliptical as they approach a shallow bottom. At the bottom, particles move back and forth only.

waves "feel" the bottom, for the distortion of the orbits into ellipses causes the whole wave to decrease its velocity. While the wave slows down, its period remains the same—the waves keep coming in from deeper water at the same rate. As a consequence, the wavelength shortens, because all of these waves must follow the fundamental law of motion:

$$\text{wave velocity} = \frac{\text{wavelength}}{\text{wave period}}$$

which is usually abbreviated to $V = L/T$. A further consequence of this change is that the wave grows higher and steeper and the wave crests become sharper. The wave **steepness,** which is defined as the ratio between its height

The whitecaps seen in strong winds far from shore in deep water are not the same as breaking waves. They are caused by the wind blowing off the top parts of wave crests.

Figure 10-13
Effect of wind of force 8 (Beaufort scale; see Table 10-1) on the surface of the sea. Wind speed, 65 km/hr (39 mi/hr); wave period, 6 sec; wave height, 5 m (17 ft). [From Atmospheric Environment Service—Environment Canada.]

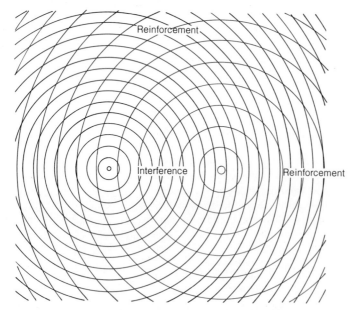

Figure 10-14
Waves from two storm centers interfere and reinforce each other, just like ripples from two pebbles tossed into a pond. At some distance from the storms, the waves will appear to come from the same general direction but with different wavelengths.

and the wavelength, increases to the point at which the water can no longer support itself, at a ratio of about 1 to 7, and the wave breaks with a crash. The depth of the water at this point is about 1.3 times as great as the wave height. The distance from shore is highly variable, depending on how rapidly the bottom shallows. On a steeply sloping bottom, many small waves will break right at the shore. Sandbars and gently sloping bottoms will cause the waves to break farther out. Thus, the location of the **surf zone,** where the waves break, is a good guide to the depth of the water.

Now contrast this picture of regularity with what you see at the beach during a storm or a strong wind. Though the waves still break on shore with some semblance of regularity, the whole scene is much more wild and confused. In deeper water, whitecaps are everywhere, the surface of the water is rough with ripples, or little waves on big ones, and no distinct wave pattern can be seen. We can find the key to all by watching a calm sea surface as still air is freshened by a breeze. Ripples, tiny waves less than a centimeter high, take shape as the breeze comes up. As the wind increases, the ripples grow into full-sized waves, the size depending on the speed of the wind (see Table 8-1), how long it blows in any one direction, and the distance that the wind blows over the water, which is called the **fetch** of the wind. The energy of motion of the wind is thus transferred to the water, much in the way that a child's energy is transferred to a toy automobile—the longer and harder he pushes it, the faster it goes.

Storms make irregular choppy patterns of large waves that radiate outward from the storm area, just as dropping a pebble into a still pond makes ripples that move out as ever widening circles. As the waves leave the storm area, they become more regular swell of lower height, which can travel hundreds of kilometers. Some such swells have been shown to cross the width of an ocean. Now we can begin to see why waves of different heights and periods break against the shore. Let's return to the pebbles dropped in a pond: Dropping two pebbles in different places in a pond will produce ripples that cross and interfere with each other in some places but that, in areas far from the source, will appear to merge into two different, approximately parallel sets. In a similar way, two storms will produce waves of different sizes and periods that interfinger as they approach the shore. Timing the periods and sizes of waves at the shore can give you a rough idea of the many storms near and far that generated the swell. The Pacific shores of North America are far better for surfers because waves from the many storms in various parts of the great expanse of the Pacific Ocean are reinforced by prevailing westerly winds as they roll eastward. Surf along the Atlantic shore is smaller because the westerly winds blow against the advancing waves and decrease their effect. The best surfing on the Atlantic is on its eastern shore—along France's coasts, for example.

Wave Refraction. There is one more piece of the story to be explained: those parallel lines of waves that bend toward the shore as they approach (Fig. 10-10). As a wave approaches the shore at an angle, the parts closest to shore will feel the bottom first, the circular orbits becoming elliptical, and so that part will slow down; each successive segment along an individual wave crest meets the shallowing bottom and also slows. Meanwhile, the segment closest to shore has moved into even shallower water, and thus slows even more. In this way, not by separate segments but in a continuous transition along the wave crest, the line of the wave bends as it slows, in a process called **wave refraction** because of its similarity to the bending of light rays in optical refraction. The process can be compared with ranks of marching soldiers turning a corner, the ones closest to the corner marching most slowly and the farthest ones most quickly.

Wave refraction produces some special effects on an irregular shoreline with indented bays and projecting headlands. Around the headlands, the water shallows more quickly than the surrounding deeper water on either side, and the waves are refracted—bent—toward the projecting part of the shore from both sides. The waves converge around the point of land and expend proportionately more of their energy breaking there than at other places along the shore. Thus, erosion by waves is concentrated at headlands and tends to wear them away more quickly than along straight sections of shoreline. Conversely, wave refraction operates in a bay to make the waves diverge and expend less energy: the waters there are deeper, so the waves are refracted to either side into shallower water. The minimal wave energy expended along the inner shores of bays makes the water quieter there, making secure places for mooring ships. It is in bays that beaches form on an irregular shoreline of headlands and indentations. To explore more of the interactions of waves and beaches, we should take a closer look at how beaches are affected by the waves.

Storm waves can build to awesome heights. Sea captains have estimated wave heights greater than 25 m (80 ft) in hurricanes. One giant wave was estimated, by careful sighting by an officer of a U.S. Navy ship, to have been about 35 m (115 ft) high!

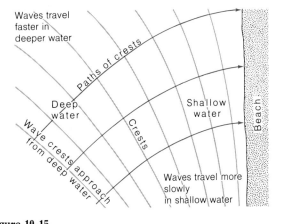

Figure 10-15
Wave refraction, the bending of wave crestlines as they approach a shore from an angle. The part of the wave that first encounters shallow water slows in speed while that part of the wave still in deeper water continues to move with its original speed, making the wave change angle, just like a rank of marchers wheeling around a corner.

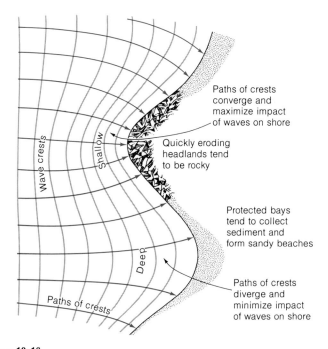

Figure 10-16
Wave refraction around a headland and bay. Because of the configuration of shallow and deep water around projections and indentations of the shoreline, wave energies are concentrated at headlands and dispersed at bays.

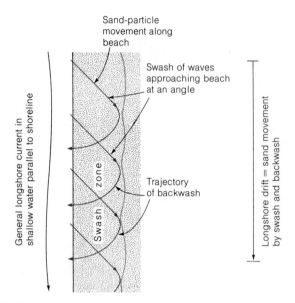

Figure 10-17
Longshore drift is the zig-zag movement of sand grains thrown up on the shore by waves approaching at an angle and washing back out at approximately right angles to the beach, thus causing the sand to progress down the beach in the direction toward which the waves are angled. Longshore current in the shallow water is created in the same way, by the zig-zag movement of water.

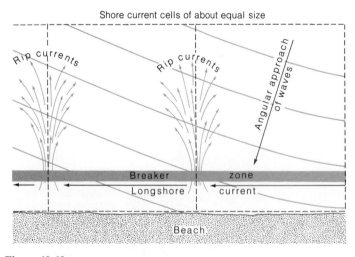

Figure 10-18
Rip currents flow out from the shore at certain points, usually regularly spaced, so that the shore can be divided into cells of water circulation along the beach. As a result of oblique wave attack, which forms the longshore current, the water tends to pile up, forming a rip current that breaks through the surf zone, fans out, and becomes dissipated.

Longshore Drift and Longshore Currents.
One of the more effortless kinds of observations the student of beaches can make is of the manner in which the waves roll up onto the sloping front of the beach, the **swash,** and fall back down again, the **backwash.** The swash of a wave has enough current competence to lift up sand grains and carry them along, in the same way that river currents do. Strong waves are competent to lift up and move large pebbles and cobbles. The backwash carries particles back down again to about their original positions on the slope. Because, despite wave refraction, waves usually break at some small angle to the shoreline, the swash moves up the beach slope at a small angle. But backwash runs down the slope at right angles, down the steepest slope available to it. Thus the sand grain in one swash-and-backwash cycle is displaced along the shoreline by a small amount. The net result is a zig-zag path in a direction along the shore that is determined by the wave direction. This **longshore drift** of sand on a beach, which is an imperceptibly slow movement to the observer of an hour or a day, has been demonstrated by experimenters using a tracer—slightly radioactive sand grains (though not radioactive enough to be dangerous to anyone).

Coupled to longshore drift is the **longshore current,** which is induced by waves approaching the shoreline at an angle: the water is transported along the beach, just as the sand grains are, by the combination of swash and backwash. The water transport creates the current, which is strong enough to carry sand grains along in shallow offshore zones. Longshore currents build up with increasing distance down the shore, and the water imperceptibly piles up—the difference in height is too small to see or measure—until a critical point is reached. There, the water breaks out to sea at right angles to the shoreline, through oncoming waves, to form a rapidly moving **rip current.** The combination of angular waves, longshore current, and rip current makes a closed loop along which the water continually moves. A long beach will typically embrace many such loops.

The spacing, intensity, and precise location of the rip currents are controlled by wave angle, wave height and period, and the topography of the beach, but the relation between these factors is so complex that exact predictions are very difficult to make. Rip currents are dangerous to swimmers and surfers, however, and a knowledge of their characteristics may help to save

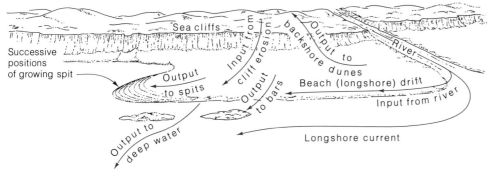

Input	**Output**
Cliffs back of shore eroded by waves	Sedimentation in deep water by rip currents and waves
Beach eroded by longshore drift and current	Growth of beaches (including spits and bars) downcurrent due to deposition of sand by longshore drift and current
Rivers upcurrent eroded by longshore drift and current	Growth of backshore dunes due to deposition of sand by offshore winds

Figure 10-19
The beach budget is a complex balance between erosion and sedimentation in which such forms as spits and bars grow as beach cliffs and other sources supply sand. If input is out of balance with output, the beach will tend to grow or erode.

lives. They can flow at a velocity more than 1 meter per second, too strong a current for inexperienced swimmers or children to fight against. The best way to get out of them was pointed out by Francis Shepard, an American marine geologist. (Shepard was one of the first to recognize the significance of rip currents and to stop calling them by the colloquial name "rip-tides," for they have nothing to do with tides.) Because they are narrow currents, the best way to avoid being carried out to sea is to swim parallel to the shore and not fight the current at all. In a short distance, the swimmer will be out of the current and can easily swim with the waves into shore.

It is best, of course, to avoid rip currents entirely. They can usually be detected by the lack of breaking waves, for the current both erodes a deeper channel and hinders the advancing waves. A good place to watch for them is at a bend or slight indentation of the beach where the water seems deeper than usual.

The Beach Budget If sand constantly leaves the beach by longshore drift and current, why doesn't the sand eventually disappear? Though this does not happen on natural beaches, it may very well happen when naïve builders or engi-

neers interfere with nature in certain ways. To understand why, we have to make an input-output budget for the beach, averaged over a significant time, such as a year. Because wind directions change from day to day, the drift may go one way one day and reverse itself the next as the waves approach from the opposite direction. On a few coasts, the net movement for the whole year will be zero, but on most there is a prevailing direction, and that will be the direction of net movement of sand. In a bay, where waves diverge because of refraction, the sand is transported from both sides to the central beach, where it accumulates. In contrast, any sand at a headland is soon transported away from it, and bare rocky shores are the rule in such places.

What happens at the end of a beach, as where a straight shoreline turns a sharp corner? Any sand in longshore transport will be carried off the end of the beach and into the deeper water beyond, where it gradually builds up a submerged bar. With continued growth, it rises above the surface and so extends the beach as a narrow **spit** of sand. From the shapes of spits and bars, a geologist can infer the direction of longshore transport; from that, he can predict the predominant directions of longshore currents and, thus, the average wind and wave directions. Favorite resorts in many parts of the world are on sand beaches that have been extended for great distances by longshore currents.

There is another output. Any beach will "leak" sand to the deeper water offshore, mainly because of rip currents and intense storms. Once there, it is rarely moved, for only the highest waves can stir up sand that lies more than 10 meters deep. This sand, therefore, is permanently lost by the beach. In shallow zones of the beach, sand may move in and out from the shoreline in a pattern related to wave activity. In times of intense storms and high waves, much of the beach above the normal high-water mark may be removed to the submerged nearshore area. In periods of relatively calm weather, that

sand will gradually be shifted back up the beach, and the beach will widen. A typical seasonal fluctuation of this kind is shown by some beaches that narrow during the stormy winter period and broaden during quiet summer weather.

If sand moves down the beach and extends it, there must be an input of sand to balance this output. Erosion of cliffs and headlands supplies some of the material, but much of it is brought to the shore by rivers. A river tends to drop its sediment to form a delta as it meets the ocean. Where longshore currents are strong, however, deltas never get a chance to form, because the sediment is quickly distributed to beaches, to bars, and offshore along the coast. Where sea cliffs are of sandy sediment, much replenishing sand is produced by erosion. Because cliffs of harder rock are broken into sand too slowly to keep pace with longshore transport, beaches do not readily form downdrift from them.

Beaches export sand in another direction—landward, to form sand dunes. Sea breezes and winds blow sand inland to form the dune ridge common to most beaches. That sand may be blown many meters high and accumulate as thin dunes even on top of high bluffs. We can summarize a simplified budget of a beach, or any segment of it, as follows, neglecting short-term fluctuations from beach to shallow water during storms and calm periods. If input exceeds output for some months or years, the beach will grow; if output consistently dominates over input, the beach will shrink, sometimes to the vanishing point.

In the natural state, beaches tend to maintain a balance between input and output. But most beaches in populous sections of the country are not in the natural state: people build cottages, pave beach parking lots, erect sea walls to "protect" the beach, and construct piers and breakwaters. The usual consequence, unless the developers or engineers responsible are aware of the dynamics of the beach, is to make the beach shrink in one place and grow in another. The classic example is a narrow pier built out from shore at right angles to it. Much to the surprise of the builders, the sand, during the following months and years, disappears from one side and enlarges the beach greatly on the other. This is an expensive way to find out that there is a longshore current on that beach. The current and drift bring sand toward the pier from the upcurrent direction (the dominant wind direction, usually) and, stopped at the pier, dump the sand there. On the downcurrent side of the pier, the

Figure 10-20
Construction of piers (frequently called "groins") along a shore to control erosion of a beach may produce unwanted changes if longshore current and drift are not considered. A typical change induced is erosion downcurrent of the pier.

current and drift pick up again and erode the beach. On this side, however, there is no replenishment of sand by the current because it is blocked by the pier, so the beach shrinks and disappears. If the pier is removed, the beach will relax to its original state. It is important to learn that a beach is a dynamic form, and any disturbance of its input-output balance, by altering either the source of material or the transport mechanism, will affect it in predictable ways. Thus construction on (or other alteration of) the dunes or bluffs at the back of a beach may strongly affect the width of the beach by changing its supply of sand.

One of the consequences of oil spills from tankers offshore is the fouling of beaches by heavy oils that gradually alter to tarry or asphalt-like lumps and layers. The oil seeps into the pores of the sand and binds it together. Temporarily, the beach may be a disagreeable mess, but sooner or later, because a beach is constantly in motion, it will cleanse itself. The oil lumps are broken up, dispersed, and mixed with the immense volume of sand on the beach. The problem is that the process may take many months or years, which makes the beach's ability to cleanse itself a small consolation to the animals and people that populate it in the meantime.

TIDES

One subject that philosophers and scientists of ancient Greece did not cover was the tide, the daily rise and fall of the sea. Ancient observers of the sea in places as widely separated as China and Iceland, however, devoted much thought to the subject. The Greeks were observant enough—they just happened to live on a large inland sea with almost no tide, whereas the people of civilizations that developed along oceanic coasts were familiar with the daily alternation of high and low water. By modern times, it had long been known that there was a relation between the position and phases of the Moon, the heights of the tides, and the time of day at which the water would reach its highest level. It was not until Isaac Newton formulated the laws of gravitation, however, that the tides were understood to be the result of the pull of the Moon and the Sun on the oceans.

The Earth and the Moon attract each other strongly with a gravitational pull that is slightly greater on the sides of the two planets that face each other. The net gravitational attraction of

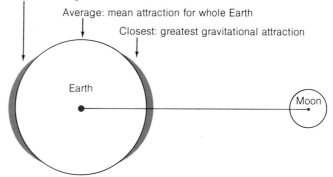

Figure 10-21
Moon's gravitational attraction causes two bulges of water on the Earth's oceans, one on the nearest side and one on the farthest side. As the Earth rotates, the bulges always face the Moon. Thus two high tides (bulge closest to Moon and bulge farthest from Moon) pass each point on Earth's surface each day.

the Moon for any point in the Earth is the vector sum (addition including direction as well as magnitude) of the large constant attractive force that is considered to act as if all of the Earth's mass were concentrated at its center and the small deviation that varies from point to point in the Earth proportional to its distance from the Moon. That deviation is the tide-producing force. This force causes a slight bulge in the solid Earth, the oceans, and the atmosphere (and the Moon, too, of course). The deformation in the solid Earth is too small to be observed, except by sensitive instruments, but the much larger bulge in the water is easily seen as the tide. The net gravitational attraction for the water of the oceans facing the Moon is at a maximum. On the side away from the Moon, the net gravitational attraction for the ocean water at the surface is at a minimum. As the Earth rotates, the tides move around it, one always facing the Moon, the other directly opposite.

The Sun, though much farther away, has so much more mass that it, too, causes tides. The Sun tides are a little less than half the height of Moon tides. The two sets of tides are not synchronous, those related to the Sun coming every twenty-four hours, once each "solar" day. The time of rotation of the Earth with respect to the Moon is a little longer than the solar day: it is twenty-four hours and fifty minutes, because the Moon is moving around the Earth. In that twenty-four hours and fifty minutes, the "lunar" day, there are two high waters, with two low waters in between.

1976 was a bad year for tanker oil spills. The worst came in December, when the ARGO Merchant, an aging ship under Liberian registry, ran aground on Nantucket Shoals, off the coast of Massachusetts. Almost 7.6 million gallons of oil, the entire load, was spilled as the ship broke up in high seas. Luckily the winds were offshore much of the time, so that little oil washed up on the shore.

a

b

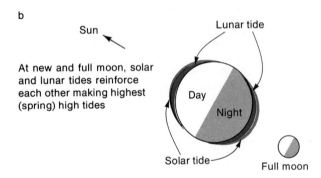

At new and full moon, solar
and lunar tides reinforce
each other making highest
(spring) high tides

c

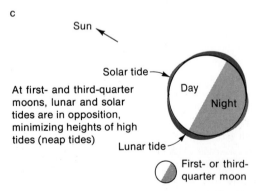

At first- and third-quarter
moons, lunar and solar
tides are in opposition,
minimizing heights of high
tides (neap tides)

Figure 10-22
The relative positions of Earth, Moon, and Sun determine the heights of high tide
during the lunar month. The highest high and lowest low tides (spring tides) come
at new and full moons; the lowest high and highest low tides (neap tides) come at
first- and third-quarter half moon.

When the Moon, Earth, and Sun line up, the combined gravitational pull of Sun and Moon reinforce each other and produce very high tides, the **spring tides.** Such high tides come every two weeks at full and new Moon. The lowest tides, the **neap tides,** come between, at first- and third-quarter Moons, when the Moon and Sun are at right angles to each other with respect to the Earth. The above account describes the equilibrium tide, that is, one that is theoretically calculated for a uniform globe. The heights of the actual tides are very different in various parts of the oceans. Because the oceans are of various shapes and sizes, the water of the tide responds in complex ways. It is a bit like connecting a great number of large and small pots and bowls in a complicated pattern and sloshing water back and forth between them. Thus, in Hawaii, the difference between low and high water is only about 0.5 meter; at Seattle, however, it is about 3 meters (10 feet). Extraordinary tides occur in a few places, such as the Bay of Fundy, where the tidal range can be more than 12 meters (40 feet). Inland lakes, such as the Great Lakes, are virtually tideless. Tides are calculated for years ahead with great precision by computers for many of the world's coastlines, especially those with important commercial shipping and harbors.

Along shallow coasts, tidal movements give up energy through friction of the water with the sea floor—energy that must ultimately come from the rotation of the Earth and Moon. That frictional loss is enough to slow the rotation of the Earth by a very small amount. The average length of the day has been calculated to have lengthened by 0.001 second in the past 100 years. That may seem negligible, but over many millions of years of geologic time, that amount of slowing can mount up. The Earth must once have been rotating much faster, though the time of its revolution around the Sun was unaffected. The Moon's rate of revolution about the Earth would have been faster, and the Moon would have been closer to the Earth. That means that the tides would generally have been much higher, that there were many more days in a year, and that the days were shorter.

Striking support for this last idea came from the world of fossils. Corals, tiny marine animals that secrete calcium carbonate and make modern coral reefs, lay down a microscopically thin layer of calcium carbonate each day; the layers laid down in summer are thicker than those laid down in winter. Careful counting of these layers in fossil corals has convinced many paleontolo-

Figure 10-23
Aerial view of a barrier island (white) that was breached by a hurricane in September 1947, after which a lobate tidal delta formed between the island and the mainland. [Courtesy of M. M. Nichols, U.S. Department of Agriculture.]

gists that, 400 million years ago, there were nearly 400 days in a year. Evidence of stronger tides is not so good, but some geologists who study tidal sediments of the past think they can see the effects of stronger **tidal currents,** the rapid movements of water in shallow parts of the oceans.

Tidal Currents. The movement of tidal waters near shorelines causes tidal currents that can reach speeds of a few kilometers per hour. As the tide rises, the water flows in toward the shore as a **flood tide,** moving into shallow coastal marshes and up small streams. As the tide passes the high stage and starts to fall, the **ebb tide** moves out, and low-lying coastal areas are exposed again. Such tidal currents cut channels through **tidal flats,** which are muddy or sandy areas that lie above low water but are flooded at high water. Tidal flats may be narrow strips seaward of the beach, or they may be extensive areas covering hundreds of square kilometers. When the tide advances on some wide tidal flats, it may move so rapidly that areas are flooded faster than a person can run. The tidal-flat

beachcomber is well advised to consult a local tide table before wandering.

Tidal flats may be separated from the open sea by long sand bars or **barrier islands** parallel to the shoreline. The islands are bars of sand that have been built up above the high-water level and are stabilized by vegetation. The barrier islands or bars are broken by occasional tidal channels through which the water rushes in a strong current. Outside these channels, tidal currents may create tidal deltas of sand transported from the tidal flat during ebb tides. The study of the effects of tidal currents on sediment in the modern world has been applied to sediments of the past. Geologists have thus inferred many deposits to be of tidal-flat and channel origin.

CONTINENTAL SHELVES

Bordering the North American coasts of the Atlantic and the Gulf of Mexico are broad, shallow sea-floor platforms that, though submerged, are clearly parts of the continental mass.

Figure 10-24
Two views of a three-dimensional model of the Atlantic continental shelf, slope, and rise of part of
North America. (Top) View looking northwest; Florida is in the foreground, Nova Scotia and part of
the Grand Banks at the far edge. (Bottom) Close-up of the section from Nova Scotia at right to New
York and Long Island at left. Near the left margin is the Hudson submarine canyon, and in the middle
foreground is the area of Georges Bank, off Cape Cod. [Courtesy of K. O. Emery and E. Uchupi,
Woods Hole Oceanographic Institution.]

Figure 10-25
An echo-sounding profile of the Congo submarine canyon off the west coast of Africa (Republic of Zaire.) The bottom of the canyon at this point is about 3000 m below the sea floor of the continental shelf; at the top, the canyon is more than 10 km wide. The heavy black horizontal lines in the water at the top of the recording are artifacts of the process. The wavy lines below the sea-floor surface are sound reflections from bedding planes in continental shelf sediments, somewhat deformed because of mild tectonic disturbance. [From K. O. Emery, Woods Hole Oceanographic Institution.]

These platforms, and similar ones around other continents, the **continental shelves,** extend from the edges of the continent to a depth of a few hundred meters, where they give way to steeper slopes that go down several thousands of meters to the main ocean floor. For most of the first century of ocean exploration, marine geologists were satisfied to say that continental shelves extended to depths of about 200 meters (650 feet), where, for the most part, the continental slopes started. Then, growing interest in the economic uses of the sea, from fishing to mining, provoked international legal discussions of the territorial rights of nations to the continental shelves. Marine geologists, finding that the old definition was too arbitrary, began to be more precise: in a United Nations' report of 1957, they recommended a 650-meter depth limit, one that would include all of the world's continental shelves. Legal questions sometimes impose themselves on scientific matters in this way.

Continental shelves vary widely in width, but they average about 65 kilometers; the general slope of the surface is slight, the angle of inclination averaging only 0°07′. Most of the surface is fairly uneven, with small hills and ridges alternating with basin-like depressions, broad valley-like troughs, and occasional narrow, steep-walled valleys called **submarine canyons.** Most areas of the continental shelves were above sea level during the Pleistocene glaciations and, as we noted in Chapter 9, much of erosional and sedimentational character of their surface was formed then. Waves and tidal currents acting on the shelves since the last glaciation have modified the surface, mainly by depositing sand near the shoreline and silts and muds in the deeper water farther from shore. Pleistocene relic sands may be found at shallow depths far out on the shelf, even near the shelf edge, as on Georges Bank southeast of Cape Cod, one of the famous fishing grounds of the Atlantic. These sands are now being dispersed,

Beam of sound waves
travels to bottom
and is
reflected back to
microphone at ship

$$\text{Velocity} = \frac{\text{distance}}{\text{time}}$$

$$\text{Distance} = \underset{\text{(down and up)}}{2 \times \text{depth}} = \underset{\text{(known)}}{\text{velocity}} \times \underset{\text{(measured)}}{\text{time}}$$

Figure 10-26
Echo sounders sense underwater topography by beaming sound waves to the bottom and measuring the time required for the beam to be reflected back to the ship.

redistributed, and altered by modern processes. There are about 400 billion tons of this sand in the top 3 meters (10 feet) of sediment off the northeastern coast of the United States, enough to supply the needs of nearby areas of thousands of years, a valuable sea-bed resource.

Continental shelves may be narrow and broken by isolated deep basins and high ridges or escarpments, as off the coast of California, where water hundreds of meters deep may be within sight of land. This coast bears all of the topographic earmarks of a tectonically disturbed area, which is in keeping with the highly faulted and deformed coastal belt just above the water. Some narrow shelves, however, show little or no evidence of tectonic disturbance. One of the best known of these is off the east coast of Florida, where the powerful Gulf Stream, a rapidly flowing current of water, runs close to shore.

Oceanographers have mapped continental shelves—and the rest of the ocean floor—with a shipboard instrument called an **echo-sounder.** This instrument, sometimes called a **fathometer,** * or **depth-recorder,** works by sending

---

*From "fathom," the traditional nautical measure of depth, equal to 6 feet.

sound waves from the ship to the bottom. The sound waves reflected from the bottom are picked up by sensitive detectors on the ship. From the measured delay in time and the known speed of sound in water, oceanographers can determine the depth. As the ship cruises along a straight course, a two-dimensional profile of the topography is traced out automatically; from many such profiles a bathymetric map is constructed. A limitation of the accuracy of such maps is the assumption that the places between widely spaced profiles have something like the same shapes and forms that we are used to seeing in three-dimensions on land. This limitation is partly overcome by a series of very closely spaced profiles in a regular grid. One view of ocean-bottom topography drawn on this basis is given in Figure 10-31, a section of a map prepared by geologists at the Woods Hole Oceanographic Institution.

In the last few years submarine geologists have used new instruments, such as echosounders towed along the bottom, to get a better idea of the topography. These "deep-towed" vehicles, or "fish," are equipped with other geophysical instruments, such as magnetometers. Even better and more detailed information

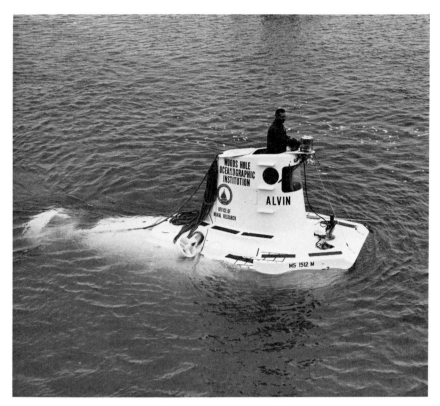

Figure 10-27
The deep submersible vessel Alvin, designed to conduct geological and biological exploration of the sea floor. [Courtesy of Woods Hole Oceanographic Institution.]

on bottom topography is obtained by the use of side-scanning sonar, a method that uses sound waves sent out so that they graze the bottom at low angles, scanning a wide area on both sides of the ship. Last but not least is direct observation of the bottom by marine geologists in deep-diving manned submersibles such as that shown in Figure 10-27. In these vessels scientists can see—and photograph—all of the details of the bottom down to depths of thousands of meters. Equipped with mechanical arms, they can break off pieces of rock or scoop up samples of sediment and bring them back to the laboratory.

The internal structure of broad, gently sloping continental shelves was worked out mainly by geophysicists at the Lamont Geological Observatory of Columbia University during the 1950s. They sent very strong sound waves down through the water, which penetrated the sediments and were reflected back to their oceanographic research ship in the same way as ordinary echo-sounders. From the way in which the sound waves were reflected by layers of sediment and rock they were able to deduce the structure of the shelf: a pile of sediment several

kilometers thick built out from the continent. The suspicion that the shelves had such a structure had early been stimulated by speculation on the narrowness of the Florida shelf near the Gulf Stream. There, it was thought, the current in the sea was so fast—up to about 10 kilometers per hour—that the sea floor was kept scoured clean of sediment. Farther north, where the Gulf Stream moved out to sea, the continental shelf widened and was discovered to consist of sedimentary layers. In the summer and fall of 1976, geologists of the United States Geological Survey began a program of drilling at sea on the Atlantic continental shelf. Their findings have corroborated many of the deductions made from geophysical evidence.

In the past few years, the implications of plate-tectonic theory for continental-shelf development have been assuming increasing importance. According to some of these ideas, the continental shelves of the Atlantic Ocean type are thought to have originated as the trailing edges of continental margins on plates that broke apart and have been moving away from each other ever since the Atlantic Ocean started

Figure 10-28
A profile of the Atlantic continental margin of North America off southern New England based on seismic data. Stratification, based on continuous seismic profiling, is shown diagrammatically for the younger sediments. [From K. O. Emery and E. Uchupi, *Atlantic Continental Margin of North America*. Copyright 1972 by American Association of Petroleum Geologists.]

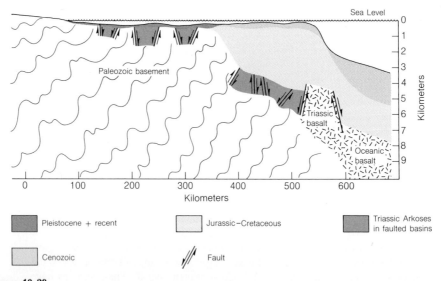

Figure 10-29
Geological cross section, somewhat schematic, of the Atlantic continental shelf from Maine south across Gulf of Maine and Georges Bank to continental rise. The Jurassic and later sediments were deposited over a multiply faulted, rifted basement of Triassic red beds and basalts that overlie metamorphosed Paleozoic rocks. [After R. D. Ballard and E. Uchupi "Triassic Rift Structures in the Gulf of Maine," *Bull. American Assoc. Petroleum Geologists*, vol. 59, pp. 1041–1072, 1975.]

1. Beginning of continental rifting: downfaulted valley formed over upwelling zone of basaltic magma.

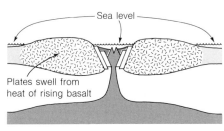

2. Mid-ocean ridge formed as narrow sea opens at spreading center.

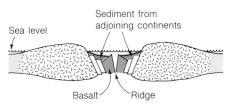

3. As plates move away from ridge they cool and subside, their edges receiving more sediment.

Figure 10-30
As two continental masses on lithospheric plates diverge at a mid-ocean ridge, the plates cool and contract, and their trailing edges subside, the newly formed continental shelves receiving terrigenous erosional detritus from the continents. See also Figure 19-16.

opening about 180 million years ago. The broken, rifted margin was heated up by the upwelling of basaltic magma that formed the newly created spreading center, the mid-Atlantic ridge. As the edge of North America moved away from the ridge, it started to cool. As it cooled, the lithosphere contracted, the surface subsided below sea level, and erosional debris from the continent accumulated on its seaward edge. As the Atlantic widened, the shelf, slope, and rise gradually built out from the continent as the edge of the plate continued to contract and subside (see Fig. 10-30).

Narrow, tectonically deformed continental shelves, such as those of the Pacific, are characteristic of continental margins that coincide with the leading edges of lithospheric plates where they terminate at transform faults or subduction zones. In that tectonic environment, continental shelves accumulate sediments, but they are likely to be deformed as well as affected by volcanism and metamorphism. Much remains to be learned of these kinds of coasts, where sedimentation in deeper water plays a relatively more important role.

CONTINENTAL SLOPE AND RISE

Continental shelves are abruptly terminated by the **continental slopes,** which have an average inclination of about 4°—a drop of about 70 meters in a horizontal distance of 1 kilometer. That is a healthy slope, but not exactly a steep cliff, as one might gather from diagrams that greatly exaggerate the vertical scale, such as Figure 10-28. The sediments of most slopes are muds and silt, derived from continental erosion, that have been carried across the shelf and draped over the edge. Like the surface shelf sediments, much of the uppermost layers of mud on the slope was deposited when sea level was lower during the Pleistocene glaciations. Geophysical exploration of the slopes below broad continental shelves reveals inclined layers of sediment that have been deformed a little by slumping and sliding down the incline. In contrast, continental slopes of tectonic coasts may be steeper, and older rock may be mantled with only a thin veneer of sediment. Rock outcrops are common on such slopes.

The lower parts of many continental slopes become gentler and merge into a more gradually sloping apron of sediment extending into the main ocean basins. These aprons are the **conti-**

Shelf   Slope   Rise

0   50   100   150 km

Figure 10-31
Map of continental shelf, slope, rise, and Hudson Canyon off New York City.
[From K. O. Emery, Woods Hole Oceanographic Institution.]

nental rises. Their average inclination is less than half a degree, only about an eighth of that of the continental slope; but they extend for hundreds of kilometers, whereas continental slopes have an average width of only 20 kilometers. Rises are fairly smooth topographically, being broken only by an occasional seamount, submarine canyon, or channel. The rises are piles of muddy, silty, and sandy sediments, kilometers in thickness, that have been carried from the continental shelf, down the slope, finally coming to rest on the deep-sea floor.

The continental slope is typically gullied by many valleys and interrupted by occasional submarine canyons. The appearance of the slope suggests erosion, as do the canyons, but we cannot draw again on the Pleistocene lowering of sea level for an explanation, because even the wildest estimate of sea level lowering would not envision the drop of thousands of meters that would be necessary to expose some of these slopes to land erosion processes. The erosion must have a marine explanation. The explana-

tion came in a rush of developments around 1950, when a hypothesis about a previously unknown type of sedimentation was proposed. The hypothesis was largely accepted after stormy debate among sedimentary geologists that rivaled more recent debates about plate tectonics. The hypothesis proposed a new type of current, called a **turbidity current,** and its characteristics ultimately helped to explain submarine canyons, the gullies on continental slopes, the formation of continental rises, and the flat plains that cover large areas of the deep-sea floor, the **abyssal plains.**

TURBIDITY CURRENTS

Strictly speaking, such currents were not new to science in the 1950s. The idea was born in the latter part of the nineteenth century in Geneva, Switzerland, where the Rhone River enters Lake Geneva. The river water is cold and full of suspended clay from the meltwaters of alpine

Figure 10-32
A thick sequence of graded turbidite beds. The lighter, thicker units are sandstones that are coarsest at an abrupt base and grade upward through finer grain sizes in to the darker shale beds. Each pair of sandstone-shale units represents one turbidity flow in a deep marine basin. Miocene of the Apennines. [Photo by P. E. Potter. From F. J. Pettijohn, P. E. Potter, and R. Siever, *Sand and Sandstone.* Copyright 1972 by Springer-Verlag New York, Inc.]

glaciers, and, at that time, when the lake was unpolluted and clear, the river water could be seen through the still lake water above, moving along a channel on the bottom as a distinct muddy current. The river water is denser than the overlying lake water, primarily because of its suspended sediment load and secondarily because it is colder. Being denser, it sinks to the bottom and runs downhill along it. The difference in density also acts as a barrier that slows down mixing of the current with the overlying waters, and so the current maintains itself for a long distance until it reaches the flat bottom of the lake. There it fans out in a thin sheet of muddy water and loses momentum, gradually coming to a stop, the suspended sediment slowly settling out on the bottom as a thin layer. This general kind of current, a **density current,** is known also from oceans, where such currents can arise because of differences in temperature or salinity alone; colder and saltier water is denser. The name turbidity current is applied to density currents that owe their density to suspended sediment.

Turbidity currents became a subject of mild interest in the 1930s as possible eroders of the submarine canyons that were then being extensively mapped. It was not until the late 1940s, however, that they became a focus of activity for marine and land geologists alike. The man who sparked much of that resurgence of interest was a Dutch geologist, Philip Kuenen, who combined his experience as an oceanographer and field geologist with a series of important laboratory experiments. Kuenen produced turbidity currents and studied their dynamics in his laboratory by pouring muddy water into the end of a flume with a sloping bottom. He showed how such currents can move swiftly, at many kilometers per hour, the speed depending on the steepness of the slope and the density of the current. Because of its speed and turbulence, a turbidity current was able to transport large quantities of sand introduced with the suspension or picked up by the current as it flowed over a sandy bottom. The sediment layers produced by settling after the current started to lose speed formed a **graded bed**—that is, a bed with coarse material at the bottom, grading upward to fine material at the top. Each turbid flow pro-

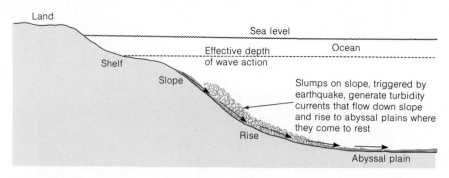

Figure 10-33
Typical formation of turbidity currents in the ocean. Slumps on the continental shelves generate turbidity currents that flow downslope to abyssal plains, where they gradually slow to a
stop and deposit turbidite sediments.

duced a single graded bed; using a series of
flows, Kuenen produced a sequence of graded
beds.

The brilliant next step was the recognition of
such graded beds on land, thick marine sandstone and shale sequences produced long ago
under water as the product of such currents. The
final step was tying all this together with what
was being learned about the sediments and topography of the sea floor to formulate a hypothesis. Turbidity currents are formed by large
slumps of mud and sand draped over the edge of
the continental shelf onto the continental slope.
The sudden slump or slide, perhaps triggered by
an earthquake, throws mud into suspension,
creating a dense turbid layer, which then starts
flowing down the slope, eroding and picking up
sediment as it picks up speed. These currents
gully the slope and excavate submarine canyons.
As the turbidity current reaches the change of
inclination where the slope meets the continental rise, the current slows, and some of the
sediment starts to settle. Many currents continue
across the rise, cutting channels as they go, to
reach the level bottom of the ocean basin, the
abyssal plain, where they fan out and come to
rest. The deposits of the rise and abyssal plain
are graded beds of sand, silt, and clay; **turbidites** was the name coined for them.

Revolutionary as these ideas were, confirmation soon started rolling in. A series of sudden
breaks in trans-Atlantic telephone and telegraph
cables on the continental slope and rise off the
Grand Banks of Newfoundland had taken place
in 1929 following an earthquake. The locations
of the breaks were plotted on a map and the
times of breaking were noted. A pattern quickly
became clear. There was a rapid breaking of

cables high on the slope, followed by a sequential rupturing going down the slope and farther
from the epicenter of the earthquake. But the
breaks downslope occurred much too long after
the earthquake to have been caused by earthquake waves. The turbidity-current hypothesis
gave the only really plausible explanation: the
earthquake provoked a slump that activated a
turbidity current so fast and powerful that it
snapped cables as it raced down the slope and
rise. The current maintained itself for at least
700 kilometers and was calculated to have
reached speeds of 40–55 kilometers (25–34
miles) per hour. Sediment cored from the deep
sea near the path of cable breaks showed a thin
graded bed at the surface, probably the material
settled from the current. Similar patterns of
cable breaks on continental slopes in other parts
of the world showed up as records of cable
companies were searched.

The most compelling evidence of turbidity
currents was the distribution of turbidite sediment in the oceans. No other mechanism could
as simply or satisfactorily explain how coarse
sand particles could be transported to deep waters beyond the reach of waves and tidal currents. How else could graded beds have filled in
the abyssal plains, the lowest parts of the ocean
basins? The turbidity-current hypothesis was
especially attractive because it simultaneously
explained the formation of the slope, rise, and
plain.

Turbidity currents have not explained everything. Though much is known about the physics of density currents, we have still much to
learn about the complex workings of turbidity
currents. Turbidity currents may not be the sole
agent responsible for excavating submarine can-

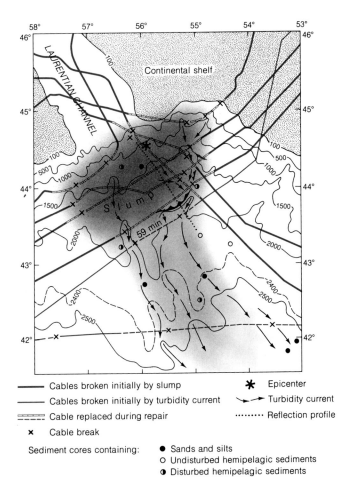

Figure 10-34
Map and seismic reflection profile of Grand Banks area where cable breaks signalled the beginning of a slump and turbidity current. [From B. Heezen and C. L. Drake, Copyright 1964 by American Association of Petroleum Geologists.]

260

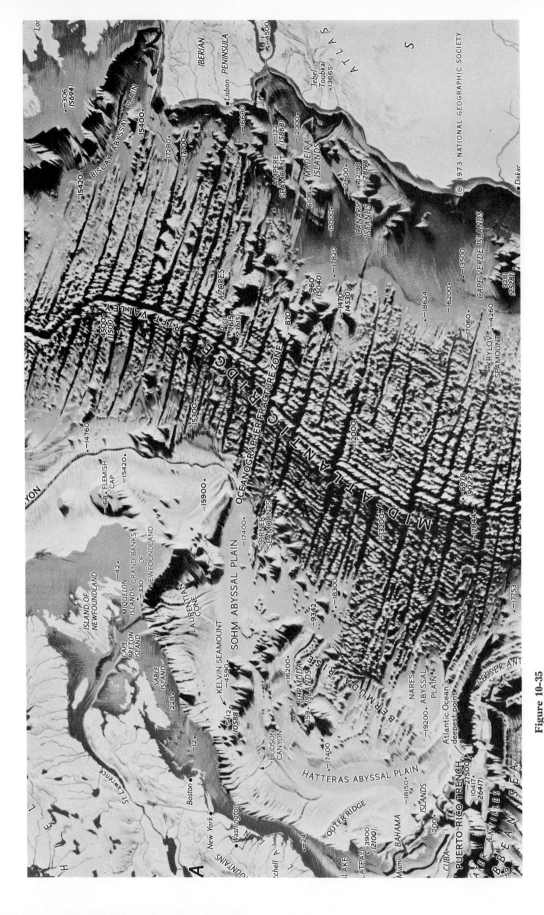

Figure 10-35
An artist's representation of the floor of the North Atlantic Ocean based on bathymetric studies of Bruce C. Heezen and Marie Tharp of the Lamont-Doherty Geological Observatory. Depths shown in feet below sea level. [Painted by Heinrich C. Berann; copyright © 1968 National Geographic Society.]

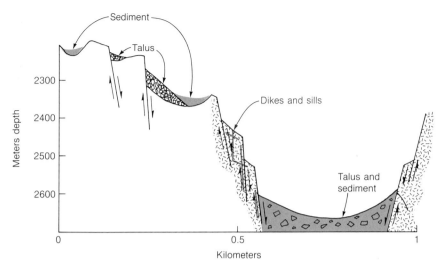

Figure 10-36
Detail of a portion of the central rift valley of the mid-Atlantic ridge in the FAMOUS (French-American Mid-Ocean Undersea Study) area southwest of the Azores Islands. The deep valley, the narrow site where most of the basalt is extruded, is bounded by a series of faults that have created local depressions where basalt talus blocks and pelagic sediment have accumulated. [Modified from "Transform Fault and Rift Valley from Bathyscaph and Diving Saucer," *Science,* vol. 190, pp. 108–116.]

yons in solid, hard rock, and there is also some evidence for the existence of localized deep-ocean currents that can also transport sand. Like other major theories, the turbidity-current idea has become more complicated as it has been worked out in more detail. More recently, however, this important simplifying hypothesis, linked to the history of the oceans and continent edges, has become a vital part of plate-tectonic theory and its applications. This has come about as a result of careful consideration of the topographic and geophysical profiles of the oceans.

THE PROFILE OF THE OCEANS

The Atlantic Ocean is fairly symmetrical about the mid-Atlantic ridge, and is bounded on both sides by continental shelves, slopes, and rises. At the ridge, a high, rough topography of basalt is created by the upward movement of material from the partially molten asthenosphere to create new oceanic lithosphere.

Much detail of the ridge topography and structure in one area has been mapped by project FAMOUS (French-American Mid-Ocean Undersea Study) in 1973 and 1974. FAMOUS concentrated on a small area centered around

36° 50′ N, southwest of the Azores Islands. In addition to detailed shipboard geophysical work, three deep-sea submersibles, the French *Archimède* and *Cyana* and the American *Alvin* dove into the rift valley many times to map and collect samples. They discovered that the intense activity of downfaulting, extrusion of lava, and intrusion of dikes and sills was confined to a narrow central portion, little more than a kilometer wide (Fig. 10-36).

Another spreading center, the East Pacific rise, arches upward from the sea floor in the Southeastern Pacific Ocean. Though it has the same general character as the mid-Atlantic ridge, it is a broader, lower feature, a reflection of the higher speed of spreading at this zone. As the new crust is created at a more rapid rate, it moves laterally fast enough so that it is not uplifted as much as slower-spreading ridges, such as the mid-Atlantic.

Away from the ridge, the topography becomes lower and less rugged, a region of **abyssal hills,** as the lithosphere subsides as a result of cooling. The slopes become thinly covered with the fine sediment that accumulates slowly over all of the ocean floor. As the lithosphere sinks more, it becomes swamped by turbidity-current deposits that bury the varied hilly topography and create

Figure 10-37

Topographic and geophysical profiles of the Atlantic Ocean. (Top) Geophysical and topographic cross section deduced from seismic measurements and echo-sounding profiles from New York to the northwest coast of Africa. [After B. C. Heezen, "Physiographic Diagram of the North Atlantic Ocean," p. 102, Figure 49. Copyright 1959 by Geological Society of America.] (Bottom) Topographic profile of the floor of the Atlantic from Martha's Vineyard, Massachusetts, to Gibraltar. A portion of an abyssal plain extends from 750 miles to about 1000 miles off the east coast of the United States. The island at 2300 miles is one of the Azores. [From B. C. Heezen, "The Origin of Submarine Canyons." Copyright © 1956 by Scientific American, Inc. All rights reserved.]

a level abyssal plain. Closer to a continent, the plain becomes a continental rise, with the original basalt topography buried under many kilometers of turbidite.

Isolated volcanic islands dot the ocean floors. Some are active, such as those of the Hawaiian Islands. Others are extinct and may be covered over completely by coral reefs, such as the atolls of the Pacific Ocean. Isolated subsea mountains with the same shape as volcanoes are found rising from the ocean floor. These **seamounts,** like volcanic islands, may occur as clusters or chains; where closely spaced, chains of seamounts merge to become **aseismic ridges.** Many seamounts have flat tops formed by erosion of the volcano top during emergence; such seamounts are called **guyots** (named after the first professor of geology at Princeton University). All of these volcanic mountains are produced by plates riding over hot spots in the mantle, regions where basalt is steadily rising (see Chapter 14).

How this came to be is the subject of much speculation, a subject we can call "paleo–plate tectonics." It is the same picture we discussed on page 255. As the Atlantic Ocean opened up, the first sediments deposited in the narrow rift-valley ocean, which was perhaps something like the Red Sea is today, were coarse turbidites flowing into deep waters at the steep, newly broken edges of the continental plates. As the plates separated farther, continental shelves were built up over the trailing edges of the plates as they subsided, and the sediments being deposited on the rise built up to form a thick pile that merged with the continental slope. With continued spreading of sea floor, the turbidites began to fill in the low spots on the rough, basaltic, oceanic crust, gradually building up to form the abyssal plains. This conception ties together tectonics and turbidite sedimentation in a consistent theory that explains much of what we know about the Atlantic Ocean today.

The Pacific Ocean is not so easily fitted into such a simple scheme. Continent edges there are narrow, and deep basins may be filled with turbidites very close to shore. Thick accumulations of turbidites are found as submarine fans or subsea deltas where submarine canyons that start near the shore empty onto the deepsea floor. Turbidite sediments form in trenches, the subduction zones in which oceanic crust is consumed as it turns downward into the asthenosphere. Many of these turbidites are crumpled and folded, scraped off, and plastered against the overriding plate edge. Much of the sediment may not be carried down with the oceanic crust along the subduction zone because the sediment, saturated with water, is much less dense than basalt and tends to "float" at the surface of the lithosphere. Some, of course, may be dragged down, mixed with volcanics and other sediments, and metamorphosed by pressure and heat as it goes down.

We have given emphasis to turbidity currents because they are major sediment eroders and transporters, but they are not the only (or even the major) currents of the oceans, nor are turbidites the only significant sediment type of the deep sea. The general circulation of the oceans, and of the atmosphere above them, is responsible for the patterns of transport of much of the fine-grained sediment of the sea.

OCEANIC CIRCULATION AND TRANSPORT OF TERRIGENOUS SEDIMENT

For centuries, mariners have known that there are surface currents in the sea that can either speed a ship on its course or hinder its progress. At least as early as 800 B.C., the Phoenicians and Greeks knew the currents of much of the Mediterranean Sea. Homer's *Odyssey* mentions the treacherous waters of the Strait of Messina between Italy and Sicily. In North America, it was that versatile politician-publisher-scientist Benjamin Franklin who started the serious study of ocean currents by publishing the first chart of the Gulf Stream.

Early investigations of currents made use of drift bottles—floating bottles set free in the ocean with cards inside asking the finder (for a small reward) to return the card with information about the date and place of its recovery from the sea. Modern physical oceanographers have invented instruments to measure directly the speed and direction of currents. Current speed is now most frequently measured by ro-

Homer warned that the main danger in navigating the Strait of Messina was the whirlpool Charybdis, (now known as Garofalo). The whirlpool lies opposite Scylla (now Scilla), a rock near the Italian shore that, according to Homer, was inhabited by a creature whose name was also Scylla, a six-headed monster with an appetite for sailors. The expression "between Scylla and Charybdis," which is descriptive of situations in which the avoidance of one danger means exposure to another, has survived to this day.

Figure 10-38
Continuous seismic profile, showing a continuous cross-sectional view of the geological structure of the
deep ocean floor flanking the mid-Atlantic ridge. The profile was obtained in June of 1967 by means of a
seismic recording system carried on board the Teledyne Exploration Company's vessel *Stranger*. The profile
shows a part of the western abyssal plain at the flank of the ridge. In this region the sediments are compar-

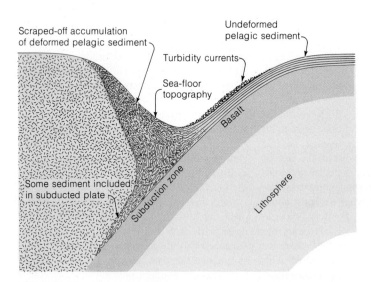

Figure 10-39
Sedimentation and deformation of sediment in an oceanic trench-subduction
zone. Much of the pelagic sediment and turbidity current deposits in the
trench are "scraped off" as the oceanic plate moves down the subduction
zone, the sediments being of much lower density than the underlying lithospheric rocks. Some sediment may be carried along with the subducting plate.

atively flat and uniform, estimated to be from 1000 to 1500 m (3300 to 5000 ft) thick. The depth from surface to sediments is about 5300 m (17,500 ft). The irregular basaltic basement protrudes through the sediments at left and dominates the topography to the right, closer to the ridge. [Courtesy Teledyne Exploration Company.]

tating vanes attached to a meter that gives the number of rotations per minute and the direction. These current meters can be attached at various depths to a moored cable and the data electronically recorded. Current depth and current speed at depth can also be determined by means of the Swallow float (named after its inventor, the English oceanographer John C. Swallow), a closed aluminum tube designed to float at various levels in the water. The Swallow float includes a sound source—usually called a "pinger" because of the sound it makes—that is picked up by sensitive microphones attached to the research ship. Thus, as the float moves in the current, the ship is able to follow its position. Currents can be inferred indirectly from photographs of rippled and scoured bottom sediment, though it is difficult to calculate current velocities exactly from such data.

The surface currents of the oceans can be simplified into a pattern of large closed loops, called **gyres** (Figs. 10-42 and 10-43). The main currents are the outside paths of the gyres. Two subtropical gyres lie on either side of the equator, the northern one rotating clockwise and the southern one counterclockwise. Between the westward-flowing equatorial currents that are parts of these gyres, there is an oppositely directed eastward flow, the Equatorial Countercurrent. North and south of the subtropical gyres are smaller subpolar gyres; each of these rotates in a direction opposite to that of its companion subtropical gyre. The close correspondence between the gyres and the directions of the prevailing winds over the oceans shows that the winds and currents are linked: the winds constitute the primary driving mechanism for the surface currents of the ocean.

Even satellites have been used to map ocean currents. Using infrared-sensitive instruments, these satellites can make high-quality images of the surface temperatures of the sea and so distinguish warm- and cold-water currents.

Surface
float with
radio, light

Density of sea water (g/cc)

1.023
1.024
1.025
1.026
1.027
1.028

Sound
signals
sent to
tracking
ship

Float slowly
drifts with
current

Density of sealed float
adjusted to = 1.027

Temperature-depth
recorder

Float

Current meter

Pinger
sound source

Anchor

Figure 10-41
Ripples indicative of high flow velocities formed in coarse sand, with sandy gravel
in upper left corner. Ripples indicate strong westerly bottom current flow at a
depth of 490 m in the Strait of Gibraltar. [From G. Kelling and D. J. Stanley,
"Sedimentary Evidence of Bottom Current Activity, Strait of Gibraltar Region."
Marine Geology, 13:M51-M60. Copyright © Elsevier Publishing Co., Amsterdam,
1972.]

Figure 10-40
Devices such as current meters and
the Swallow float are designed to
measure deep currents in the ocean.
Before the float is lowered, its density
is adjusted to that of the water at the
depth to be tracked. It then sinks to
its equal-density level and begins to
drift with the current, sending out
sound signals as it floats with the current. The density of ocean water varies from place to place depending on
the salinity and temperature. Current
meters, temperature-depth recorders,
and other instruments are moored by
cable to an anchor.

The most famous ocean currents are the
north-south sections of the gyres. The north-
flowing Gulf Stream is the strong western part
of the North Atlantic subtropical gyre. The
south-flowing California Current is the weak
eastern section of the North Pacific subtropical
gyre. The east-west equatorial currents flow at
speeds of 3-6 kilometers (2-4 miles) per day;
thus they move slowly enough to adjust to the
hot latitudes through which they flow. In contrast, the Gulf Stream flows more than an order
of magnitude faster, 40-120 kilometers (25-75
miles) per day, so that it does not have time to
adjust to its climatic surroundings. Thus the
Gulf Stream remains a warm current in the cold

North Atlantic, only slowly transferring heat to
the colder air above it. Such warm-water flows
contribute significantly to heat transfer from one
part of the globe to another.

The prevailing winds can cause vertical
movements in the sea, sometimes causing deeper
waters to move up to the surface—**upwelling**—or surface waters to move to lower
depths—**sinking.** Most deeper waters of the
ocean are colder than those at the surface; therefore, when they reach the surface, they cool the
air, which causes fog to form. This is what
causes the foggy summer weather familiar to
people who live along much of the Pacific coast
of North America. Upwelling and sinking near

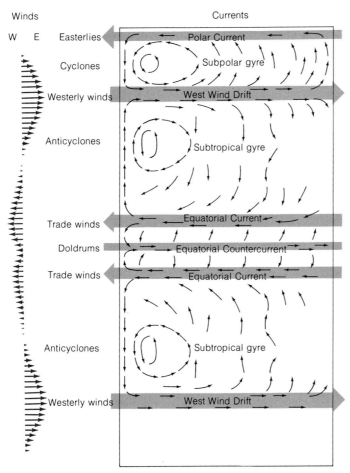

Figure 10-42
Idealized ocean, rectangular in shape and subject only to the horizontal wind forces shown by the broad, gray arrows, would have the circulation patterns indicated by the black arrows. Approximate relative velocities of surface winds are indicated at left. This diagram is schematic for the surface only. [From W. Munk, "The Circulation of the Oceans." Copyright © 1955 by Scientific American, Inc. All rights reserved.]

coasts, in most places, affects the water to a depth of about 100–200 meters (300–650 feet).

Upwelling is important for its biological side effects. Deeper waters tend to be rich in nutrients, because the sparse marine life at depth is unable to utilize most of the phosphate, nitrate, and other dissolved matter in it. When that rich water reaches the sunlit surface, where organisms can thrive in abundance, the biological populations expand in response to the nutrients. Microscopic plant life blooms, and fish populations that live on it expand in proportion.

Vertical Ocean Circulation. Imagine the Atlantic or Pacific Ocean as an elongate oval soup bowl stretched out in the north-south direction with the cold polar waters at opposite shallow edges and the equatorial waters in the middle. The surface waters are warm near the equator—around 25°C or warmer—while those in the Arctic and Antarctic are quite cold—about 0°C or a little above. Because cold water is denser than warm, the polar waters tend to sink and slide along the bottom toward the equator. As they do, they push in front of them the deeper waters, which tend to rise near the equator, being displaced from both directions. This simplified model explains how it happens that, just below the shallow, warm waters of the equatorial ocean, the deeper waters are cold.

Figure 10-43
Major ocean currents shown on a map centered on the South Pole. The major gyres can be identified and compared with the idealized drawing of Figure 10-42. [From W. Munk, "The Circulation of the Oceans." Copyright © 1955 by Scientific American, Inc. All rights reserved.]

Figure 10-44
Generalized vertical circulation of the Atlantic Ocean. (a) An ideal model of a North-South ocean that is cooled at the poles and warmed at the equator. Colder waters sink because they are denser, replacing warmer water, which rises. (b) Simplified model of Atlantic Ocean circulation, showing how Antarctic bottom water flows along the bottom more than 20° north of the equator, displacing the Arctic bottom water to an intermediate level.

Because the dense, cold waters move slowly and mix with surrounding waters very slowly, they tend to retain their original temperature and salinity (saltiness of the water varies slightly from place to place in the ocean). Thus the distinctive temperature and salinity of such waters allows them to be identified as large bodies, or **water masses,** and allows their place of origin to be determined. North Atlantic deep water can be traced from its polar origins in this way, as it sinks and moves southward. Before it reaches the equator, it meets and rides over a mass of still colder and denser water, Antarctic bottom water, which has worked slowly northward from the cold Antarctic Sea.

The topography of the ocean floor affects deep-water currents. They may be blocked by ocean ridges or they may flow through gaps or breaches in a ridge. The water masses are density-driven, so they follow topographic highs and lows just as turbidity currents do.

The density-driven vertical circulation is much slower than the wind-driven horizontal circulation at the surface. Deep waters rise at the equator at speeds of only 2–5 meters (6–15 feet) per year. Polar waters take about 1000 years to circulate, a number that may be an important practical matter before very long. If pollutants are introduced into high-latitude bottom waters, they will not rise to the surface near the equator for hundreds of years. Thus radioactive waste materials might lose a significant amount of

their damaging radiation before they come back to the surface. On the other hand, once introduced to such a slow moving system, toxic materials may remain in circulation for a very long time.

The precise measurement of the chemical composition of sea water in various parts of the ocean is necessary to an understanding of the details of ocean circulation. The data will enable oceanographers to understand how and where natural and man-made chemical substances are introduced and how they are distributed throughout the world's oceans. Designed to do just that is GEOSECS (Geochemical Ocean Sections), one of the major programs of the International Decade of Ocean Exploration, a multinational cooperative study of the oceans from 1970–1980. This large-scale geochemical study of the seas has now been largely completed and has taught us much about the movements of water masses, the distribution of radioactive substances in the oceans, and the fate of carbon dioxide as it moves from the atmosphere to the oceans (See Chapter 12). In addition, GEOSECS has given us new understanding of the nature and distribution of particulate matter in sea water (Fig. 10-45); such particles, after all, are the raw material of sedimentation in the deep sea.

Deep-sea Sedimentation. The general circulation of the ocean is too slow to accomplish

Figure 10-45
A longitudinal section of the North Atlantic Ocean showing the dry weight of particulate matter as mapped by GEOSECS. Vertical lines of dots show position of GEOSECS stations. [After Brewer and others, "The distribution of particulate matter in the Atlantic Ocean," *Earth and Planetary Science Letters,* vol. 32, 1976.]

much erosion, except where such strong currents as the Gulf Stream travel along the shallower edges of the sea. Slow-moving currents do have enough mild turbulence, however, to keep fine-grained sedimentary particles suspended for a long time before they settle through the great depths of water to the bottom. Though sea water may appear clear and transparent, careful filtering of large volumes of deep water, such as of 100-liter samples (about 25 gallons), can extract a few thousandths of a gram of suspended mineral solids. The particles are smaller than 0.025 millimeter, and a great many of them are 0.001 millimeter or less. Identification of the particles shows that they include fragments of clay minerals, quartz, feldspar, and other common minerals produced by the weathering of rocks on the continents. These particles in the water are of the same general kind as those that constitute **pelagic sediments,** the gray and brownish muds that cover much of the varied topography of the deep-sea floor. There is little question that the muds on the bottom were formed by the slow, steady settling of land-derived erosional debris through the great depths of water.

Particles so small take a long time to settle through the water, for their rate of fall is slowed by the frictional resistance of the water. Even in perfectly still water, a particle 0.001 millimeter in diameter would take months to fall several kilometers to the deep-sea bottom. The settling is made even slower by the slow horizontal and vertical movements of the water which may lift the particle up again, extending its lifetime as a suspended particle for many years. Some oceanographers have estimated that it may take several hundred years for some of the smallest particles to finally reach the bottom.

Because the particles take so long to settle, they may be carried greater distances by horizontal ocean currents. A particle dropped into the Gulf Stream off North Carolina might end up on the bottom off the west coast of Europe. Patterns of bottom sediment have been mapped, revealing how distribution patterns are affected not only by strong currents like the Gulf Stream but the many lesser currents of the ocean.

The rates at which these particles are laid down as sediment are extremely slow, in most places about 1 millimeter every 1000 years. At that rate, an ocean bottom 4 kilometers deep would take 4 billion years, almost the whole age of the Earth, to fill up! Of course, the ocean bottom does not stay still for that long: as part of

Figure 10-46
Foraminiferal ooze dredged from a depth of 450 m off the coast of Central America. Enlargement about 15×. [Photo by Patsy J. Smith, U.S. Geological Survey.]

a lithospheric plate, it is moving horizontally at the rate of a few centimeters per year, eventually to be subducted into the mantle.

Though geologists have always known that wind transport plays some role in the deposition of pelagic sediments, it was only in the last decade that they began to realize how important that role is. That realization came as the result of oceanographic research ships taking air samples at sea, partly to test patterns of global air pollution, and was confirmed by melting down samples of ice from the Greenland and Antarctic glaciers and measuring the amount of airborne dust that had fallen there, far from the effects of human industrial pollution. This steady worldwide dust contribution forms about 10 percent of the pelagic sediment. At some times, particularly when there are violent volcanic eruptions, the proportion may be much greater.

Another important component of pelagic sediment is the calcite (calcium carbonate) shell material of pelagic foraminiferans, tiny single-celled animals that live in the surface waters of the sea. Though they are moved about by currents, most are large enough to fall relatively quickly to the bottom when they die. There they accumulate as **foraminiferal oozes.** Very early

Figure 10-47
Scanning electron micrograph of a Pleistocene foraminifer (*Proteiphidium orbiculare*). Enlargement about 140×. [Photograph by T. Cronin.]

Figure 10-48
The calcium carbonate compensation depth is the level in an ocean below which the calcium carbonate of foraminifera and other shelled organisms that have settled from surface water will dissolve. The depth, which is a zone rather than a sharp boundary, varies some from ocean to ocean.

The dissolution of calcium carbonate in the deep ocean has become important in consideration of the future impact of the carbon dioxide injected into the atmosphere by our burning of fossil fuels. As more carbon dioxide enters the ocean by absorption from the atmosphere, calcium carbonate shells become soluble—just as the weathering of limestone on land is promoted by carbon dioxide in rain (Chapter 4). This shell dissolution is a way the oceans have of taking up part of the extra carbon dioxide.

in the course of marine geologic exploration, it was discovered that oozes were abundant at depths less than about 4000 meters (about 13,000 feet) but rare in the deepest waters of the ocean. This could not be attributed to a lack of shells supplied by foraminifers, which live near the surface and, thus, are unaffected by the depth of the water. A closer look at many sediments from deeper water showed a few foraminifers, usually the larger and thicker-shelled ones.

At the same time, physical oceanographers were pointing out that the deeper waters of the oceans were colder, under higher pressure, and contained more dissolved carbon dioxide (from colder polar waters) than shallower waters. Each one of these factors contributed to making calcium carbonate more soluble at depth than at the surface. Then came the hypothesis: no matter how abundant the shelled organisms are in the surface water, as their shells fall into the deeper waters that are undersaturated with calcium carbonate, they will dissolve, either while settling or soon after they come to rest on the bottom.

An ingenious test for this hypothesis was made by an oceanographer at Scripps Institution of Oceanography, who reasoned that, with modern instrumentation, he ought to be able to observe directly any rate of solution. He took carefully machined, accurately weighed, perfect spheres of calcite, and lowered them over the

side of a ship to various depths for various periods of time, and then brought them back up to weigh again. There was no change in the shallow depths, but he found a loss of weight in deeper waters, coupled with etched pits and irregularities, which confirmed that calcite was rapidly dissolved there.

The depth of water below which calcium carbonate starts to dissolve is called the calcium carbonate **compensation depth.** It has become important to an interpretation of the evolution of the ocean basins, using plate tectonics as a model, that has resulted from the National Science Foundation's program of deep drilling of sea-bottom sediments. Drilled samples from some parts of the ocean that are now below the compensation depth show that, some millions of years ago, calcium carbonate was abundant in the sediments. Does this mean that the compensation depth of the oceans has changed with time? That would imply that there had been some drastic change in the circulation patterns of the ocean. The movements of oceanic lithospheric plates offered another alternative. As part of a plate was formed at a ridge or rise, it would have been topographically high, above the compensation depth and the resting place for much carbonate sediment, just as the mid-Atlantic is today. As that portion of the plate moved away from the ridge, it would have subsided gradually as it cooled, eventually passing below the compensation depth, after which time

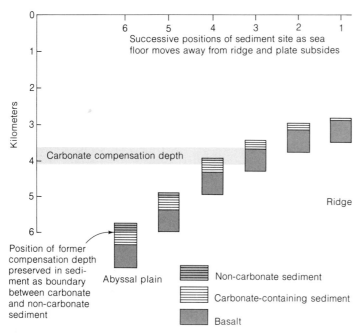

Figure 10-49
As a site of sedimentation is transported away from a mid-ocean ridge by plate movement, plate subsidence moves the site downward with respect to sea level, eventually below the calcium carbonate compensation depth. At that point, carbonate sediment is succeeded by noncarbonate deposits.

it would no longer have received much calcium carbonate sediment. This hypothesis is now being actively pursued with the aim of tracing the rates and paths of movement of oceanic plates in many parts of the oceans.

Calcium carbonate oozes are the most abundant of the biologically produced sediments on the sea floor. Oozes of silica—a noncrystalline form of silicon dioxide, like opal—form, in much the same way as calcium carbonate oozes, from the silica shells of diatoms, an abundant class of green, unicellular algae found in the surface waters of the oceans. These **diatom oozes** are found mostly in the Pacific and Antarctic oceans. Their distribution is governed partly by the abundance of nutrients at the surface. Even where the living organisms are abundant, however, diatom oozes are found only if there is little detritus from land erosion. In many places, such detritus forms the bulk of the sediment and so dilutes the slowly accumulating shells of diatoms and other silica-secreting organisms.

Some components of deep-sea sediment are formed by chemical reactions of sea water with the surface of the sediment. The most prominent of these are manganese nodules, those black lumpy accumulations first found by the *Challenger* expedition, which form at the surface of the sediment over many large areas of ocean bottom. Manganese nodules are estimated to cover as much as 20-50 percent of the Pacific Ocean floor. They form slowly as dissolved manganese and other metals, such as nickel, are precipitated both from the overlying sea water and from the sea water trapped in the pores of recently deposited sediment. The nature of the chemical reactions that form the nodules has long been a subject of scientific research. Recently, as geologists have become more concerned with conservation of natural resources and new sources of manganese ores, they have been estimating the amounts of manganese that could be recovered economically from the sea floor. At this time, the nodules are too expensive to recover, although they are relatively high-grade ores; but eventually, perhaps soon, the cost of mining land deposits of manganese mining a practical matter may become economic. When that time comes, marine geologists and biologists will no doubt have to file some statements on the environmental impact of such mining activity on the water, the sediment, and the biological habitats of the deep sea. In order to do that, we will have to learn a great deal more about the deep sea than we now know.

The two concerns of practical importance—the utilization of the ocean for its mineral and food resources, and the pollution of the ocean by using it as the garbage can of the world—are intertwined. It is impossible to use the ocean's resources without interfering with it in some way. The imperative is to do so in such a way that the alteration will not be damaging or irreversible. The production of oil on continental shelves need not permanently disrupt the biological population of the oceans nor destroy the adjacent beaches, *if* there is sufficient geological knowledge and rigorous enforcement of fail-safe engineering procedures for the prevention of accidents. The oceans can be self-cleansing if oil spills are few and far between. It is heedless dumping of wastes on a global scale that will overload the capacity of the world ocean to maintain its equilibrium.

SUMMARY

1. Wave action is the major erosional agent operating along coasts. Rates of erosion by waves are fastest on shorelines of unconsolidated materials.

2. The shape of a shoreline is determined by wave erosion, modified by tectonic uplift or subsidence, sedimentation, and eustatic changes in sea level.

3. Waves are generated by wind, and are described by their wavelength, height, period, and velocity. Surf is the product of waves entering shallow water. Waves are radiated outward from storms at sea, their places of formation.

4. Wave refraction, the bending of waves as they approach shorelines, is controlled by the shape of the shoreline and the wind direction. Wave refraction affects erosion and sedimentation on beaches, and is also responsible for longshore currents and rip currents.

5. A beach is a dynamic form that is the result of a balance between material eroded from it and material transported to it along the shoreline. It can be described by a budget relating input and output. Man's interference can drastically alter the budget of a beach and, thus, its shape and size.

6. Tides originate from the gravitational pull of the Moon and Sun. Tidal currents are produced that are important distributors of sediments in tidal channels and tidal flats.

7. Continental shelves, slopes, and rises characterize the edges of continents. They are formed by sedimentation of erosional debris from the continents accumulating at the deep-water margin.

8. Formed by the suspension of mud in waters, turbidity currents are density currents that erode submarine canyons, gully the continental slopes, and deposit distinctive graded sediments, turbidites, on the continental rise and abyssal plain. Such currents are the agents of transport of coarser materials to the deep sea.

9. Plate tectonics explains the development of the profile of the oceans in terms of crust forming at the ridges, moving laterally away, and being covered with deep-sea sediment.

10. The horizontal circulation of the oceans is wind-driven into major and minor gyres. The Gulf Stream is the northward-flowing part of one of these, the North Atlantic subtropical gyre.

11. The vertical circulation of the oceans is a response to the greater density of masses of colder water formed in the polar oceans.

12. Pelagic sediments are combinations of fine-grained terrigenous clays, some water-borne and some transported by wind, combined with the calcareous or siliceous shells of small organisms, foraminifers and diatoms that live in the uppermost layers of the oceans.

EXERCISES

1. A certain stretch of shoreline includes a steep headland of sandstone with bays on both sides. Where would you expect to find the best beaches for swimming? How might you tell the direction of longshore currents from the distribution of beach sand?

2. Low submarine ridges of sand on the continental shelf off the northeastern coast of North America have been interpreted as former beaches. What sequence of geologic events can you hypothesize that would support this interpretation?

3. After a period of calm winds and no breakers along the northeastern shore of the United States, an intense storm with high winds passes over the area, followed by another period of calm. Describe, the state of the surf along the beach during the storm and several days afterward.

4. What times(s) during one month that you have to spend at a rocky seashore would you pick to observe the maximum exposure of a wave-cut terrace? What time(s) to observe maximum erosion of a headland?

5. How might you account for the contrast between the broad continental shelf off the East Coast of North America and the narrow, almost nonexistent one off the West Coast?

6. Hoover Dam was built across the Colorado River in southern Nevada. When the river valley was flooded for many kilometers upstream, forming Lake Mead, engineers noted turbid muddy waters at the foot of the dam beneath clear waters above. How might this mud suspension have been produced?

7. Why would you expect thicknesses of pelagic sediments in depressions near the mid-Atlantic ridge to be much less than in depressions at the flanks, far distant from the Ridge?

8. Where would you be more likely to find foraminiferal oozes on the sea floor, on a mid-ocean rise or ridge or on an abyssal plain? In which of these two provinces would you be more likely to find turbidites? In what particular situation might you possibly find both kinds of sediment interlayered?

BIBLIOGRAPHY

Bascom, W., *Waves and Beaches.* New York: Anchor Books (Doubleday and Company, Inc.), 1964.

Heezen, B. C., and C. D. Hollister, *The Face of the Deep.* New York: Oxford University Press, 1971.

Heirtzler, J. R., and W. B. Bryan, "The Floor of the Mid-Atlantic Rift." *Scientific American,* August 1975.

Inman, D. L., and B. M. Brush, "The Coastal Challenge." *Science,* v. 181, pp. 20-32, 1973.

Moore, J. R. (editor), *Oceanography: Readings from Scientific American.* San Francisco: W. H. Freeman and Company, 1971.

Ross, D., *Introduction to Oceanography* (2nd ed.). Englewood Cliffs, New Jersey: Prentice-Hall, Inc., 1977.

Shepard, F. P., *Submarine Geology* (3rd ed.). New York: Harper & Row, 1973.

Turekian, K. K., *Oceans* (2nd ed.). Englewood Cliffs, New Jersey: Prentice-Hall, Inc., 1976.

11

SEDIMENTATION AND SEDIMENTARY ROCKS

Sedimentation is the final stage of a process that begins with erosion and transportation of eroded materials to sites of deposition. Physical sedimentation is the deposition of such materials in the lowest places to which air and water currents can transport them. Chemical sedimentation is mainly the process by which sea water keeps its composition constant by depositing precipitates to balance the input of dissolved weathering products by rivers. Calcium carbonate makes up the largest volume of chemical sediment, and much of it is extracted from sea water by invertebrates and secreted as shells. Silica-rich sediments are also largely produced by organisms, mainly the diatoms. Bacteria play an important role in sulfide sedimentation in environments lacking oxygen. Gypsum and salt form from the evaporation of sea water in isolated basins. Sediments show the impress of the geomorphic environments in which they were deposited. Tectonism controls both subsidence in the depositional area and weathering at the source of the erosional debris. Chemical and physical changes after deposition result in lithification and many other alterations of composition and texture.

Sedimentation, which means settling out of suspension, or deposition in a layer, is a word with many associations. The engineer designing a dam on a river for flood control worries about sedimentation filling the reservoir in back of the dam. The ship's captain navigating through sandy areas near shore is concerned that the shifting patterns of sedimentation may have built up shoals on which he may run aground. Geologists are concerned with all of the varied kinds of sedimentation on the surface of the Earth and how they play a role in the overall dynamics of the planet. Sediments include solid materials physically deposited by wind, water, or ice and dissolved substances chemically precipitated from oceans, lakes, or rivers. Physically deposited sediments have been discussed in relation to erosion and transportation in Chapters 5 through 10; here we will consider them in relation to chemically deposited sediments and in the context of the accumulation of sediments in general.

SEDIMENTATION AS A DOWNHILL PROCESS

Physical sedimentation starts where transportation stops. When the wind dies down, dust settles; when water currents decrease their speed, sand settles. On Earth, physical transportation and sedimentation follow a general downhill trend in response to gravity, from rock falls and mass movements downslope to river systems, and then down to the sea. In running water, sedimentation is a one-way street, each temporary stage of transport and sedimentation carrying the sediment farther toward the bottom of the deep sea. Much of it is permanently dropped along the way and never reaches the end of the line. Eolian sedimentation is different, for winds may blow material from low to high places and back again. But in the long run, eolian sedimentation is effectively a one-way street, too: Once windblown material drops to

Though the dissolved salt in sea water does not evaporate, the air above the ocean always contains some small crystals of sea salt that are left floating after droplets of sea spray from breaking waves have evaporated. This salty air causes automobiles near the ocean to rust much more than those inland, because the salt is corrosive to metal.

the ocean surface, it is trapped. It settles through the water and cannot be picked up again.

Chemical sedimentation is also a "downhill" process, but the driving force is chemical rather than gravitational. A major aspect of weathering and erosion is the chemical decay of rocks exposed to the water and carbon dioxide of the atmosphere. In the course of decay, ions from the rocks are dissolved, and rivers carry them to the sea (see Fig. 6-19). The ocean may be thought of as a huge chemical reservoir: water continually evaporates from the surface, and fresh river water runs in to replenish it. Although that keeps the amount of water fairly constant, it works also to enrich the sea in the dissolved ions: evaporation takes away only the water; the ions do not evaporate. Yet the sea maintains the same salinity. It does so because of sedimentation of the dissolved material as chemical precipitates. Totalled over all of the

oceans of the world, those precipitates must balance the total inflow of ions released by weathering and brought in by rivers.

Understanding the nature of both physical and chemical sedimentation processes, the geologist can work backwards from the properties of a sedimentary rock to deduce its history. He can read that history in terms of the distribution of land and sea, mountains and plains, deserts and swamps—in other words, **the paleogeography** of the ancient time during which the sediment was formed.

Many sedimentary geologists start by analyzing the physically deposited sediments, for they are the most useful in deciphering the major tectonic elements of paleography: the uplands that are the source of detritus, the low basins that receive the sediment. They also are a key to the nature and geography of the transportation network by which the solid products of erosion are carried to sedimentary environments.

CLASTIC SEDIMENTS

How are we to discover what we want to know about transportation and deposition of solid particles, particularly in relation to the tectonic and erosional forces that produce detritus? **Clastic** sediments, those made up of particles broken and weathered from pre-existing rock, tell that story, much of which has been covered in earlier chapters on erosion and transportation. These sediments are also frequently referred to as **detrital,** for they are made up of the detritus of erosion. Clastic sediments—shales, sandstones, and conglomerates—are far more abundant than the chemical precipitates. They constitute well over three-quarters of the total mass of sediments in the Earth's crust, and, of that fraction, shale is by far the most abundant rock type, being about three times as common as the coarser clastics. Clastics dominate because mechanical erosion is constant and widespread over the Earth.

Sedimentation of particles is largely controlled by the strength of the currents that carry them: the larger the particles, the stronger the current must be in order to carry it. It was natural, then, for geologists to distinguish the various clastic sediments on the basis of particle size. Such a division reflects the conditions of sedimentation: A gravel, or its lithified equivalent, conglomerate, calls to mind strong currents of rapidly flowing rivers in mountains, or high waves on a rocky beach. Mud, or its rock equiv-

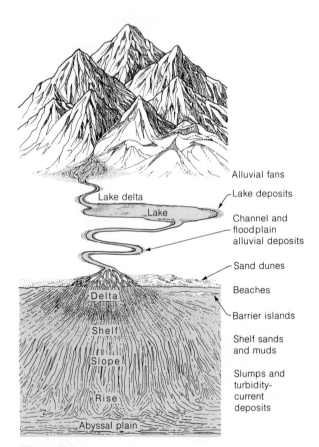

Alluvial fans

Lake deposits

Channel and floodplain alluvial deposits

Sand dunes

Beaches

Barrier islands

Shelf sands and muds

Slumps and turbidity-current deposits

Lake delta

Lake

Delta

Shelf

Slope

Rise

Abyssal plain

Figure 11-1
The downhill path of transportation and deposition takes material from the heights of mountains to the depths of the oceans, many different sedimentary environments being encountered along the way.

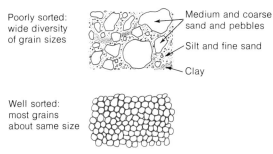

Poorly sorted:
wide diversity
of grain sizes

Medium and coarse
sand and pebbles

Silt and fine sand

Clay

Well sorted:
most grains
about same size

Figure 11-2
Sorting of sedimentary particles produces sediments with a small size range of particles. See also Figures 4-15 and 11-3.

Table 11-1
Classification of sand by grain size

Classification	Grain size (mm)
Very coarse sand	1.0–2.0
Coarse sand	0.5–1.0
Medium sand	0.25–0.5
Fine sand	0.125–0.25
Very fine sand	0.0625–0.125

alent, shale, suggests quiet waters that allow the finest particles to settle. Sand and sandstone imply moderate currents, such as those of rivers and shores, as well as the strong winds that blow sand into dunes.

Sand and Sandstone. Sandstone, more than any other clastic sediment, contains easily read information about its origin. Sand particles are large enough to be seen with the naked eye, and, under a microscope, the minerals can be identified by their optical characteristics and their textures can be studied. In contrast, most of the particles in shale are too fine for optical study, even with high-power microscopes. Sandstones are more abundant and widespread than conglomerates, and they tend to occur as erosion-resistant formations that make easily observed outcrops.

The range of sizes of sand and sandstone grains has been studied extensively as an aid in deciphering their origin. Table 11-1 shows how sands are divided on the basis of their average grain size. But average size does not tell the whole story. If all of the grains in a sample are close to the average size, the sand is considered well **sorted;** if there are many grains much larger and smaller than the average, the sand is poorly sorted. Because **sorting** is related to the kind of depositing current, we can distinguish between well-sorted beach or dune sands and poorly sorted turbidite sands. The degree of sorting can be measured quantitatively; this allows fine distinctions to be made as to the kind of current that transported the sand.

The shapes of sand grains can be important guides to their origin. From observation of modern sands and from experiments with laboratory-simulated transportation, we know that

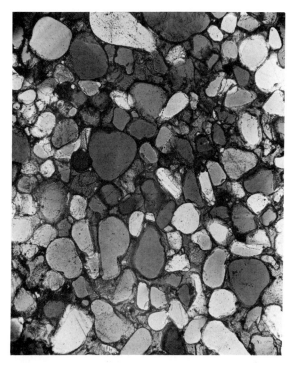

Figure 11-3
A microscopic view of a thin section of St. Peter Sandstone (Ordovician) of Illinois. All of the grains are well rounded and well sorted by the action of transporting currents. Almost all of the grains are quartz. (Magnification 44×.) [From *Sand and Sandstone* by F. J. Pettijohn, P. E. Potter, and R. Siever, copyright 1972, Springer-Verlag New York, Inc.]

sand grains are abraded as they get knocked against each other by currents. Grains lose their sharp edges and corners, their angular aspect, and become rounded. At the same time, they tend to assume more spherical shapes. From a look at the rounded, spherical grains of some ancient sandstones, such as that in Figure 11-3, a sedimentologist can infer that they had a long,

Figure 11-4
Map of inferred paleocurrent directions based on cross-bedding in the basal Pennsylvanian sandstones of part of the northeastern United States. General directions correspond to areas distinguished by presence or absence of metamorphic quartz pebbles. [After P. E. Potter and
R. Siever, "Sources of Basal Pennsylvanian Sediments in the Easter Interior Basin," *Jour. Geology,* v. 64, p. 242, 1956. Copyright © 1956 by University of Chicago Press.)

arduous journey. Angular grains of various shapes imply a short transportation distance.

The bedding of sand and sandstone gives even more useful information, for we can recognize cross-bedding, ripple marks, and those characteristic bedding-plane structures, such as flute casts, that are associated with turbidites (see Chapter 10). These help us to identify the sedimentary environment in which the deposit was laid down. Cross-bedding and other current structures also are guides to the current direction. They can be measured in the field to make a **paleocurrent** map, showing the directions of sediment transport. If the sandstone were deposited by a river, the paleocurrent map can be viewed as a map of the general land slope down which the rivers ran. If the bed structures of a turbidity current are measured, we can construct a paleocurrent map of the submarine slopes down which the muddy suspension flowed. Thus we can map part of the route of sediment migration from erosional source to depositional basin:

The mineralogy of sandstones is an important prerequisite for reconstructing the nature of the source areas that were eroded to produce the detritus. In Chapters 4 and 5 we discussed how chemical weathering can remove much of the feldspar from an eroding granite, so that the resulting detritus is mainly quartz, eventually producing a quartz-rich sandstone. That same granite in a rapidly eroding terrain on a mountainside can produce a feldspar-quartz mixture that will make an arkosic sandstone. But mineralogy also tells us something more of the source: the kind of rock being eroded. Certain minerals typical of metamorphic rocks, such as the silicates kyanite and staurolite (see Appendix IV), are diagnostic of metamorphic terrains formed at various temperatures and pressures. Thus we can glean something of the paleogeology of the source area by estimating the proportion of igneous, metamorphic, and sedimentary rocks being eroded there.

On the basis of mineralogy and such textural attributes as sorting, geologists have classified sandstones into several major groups. The **quartz arenites** (arenite = sand size material; drawn from *arena*, the Latin word for sand) are sandstones made up almost entirely of quartz grains, usually well sorted and rounded. **Arkoses** contain much feldspar; the grains tend to be poorly rounded and less well sorted than quartz arenites. **Lithic arenites** have a high content of fine-grained rock fragments, mostly from shales, slates, schists, or volcanics. **Graywackes** are made up of sand grains of quartz, feldspar, and rock fragments surrounded by a fine-grained clay matrix; this matrix is now thought to be formed by the squashing and alteration of soft rock fragments, such as those of shale, after deep burial of the sandstone formation. Many graywackes are turbidites (see p. 257), and some of the matrix may have been formed from the clay deposited by the muddy turbidity current.

Sands are deposited in many different environments: rivers, deltas, estuaries and tidal flats, beaches and offshore bars, continental shelves, slopes, and rises, and deep-water turbidite basins. From the shapes of sand accumulations, their types of bedding, their textures, and their stratigraphic relationships to other lithologies, we can usually infer the environment of deposition with some confidence.

Paleocurrents, grain size and sorting, mineralogy, and many other characteristics of sandstones are studied intensively by petroleum geologists, for much of the world's oil is found in the pore spaces of sandstones. Knowledge of how the sand was deposited guides geologists in their exploration for new oil fields and assists them in the reservoir engineering required to extract the oil from the ground. Such knowledge is also a necessity for the geologist seeking groundwater supplies in porous sandstone beds.

Gravel and Conglomerate. If sand grains are easy to study, the pebbles of a conglomerate are that much more so. The variety of pebbles is as great as the different kinds of outcrops from which they were eroded, and the information they provide is explicit. A granite pebble is sure evidence of the existence of a mass of exposed granite in the drainage basin of the rivers that brought the pebbles to the site of deposition. The number and size of the pebbles is directly related to the strength of the current that transported them. Because there are relatively few kinds of places in which currents strong enough to transport pebbles can flow, we can often infer the origin of the pebbles with some confidence. Mountain streams carry gravels, and alluvial

Figure 11-5
Conglomerate and associated sandstone, Puente Hills, California. [From *Geology Illustrated* by J. S. Shelton. W. H. Freeman and Company. Copyright © 1966.]

fans are among the important places in which they are dropped. Many river channels carry pebbles in their upper and middle reaches. Beach gravels are common along rapidly eroding coasts of hard rocks. Glacial outwash typically contains much gravel.

Because pebbles and cobbles abrade and become rounded very quickly in the course of transport, their shapes and the roundness of edges and corners are good guides to the distance they have traveled from their source area. Maps of average or maximum pebble size can be made that show a steady decrease in pebble diameter in a certain direction. In some studies, cross-bedding in the formation shows the same direction. Because there is a limit to the size of pebble any river can carry, generally about 25 centimeters in diameter, one can project upstream from measured sizes, knowing the rate of size increase from the map, to the position where 25-centimeter pebbles would be found. That would be the source area. In this way, ancient mountain fronts have been deduced from sediment characteristics.

Conglomerates can be of local origin within the sedimentary environment. Strong storm waves can tear up previously deposited, partly compacted sediment and redeposit the irregular pebbles in a new matrix of sand or mud when the storm dies down. This happens most commonly with such fine-grained deposits as shales. The boulders and cobbles of a coral reef that accumulate along its margin as a talus slope may also form conglomerates. Gravel talus slopes resting against continental mountains are continually stripped away by erosion, and so are poorly preserved in the rock record.

Mud and Shale. The fine-grained sediments of the Earth, which are the most abundant and widespread, reveal the least about their formation. All too often, their outcrops are completely covered with soil or rubble. The material itself must be studied mainly by X-ray diffraction or chemical methods. Much of what we can determine from shales about their formation is a general deduction from their fine grain size: they are the result of slow settling from very gentle transporting currents.

On a river floodplain, muds and silts may be deposited from a waning flood or in an oxbow lake formed from a cut-off meander. Muds are left behind by ebbing tides along many tidal flats where wave action is not great. Below the depth of effective wave transport, mud settles over much of the deeper parts of continental shelves, slopes, and rises. This slow, steady deposition of fine particles also makes its contribution to the extensive deep-sea sediments that blanket ridges, trenches, abyssal hills, and abyssal plains. Mud deposited by waning turbidity currents accounts for much of the sediment of abyssal plains.

Many muds and shales are mixed with chemical sediments; calcareous shale and shaly limestone are the most prominent types. Cherts, evaporites, and other chemically precipitated rocks may be mixed with mud, and some sediments grade from one pure rock type to the other with all the intermediate transitions. Frequently, it is this chemical component that gives the shale a distinctive character and, thus, a name. Black or organic shales are those that contain abundant organic matter, which is evidence of formation in a poorly oxygenated environment that allowed the organic compounds to escape oxidation and decay. Ferruginous or iron-rich shales are those rich in such iron minerals as hematite.

Perhaps the major significance of shales lies in their mineral composition. Most shales are at least one-third clay minerals; thus, they represent what we might call the dregs of weathering. Each shale bed is evidence of the weathering of a great volume of feldspar and other silicate minerals to produce kaolinite, illite, montmorillonite, and chlorite, the major groups of clay minerals.

Though shales may not provide the best indication of the geological conditions at their time of formation, they are economically very useful as the raw material for brick, tile, china, and pottery of all kinds. Mixed with limestone, shale becomes the raw material for Portland cement, the common cement used in making mortar and concrete. At this point in history, one kind of shale stands out as most valuable: oil shale. One of the world's major oil-shale reserves is in the western United States. The Green River Shale

Figure 11-6
Change in pebble size associated with cross-bedding directions in the Triassic Bunter Sandstone of France and Germany. Note the increase in the thickness of sandstone in the down-dip direction of cross-bedding; this increase is associated with aggradation of an alluvial plain. [From P. E. Potter and F. J. Pettijohn, *Paleocurrents and Basin Analysis,* Copyright 1963 by Springer-Verlag New York, Inc.]

owes its high oil content to the geological transformation of abundant algae and other organisms that grew in an enormous lake that covered parts of Wyoming, Colorado, and adjacent states. The Green River Shale has, in addition to its high organic content, a most unusual group of chemically precipitated minerals, the product of alkaline conditions in the lake.

CARBONATE DEPOSITION

The most abundant chemically precipitated sediment, limestone, best illustrates how and where chemical sediments form. Limestone—$CaCO_3$—and the related rock dolomite—$CaMg(CO_3)_2$—are often called, from their chemical composition, **carbonate rocks,** or, more simply, **carbonates.** The ocean is the scene of immensely varied kinds of carbonate sedimentation, from the formation of pelagic foraminiferal oozes in the deep sea (Chapter 10) to shallow-water accumulations of sand and mud made up of calcium carbonate. The chemical basis for carbonate sedimentation is the relative abundance of calcium and bicarbonate ions in sea water. The equation for carbonate sedimentation is:

calcium ion + bicarbonate ion →
$\quad$ Ca^{++} $\qquad$ HCO$_3^-$
$\qquad$ calcium carbonate + hydrogen ion
$\qquad\quad$ CaCO$_3$ $\qquad\qquad$ H$^+$

At equilibrium (or saturation) there is, together with the solid calcium carbonate, a concentration of calcium and bicarbonate ions in solution whose (multiplication) product is constant. The precipitate may form if there is more calcium than bicarbonate, or vice versa, as long as their product exceeds the saturation value.

Two forms of calcium carbonate can precipitate, the hexagonal mineral calcite or the orthorhombic mineral aragonite. If the precipitation proceeds undisturbed and very slowly from slightly supersaturated solutions, calcite will form and remain stable indefinitely—a criterion for chemical equilibrium. In most precipitations, however, aragonite will form first, and then very slowly—sometimes over a period of many years—will transform to calcite. Most modern carbonate sediments are a mixture of the two forms, partly because the shells of organisms that contribute to carbonate sediments may be either or both. Almost all ancient limestones are calcite, because enough time has

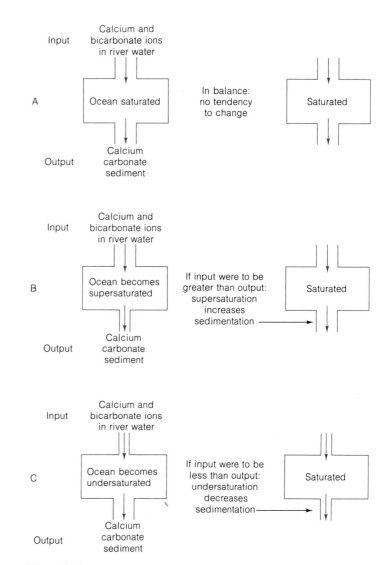

Figure 11-7
The feedback system that keeps the oceans approximately saturated with calcium carbonate. If river input increases (or decreases), the system will respond by increasing (or decreasing) the amount of sedimentation.

elapsed for all of the unstable aragonite to have changed to calcite.

In most of the oceans, sea water is fairly close to being saturated with calcium carbonate—that is, a chemist would expect that calcium carbonate would be precipitated if very many calcium or bicarbonate ions were added to it. The warm surface waters of many tropical areas are slightly supersaturated, whereas colder waters in high latitudes or at great depths are slightly undersaturated. This makes reasonable the notion that the ocean as a whole stays near the saturation point by a steady-state process. What would happen, then, if the inflow of river water stayed the same but its content of calcium and bicarbonate ions were to drop for some reason? The oceans would become undersaturated with calcium carbonate, and carbonate sedimentation might be expected to slow down or stop. Similarly, if the influx of those ions were greater, we would expect the ocean's composition to move toward supersaturation, thus stimulating more calcium carbonate sedimentation.

Thus, at first sight, the ocean seems to be a reasonable chemical system whose behavior is predictable. A closer look, however, shows that an important part of the system has not been taken into account—the biological world.

Biological Precipitation. Almost everywhere in the oceans, carbonate sediment is made up of the shells of organisms rather than of inorganic precipitates. Apparently, the conditions for precipitation are right, but it is accomplished by the organisms extracting calcium carbonate from the water for their shells rather than by inorganic precipitatation directly from the water, as in the laboratory. Areas of extensive carbonate sedimentation are restricted to warm tropical seas, which shows the general correspondence in such places between the chemical condition of slight supersaturation and the high populations of organisms whose shells make the sediments. Shelled organisms live in colder undersaturated waters, but the shells tend to dissolve after the organisms die; the shells of pelagic foraminiferans, for example, settle into deeper waters below the calcium carbonate compensation depth, as we pointed out in Chapter 10. Carbonate-secreting organisms and carbonate sediments are also found in fresh-water lakes, some of which are saturated and some of which are not.

An enormous array of organisms, from primitive one-celled animals to the common oysters, clams, and other highly evolved invertebrates, secrete some calcium carbonate. Carbonate-secreting plants range from primitive algae to some higher plants, such as some aquatic grasses. Vertebrates (and some invertebrates) do not secrete calcium carbonate but, rather, harder calcium phosphate minerals to form bone and teeth. The physiology of carbonate and phosphate secretion varies greatly among the many groups of organisms, and much remains to be learned about it.

Carbonate-shelled organisms live in dependence on the sea (or lake) water around them, which provides nutrients and the dissolved materials from which they make their shells. They also live in a complex of intertwined relations with the other organisms in their habitat. The entire web of interdependence of organisms and their environment is the subject of the science of ecology. Because the ecological study of carbonate-secreting organisms and carbonate sediments in various environments has been carried on vigorously in the past two decades by geologists and paleontologists, we have learned how limestones are made. One sort of habitat, in particular, has always captured the attention of scientists—the coral reefs of tropical seas.

Coral Reefs. From 1831 to 1836, Charles Darwin sailed on the *Beagle* as naturalist-scientist for a British surveying expedition, a voyage made famous because it allowed Darwin to observe and collect the great variety of organisms that laid the foundation for his theory of organic evolution. One of the products of the voyage was his analysis of Pacific coral reefs. Darwin was one of the first to explore in detail the relation of organisms to their geologic environment. Many of his ideas on coral reefs are still accepted today. More than a hundred years after the *Beagle* sailed, the coral reefs of the South Pacific became battlegrounds of World War II, and military and engineering needs sparked new observations. After the war, two coral reefs were used for atomic bomb testing, and the name of one of them became famous: Bikini (the other was Eniwetok). To geologists, those reefs became famous because of an extensive mapping and drilling program that was undertaken to determine the origin and dynamics of reefs so that the effects of bomb testing could be assessed.

The major physical characteristics of a coral island or **atoll** are: (1) an outer wave-resistant reef front, a steep slope facing the open ocean; (2) a flat reef platform in back of the reef and extending toward the island; (3) a shallow lagoon in back of the reef platform, protected from the waves by the reef; and (4) the island itself. Some atolls have no central island, just a more or less circular reef, parts of which may be above water and forested, surrounding a central lagoon.

The main part of the reef tract is made up of actively growing coral, an organism that grows as colonies of great numbers of individuals joined to each other. The coral secretes its calcium carbonate as it grows, cementing itself to

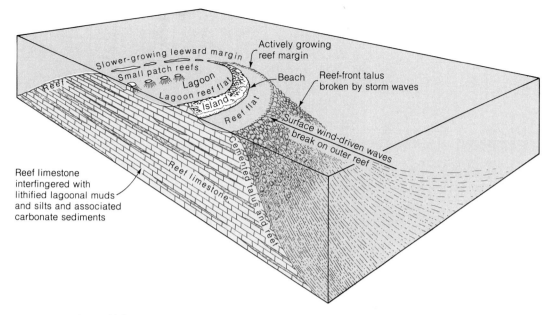

Figure 11-8
Diagrammatic drawing of a reef. The reef tends to grow more rapidly on the windward side, where waves bring fresh nutrients from deeper, open waters to the organisms.

the carbonate remains of dead coral below, and the reef grows outward. The living stalks of coral get their food from tiny bits of organic matter brought to them by waves coming in from the open ocean. Reef-building corals need light to grow because they live in **symbiosis** (that is, in a mutually life-supporting relationship) with small green algae (zooxanthellae) that live in the translucent coral tissue and need light to live. The coral provides protection for the algae and the algae provides photosynthetic oxygen for the coral. The light requirement limits coral growth to shallow waters, less than about 20 meters (65 feet) because, as transparent as it may seem, sea water gradually filters out more and more light the deeper it gets.

Living in association with the coral are various kinds of coralline algae, which also secrete carbonate and thus help to cement the whole structure into a massive rock terrace. On the reef platform live many species of shelled and soft invertebrates. In the lagoon live many other kinds of organisms. The organisms feed upon each other, and, in the process, the shells or other hard parts of the prey organisms are broken up into sand-, silt-, or clay-sized particles. These, together with the physical erosion of the reef front, which produces fragments of coral and coralline algae, provide the carbonate sand of the island beaches and some of the fine carbonate mud that floors parts of the lagoons.

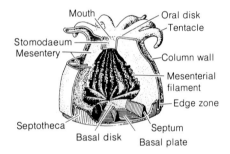

Figure 11-9
Cutaway drawing of a typical coral, showing the relation of the soft body parts (mesentery) to the skeleton parts of calcium carbonate; basal plate and septum. [After *Treatise on Invertebrate Paleontology,* Geol. Soc. Am., and University of Kansas Press, 1956.]

Some of the mud comes from microscopic particles secreted by algae; some of the rest may be produced by nonbiological precipitation from warm lagoon waters that become supersaturated with calcium carbonate as a result of evaporation.

A seasoned observer can deduce where samples of reef sediment came from just by looking at the sediment and the kinds of shells in it. Hard, cemented rock made up of coral and coralline algae come from the reef front. Sediments from the main reef platform may contain

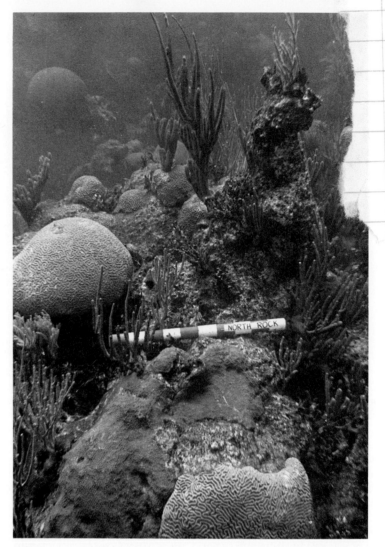

Figure 11-10
An underwater photograph of a coral reef knoll in a few meters of water near North Rock, Bermuda. The scale is 50 cm long. Below the scale is a sheet-like encrusting coral colony. At left center and lower right are large heads of brain coral. The branching, tree-like forms are sea whips and sea fans. [Photo supplied by Peter Garrett.]

many kinds of clams and other shells, sometimes with some carbonate sand from the erosion of the reef. The lagoon is dominated by muds, sometimes built up into small mounds, occasionally spotted with little coral "heads" growing here and there. The beaches are where the sand accumulates. The geologist uses this information to infer the nature of ancient reefs formed in the seas of the past—such as the reefs of the Silurian Period, the remains of which lie in a belt across what is now Indiana, Illinois, and Wisconsin, or the great reefs of Permian age in west Texas.

Origin of Coral Reefs. Ever since Darwin first studied reefs, geologists have wondered about how they form. At first sight, there appears to be a paradox. How can corals, which need light to live, build islands that reach to the surface from the floor of the deep sea thousands of meters below? There is no conceivable way that the level of the sea could once have been low enough for coral to have formed so near the bottom, nor is there any evidence that much of the floor of the ocean was ever structurally elevated to sea level, which would have allowed the corals to begin growing. The clues Drawin saw

Figure 11-11
The Guadalupe Mountains of West Texas from the south. The drawing below is a reconstruction of the sedimentary environment associated with a great reef that existed here in Permian times. [From *Geology Illustrated* by John S. Shelton. W. H. Freeman and Company. Copyright © 1966.]

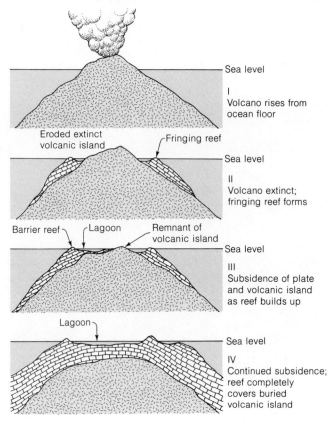

Figure 11-12
Evolution of a coral reef from a subsiding volcanic island. In most respects this chain of events was first proposed by Charles Darwin in the nineteenth century. The framework of plate tectonics provides an explanation for the subsidence of the islands.

were **fringing reefs,** reefs similar to atolls growing around the edges of volcanic islands. Other islands were mostly coral, but there was a remnant of volcanic rock. The theory he proposed over a century ago remains the most probable explanation.

The process starts with a volcano being built up from the sea floor. As the volcano stops its eruptive activity—temporarily or permanently—corals and coralline algae colonize the shore and build a fringing reef around the volcanic island. The central volcano may then be lowered almost to sea level by erosion. If such a volcanic island sinks below the waves as a result of some tectonic movement, actively growing coral and coralline algae may keep pace with the sinking and build up the reef. In this way, the volcanic center may disappear, to be replaced by an atoll with a central lagoon. One of the results of the deep drilling on Bikini and Eniwetok atolls was striking confirmation of this theory:

volcanic rock was penetrated by the drills deep below the coral of the island. Oceanographic research parties have mapped many submerged flat-topped volcanoes that once must have stood above sea level and been eroded, but then subsided below sea level too fast for coral growth to keep up. More recently, as we will see in Chapter 19, plate-tectonic theory has proposed an explanation of the subsidence of volcanic islands on oceanic lithospheric plates as part of the process of sea-floor spreading. Of course, some coral islands have a much more complicated history, and sea-level changes during the Pleistocene affected all of the reefs then in existence.

Fascinating as coral-reef islands are, they account for a relatively small proportion of the carbonate sediment produced in the ocean. By far the largest bulk of carbonate sediments similar to the ancient limestones formed on the continents are formed on shallow-water platforms near or attached to the continents.

Figure 11-13
Map of carbonate sediments in the Bahama Islands. The reef fronts and islands are on the eastern margins of the banks, facing the westward-blowing trade winds. [After N. D. Newell and J. K. Rigby, "Geological Studies on the Great Bahama Bank," Soc. of Econ. Paleontologists and Mineralogists Spec. Paper No. 5, 1957.)

Figure 11-14
Cross section of an oolite, made up of concentric shells of calcium carbonate (aragonite) precipitated as the grain was rolled and suspended in current-agitated waters. Typical oolites range in size from 0.25–2.0 millimeters in diameter.

Carbonate Platforms. One of the best examples of a carbonate platform is the area of the Bahama Islands and the shallow banks surrounding them. This region of about 155,000 square kilometers (about 60,000 square miles) is a flat-topped shallow platform, on the west separated from the mainland of Florida by the narrow, deep Straits of Florida and on the east dropping abruptly more than 3600 meters (about 12,000 feet) to the deep ocean floor. Most of the platform is only a few meters below sea level, and it is dotted with many small islands. Coral and algal reefs are found on the eastern edges of the platform where the southwestward-blowing trade winds bring open-ocean water rich in nutrients to the organisms of the actively growing reef tracts. Much of the area of the shallow banks to the west is covered with carbonate sand and mud particles with essentially no land-derived detrital material, for supply of sediments from the continent is cut off by the Straits of Florida. The lack of terrigenous erosional debris is important because it allows life to be abundant on the platform: many of the organisms that live there might be rapidly "smothered" to death if there were a significant amount of noncarbonate clay- and sand-sized particles present.

A distinctive kind of carbonate sand, **oolite,** is formed where strong tidal currents flood the banks each day. Oolites are more or less spherical grains of aragonite that are made up of concentric layers surrounding a nucleus, like the structure of an onion. Most of the nuclei are fragments of shells. These nuclei get coated with layers of aragonite as the tides bring in cold ocean waters that become supersaturated with calcium carbonate as they warm and evaporate on the shallow banks. The currents are strong enough to keep the grains rolling or suspended in the water, and, as a result, they get coated with precipitate on all sides. The limit to growth of the oolites is determined by the maximum grain size that can be moved by the current.

The variety of types of carbonate sediments found on the Bahamas is exemplified by a cross section of one of the islands, Andros, and the banks west of it (see Figure 11-15). The reefs on the east shore protect a narrow muddy lagoon, which lies in front of a sand beach on the island, like the lagoon of an atoll. The western side of the island leads down to a tidal flat. The tidal flat is covered with muds, sometimes finely rippled, interrupted by tidal channels, and in many places overgrown with **algal mats,** interwoven mucilaginous surfaces of blue-green algae. This

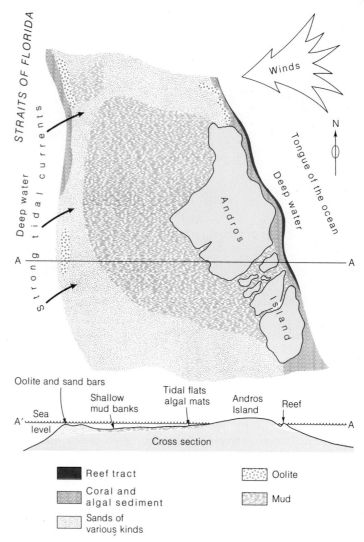

Figure 11-15
Map and cross section of Grand Bahama Bank west of Andros Island.
[After various sources.]

sticky surface traps fine carbonate sediment and, as the algae grow around and upward through the carbonate, the sediment is incorporated in a layered mixture. In this way, the algae produce the layered structures called **stromatolites** that are found in many tidal-flat limestones. These structures have achieved great importance as evidence of algal life far back in the Precambrian. Also found on tidal flats are areas in which the calcite and aragonite of the original sediment have been transformed into the calcium-magnesium carbonate mineral dolomite, $CaMg(CO_3)_2$. In these areas, the sea water in the pores between the grains just below the surface has become enriched in magnesium ions owing

to evaporation. That increase in magnesium promotes the exchange of some magnesium for calcium ions in the carbonate mineral, converting it to dolomite. Many ancient dolomites show evidence of this kind of tidal-flat origin.

Below the tidal flats west of Andros are extensive shallow banks, only a meter or two deep in many places, where the water is quiet and the bottom is carbonate mud. Some of the mud is in the form of soft pellets, produced as fecal pellets by the many kinds of organisms living on the bottom. Typical is a marine worm that feeds by eating the mud, extracting for food the small amount of organic matter it contains, and excreting the bulk of the carbonate mud as pellets.

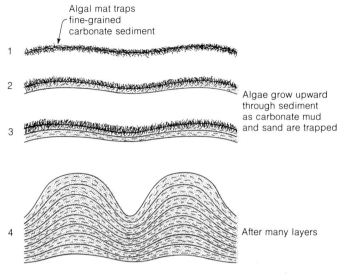

Figure 11-16
Stages in the growth of a stromatolite formed by the sediment-trapping action of algae. As the sediment accumulates, the algae continue to grow upward while the previously deposited layers become cemented and lithified. The convex upward structures vary greatly in all dimensions and in their regularity, ranging in size from a few centimeters to more than a meter in diameter. The laminae are typically a few millimeters thick. A good example of one kind is shown in Figure 12-5.

Figure 11-17
The formation of a stalactite and a stalagmite follows a drip of calcium-carbonate-saturated water from a cave ceiling.

In the mud area lives a variety of algae that secretes microscopic needles of aragonite, about 0.003 millimeters long. Aragonite needles of similar size and shape occur abundantly in the mud. A small part of the carbonate mud may also be the result of nonbiological precipitation from the warm, supersaturated water of the banks, which can also produce aragonite needles. Most of the fine sediment is from algal precipitation and the wearing down of coarser shell materials by abrasion and animal ingestion.

On the far western side of the banks west of Andros, the movement of the water becomes greater, and the currents winnow out the fine material. Waves and tidal currents move sand consisting of broken pieces of shells into submarine dunes and bars much like those formed by currents in large rivers or those found on shallow continental shelves in noncarbonate terrains.

Armed with the information about Pacific atolls and carbonate platforms like the Bahamas, geologists have learned to recognize many different kinds of ancient limestones that originated long ago in similar situations. Thus, they have been able to make maps of ancient reef tracts, extensive tidal-flat areas, sand banks, and the other kinds of shallow-water areas in which animals, plants, and the physical environment interact to produce carbonate deposits. To these must be added the deeper-water environments of the ocean, where oozes form, later to be changed into chalk. A paleogeographic map of North America showing areas of carbonate deposition during one time period is shown in Figure 22-50.

Not all carbonate deposits form in the sea. Calcium carbonate is deposited as crusts and layers around hot springs, both by algae that grow in the hot water and by nonbiological precipitation. The deposits are **tufa,** which is porous and easily broken, and **travertine,** a denser variety that is familiar because of its wide use as a decorative stone for building facings and table tops. Carbonate is also found in **stalagmites** and **stalactites** in caves formed by groundwater in limestone formations. Evaporation of carbonate-saturated groundwater dripping from fractures in the cave roof forms the needle-like stalactites. The stalagmites build up from the floor as the drips fall on that spot. Carbonate sediments can form in lakes from algal activity and nonbiological precipitation. They range from such salty lakes as the Great

Figure 11-18
Two species of modern diatoms filtered from sea water. These photographs were taken with a scanning electron microscope at very high magnifications. The long dimension of each species is about 10 micrometers. [Photos by C. Stein and A. Eaton.]

Salt Lake and the Dead Sea to the fresh-water lakes of northern temperate regions, such as those of Minnesota and Wisconsin.

THE VARIETY OF BIOLOGICAL SEDIMENTATION

Though calcium carbonate is the most abundant biological sediment, there is a great variety of other sediments whose formation is wholly or partially controlled by the biological world.

Silica. The deposition of silica (SiO_2) has some similarities to the deposition of carbonates. Most of the silica of biological origin is secreted by single-celled organisms. The most important are small algae called **diatoms** that populate much of the surface layers of the ocean and fresh-water lakes. These little organisms are extraordinarily efficient in removing silica from sea water to make their shells, which are an amorphous form of silica similar to opal in crystal structure. In contrast to the marine carbonate-secreting organisms, which live in waters that are nearly saturated with calcium carbonate, diatoms can extract silica from very undersaturated solutions. When diatoms growing in a laboratory aquarium use up all of the dissolved silica in the water, they will start to use dissolved silica etched from the glass walls of the aquarium, but how they do it is still a mystery. In addition to diatoms, there are small single-celled animals called **radiolarians** that are related to calcareous foraminifera and live much like them. Some kinds of sponges secrete silica, too. When diatoms and radiolarians die, they sink to the bottom of the sea and accumulate in the sediment. Under areas of high biological productivity, where silica-secreting organisms are abundant because of a high supply of silica and other nutrients in the water, the silica shells of dead organisms rain down and form silica-rich **diatom ooze** and **radiolarian ooze.** When these oozes become cemented and hardend into rock, they are called **diatomite** and **radiolarite.** Diatomite is a useful rock: because of its high porosity, it has been used in filters and as fillers, and it is sometimes used as a mild abrasive. Some of the best known diatomites are in the Monterey Formation, which is exposed in many places along the coastal regions of central and southern California. Many ancient **cherts,** hard and dense silica-rich rocks, originated as diatomites or radiolarites and later became strongly lithified as they recrystallized to a very fine-grained rock composed of microcrystalline quartz.

Sulfide. Organisms may control chemical sedimentation indirectly by changing the chemical conditions in the environment. One important example is the formation of ferrous sulfide (FeS_2), the mineral pyrite, by the indirect action of bacteria. The bacteria are in the same group as those that cause the noxious smell of rotten eggs. The smell is the gas hydrogen sulfide (H_2S). This gas is produced in sediments or sea water when these bacteria chemically change sulfur from its oxidized state, as the sulfate (SO_4^{--}) dissolved in sea water, to its reduced state, sulfide (S^{--}). These primitive bacteria, which can grow only in the absence of oxygen and so cannot respire as most organisms do, get their energy by converting the oxidized sulfur ion from its $+6$ state in sulfate, where the atom has lost 6 electrons, to the -2 state in sulfide, where the atom has gained 2 electrons. The hydrogen sulfide produced, itself a powerful reducing agent, changes ferric iron (Fe^{+++}) to ferrous iron (Fe^{++}) and precipitates the highly insoluble pyrite.

The presence of decaying organic matter is necessary for the H_2S bacteria to thrive; this decay keeps the immediate environment free of oxygen. In most normal oxygenated or aerated environments, organic matter decays by using up oxygen, essentially as a slow combustion process similar to the way we respire:

$$\text{organic carbon} + \text{oxygen} \rightarrow \text{carbon dioxide}$$
$$\text{C} \qquad\qquad \text{O}_2 \qquad\qquad \text{CO}_2$$

As the oxygen is used, it is replenished by free mixing with the atmosphere, of which one-fifth is oxygen. In most shallow parts of the ocean, the mixing of the water by waves and currents keeps the water well aerated. In the deep ocean, the rate of replenishment is slower, taking as much as a thousand years; but, because there is relatively little organic matter in the deep sea, the oxygen does not completely disappear.

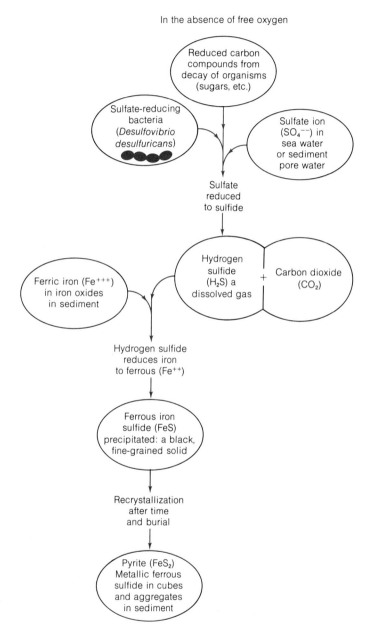

Figure 11-19
Pyrite, ferrous sulfide (FeS_2), is formed by a chain of reactions that starts with the reduction of sulfate (SO_4^{--}) from sea water by sulfate-reducing bacteria living in an environment free of oxygen.

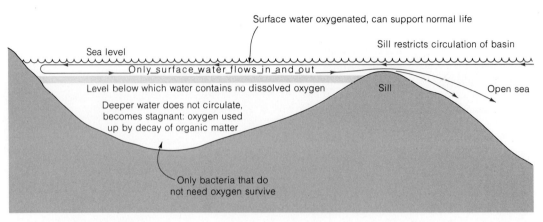

Figure 11-20
Sea basins separated from the main body of open sea water by sill may become deoxygenated as the water below the sill level stagnates from lack of circulation.

Deoxygenation is the explanation for the black sands and muds just below the surface of many tidal-flat sediments. A quick scoop of the sediment will let you smell a whiff of hydrogen sulfide. The blackness comes from the first form of ferrous sulfide precipitated, a finely dispersed black substance that slowly transforms to crystalline pyrite.

The oxygen *can* totally disappear in two situations: if there is a great amount of decaying organic matter in the sediment, such as in some biologically productive areas of tidal flats, the oxygen, slowly permeating into the sediment by diffusion, gradually is depleted by biological activity, and the sediment becomes reducing—that is, lacking in oxygen. When that happens, the bacteria that produce hydrogen sulfide become active, and pyrite is eventually formed.

In some areas of the sea, deep basins may be cut off from replenishment by aerated waters by a **sill,** a topographic ridge or barrier that prevents free circulation and mixing. In such a place, the waters of the basin do not mix well with oxygenated surface waters because the depth is too great for the deep waters to be affected by waves, and the greater density of those waters (caused by low temperatures) prevents general mixing by convection. Here again, as organic matter decays, oxygen is used up and replenishment by mixing with the aerated waters above is too slow; thus, bottom waters and sediment become reducing. Many fiords— drowned valleys scoured well below sea level by glaciers—have sills at the seaward end formed by terminal moraines or by the limit of the scouring action of the glacier. This causes them to be reducing below the level of the sill.

The deoxygenation of surface waters can also be brought about by some forms of pollution. When abundant phosphate, one of the important nutrients of organisms, pollutes a lake or river, the algae and many different aquatic plants will flourish, sometimes to the point of glutting the surface waters, a process called **eutrophication.** When these organisms die, their abundance is transferred to the bottom, where the extensive decay uses up oxygen faster than it can be replenished. The result is a great shift in animal populations, as fish and other organisms that need oxygen are cut off from much of the lake. The lake is not "dead," a term that many people have applied to Lake Erie; but its population has been drastically altered, and many species have disappeared, especially popular food and sport fishes, while "scummy" algae and weeds thrive.

Coal. Lack of enough oxygen to decay vegetation completely on land is responsible for the formation of one of our most valuable sediments, **peat,** and its lithified equivalent, **coal.** The abundant plant fossils in coal beds indicate that they originated in fresh-water swamps, much as peat bogs form now. As the luxuriant plant growth of such a swamp dies, it falls to the waterlogged soil. The water and rapid burial by falling leaves protect the twigs, branches, leaves, fruit, and seeds from oxidizing, just as thick leaf mats in some forests protect the lower layers from complete decay. The vegetation accumulates and gradually turns into peat, a porous brown mass of organic matter in which twigs, roots, and other plant parts can still be recognized. After more burial and chemical transformations of the aging organic matter, the peat becomes **lignite,** a very soft coal-like material. Greater depth of burial, longer time, and higher

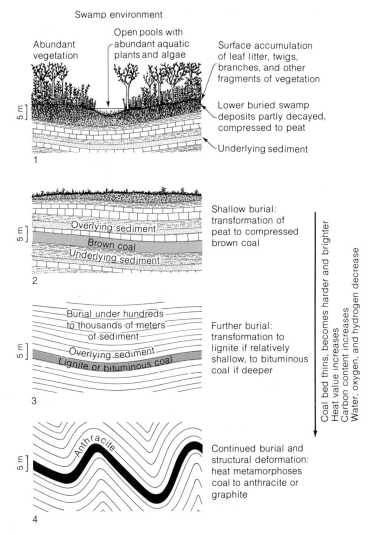

Figure 11-21
The process by which coal beds form begins with the deposition of vegetation.
Protected from complete decay and oxidation in a swamp environment, the deposit
is later buried and subjected to mild metamorphism, which transforms it into lignite, bituminous coal, or anthracite, depending on depth of burial, temperature, and
amount of structural deformation.

temperature may ultimately metamorphose the
lignite into **bituminous coal,** or **soft coal,** and,
in extreme cases, to **anthracite,** or **hard coal.**
The greater the metamorphism, the harder and
brighter the coal and the higher its heat value.
There is little doubt that, as our energy needs
continue to grow and as oil and gas are less able
to satisfy the demand for fuel, coal is becoming,
once again, as it was up to about forty years ago,
an extremely important chemical sedimentary
rock.

OTHER CHEMICAL SEDIMENTS

In an arid climate, the same general kind of
barred basin that restricts circulation and causes
deoxygenation can be the scene of a different
kind of sedimentation—salt deposition.

Evaporites. Sediments composed of the mineral halite, or rock salt (NaCl), the calcium
sulfate minerals gypsum ($CaSO_4 \cdot 2H_2O$) and

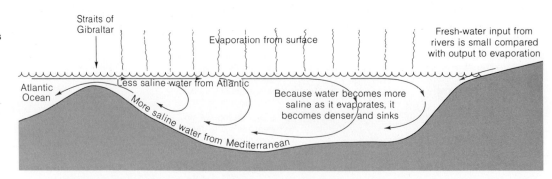

Figure 11-22
Simplified diagram of circulation of the Mediterranean Sea through the Straits of Gibraltar. Because influx of fresh water from rivers into the Mediterranean does not balance evaporation from the surface, there is an inflow of water from the Atlantic Ocean to replace sinking surface water that has become more saline and thus denser as a result of evaporation.

anhydrite ($CaSO_4$), and many other less abundant salts formed by the evaporation of sea water are called **evaporites.** The thin crust of salt formed when a pond of sea water dries up is easy to observe along many shorelines, but not much salt forms in such a situation. The ratio of salt to water is such that, for every liter of sea water evaporated, about 35 grams (a little more than 1 ounce) of solid salt will crystallize. How much sea water had to evaporate, then, to produce an evaporite formation 100 meters thick, 50 kilometers wide, and 100 kilometers long? The volume of the evaporite, about 5×10^{11} cubic meters, at an average density of about 2.3 grams per centimeter, weighs about 1.15×10^{18} grams, which represents the salt evaporated from about 3.3×10^{16} liters of sea water (approximately 8.7×10^{15} gallons)! A single pond containing that much water would have a volume of well over 30,000 cubic kilometers. In other words, the water would have had to be more than 6 kilometers deep over the area covered by the formation, much more than the average depth of the oceans. This absurd conclusion alone led geologists to suspect that there must be some natural mechanism that constantly replenishes the sea water as it evaporates.

The study of the minerals formed by sea-water evaporation provided another lead. The first experimental evaporation of sea water was performed in 1849 by Usiglio, who showed how a sequence of minerals would be precipitated as evaporation proceeded, starting with calcium carbonate and calcium sulfate, progressing to sodium chloride, and then, in the final stages, to magnesium and potassium minerals. The important point, one that was amplified and care-

fully worked out in detail much later, was that a distinctive sequence involving a complex order of precipitation of many minerals would characterize complete evaporation. Some evaporites show those sequences and are interpreted as simple desiccation products. Yet a great many thick evaporite deposits consist only of gypsum, or anhydrite and halite, or a combination of the three. Did incomplete evaporation go only so far as to produce halite, in which case an even greater volume of water would have been required? Why are there so few evaporites that contain the last salts to precipitate just before complete drying?

A resolution of these difficulties came with the theory that typical evaporite sequences are deposited in relatively shallow arms of the sea, or in basins connected to the sea by narrow openings. As surface water evaporates from the basin, the dissolved materials become more concentrated, normally by limestone deposition, until the first evaporite precipitate, typically gypsum, starts to form. The concentrated solution formed at the surface, called a **brine,** is denser than the water below by virtue of its greater content of dissolved salt, and so tends to sink to the bottom. As it does, normal sea water flows in at the top, through the seaway from the open ocean. A continuous circulation pattern is set up by the denser brine flowing out through the bottom of the seaway. Thus, a steady-state system is created in which gypsum is continually removed as a precipitate while sea water circulates through the evaporite basin. Circulation of this sort occurs in the Mediterranean Sea and the Straits of Gibraltar. Atlantic Ocean water flows in at the top of the straits to the saltier

Usiglio simply filled a bucket with water from the Mediterranean Sea, took it to his laboratory, and let it evaporate. Though he did crystallize many minerals found in natural salt deposits, his results were erratic, since his methods were primitive by modern standards. Half a century later, a Dutch chemist, van't Hoff, tackled the same problem with more advanced laboratory methods but, more importantly, with a deep theoretical understanding of the newly developing science of physical chemistry. His results, a detailed sequence of minerals precipitated as evaporation proceeded, still stand today as a triumph of experimental geochemistry.

Mediterranean, which has a high evaporation rate, and saltier Mediterranean bottom water flows out to the Atlantic through the bottom of the straits. The Mediterranean, however, does not evaporate sufficiently now to form gypsum. Alternative circulation patterns have been proposed, including ones in which the dense brines move down into and through permeable sediment below the basin and reappear along lower slopes of an adjacent ocean basin. This mechanism also works for evaporites formed on evaporating tidal flats, where the brine formed by evaporation sinks into the upper unsaturated groundwater zone, slowly precipitating gypsum as it moves down.

SEDIMENTARY ENVIRONMENTS

How does one make order out of the almost bewildering array of different kinds of sediments of all ages and take advantage of all the information they contain about what the earth was like when they were deposited? One way is to use the concept of the **sedimentary environment**—that is, all of the important physical and chemical factors or variables that control the formation of a particular sedimentary type.

We might describe a sedimentary environment in a limited way by making a statement about the average kinetic energy—that is, the energy of motion of its water; thus, we might thereby lump together deposits of point bars in rapidly flowing rivers, sandbars off a beach, and some turbidity-current deposits on the continental rise. Or we might characterize a chemical environment by saying that the water is relatively pure—that is, fresh. That would put together soils, sediments formed in rivers and lakes, and permeable rocks through which fresh groundwater percolates. These kinds of environmental definitions limited to one variable generally fail to be useful because they lump rather diverse sediment types and are not easily used for reconstructing the past.

A more useful general definition of a sedimentary environment is one that emphasizes the geomorphologic approach as a meaningful way to group the variables. Thus we might describe a lagoonal environment as one of limited area, separated by some barrier from the open sea, in which the water is relatively calm and the depths shallow; some varieties may be further characterized by restricted circulation and lack of oxygen in bottom waters, and reef lagoons may be

distinguished as a special type. This approach, which unites all the variables by the geometric shape of the place and its relation to adjacent environments and larger geographic and geologic elements of the Earth's surface, has proved most useful.

The geomorphologic definition has another advantage. It fits with the habitats of the organisms that live in and upon the sediment and modify it. Worms, burrowing clams, crustaceans, and other kinds of organisms get their food by eating sediment and digesting the minute quantities of organic matter deposited in it. They excrete the unused inorganic bulk of the sediment, leaving a record of burrows, tracks, and trails, which the geologist recognizes as the hallmarks of **bioturbation,** the reworking of sediment by organisms.

Table 11-2 lists some major sedimentary environments and their characteristics. Many more could be listed, and many can be subdivided into smaller units, down to small areas that have been called "microenvironments." Environments may be mixed and not entirely sedimentary. For example, environments around volcanic islands may be characterized by mixtures of shallow- and deep-water sediments (derived by the erosion of the volcanic rocks on land) with submarine volcanic flows and pyroclastic deposits from violent eruption. What is important in any such use of a particular environmental designation is that a set of rock characters—the only evidence a geologist sees—should be associated with a geomorphologic environment in which certain well-defined processes operate.

For instance, we know that at present (a point in geologic time), well-sorted sand is being deposited at the shore and in very shallow nearshore waters; farther out, in deeper waters of the continental shelf, silts and muds are being laid down. Still farther out, on the continental slopes and rises, turbidity currents are depositing sand, silts, and mud. Another example that shows such lateral gradation of sedimentary environments is found in the different kinds of carbonate sediments that are deposited in different portions of a coral reef at the same time. To characterize such contemporaneous assemblages of sediments, we use the word **facies** to emphasize the lithologic aspects of sediments deposited in different environments at the same time in history. The reason why geologists have concentrated on this idea of sedimentary environment is that it has been immensely useful in reconstructing the history of the Earth in past epochs. The construction of a paleogeographic

A recent hypothesis, based on Deep Sea Drilling Program holes in the Mediterranean that contain abundant evaporite, proposes that the Mediterranean was cut off from the Atlantic at Gibraltar about 6 million years ago and dried up completely to form a temporary salt-covered desert.

Table 11-2
Major sedimentary environments

Environment	Sediment types
Dominantly detrital	
Alluvial	Moderate to poorly sorted point bar and channel sands and gravels interbedded with sandy shales; occasional coal or peat beds; very coarse debris in alluvial fans.
Deltaic	Well-sorted bar-finger sands and delta-front silts and clays interbedded with marine clays and coastal swamp deposits.
Tidal	Moderately sorted tidal-channel sands, silts, and muds; abundant invertebrate faunas; pyrite in black deoxygenated layers below surface in some places.
Beach and bar	Well-sorted sands and occasional gravels with well-rounded and worn grains interbedded with marine and nonmarine deposits.
Shallow-water marine (continental shelf)	Sands, silts, and muds with variable marine fauna distributed in sheet-like geometry and interbedded frequently with some carbonate sediment.
Deep-sea turbidite (continental rise, abyssal plain, and trench)	Graded sequences of poorly sorted sand to fine clay-size particles interbedded with pelagic clays; some individual units can be traced laterally for long distances.
Deep-sea pelagic (abyssal hills, and abyssal ridges and rises)	Fine clay, some of windblown origin, very finely laminated, frequently with manganese nodules or crusts, interbedded with carbonate or siliceous oozes.
Dominantly chemical	
Reefs	Complex of carbonate rock types, from massive cemented reef rock of corals and/or algae to back-reef carbonate sands, lagoonal muds, and beach sands.
Carbonate platforms	Great variety of reef, lagoonal, tidal-flat, and shallow-bank deposits of oolitic and shell-fragment sand, and algal-mat and fine-grained carbonate muds.
Deoxygenated barred basins	Pyrite-rich and organic-rich muds with no bottom-dwelling marine fauna.
Restricted evaporite basins	Gypsum, anhydrite, halite, and other salts interbedded frequently with carbonates and some muds.

map is based on the analysis of the facies that formed at the same time in the past in different sedimentary environments.

The historical geologist who deduces an off-shore shale facies, a nearshore and shoreline sandstone facies, and an alluvial sandstone-siltstone facies and can plot their areal extents on a map has thereby reconstructed the position of the ancient shoreline and the land and sea environments associated with it. If at the same time he can infer the composition of the source rocks of the clastic sediments, he can draw some paleogeology on the paleogeographic map.

If he then sets about drawing maps of the same area for two successive time periods in Earth history, he can see how things changed. Such mapping commonly reveals a shift in the position of the shoreline. A shift showing that the sea later covered more of the continent's edges, or even its interior, than previously indicates a **transgression** of the seas on the continents. A map constructed for a still later period might show that the transgression was followed by a **regression,** during which the seas withdrew (see Fig. 11-23). Transgressions and regressions may be the result of local tectonic movements that elevate or depress that portion of the continent relative to sea level. But other lateral movements of shorelines may be the result of a general rise or lowering of sea level all over the world, changes we call **eustatic.** The causes of eustatic changes in sea level that affect entire oceans must be on a grand scale. One well-known cause is a glacial age, when the conversion of huge amounts of sea water to ice decreases the volume of sea water (see Chapter 9). Another is a change in the oceans' capacity, which can be related to periods of faster and slower sea-floor spreading (see Chapter 19). The Cretaceous Period, for example, has long been known to be a time of extensive transgression of the seas on continental platforms. Evidence from the oceans indicates that it may have been a time of rapid spreading, when the volume of rapidly moving oceanic lithosphere would have been puffed up due to heat expansion, thereby

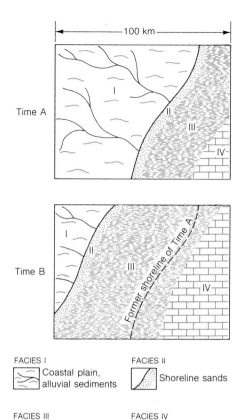

FACIES I
Coastal plain,
alluvial sediments

FACIES II
Shoreline sands

FACIES III
Marine offshore
muds

FACIES IV
Carbonate shelf
sediments

Figure 11-23
Paleogeographic maps based on environments deduced
from sedimentary facies for two time periods, *A* and *B*,
where *B* may be a million years later than *A*.

in the probability of preservation, and the differences are related, in part, to the rapidity of sedimentation and burial. In the deep sea, deposits slowly accumulate at very low rates, only a few millimeters every thousand years. Once deposited, most of these deep-water sediments are unlikely to be eroded and redeposited, because bottom currents strong enough for the task are rare. That is the reason why deep-sea pelagic sediments offer the most complete historical records of organic evolution, of temperature changes during ice ages, and of other geologic patterns.

In contrast, the shallower waters of the continental shelf deposit sediments at much higher rates—many centimeters every thousand years, on the average. These sediments get buried faster, but waves and currents are much more likely to scour the bottom and rework it mechanically. Furthermore, the higher the sedimentary accumulation, the more the waves are likely to rework and redistribute it, so that there is a level of sedimentation above which accumulation stops. The importance of **subsidence** of the crust is that it allows sedimentation to continue and the accumulation to build up. This process is one of slight positive feedback, in the sense that tectonic subsidence is reinforced by the sedimentary load. The further sedimentation proceeds, the greater the weight on the crust, because each layer of sediment is much denser than the sea water it replaces. The effect of the

lowering the general volume of the ocean basins and raising sea level. By linking local changes in environment to larger causes of sea-level change, the historical geologist can define the complex way in which the surface of the planet responds to its interior motions.

BURIAL AND ACCUMULATION OF SEDIMENT

A bar in a river may exist for only a few months, from the high-water stage that formed it to the next stage, which destroys it. Of all the sediments that are made day by day, only a small fraction is preserved and gives us a record of geologic time. Sedimentary environments differ

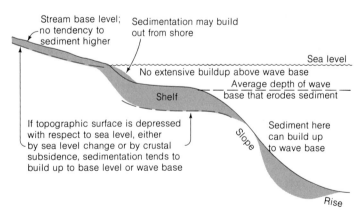

Figure 11-24
Sedimentation is closely dependent upon subsidence in those environments where the site of deposition is close to either base level of erosion on land or wave base in the sea.

weight is to push down the crust (see the discussion of isostasy in Chapter 18), allowing still more sedimentation to proceed. This process does not continue endlessly, nor can it account for all of the subsidence shown by most continental shelves. The reason for this is that, as subsidence continues and sediments get laid down, more and more of the crust at that point consists of sediments; because these are much less dense than average crust, the effect of additional sediment tends to become negligible. Subsidence initiated by tectonic mechanisms and enhanced by sediment weight is evidenced by great thicknesses of sediments.

Geosynclines. The first theorizing about the evidence of sediments of great thickness did not come from modern oceanographic study of the continental shelves, but from the field work of the State Geologist of New York in the middle of the nineteenth century, James Hall. As a result of extensive mapping of sediments of the Appalachian Mountains, correlating them stratigraphically, and measuring their thicknesses, Hall concluded that there were many tens of thousands of feet of sediment that had accumulated in a long, relatively narrow trough bordering the continent. He envisioned it as having been something like a large downfold in the surface that steadily accumulated sediment as it subsided. Later, the name **geosyncline** was applied to the sediment-filled trough.

Geosynclines vary from a few tens of kilometers to hundreds of kilometers wide, and they may be thousands of kilometers long. The nature of the sediments they contain gives us a good picture of their origin, for some are turbidite sands formed in deep water and others are shallow carbonate platform limestones; in some places, alluvial deposits are also found. A great many of the sediments are shallow-water ones, including many of those near the bottom of the trough. The great thickness and the widespread distribution of such shallow-water deposits in geosynclines indicate that they were not deep trenches in the ocean that were gradually filled to the surface. On the contrary, as Hall reasoned, the evidence points to a gradually subsiding mobile belt that generally received sediment in proportion to its sinking, but whose surface was shallow most of the time.

Many geosynclines can be subdivided into an inner belt closer to the continental platform, the **miogeosyncline,** and an outer belt closer to an ocean basin, the **eugeosyncline.** The miogeosyncline tends to be filled with lesser thicknesses of limestones, shales, and alluvial sandstones, though other kinds of sediment may also be found. The greater thicknesses of the sediments in the eugeosyncline consist of turbidite sandstones and shales, pelagic limestones and shales mixed with volcanic rocks, submarine basalts, and ash falls and flows. The explanation of the origin of geosynclines in terms of plate-tectonic theory is outlined in Chapter 10 and given in detail in Chapter 19.

Structurally deformed, metamorphosed, and injected with igneous intrusions, geosynclines were the forerunners of the major mountain chains of the world: the Alps, the Himalayas, the Appalachians, and the Western Cordilleran belt of the Americas. Only in the youngest mountain belts are the youngest geosynclinal beds preserved. As the mountains wear away, older and older sedimentary rocks are stripped off by erosion, in many places uncovering igneous and metamorphic rocks below. As geologic time goes on, the less likely it is that sediments uplifted into mountain ranges will survive erosion. In general, less and less sediment is found preserved as one moves back through the history of the Earth.

Continental Platforms. Wide areas of the North American continent between the Appalachians and the Rocky Mountains have been relatively stable at least since the Cambrian Period began. Sedimentary accumulations are much thinner than in the geosynclines to the east and west, though there are a number of sedimentary basins, such as the Illinois Basin, that have received as much as 3000 meters (10,000 feet) of sediment. Deep-water formations are conspicuously absent, and many of the sediments are shallow carbonate-platform sediments and alluvial (or near-shore marine) sandstones and shales. Individual formations more or less continuous with those in geosynclines are much thinner on the platform. Subsidence has been much less on the platform, and no great mountain-making episodes have affected it. Conversely, erosion has not eaten so deeply into the surface sedimentary rocks, so that Precambrian igneous and metamorphic rocks, the basement, are exposed only in a few places, such as in the Ozark Mountains or the Black Hills. The key feature of platform sedimentation is not so much in sediment types and the environments in which they formed, for there is almost complete overlap with geosynclines in that regard, but in the thinness of the accumulation, a response to only mild and intermittent subsidence.

Subsidence, which influences environment and thickness of accumulation, is only one as-

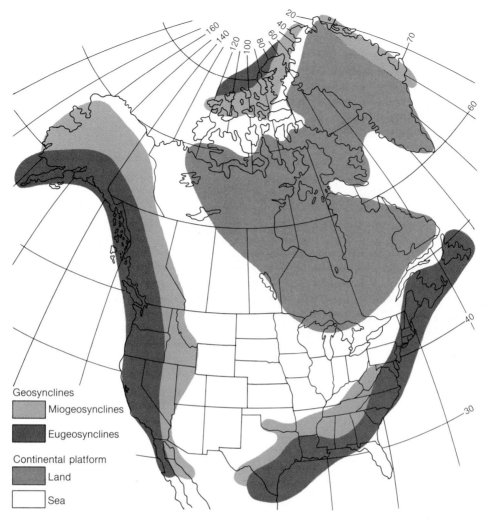

Figure 11-25
Paleotectonic map of North America for the Cambrian, Ordovician, and Silurian, showing
outlines of geosynclines bordering the North American continent. [After *History of the Earth*
(2nd ed.) by Bernhard Kummel. W. H. Freeman and Company. Copyright © 1970.]

Figure 11-26
Diagrammatic cross section of a geosyncline and adjoining platform area. The platform and
miogeosyncline differ largely in thickness of sediment, whereas miogeosyncline and eugeosyncline differ also in kinds of sedimentary rocks.

pect of the tectonic control of sedimentation. Just as important is the indirect effect that tectonics has on the mineral composition of detrital sediments.

TECTONICS AND SEDIMENT COMPOSITION

Contrasts in the mineral composition of clastic sediments can be startling. For example, compare two alluvial sandstones, an arkose and a quartz arenite. The arkose may contain as much as 30–40 percent feldspar, the remainder quartz and other mineral and rock fragments. The grains are coarse and angular, showing little sign of abrasion. The quartz sandstone may be more than 95 percent quartz with no feldspar. The grains are well-sorted and well-rounded. The contrast is not in the environment, for both are alluvial but in the source of the erosional debris. The source of the arkose is likely a granitic igneous rock; the rocks eroded to make the quartz sand might well have been another sandstone.

We can generalize further about feldspar, the most abundant mineral of the crust, as a detrital mineral in comparison to quartz. As shown in Chapter 5, feldspar chemically decomposes to clay minerals, given enough time for reaction with rain and soil water. Quartz is essentially unaffected by most chemical weathering. The survival of feldspar in a weathering terrain is dependent upon the rate of chemical decomposition in relation to the rate of mechanical erosion that breaks up the rock and transports it. The ratio of chemical to mechanical erosion is related to the topography of the terrain—the more elevated and rugged the mountains, the more rigorous the mechanical erosion. Thus we may relate the abundance of feldspar to mountainous topography, which itself is the product of tectonic activity. Low-lying areas not subject to severe mechanical erosion produce detritus low in feldspar; much of the feldspar decomposes to clay before it can be transported.

This tectonic background to sediment composition is a major basis for the reconstruction of ancient tectonic events, of high mountain chains that once shed abundant detritus and are now gone. For example, the Devonian sandstones of the Catskill Mountains of New York are a very thick accumulation of alluvial and deltaic sands that were transported from a great mountain range to the east, roughly parallel to the present low hills of the Taconic Mountains east of the Hudson River. In the same way,

geologists in Canada have been able to reconstruct some fragmentary patterns of vanished mountain ranges, some more than 2 billion years old, from Precambrian sediments. Sediments are the hieroglyphics of geologic history.

SEDIMENT INTO ROCK: DIAGENESIS

Once a sediment is deposited and buried by other sediments, it is not immune to change. One has only to compare freshly deposited muds and sands with ancient shales and sandstones to see the obvious differences in hardness, cohesion, and porosity. The many processes that produce the changes that take place in a rock's composition and texture after deposition are lumped together in the term **diagenesis.** Generally, they operate to harden the soft sediment into rock—that is, to **lithify** it. Diagenesis may also alter the mineral composition by dissolving some of the original minerals and precipitating new ones.

The major physical diagenetic change is **compaction,** a decrease in porosity caused by mineral grains being squeezed closer to each other by the weight of overlying sediment. Sands are fairly well packed as they are deposited, so they compact little, even when buried deeply. Newly deposited muds, however, are highly porous: they have a high water content when deposited, often well over 60 percent, and their layers thin drastically by compaction. The porosity of a sediment may also decrease greatly from the precipitation of diagenetic minerals in its pore spaces.

Chemical diagenetic changes are the result of two general tendencies. The first is a gradual approach toward chemical equilibrium of the nonequilibrium mixture of diverse minerals from many different kinds of rock that have been brought together as detritus in the sediment (and, perhaps, mixed with some chemical precipitate from the environment, such as calcite). Thus, sedimentation may mix minerals from two very different kinds of igneous rocks, minerals that would have been incompatible under the original conditions of formation of the igneous rocks, such as a sodium-rich plagioclase feldspar from a granite and a calcium-rich one from a basalt. Diagenetic chemical changes tend to dissolve the calcium-rich feldspars and precipitate sodium-rich feldspars, thus moving the rock toward chemical equilibrium—namely, a more homogeneous plagioclase composition. A different example of lack of equilibrium is a grain of aragonite in a carbonate sediment, which, given enough time, tends spontaneously to change to calcite, which is the form of calcium carbonate stable at low pressures and temperatures. This tendency to equilibrium results in many other chemical reactions between incompatible or unstable minerals, which result in the formation of new minerals and, thus, bring the rock to a new composition in equilibrium with its surroundings.

The second tendency is for a sediment to be buried more or less deeply in the crust. As a sediment is buried, it becomes subjected to increasingly high temperatures—on the average 1°C for each 30 meters (100 feet) of depth (see Chapter 13)—and high pressures—on the average about 1 atmosphere for each 4.4 meters of depth (1 pound per square inch for each foot of depth). As minerals and the surrounding groundwater in pore spaces are heated up and put under greater pressure, they tend to react chemically to form new minerals. This process, when carried far enough, becomes metamorphism, in which the entire character of the rock alters. The boundary between diagenesis and metamorphism is somewhat arbitrary, usually drawn at a temperature of about 300°C.

The list of specific diagenetic changes is great. Few of these are universal; their occurrence depends on the geologic situation. A few important examples include the change of unstable opaline silica shells of diatoms to quartz, the stable form; transformation of the unstable swelling clay, montmorillonite, to a stable mica type of clay, illite; the precipitation of calcite and quartz as pore-filling cement in sandstones; and the alteration of volcanic glass to clay minerals and zeolite minerals. All of these changes must be understood before we can deduce the nature of the original sediment that was laid down, which we need to do in order to interpret geologic history.

Diagenesis is of some practical value, because recovery of oil, gas, or groundwater from formations depends on the porosity of the rock, which may have been largely determined by diagenetic cementation. The formation of oil itself is a diagenetic process by which organic remains of many kinds of organisms are gradually altered to liquid petroleum or natural gas, or both. The transformation of peat through bituminous coal to anthracite is another diagenetic process. Understanding all of these processes better enables us to search more intelligently and successfully for new mineral and energy resources.

Figure 11-27
Some changes in composition and texture that are produced by diagenetic processes. Most of the changes tend to transform a loose, soft sediment into a hard, lithified sedimentary rock.

SUMMARY

1. Physical sedimentation is controlled by gravity, and chemical sedimentation is dominated by precipitation from sea water, which keeps the ocean constant in composition.

2. Carbonate sediments form from supersaturated sea water in warm parts of the ocean's surface, primarily through the activities of organisms that secrete carbonate.

3. Coral reefs and atolls are built by large communities of carbonate-secreting corals and coralline algae. Their structure of reef front, lagoon, and island is made by the complex interaction of many kinds of organisms and the sea. Reefs form around originally volcanic islands, which may later erode and subside to be covered over by reef.

4. Carbonate platforms near or attached to continents in tropical seas account for most of the shallow-water carbonate sediments of the world. Oolite, carbonate sands, muds, and tidal-flat deposits, such as stromatolites, are characteristic of the various environments of the shallow bank areas of the Bahama Islands.

5. Silica is secreted by diatoms, radiolarians, and sponges. Siliceous oozes and cherts are formed by the sedimentation of the skeletons of these organisms on the sea floor.

6. Precipitation of sedimentary sulfides is accomplished by the action of sulfate-reducing bacteria on organic matter in such deoxygenated environments as silled basins or tidal flats.

7. Coal is formed by the partial decay and transformation of organic matter laid down in swampy environments. Vegetation is first changed into peat and then, in an ascending series of metamorphic stages, to lignite, bituminous coal, and anthracite.

8. Evaporites are deposited in restricted basins of the sea in which evaporation continues to produce precipitates of gypsum and salt as sea water is replenished by a connection to the open sea. Some evaporites form from complete desiccation. Others form by evaporation on tidal flats in arid environments.

9. Clastic sediments are divided into conglomerate, sandstone, and shale on the basis of grain size, which is a reflection of current strength.

10. A study of the grain size and bedding characteristics of sand and sandstone gives information on current type and direction. Paleocurrents are inferred from cross-bedding and other directional structures.

11. Gravel and conglomerate are formed by strong currents characteristic of rapidly flowing rivers and strong waves. Pebble size and roundness can be used to infer the distance of transport from the sediment source area.

12. Mud and shale are deposited from settling of fine material from slow or waning currents on river floodplains and in deeper marine environments. Many shales are mixed with chemical components. The clay minerals of shales come from the weathering of silicate minerals.

13. Sedimentary environments are described in terms of geomorphology, which links important sedimentary characteristics to particular geographic locations.

14. Sediment accumulates as a result of subsidence in the depositional area. Geosynclines, which are the sites of great accumulations of sediments, can be subdivided into miogeosynclinal and eugeosynclinal tracts.

15. A continental platform is a large area of a continent over which subsidence has been slight for a long time. As a result, sedimentary accumulations on such platforms are thin.

16. Tectonic control of sediment composition is evidenced by the ratio of quartz, a stable mineral, to feldspar, an unstable mineral in weathering environments. Mountain-building results in more rapid mechanical erosion of feldspar; thus, abundant feldspar in sediments indicates tectonism.

17. Diagenesis is the process by which sediments are changed physically and chemically and lithified, partly as a result of burial and increases in temperature and pressure.

EXERCISES

1. A few years ago some marine biologists thought that dynamiting certain areas of a coral reef for engineering purposes was upsetting the ecological balance of the reef and would lead to the death of large populations of corals. Their fears have not been substantiated (so far), but if they had been right and all of the corals had died, what events might characterize the further evolution of the reef? Could you recognize these events from the sediment produced?

2. What reasons can you think of why the Pacific Ocean has so many coral atolls and the Atlantic so few?

3. Early in the Precambrian era there were no carbonate-secreting organisms. Assuming the oceans, with that exception, were much like those of today, where and what kind of carbonate sediment, if any, would you expect to have been deposited?

4. The Black Sea is known to lack oxygen in its deep waters. What does this suggest about the nature of the Bosporous and Dardanelles, the straits that connect the sea with the Mediterranean? What kinds of sediment might you expect to find at the bottom of the Black Sea?

5. The general oceanographic circulation conditions of some ancient evaporite basins seem to have been similar to those of some present-day deoxygenated basins, yet only some of the evaporite basins contain much organic matter and sulfides. Why might this be so?

6. A geologist has mapped a formation of a certain age as changing from a conglomerate on the western edge of his map area to interbedded sandstone and shale on the eastern edge. On the basis of this information alone, what deductions might be made about the depositional environment and paleogeography of the formation?

7. In the Mississippi delta country of Louisiana, oil wells have been drilled 7000 meters or more to penetrate Miocene formations of nearshore shallow-water sandstones and shales. How do you think this much sediment has accumulated?

8. How do you think the processes that have made mud into shale might generally differ from those that have made sand into sandstone?

9. A number of geologists estimate that 10 percent of the ocean's salt may have been removed as evaporite deposits during the Permian Period. If the ocean's volume were then the same as now, 1.37×10^{21} liters, how many kilograms of salt would have been deposited?

BIBLIOGRAPHY

Blatt, H., G. Middleton, and R. Murray, *Origin of Sedimentary Rocks.* Englewood Cliffs, New Jersey: Prentice-Hall, Inc., 1972.

Garrels, R. M., and F. T. Mackenzie, *Evolution of Sedimentary Rocks:* New York: W. W. Norton and Co., 1971.

Krumbein, W. C., and L. L. Sloss, *Stratigraphy and Sedimentation* (2nd ed.). San Francisco: W. H. Freeman and Company, 1963.

Kuenen, P. H., "Sand." *Scientific American,* April 1960. (Offprint No. 803.)

Laporte, L. F., *Ancient Environments.* Englewood Cliffs, New Jersey: Prentice-Hall, Inc., 1968.

Selley, R. C., *Ancient Sedimentary Environments.* Ithaca, New York: Cornell University Press, 1970.

12

EARTH AND LIFE

Earth is probably only one of many billions of planets in the universe on which the conditions necessary for the development of life were met. The compositions of the crust, the atmosphere, and the oceans have not only determined the course of biological evolution but have been themselves affected by life processes. The primitive Earth had an oxygen-free atmosphere conducive to the origin of life. Some time after primitive life started, photosynthesis evolved and oxygen began to build up in the atmosphere, eventually to near present levels. Life depends on the environments in which it evolved and to which it has adapted. Human activities may affect those environments seriously by increasing the levels of carbon dioxide, which might affect the global climate, and by introducing large quantities of toxic metals into the biosphere.

The Earth gives us permission to live. It provides the basics: the air we breathe, the water we drink, and the food we eat—the plants and animals that share the planet with us. For modern civilizations, it provides the mineral and energy resources necessary to innumerable systems that we take for granted, from the fertilizers required by modern high-productivity agriculture to the jet fuel required by our airliners. The surface environment of Earth plays a profound role in our lives. We can exist only in a narrow range of temperatures and pressures, and we are dependent on the abundance of many chemical compounds—water in particular. It has become abundantly clear, particularly in the past decade, that the relation between life and the environment is not one-way. Not only does the physical environment control life, the biological world has a profound effect on the environment. Rich, black soil—an environmental necessity for productive agriculture—is formed largely by the interaction of organisms with elements of the physical environment. The oxygen in the atmosphere—an element of the environment that is required by the respiratory mechanisms of all complex forms of life—has

been manufactured by green plants in the process of converting sunlight to usable chemical energy by means of photosynthesis. The human population of the Earth is increasingly altering the global environment. We add more and more carbon dioxide to the atmosphere by burning coal and oil, for example, and such pesticides as DDT have been dispersed throughout the waters of the continents and oceans.

In this chapter, we will explore the interaction between Earth and life. Why is there life here and not on the Moon? How did life start, and how did it evolve? Above all, how precarious is our existence on this planet, and what are the possible effects of our technology and growing population on our environment?

LIFE BEGINS

Throughout most of human history, the subject of the origin of life was exclusively a mythological or a theological concern. Discussion of the matter dealt mainly with the precise meaning of the revealed truth of the Judeo-Christian scriptures or that of the sacred texts or oral traditions

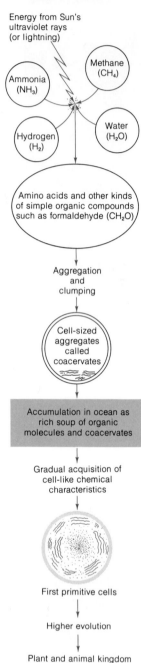

Figure 12-1
Origin of primitive organic compounds, followed by precellular evolution, leading to the first cells—a scheme first envisioned by A. I. Oparin and now accepted in a general way by most scientists studying the origin of life.

Figure 12-2
Experiment of S. L. Miller, in which amino acids were made by circulating methane (CH_4), ammonia (NH_3), water vapor (H_2O), and hydrogen (H_2) past an electrical discharge. The amino acids, collected at the bottom of the apparatus, were detected by paper chromatography. [From "The Origin of Life" by G. Wald. Copyright © 1954 by Scientific American, Inc. All rights reserved.]

of other religions; all explanations were framed in terms of the actions of a creator. Although the rise of geology in the eighteenth and nineteenth centuries (as part of the "Age of Enlightenment") permitted the age of the Earth to be discussed in scientific terms rather than in terms of a literal interpretation of the Bible, it was not until the twentieth century that scientists seriously opened the subject of the origin of life to nontheological discussion. In the nineteenth century, Louis Pasteur waged a decisive battle against the idea of "spontaneous generation" of life, challenging the commonly held view that, by some such process, maggots, flies, and bacteria came to life on rotting garbage. Pasteur showed that neither bacteria nor any other kind of life could arise from any kind of dead organic matter if it were first sterilized by heat. Life orginated only from other life, he argued. Right as he was about life as we now know it, he and others simply ignored the question of whether there was ever a beginning to the process.

In 1924 a young Russian biochemist, A. I. Oparin, opened up the whole matter by asserting that there had to have been a beginning, sometime in the early history of the Earth, and that it was possible to make some intelligent guesses about how it might have happened. He theorized that, in its early evolution, the Earth's atmosphere lacked oxygen but contained many reduced gases, such as ammonia (NH_3), hydrogen (H_2), and methane (CH_4). In that kind of atmosphere, energy in the form of ultraviolet rays from the Sun or lightning might have created organic molecules similar to the basic building blocks of life, such as the amino acids, which are molecules that form proteins when chemically strung together in long chains. Once the building blocks were formed, they might have tended to clump together in larger and larger units, which would then have begun to attain some of the characteristics of a primitive cell. All of this gradual synthesis would have taken place in the early ocean, which he de-

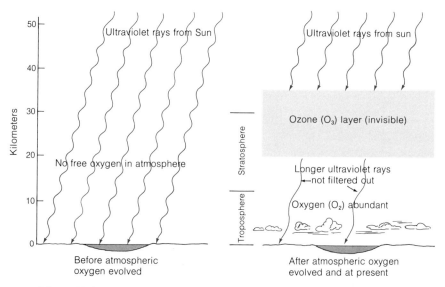

Figure 12-3
The evolution of oxygen in the atmosphere led to the formation of an ozone layer in the stratosphere as oxygen atoms and molecules combined to form the three-atom molecule O_3. This layer absorbs much of the shortwave ultraviolet rays from the sun and protects surface life from this cell-damaging radiation.

scribed as a "soup" of organic molecules. In that soup, the primitive cell-like aggregates would gradually have acquired more life-like attributes, a process culminating in the appearance of the genetic substance governing reproduction and inheritance. This stage would have marked the beginning of life. Oparin thus showed how a series of small, statistically probable chemical events could lead to the formation of life. A generation later, the DNA (deoxyribonucleic acid) molecule was shown to be the genetic substance, and its structure and mode of operation were worked out. Once DNA was formed, cells could divide, each keeping a strand of DNA, which would cause it to resemble its parent and, at the same time, would offer the opportunity for change and evolution through random alteration of the strand. (The changes in the organism produced by alterations of its DNA cause it to interact differently with the physical environment. Some changes are beneficial to the organism in its interaction with the environment and others are not; thus some individual organisms survive and others die. This phenomenon, called natural selection by Darwin, was instrumental in directing the course of evolution.)

About thirty years later, a young American graduate student in chemistry, Stanley L. Miller, devised a crucial experiment that showed how it really might have happened. He built an apparatus in which he could simulate lightning bolts in a reducing atmosphere by setting off powerful electric sparks in a glass chamber filled with a mixture of water, ammonia, and methane. After sparking such a mixture for many hours, Miller was able to identify a number of amino acids. In the last decade, partly stimulated by the space program and the search for life on other planets, the study of the origin of life has become an active science linking biology with geology and astronomy.

The essence of the theory remains much as Oparin first suggested, the important condition being the oxygen-free atmosphere. The necessity for a reducing atmosphere arises because synthesis and preservation of a variety of large organic molecules takes place easily only in such surroundings. Many now believe that the major energy source required to link small molecules together to make larger ones is ultraviolet radiation. On today's Earth, most ultraviolet light is filtered out by a layer of ozone (O_3), a three-atom oxygen molecule formed in the stratosphere from the more ordinary two-atom oxygen molecule (O_2). In the ozone layer, some oxygen molecules are split by absorption of the energy of ultraviolet rays to form single oxygen atoms.

Some scientists believe that the existence of the ozone layer may be threatened by three of man's activities: introduction of Freon (chlorofluoromethanes) refrigerant and spray propellant gases, exhaust gases from Supersonic transport (SST) planes flying through the stratosphere, and nitrogen oxide gases indirectly originating from the heavy use of nitrogen fertilizers. All three result in ozone-destructive chemical reactions that might be difficult or impossible to counteract. The ever-increasing use of nitrogen fertilizer may ultimately be limited because of this unforeseen side-effect.

Figure 12-4
Microorganisms from the Precambrian Gunflint Chert of Ontario, about 2 billion years old. The top row shows sections through three different individuals of the same alga-like organism *Eosphaera tyleri*, thought to be a free-floating colonial photosynthetic organism. The bottom row shows four different individuals of a peculiar primitive organism, *Kakabekia umbellata*, first discovered in the Gunflint Chert. [Photos by E. S. Barghoorn. From E. S. Barghoorn and S. A. Tyler, "Microorganisms from the Gunflint Chert," *Science*, v. 147, pp. 563-577. Copyright 1965 by the American Association for the Advancement of Science.]

These then combine with oxygen molecules to form the ozone, which itself absorbs ultraviolet rays very effectively. Were it not for the ozone layer, we would all be irradiated with powerful ultraviolet light, which would induce such intense sunburn that life on the surface of the land would be impossible. Strange that the rays that now tend to destroy life worked then to build it.

The early ocean "soup" was fairly dilute, perhaps with a thin scum of oily organic matter on its surface. Much current research is concerned with the next step: the making of large aggregate molecules of protein-like or DNA-like materials of the sort that led to the evolution of the first cell. Experiments are now beginning to show the nature of the many chemical steps involved in the building of life-like molecules.

Whatever these steps, the information from the Viking expedition to Mars in 1976, suggests that they either did not take place on that planet or were aborted by the long-term lack of liquid water. No form of life familiar to us has been found on the Martian surface. Our evolution as a planet may have been unique in this solar system in providing the conditions for life to begin and flourish.

THE OLDEST FOSSILS

When did all of this take place? Paleontology gives us an important date. In a dense chert in a sedimentary sequence in South Africa that is more than 3.2 billion years old, there are microscopic spherical and filamentous forms of carbonaceous organic matter that are probably fossils of primitive cells. Studies of the chemical composition of the carbon material support the microscopic evidence. If these forms are cells, then the whole process of life may have begun relatively early in the Earth's history, as early as 3.5 or even 4 billion years ago. Just as the search continues for the oldest rock, presumably igneous, there is the possibility that very old sediments will be found that will allow geologists, with certainty, to push the origin of life even farther back than 3.2 billion years (the age of the oldest known sedimentary rock containing evidence of life).

We are sure that by about 2 billion years ago, well-organized algal life was thriving. A formation that old is exposed on the north shore of Lake Superior, the Gunflint Chert; it contains a diversity of forms that are undoubtedly biological. Formations of stromatolitic limestones of about the same age have been mapped in Canada and South Africa; the stromatolites are of the same sort as those formed by algal mats today. By one billion years ago, a higher form of life may have been established: the cell with a nucleus. (Cells of this sort are the ones with which most of us are familiar, but they are restricted to relatively advanced bacteria and higher organisms; the earliest life forms, such as primitive bacteria and algae, had only nonnucleated cells.) We know of organisms from the Bitter Springs Formation of central Australia that look like they contain remnants of nuclei. The rocks of that formation have the same lithology as other Precambrian sedimentary rocks in which the oldest fossils are preserved: unmetamorphosed cherts in which there is excellent preservation of organic structures.

Some paleontologists who study the Precambrian are not so sure that these advanced types of cells appeared so early; they believe that the form of the "nucleus" is mimicked by cell degradation products and that the nuclear cell did not originate until just before the Cambrian Period, when many higher forms of organisms appeared.

The first shelled organisms appeared at the beginning of the Cambrian Period. Cambrian fossils include an incredible diversity of species of invertebrates. Just before that time, in very late Precambrian sediments transitional to the Cambrian, higher forms of multicellular (or **metazoan**) life without shells had developed. Sometime between 600 million and one billion years ago, higher forms of life evolved so rapidly that the rate of evolutionary development, compared to the rates of earlier times, could be described as explosive. From a world populated by primitive algae and bacteria, there emerged many thousands of species of animals, from sponges and mollusks to worms and trilobites. From then on came the march of evolution that paleontologists have mapped so well: the appearance of the first vertebrates, land plants, flowering plants, the dinosaurs, the mammals, and, finally, a few million years ago, the genus *Homo*.

Figure 12-5
Algal stromatolites from the 3-billion-year-old Bulawayan Limestone of Rhodesia. Typical stromatolitic, crescentic laminations are shown on a weathered rock surface. [Photo by Keith Kvenvolden.]

Figure 12-6
Organic, alga-like microscopic fossils in black chert of the early Precambrian Fig Tree Series near Barberton, South Africa. (1) Spheroidal and distorted fossils showing typical irregularly reticulate surface texture. (2) Section through one spheroid showing cell wall of variable thickness. (3) Spheroid containing "coal"-like organic material interpreted as the altered remnants of the original cell material. (4) Spheroidal fossils showing varying degrees of preservation. Diagonal layers are laminae of organic matter parallel to bedding. [Photos by E. S. Barghoorn. [From J. W. Schopf and E. S. Barghoorn, "Alga-like Fossils from the Early Precambrian of South Africa", *Science*, v. 156, pp. 508–512. Copyright 1967 by the American Association for the Advancement of Science.]

Chemical reactions in the upper atmosphere split a small number of water molecules into hydrogen and oxygen gas. A small amount of atmospheric oxygen may have originated in this way, but the rate of production by these reactions is very slow and, for practical purposes, negligible.

Figure 12-7
A late Precambrian fossil from rocks of the Ediacara Hills, South Australia. This annelid worm is one of many soft-bodied organisms whose development preceded the evolution of the shelled invertebrates of the Cambrian Period. [Photo by M. F. Glaessner.]

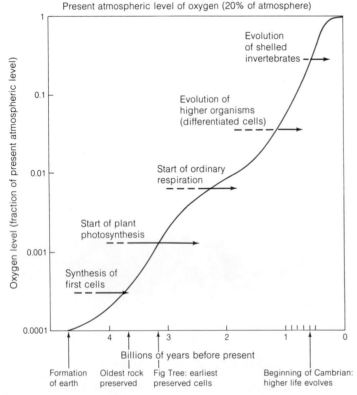

Figure 12-8
One hypothesis of the evolution of oxygen in the atmosphere in relation to the origin of life and evolution of higher organisms. There is as yet no general agreement on exactly when and to what levels oxygen accumulated in the Precambrian and how close the levels of oxygen in Phanerozoic time came to the present-day level.

Evolution of Atmospheric Oxygen. There was a radical transformation from the first life that developed in a reducing atmosphere to the kinds of organisms of the Cambrian and later periods that needed oxygen for respiration. The first organisms must have lived without oxygen, like some primitive bacteria of today, such as the sulfate-reducing species that are instrumental in precipitating pyrite (Chapter 11). At some time around 3 billion years ago, some of the primitive species must have developed one of the great biological inventions: photosynthesis.

Photosynthesis is a complex chemical process by which plants that contain chlorophyll are able to convert carbon dioxide and water into carbohydrates, the sugars needed for biological energy. In the equation below, we show the production of CH_2O, a simple formula representing all of the many carbohydrates that actually form.

$$\text{carbon dioxide} + \text{water} \xrightarrow{\substack{\text{(in the presence of} \\ \text{sunlight and chlorophyll)}}}$$
$$\quad CO_2 \qquad\qquad H_2O$$

$$\text{carbohydrates} + \text{oxygen}$$
$$\qquad CH_2O \qquad\qquad O_2$$

For each 30 grams of carbohydrate produced in this reaction, approximately 112,000 calories is converted from sunlight to chemical energy tied up in sugars, the energy that is the basis of life processes. At the same time, one molecule of oxygen is produced for every atom of carbon incorporated into organic matter.

At the beginning of the evolution of photosynthesizing plants, there were no animals to breathe oxygen, so much of the oxygen produced by photosynthesis must have started to accumulate in the atmosphere. This free oxygen made possible the beginning of a new method of utilizing energy: respiration. Respiration is oxidation of carbohydrate, which releases the energy gained from photosynthesis.

$$\text{carbohydrate} + \text{oxygen} \rightarrow$$
$$\quad CH_2O \qquad\qquad O_2$$

$$\text{carbon dioxide} + \text{water}$$
$$\qquad CO_2 \qquad\qquad H_2O$$

In this reaction, one molecule of oxygen is used up in the conversion of each atom of organic carbon to carbon dioxide. The first respirers were undoubtedly primitive bacteria that could live on small amounts of oxygen, perhaps as little as a hundredth of the amount now present in the atmosphere. This development may have taken place as early as 2.7 billion years ago. For a long time oxygen must have continued to accumulate slowly, as photosynthetic production exceeded its depletion by respiration. As a result, we can deduce that an equivalent number of organic carbon atoms were buried as organic matter in sediments. That organic matter can be looked upon as the buried excess of photosynthesis over respiration. In its simplest form the total budget since oxygen first started accumulating is given by this subtraction:

$$\begin{pmatrix} \text{number of carbon atoms} \\ \text{in organic matter} \\ \text{produced by photosynthesis} \end{pmatrix} = \begin{pmatrix} \text{number of} \\ \text{molecules} \\ \text{of oxygen} \\ \text{produced} \end{pmatrix}$$

$$-$$

$$\begin{pmatrix} \text{number of carbon atoms} \\ \text{in organic matter} \\ \text{oxidized by respiration} \end{pmatrix} = \begin{pmatrix} \text{number of} \\ \text{molecules} \\ \text{of oxygen} \\ \text{used up} \end{pmatrix}$$

$$\begin{pmatrix} \text{number of carbon atoms} \\ \text{in organic matter} \\ \text{preserved in sediments} \end{pmatrix} = \begin{pmatrix} \text{number of} \\ \text{molecules} \\ \text{of oxygen} \\ \text{accumulated} \\ \text{in atmosphere} \end{pmatrix}$$

The total amount of carbon in organisms living today is so small in comparison to the total for all the organisms that have lived in the past that it can be neglected.

Sometime just before the Cambrian, atmospheric oxygen reached levels sufficiently close to today's to allow for the rapid evolution of the higher invertebrates. For the rest of geologic time, the oxygen in the atmosphere has been maintained by the photosynthesis of the green plants of the world, much of it by green algae in the surface waters of the ocean. This story is one of the most dramatic examples of how far-reaching the consequences of the origin and evolution of life were for the surface of the Earth.

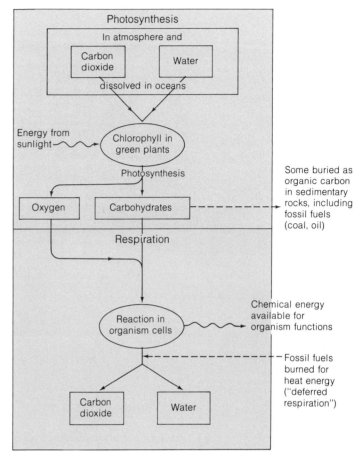

Figure 12-9
The photosynthesis-respiration couple that links organisms to the oxygen and carbon dioxide in the atmosphere and oceans.

OUR OXYGEN SUPPLY

In the late 1960s, geochemists were called upon to demonstrate that our oxygen supply was vast and that pollution would not deplete it even in the distant future. At that time, some biologists concerned with environmental quality voiced concern that pollution was endangering our oxygen supply, and posed the possibility that we might inadvertently suffocate ourselves. The concern came from reports that DDT was interfering with photosynthesis of some species of green algae. The reasoning followed that, if photosynthesis stopped all over the world, we would "soon" use up all the atmosphere's oxygen by respiration. The concern was shown to

be groundless, for there is such an immense amount of oxygen in our atmosphere and oceans (about 10^{21} grams) that, even if all photosynthesis stopped tomorrow and all other respiring life went on as before, it would be several thousand years at least before oxygen would be significantly depleted by respiration and all of the other reactions in which oxygen is used up. In addition, only some species of algae seem to be vulnerable to DDT, and there is no evidence that the Earth's major photosynthesizers, oceanic algae, are detectably affected. Some concern about the environment is justified, but there need be no fear of running out of oxygen.

Some atmospheric oxygen is used up by the oxidation of metals that occurs in the weathering of rocks, but the amount per year is very small compared with the huge quantities used by respiration and provided by photosynthesis. Accelerated burning of fossil fuels also uses up oxygen, but this amount is also too small to affect the overall picture seriously. So far, we have used up only 7 out of every 10,000 oxygen molecules by burning coal, oil, and gas, and if we were to keep burning fuel at an increasing rate until the year 2000, we would still have used up only 20 out of every 10,000 oxygen molecules.

Figure 12-10
Input and output of oxygen—atmosphere and oceans. Photosynthesis and respiration are in approximate balance and far outweigh the other inputs and outputs. The amount of oxygen in the atmosphere is so great in proportion to the output rate that even if all photosynthesis were to stop, our oxygen supply would last well over 2000 years.

EXTRATERRESTRIAL LIFE

The evolution of life on Earth was an expectable consequence of the evolution of the planet. Earth was large enough for its gravitational attraction to hold an atmosphere. The temperature of most of the surface was low enough that water was liquid. All of the chemical elements needed for our varied biological processes were present. Given this conjunction of circumstances, was it not inevitable that life forms based on the organic chemistry of carbon and water would arise? If so, then would it not also be inevitable that life is not a strange accident on a unique planet but an event that we would expect to be repeated in various places and at various times in the universe? This is the way Harlow Shapley, one of the great American astronomers of the past generation, started to think about the subject. He then made a simple calculation. How many stars had about the same composition and quality of luminosity as our Sun, and thus could heat and light a planet such

as ours? From his knowledge of our galaxy and the rest of the universe, he estimated that there were about 10^{20} stars with the proper characteristics. But how many of those stars might have a series of planets like the ones in our solar system? One in a thousand is a conservative estimate. How many of those planets might be placed, as the Earth is, just the right distance from their stars for them to have the right temperature? One in a thousand, to continue being conservative. How many of those planets might be big enough to hold atmospheres but not so big as to hold all of the hydrogen too? Again, one in a thousand. After all these and other estimates, he ended with a most conservative estimate of the number of planets in the universe on which life might be expected to develop: 100,000,000. With such a large number, he thought it exceedingly probable that life does indeed exist out there somewhere—perhaps too far ever to reach even by radio communication,

Since Shapley's estimates, others have modified the estimates of the likelihood of life existing elsewhere in the universe. Some have modified the estimates upward on the supposition that the number of planets like ours is larger; others have decreased the estimates by arguing that the probability of formation of cells and reproductive life, even given favorable conditions, is much smaller.

but there, nevertheless. Thus was born a new kind of scientific enterprise: **exobiology.**

Part of the excitement about the first trips to the Moon was the thought of confirming our ideas about the origins of life. The Moon was lacking an atmosphere; it was too hot on the day side and too cold on the night side; and there was no free water detectable. We did not expect to find life there, and we didn't. The most careful analysis of the first Moon rocks failed to reveal any signs of life, neither cells of organisms nor telltale organic molecules that could have been formed only by biological processes. So we have important negative evidence that gives us some confidence in our reasoning.

Mars is another story. Because Mars has a thin atmosphere (mostly carbon dioxide) and there is evidence of water (the geomorphology of some terrain resembles river valleys), the chances that some form of life exists—or once existed—are better than on the Moon. But no form of even very primitive life, at least as we know it on Earth, could survive for long on Mars today. One of the instruments that was landed on the Martian surface was designed to detect small quantities of amino acids in soil. The results were negative. Results of other instrumental analysis shed further doubt on the existence of life, though some exobiologists hold to their belief that we may yet turn up some evidence for it. The verdict for the present: no life on Mars now, and no evidence that there was ever enough water at the surface for a sufficiently long time to generate life.

Life in outer space? It's doubtful; but astronomers have detected small quantities of about twenty simple organic compounds in the nearly empty space between stars, one of which is formaldehyde (CH_2O), the simplest building block of carbohydrates. Some of these compounds are also found in meteorites. Thus it is apparent that the basic units of the compounds of life can be formed in space and transported by meteorites. Now we must indeed recognize the probability that life exists throughout the universe.

Back here on Earth, the importance of all of these ideas is that they make us focus on why we are here and what the conditions are for our continued existence on this planet. How stable is our environment? Can we, the members of one species, so alter the Earth that we make life more difficult for ourselves?

HIGHER FORMS OF LIFE: INTERACTIONS WITH THE ENVIRONMENT

Once the metazoans evolved, the well-known fossil record began—a record of a host of evolutionary events, as new organisms arose by the interaction of the genetic material of each species with its environment. For it is the physical and chemical environment of the Earth's surface that is the arena of natural selection that determines which species survive. But the environment is itself acted upon by the organisms. The surface of the Earth, as well as its atmosphere and oceans, have been profoundly affected by developments in organic evolution.

The shelled organisms did more than mark history with their fossil remains. The oceans became the place where organisms secreted enormous quantities of calcium carbonate, calcium phosphate, and silica to make their shells. As these animals died, new types of sediment were thus created, as well as constructional features, such as reefs. In the mid-Paleozoic, the higher plants evolved and the land surface became vegetated with coniferous trees, ferns, and other early plant species. Lushly vegetated swamps became possible for the first time, producing another kind of biological sediment, coal. Vertebrate life also had its origin in the mid-Paleozoic, beginning with the fishes, followed by the amphibians, and then the climactic evolution of the reptiles, the age of dinosaurs, in the Mesozoic. The mammals appeared in the Mesozoic too, but reached dominance only after the dinosaurs disappeared. None of these vertebrates had any significant effect on the Earth's physical or chemical environment; that was to come with the next development: the evolution of humankind. The genus *Homo* appeared on the scene only a few million years ago, and evolved to *Homo sapiens,* our species, only within the last million.

Many of the major events of organic evolution can be associated with major geologic events, such as the assembly of the supercontinent of Pangaea in the late Paleozoic. Hundreds of species of invertebrates became extinct then, and the world saw the beginning of a wholesale change in the kinds and relative populations of the different animal and plant species. As continents collided to form Pangaea, most of the expanse of shallow continental shelf surrounding each continent disappeared, leaving only one

In early 1977, the radio telescope observatory of the Max Planck Institute of Astronomy in Germany reported the detection of molecules of water in "IC133", a nebula 2.2 million light years away. This indicates that somewhere in that nebula, physical conditions are similar to those of our own solar system.

narrow perimeter around the supercontinent. During the Paleozoic the shelves had harbored the most productive biological populations. Climatic extremes, including glaciation of parts of what are now Africa, Australia, and South America, worked with geographic constriction of shelves to create environmental stresses great enough to decimate many species. When Pangaea rifted apart, forming new wide expanses of hospitable shelves, the survivors founded the new stocks of the Mesozoic world.

The major geologic event associated with our evolution and early history was, of course, the Pleistocene glaciation. Early humans learned first to take advantage of natural protected habitats, such as caves, to take refuge from the snow and ice and cold. The next step was learning to build a shelter. And that step ultimately led to our huge buildings, highways, dams, canals, and all of the other new "landforms" of the modern Earth. *Homo sapiens* is, of course, a natural species, and in that sense anything we do is "natural," but the landscape of our civilization goes so far beyond any other organism's work in modifying "nature" that our influence is clearly of a different order of magnitude. Our influence has had its negative aspects too, for inadvertently our modification of the environment to suit ourselves may have produced hazards as well as benefits.

HAZARDS TO THE ENVIRONMENT

A visit to the "environment and ecology" section of a public library or paperback bookstore may frighten you. Titles are made up of words like "crisis," "survival," "threat," and "danger." Perhaps more revealing is the use of such words as "frail" and "fragile" to describe the Earth. How do we reconcile the doomsday view with the geological evidence that the Earth is a dynamic global system that is remarkably stable in its steady-state equilibrium. To what extent have people suddenly wakened to the real possibility that we are so efficient at controlling our own environment that we may foolishly be tipping "the balance of nature" on a global scale, and to what extent have they simply become aware of what the Earth has been like all the time?

Environmental hazards divide themselves into local and regional versus global problems. Landslides and earthquakes are natural and local phenomena. We describe, in Chapter 5, how poor engineering and construction practices can precipitate landslides and, in Chapter 17, how minor earthquakes can be provoked by pumping fluids at high pressures into subsurface formations. At the opposite extreme are the global hazards, such as the worldwide increase of carbon dioxide in the atmosphere, that might influence the Earth's climate.

Many concerns for specific regions or types of environment are purely esthetic—the preservation of natural beauty, wilderness areas, and, in general, "unspoiled" landscape. To the extent that such concerns are based on uniqueness of the landscape, a knowledge of geology may be of help in our decision to preserve or modify any specific element of that landscape. We know that river gorges may be common in a variety of terrains, but there is little question that there is only one that has the magnificence of the Grand Canyon of the Colorado.

Medical Geology. The environmental hazards that are of a different sort of importance are those to public health. The link between geology and health has spawned a new field, **medical geology,** and its questions are new: Are the levels of lead in our drinking water or food much above the natural level, and, if so, are they potentially a medical danger? How widespread is mercury pollution, and how toxic are a few parts per billion in drinking water? In such matters the job of the scientist is dual. One is to measure the spread of a pollutant through the Earth-surface system of atmosphere, surface waters, biological populations, and sediments, and to determine how much man's activities are altering that spread. The other is to answer a series of medical questions. What bodily damage may result from long continued exposure to low levels of toxic metals or other pollutants? At what levels do obvious disease symptoms appear? At the extreme, what are the lethal doses? We must also consider the ill effects of deficiencies of some metals in our diet.

Most perplexing are the maps that show the incidence of certain diseases, from cancer to kidney stones, for each county or region of a country. These maps show that people living in certain areas are seemingly more prone to certain diseases than those living elsewhere. Does the incidence of a disease have to do with the kinds of people who settled in a region, or with their descendants, or does it have to do with the local geological environment that affects the water, food, dust, and anything else that may affect our health?

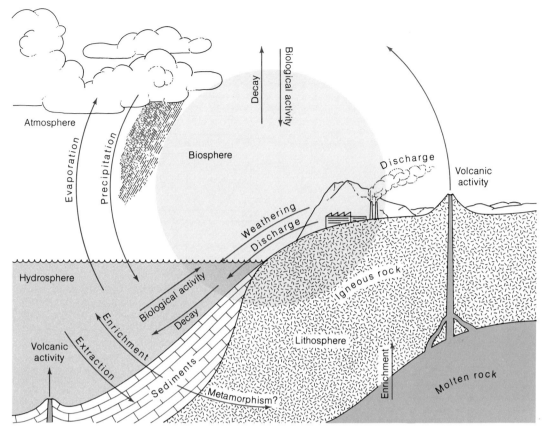

Figure 12-11
Mercury cycle disperses the metal throughout the lithosphere, hydrosphere, and atmosphere and through the biosphere, which interpenetrates all three. Mercury is present in all spheres in trace amounts, but it tends to be concentrated by biological processes. Human activities—in particular, certain industrial processes—may now present a threat by significantly redistributing the metal. [From "Mercury in the Environment" by L. J. Goldwater. Copyright © 1971 by Scientific American, Inc. All rights reserved.]

Toxic Metals. The toxic metals are some of the most serious potential offenders. Mercury, for example, which is known to be toxic, first hit the headlines a few years ago when a Canadian graduate student discovered high levels of the metal in the tissues of lake fish. We know that mercury occurs in small amounts in many rocks—about 0.2 part per million in granite and less than half that amount in the average crustal rock. The mercury in rocks is steadily contributed in small amounts to natural waters by ordinary chemical weathering processes. Most natural waters contain only a few parts per billion, and thus are harmless. Some part of the mercury in water is naturally converted to an organic form, methyl mercury, which is the form most harmful to organisms. The medical data indicate that chronic mercury poisoning

may arise from high levels (many parts per million) of the metal dissolved in water, much of it as methyl mercury. At these levels, mercury affects the nervous system in hidden ways, with few well-defined symptoms shown for long periods of time after the exposure. Acute mercury poisoning has occurred in people living around several bays in Japan, where shellfish, severely contaminated by mercury-laden industrial wastes, were eaten as a large portion of the diet. For these reasons, the World Health Organization has recommended the maximum permissible mercury level for human food, including fish, at 0.5 part per million.

Enough work has been done on the circulation of mercury at the Earth's surface to show how the interaction between the biological world and mercury in the physical environment

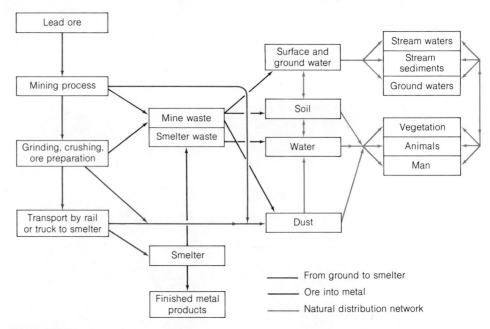

Figure 12-12
Movement of lead through surface environments, beginning with the mining of lead ore. At each stage of processing or transport, lead-rich material may get into the air or into surface waters and soil, some of it eventually to be ingested by plants and animals. [Modified from B. G. Wixson, 1973.]

works. In the past fifty years, many thousands of tons of mercury have been mined for use in electrical equipment, chemical processing plants, and in pesticides. We can look on this as an accelerated weathering process, by which much more mercury than normal is being released from rocks. Though some of the mercury in some chemical processes is reused, a great deal of it escapes into natural waters or is vaporized into the atmosphere. From there, it is distributed to lakes, the ocean, and various sedimentary environments. A fraction of the mercury, converted to methyl mercury by bacteria, is ingested by organisms and accumulates in their tissues. As larger animals eat smaller ones, more of the metal accumulates in the larger ones, so that very large fish, such as tuna or swordfish, may contain relatively large amounts, perhaps a few hundredths of a part per million. In waters that are polluted by industrial waste, the levels may be higher. Eventually, this material is absorbed by sedimentary particles, particularly the clays, and is buried out of reach of the biological system.

The serious question about mercury is, just how much does the mercury in our waters exceed natural levels, and how widespread are such high levels? It is by no means clear that, in most places in the world, natural levels have been exceeded greatly. We know of a few places where industrial wastes have been uncontrolled and the pollution has reached dangerous levels; but we have only recently begun to pay much attention to these elements, and what we need to do is monitor unpolluted and polluted natural waters and their biological populations much more carefully. In company with other toxic metals, mercury has been in the human diet at very low levels since we evolved several million years ago. Exactly what the range of those levels is—and by how much they can be exceeded without danger—remains to be determined. There is also good evidence that minimum levels of some metals are required for good health. If, as a result of our fear of absorbing "poisonous" substances, we were to try to use only distilled water for drinking and food preparation, we might produce more harmful consequences than those produced by most impurities in water. We are, after all, adapted to a natural habitat in which small amounts of almost every element are found.

Other metals have the same general cycles of behavior. The most important, from the medical point of view, are lead, cadmium, arsenic, chromium, and nickel. Lead is particularly impor-

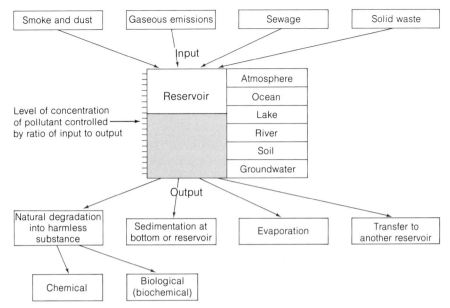

Figure 12-13
Inputs and outputs of pollutants in relation to concentration levels in reservoirs. The level is controlled by the input-output ratio. The rate of change of level depends on the rates of the processes involved.

tant, both because it is very toxic and because it is largely dispersed throughout the atmosphere from automobile and industrial emissions. Two aspects of the problem are apparent. Locally, in inner cities or near major highways, the lead levels from emissions may be very high, compared to those in suburban or rural regions; and globally, there is evidence that the entire atmosphere is being charged with more and more lead. The United States has begun the conversion to lead-free gasoline for automobiles. If and when other countries follow and this source of atmospheric lead is cut down, the problem will disappear, for lead is rained out of the atmosphere very quickly.

All environments are self-cleaning by sedimentation. Sooner or later, the contaminants we worry about will settle out of the atmosphere, lakes, and oceans. That is small consolation to most of us, because rates of sedimentation are so slow for most dissolved pollutants that, even if sources of excessive pollution are cut off, dangerously high levels may remain for a hundred years. In a particular environment, any pollutant tends toward a steady-state level that is determined by the balance between input rate from natural and human activity, its dispersal through the environment, and the sedimentation rates in that environment. Historical records show

whether the system is out of balance, whether the levels are increasing because inputs are greater than outputs. Monitoring in the future may also show how levels decrease as artificial inputs are lowered and the natural output continues. Input-output relations are shown well by the carbon dioxide system.

CARBON DIOXIDE AND CLIMATE

The small amount of carbon dioxide in the atmosphere (a little over 320 parts per million) has a profound effect on our climate. The atmosphere is relatively transparent to the incoming visible rays of the Sun. Much of that radiation is changed by reflection at the Earth's surface to infrared, invisible long-wave rays that radiate back away from the surface. The atmosphere, however, is relatively opaque and impermeable to infrared rays because of the combined effect of clouds and carbon dioxide, which strongly absorbs the radiation instead of allowing it to escape into space. This absorbed radiation then heats the atmosphere, which radiates heat back to the Earth's surface. This is called the "greenhouse effect," by analogy to the warming of greenhouses, whose glass is the

The disposal of radioactive wastes from nuclear reactors poses an increasing difficulty. Underground disposal, already tried with mixed results in several places (the permeable formations or mines leaked) is a way of artificially depositing and burying an artificial sediment, speeding to an instant a process that would take thousands or millions of years to happen naturally.

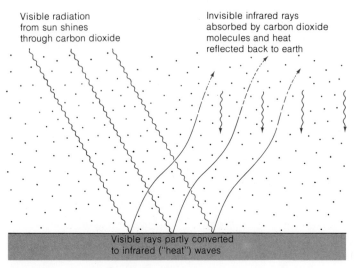

Figure 12-14
How the greenhouse effect works. Just as the glass of a greenhouse transmits light rays but holds in heat, the carbon dioxide of the atmosphere transmits visible radiation from the sun but absorbs and reflects back to Earth the infrared rays from the surface.

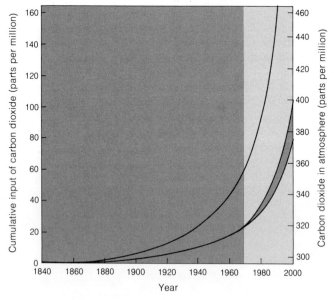

Figure 12-15
The lower curve shows the increase in atmospheric carbon dioxide since 1860, with a projection to the year 2000. The upper curve shows the cumulative input of carbon dioxide. The difference between the two curves represents the amount of carbon dioxide removed by the ocean or by additions to the total biomass of vegetation on land. [From "The Carbon Cycle" by B. Bolin. Copyright © 1970 by Scientific American, Inc. All rights reserved.]

barrier to heat loss. Any process that alters the amount of carbon dioxide in the atmosphere may conceivably affect the Earth's climate.

Since the start of the industrial revolution, about the beginning of the nineteenth century, we have been pumping carbon dioxide into the atmosphere at an accelerating rate by our burning of coal, oil, and gas. The carbon dioxide level of the atmosphere has been increasing, as shown by systematic measurements in various places in the world. In addition, calculations have been made of the amounts of carbon dioxide added to the atmosphere from the figures for fuel consumption. There is a pronounced discrepancy: the increased level in the atmosphere is not as high as would have been predicted by the additional supply. This suggests some loss or output from the atmosphere, something absorbing the extra carbon dioxide, moderating the effect of the increased input.

Much of the carbon dioxide that is "missing" from the atmosphere has been mixed with the oceans. Gas molecules of carbon dioxide in the air are in equilibrium with dissolved gas molecules in the water. As the concentration of gas in the air increases, there is a tendency toward re-establishing equilibrium: the water dissolves more gas, taking some of the excess from the air. In this way, the oceans are absorbing some of the carbon dioxide produced by the industrial revolution (about 50 percent) and keeping the atmosphere much closer to its natural levels. Nevertheless, in spite of the ocean's moderating effect, carbon dioxide levels are expected to reach about 375 parts per million by the year 2000, a significant increase over 320 parts per million in 1970 and 295 parts per million in the middle of the nineteenth century. Yet it is doubtful that this has seriously affected our climate and that it will so affect it in the next decades.

The possible increase in temperature is not great, partly because atmospheric carbon dioxide is already absorbing about as much radiation as it can and the rest will pass through unabsorbed, and partly because any rise in temperature will produce more cloudiness, which will tend to lower the radiation coming in from the Sun. The best guess now is that, in the next thirty years, the carbon dioxide effect alone will increase the global average temperature by about 0.5°C, but that the countering effect of cloud cover may moderate this almost entirely. (It is doubtful that the small increase in cloudiness would be noticed by the average person.)

A more pessimistic view is taken by Wallace

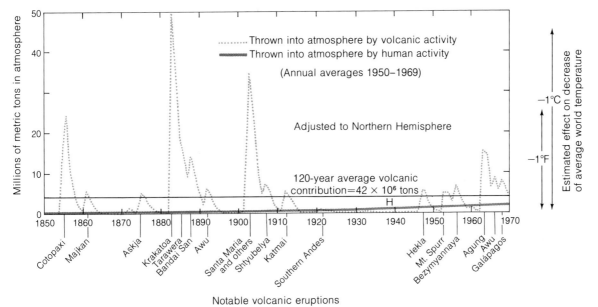

Figure 12-16
World-wide load of atmospheric dust thrown into the stratosphere by volcanic eruption since 1850 in comparison to that contributed by human activity. Peaks of volcanic activity may have an effect on world average temperature, as shown in the estimates on right side of graph. [After J. M. Mitchell, "Pollution as a Cause of the Global Temperature Fluctuation," in *Global Aspects of Pollution*. Copyright 1970 by Springer-Verlag New York, Inc.]

Broecker, a geochemist at Columbia University, who thinks that the Earth is in one of its frequent cooling periods (we have been in one since about 1940) that will bottom out in a few years. That cooling up to now had more than compensated for any warming by the additional carbon dioxide we have been pumping into the atmosphere. As the Earth moves again into one of its natural warming cycles in the next decades, Broecker suggests, the increasing carbon dioxide effect will add to it and may drive the global temperature higher than it has been in the last 1000 years.

But these kinds of calculations are subject to many uncertainties. One of the factors that is most uncertain is the role of dust. These tiny particles high in the stratosphere may reflect much sunlight away from the Earth and so decrease the amount of available radiant energy that warms the surface. The amount of man-made dust has become measurable, but at present is small compared to that of volcanic dust from major eruptions (see Fig. 12-16). The Earth's atmosphere, at least in historic times, has quickly recovered from a few relatively large eruptions as rainfall precipitated out the dust. It is possible, however, that an exceptionally long

string of big eruptions, such as those geologists know of in the past, could have an important long-term cooling effect. The injection of much additional dust by industrial and agricultural activities over the next decades could also have an effect.

The issue is important because an increase in the average temperature of only a few degrees could lead to the melting of glacial ice, a rise in sea level, and flooding of coastal regions. Too important to be left to calculations that depend upon current uncertainties, levels of carbon dioxide and dust continue to be monitored by research laboratories so that we may better predict what will happen in the future.

USING LAND WITH GEOLOGICAL FORESIGHT

Life is not all hazards. Part of our concern for the environment stems from feelings that we may not be making the most sensible decisions about our use of land. A geologist can foresee the unhappy consequences of scalping a hillslope of soft, potentially waterlogged formations and building many small homes on the resulting unstable tract. The location of highways, dams and reservoirs, strip and underground mines, large-scale tract housing, and many other enterprises is best not left to chance development, for the costs of unwise choices are too often borne by the community as a whole. Though zoning regulations on building are traditional in many urban areas, they rarely take geological realities into account.

Any construction has to be firm on its foundations, but that is only one aspect of the problem. Builders have to take into account what will happen to the foundations if water from many septic tanks waterlogs the soil. Underground piping of gas, water, and sewage may be affected by slumping, landslides, or earthquakes. Engineering in areas of permafrost requires special precautions, as builders of the Alaska pipeline found. Discharge of sewage from septic tanks may find its way into subsurface water supplies, contaminating them with dissolved chemical substances. Garbage disposal is an increasing problem as communities move against open dumps and uncontained burning of trash. One response, spreading the garbage and covering it with soil as sanitary landfill, may also result in groundwater contamination if the proper site is not chosen. The formations below the landfill should be sufficiently impermeable to prevent downward seepage into the water table.

The underground disposal of radioactive waste, mainly of high-level material from nuclear reactors, but also from the increasing amount of low-level radioactive garbage from hospitals and laboratories, is fast becoming one of the most important issues in waste disposal. It is a public issue that will be crucial to any large expansion of nuclear power plants. In particular, it is worrisome for the planned development of fast breeder reactors, which produce the element plutonium. A major component of atomic bombs, plutonium is also one of the most toxic substances known. As little as a few thousandths of a gram (a few hundred-thousandths of an ounce) is enough to kill a person.

Land-use planning may have to take larger regions of the land into account. Is it wise, for example, to plan for the urbanization of an area known to be the recharge of an underground aquifer that supplies drinking water to the population? Another question is one of surface-water storage. There is always the temptation to drain marshes and swamps and build on the reclaimed land, but there is usually little realization that such places are important storage depots for water (see Chapter 6). Once the wetlands are drained and paved, the area is much more subject to flash flooding: because there is no opportunity for the water to soak into the ground, it runs off immediately.

There are many other choices to be made that involve evaluations of the suitability of land for agriculture, recreation, or transportation. Once the suitability of a given piece of land is determined, we must still face the priority problem: we must determine whether one use of the land is more important than another. Those priorities, such as designating land for recreation rather than building development, are socially and politically determined, but the choices among the alternatives have to be illuminated by geological knowledge. If we are to live with development and utilization of land and resources for different purposes, it ought to be based on planning that is as intelligent as possible. The geological contribution is an understanding of how all contemporary surface processes are related, and how the crust of the Earth beneath has been patterned by past geological events.

SUMMARY

1. The origin of life on Earth came early in the planet's history as a response to the reducing composition of the primitive atmosphere. Energy, probably as ultraviolet radiation, produced small to medium-size organic molecules, such as amino acids, which then grew to larger sizes. Ultimately, the molecules became extremely complex and evolved into true cells.

2. The oldest fossils are primitive cells of Precambrian bacteria and algae found in chert beds. The oldest known are 3.2 billion years. By 2 billion years ago, algal life was well established. By the beginning of the Cambrian period, higher forms of life had evolved and shelled organisms started to provide a good geologic record of evolution.

3. Atmospheric oxygen started to evolve as a result of the development of photosynthesis by early single-celled plants; during the Precambrian, it gradually accumulated to levels close to that of today. Our oxygen supply is now so great that there is no cause for fear that it will be depleted.

4. It is likely that life exists elsewhere in the universe. No life has been found on the Moon, and so far we have not found it on Mars.

5. Environmental hazards—local or global—may be primarily esthetic, or they may be related to problems of health or safety. Medical geology relates levels of potentially harmful substances, such as lead or mercury, to sources of pollution, to dispersal in the environment, and to rates of removal of pollutants by sedimentation.

6. Global environmental problems are illustrated by carbon dioxide, which has been increasing in the atmosphere as a result of burning fossil fuels. Much of the increase has been absorbed by the oceans. The small increase in temperature expected to be produced by the carbon dioxide increase will probably be balanced by increased cloudiness, so the world's climate will not be significantly affected.

7. Intelligent decisions on the use of land in urban and rural areas for various purposes depend on a knowledge of geological processes and the local geological situation.

EXERCISES

1. Construct a table showing the ranges of temperature, pressure, and atmospheric composition that make life possible in the form that we know it on Earth. Which, if any, of the other planets might satisfy all of the conditions?

2. Suggest the probable changes in the composition of the Earth's atmosphere in the next several thousand years if all photosynthesis were to stop suddenly today.

3. If you were part of a team of scientists planning a hypothetical manned landing on Mars, what sorts of things would you ask the astronauts to look for as evidence of life of any kind on the surface? What kinds of organic molecules would you presume to be evidence of life?

4. An unsubstantiated report suggested that very high amounts of aluminum in the diet might be harmful to health. From what you know of geochemical and environmental cycles, as well as your knowledge of common aluminum products, suggest possible routes by which people might be subject to unusually high aluminum intake.

5. If you were the mayor of a coastal city, how might you react to a report that some engineers wanted to melt the polar ice caps to produce large quantities of fresh water?

6. A land developer would like to build many houses on a shoreline strip of low-lying coastal marsh below bluffs of relatively unconsolidated shales and sandstones 100 meters high. What geological reasons can you think of that would make you argue against such a development?

BIBLIOGRAPHY

Laporte, L. F., *The Earth and Human Affairs,* San Francisco, Canfield Press, 1972.

Goldwater, L. J., "Mercury in the Environment." *Scientific American,* May 1971. (Offprint No. 1221.)

McHarg, I. L., *Design with Nature.* New York: Natural History Press, 1969. (Also issued in paperback by Doubleday/Natural History Press.)

Oparin, A. I., *The Origin of Life.* New York: Macmillan, 1938. (Reprinted in paperback by Dover Publications, Inc., New York, 1953.)

Shklovski, I. S., and C. Sagan, *Intelligent Life in the Universe.* New York: Holden-Day, Inc., 1966. (Reprinted in paperback by Dell Pub. Co. (Delta), New York.)

Singer, S. F., *Global Effects of Environmental Pollution.* New York: Springer-Verlag, 1970.

Wald, G., "The Origin of Life." *Scientific American,* August 1944. (Offprint No. 47.)

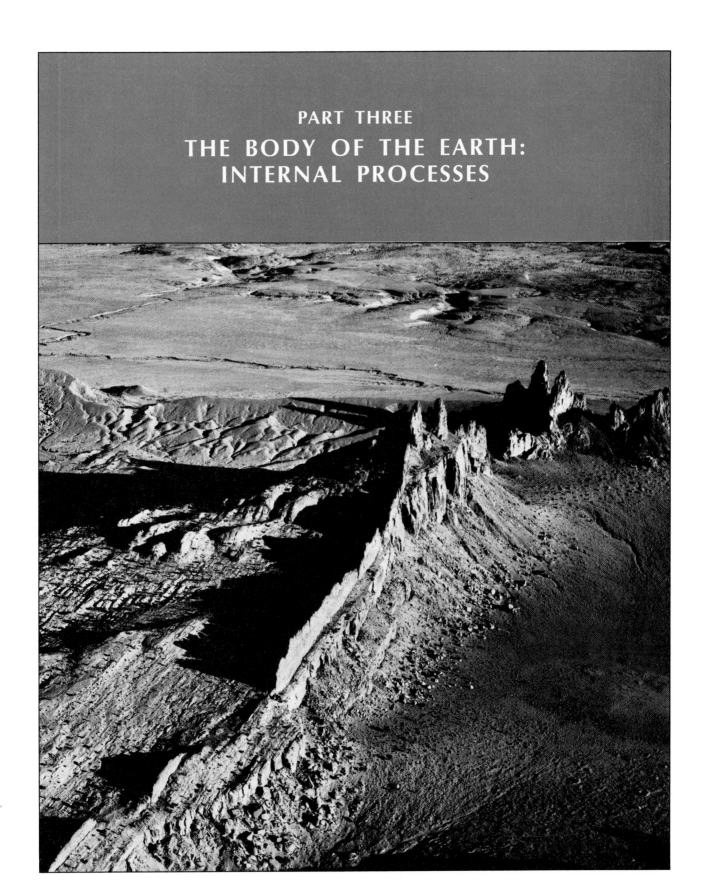

PART THREE
THE BODY OF THE EARTH:
INTERNAL PROCESSES

The materials that make up the atmosphere, the ocean, and the rocky skin of the Earth, and the forces that deform the outermost layers, have their origin in the deeper interior. The internal heat of the Earth provided the energy that led to the formation of plates and their embedded continents, and it provides the energy that keeps the plates moving. These deep-seated forces are so powerful as to cause earthquakes and volcanic eruptions and to form deep-sea trenches, geosynclines, and mountain belts, mainly in association with plate boundaries. The geologist can only infer the properties of the deep interior, using as clues the nature of plate motions, the materials brought up by volcanoes, and physical measurements of such phenomena as heat flow, variations in the magnetic field and gravity, and the travel times of seismic waves. Man's first explorations of other planets will enable him to test his theories of Earth's evolution in the perspective of other bodies that have evolved differently.

13

THE INTERNAL HEAT OF THE EARTH

Earth's internal engine is driven by radioactively generated heat and heat left over from the differentiation that took place early in the planet's history. The work done by the engine registers on the surface in the form of plate motions, earthquakes, mountain-making, and volcanic eruptions. In fact, almost all of geology is ultimately related to Earth's internal heat.

Three hundred years ago the English physicist and chemist Robert Boyle wrote on the nature of terrestrial heat with a prescience that was truly remarkable. In a recent historical review the following quote was reprinted from Boyle's book *Of the Temperature of the Subterraneal Regions as to Heat and Cold:*

"... it seems probable to me, that in these yet inpenetrated Bowells of the Earth, there are great store-houses of either actual Fires, or places considerably Hot, or, (in some Regions) of both; from which Reconditories (if I may so call them) or magazines of hypogeall heat, that quality is communicated, especially by Subterraneall Channells, Clefts, Fibres or other Conveyances, to the less deep parts of Earth, either by a propagation of heat through the substance of the interposed part of the Soil . . . Or else, (which is perhaps the most usuall way,) by sending upwards hot minerall Exhalations and Steams."

Boyle anticipated many of the ideas we will take up in this chapter—for example, the temperature increase with depth caused by internal heat sources and the transfer of heat to the surface by conduction and the motion of hot matter.

The evidence of Earth's internal thermal energy is everywhere. Boyle cited volcanoes, hot springs, and the elevated temperatures in mines and boreholes to document the flow of heat from the interior to the surface. Today we would add such examples as global plate motions, earthquake activity, and the uplift of mountains, all of which represent mechanical work whose ultimate source of energy is the heat in the interior.

Despite these ubiquitous manifestations of internal heat, we cannot positively reconstruct Earth's thermal history by working backward in time from present-day observational data. It would be like trying to write a history of civilization on the basis of what is in today's newspaper. An infinite number of thermal histories could have caused our planet to evolve to its present state. Nevertheless, we can make plausible models by invoking as always our general knowledge of the Earth and the other planets and making the best use of such data as that gained from studies of heat flow, radioactivity, the ability of rocks to transmit heat, rheological (flowage) properties of heated rock, and travel times of seismic waves. We have no guarantee that these models correspond to anything that happened, but they do provide insight about the

Figure 13-1
Geothermal power plant at The Geysers, Sonoma County, California. Heat from
the interior converts water to steam, which is piped through turbines to generate
81,000 kilowatts of electrical power. [From U.S. Geological Survey.]

present thermal state of Earth as well as its possible history.

Before we consider the source of Earth's internal heat and how this heat is transferred to the surface, we give a brief overview of the thermal history of the Earth, summarized from Chapter 1.

HEAT PRODUCTION AND TRANSFER IN THE EARTH

Heat Sources. Radioactivity and the conversion of gravitational to thermal energy are thought to be the major sources of internal heat. The processes of planetary accretion and adiabatic compression warmed the interior, and Earth started on its evolutionary course about 4.7 billion years ago with an initial temperature that may have been somewhere near 1000°C. Radioactivity then took over, and the internal temperature began to rise. Core-mantle separation was triggered perhaps 4 or 4.5 billion years ago, when the temperature rose to the melting point of iron. The sinking of vast drops of iron to the core would have liberated some 2×10^{37} ergs of gravitational energy in the form of heat. This source of heat was great enough to produce

extensive melting and reorganization, resulting in a differentiated Earth, zoned into core, mantle, and crust.

The principal types of rocks that make up the Earth's crust are granites and basalts. Seismologists and petrologists tell us (Chapters 14, 15, and 17) that peridotite is an excellent candidate for the major constituent of the mantle. The heat produced in these rocks by the radioactive disintegration of uranium, thorium, and the radioactive species of potassium can be determined in the laboratory. Table 13-1 summarizes the results. Because the radioactive elements like uranium have become concentrated in granite as a by-product of Earth's early differentiation, this common rock leads in radioactive heat production.

Within each gram of granite about 300 ergs of thermal energy is produced per year. It is easy to see by multiplying this number by 2.7×10^{25} grams—the number of grams of granite in a hypothetical spherical shell 20 kilometers thick and of the same diameter as Earth—that some 10^{28} ergs of thermal energy can be produced by an outer layer of granite only 20 kilometers thick. This is equal to the total heat reaching the Earth's surface each year as determined by measurements. It is about 1000 times more than

One calorie (cal) of heat will raise the temperature of one gram of water by 1°C. One cal = 4.18×10^7 ergs. One μcal = 10^{-6} cal. A megaton nuclear explosion releases 4×10^{22} ergs.

the energy released each year in earthquakes, and it is about 250,000 times more than the energy of a 1-megaton nuclear explosion! This simple calculation not only demonstrates the importance of radioactivity as a present-day heat-producing agent but also gives some measure of the total volume of granite in the Earth's crust, for a layer much more than 10 to 20 kilometers (6 to 12 miles) thick would generate more heat than that observed. We will see that much of the heat flowing out of the continents originates in the radioactivity of near-surface granitic rocks, whereas heat flow from the sea floor, where there is no granite, has a deeper source.

Heat Flow by Conduction. Heat is energy in transit. It may seem obvious that heat flows from regions of high temperature to regions of low temperature—or in the example of our planet, from the interior to the surface. Not so obvious is the mechanism of heat flow or the rate at which it occurs. Heat energy in a solid exists as the vibration of atoms. The intensity of the vibrations determines **temperature.** Heat is **conducted** when the thermally agitated atoms and molecules jostle one another, thus mechanically transferring the vibrational motion from the hot region to the cool one (Fig. 13-2).

The quantity of heat transferred per unit time between two points is proportional to the *temperature difference* per unit distance and to the property called **thermal conductivity,** which differs for each substance and is a measure of its ability to conduct heat. Rock is a very poor heat conductor: it has a very small thermal conductivity. To transfer heat through only 10 meters (30 feet) of rock takes about three years, which is why underground pipes don't freeze and why underground vaults maintain nearly constant temperature despite large seasonal temperature fluctuations at the surface. A lava flow 100 meters (300 feet) thick would take about 300 years to cool. Heat entering one side of a plate of rock

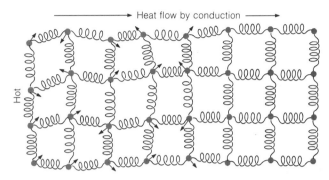

Figure 13-2
Schematic representation of heat flow by conduction through a solid. Interatomic forces that bind atoms to each other are indicated by springs. Heat applied at the left induces thermal agitation of the atoms. Heat is conducted when the vibrations gradually spread to the right.

400 kilometers (250 miles) thick would take about 5 billion years to flow out the other side. In other words, if the Earth were to have cooled by conduction only, heat from depths greater than about 400 kilometers would not yet have reached the surface!

When a substance is so hot that it begins to glow, like a red-hot poker, heat can be transferred by radiation, most of which is emitted in the near infra-red and visible region of the spectrum. This **radiative transfer** can be a more efficient process than conduction in some materials, but the minerals in Earth's interior are relatively opaque, reducing the efficiency of heat loss by this means, so that it is probably less important than conduction. There is no question that heat conduction must be an important agent of heat transfer in the interior, but it may be overshadowed by convection.

Uranium is one of the heaviest elements, yet it became concentrated in the outermost layers of the Earth instead of sinking to the core. This is an example of how chemical affinity can be important as well as gravity in determining where elements end up. Uranium has a strong attraction for oxygen, which is most abundant in the crust. Oxygen migrates upward because it forms lightweight and easily meltable compounds with calcium, sodium, potassium, aluminum, and silicon.

Beer does not freeze in Moscow "in cellars that were not above 12 or 14 foot deep" (Robert Boyle, 1671).

Table 13-1
Radioactive heat production in common igneous rocks.

Kind of rock	Amount of radioactive element in rock (parts per million)			Amount of heat produced (ergs/gram/year)
	Uranium	Thorium	Potassium	
Granite	4	13	4	300
Basalt	0.5	2	1.5	50
Peridotite	0.02	0.06	0.02	1

Figure 13-4
Convection in a coffee cup. A thin layer of white dust on the surface shows a cellular pattern that marks regions of rising columns of hot fluid. Dark lines mark regions where the spreading, cooled liquid descends into the body of the fluid. [Photo by V. J. Schaeffer, State University of New York, Albany.]

Figure 13-3
A familiar example of convection is seen when water is heated in a coffee pot.

The silicon compound "Silly Putty" illustrates how a solid can flow over long periods. One can bounce it like a ball or break it with a sudden blow, but a ball of Silly Putty will flow into a pancake shape under its own weight if left on a table overnight.

Lead weight placed on top of wax

Many hours or days later, lead sinks into the viscous material

Figure 13-5
Materials can behave as solids over short times and as viscous fluids over long intervals. Cold wax is a solid, but a lead ball placed on top of the wax slowly sinks into the interior in a few hours or days, as if the wax were a viscous fluid. Earth's mantle is supposed to show this dual behavior, permitting slow convection to occur.

Heat Flow by Convection. The phenomenon called **convection** (Fig. 13-3) is rather common. One can see it happening in a cooling cup of coffee (Fig. 13-4) or in a rapidly heating kettle of water. Because liquids conduct heat poorly, a kettle of water would take a long time to heat to the boiling point if convection did not distribute the heat rapidly. Convection is at work when a chimney draws, or when warm tobacco smoke rises, or when cumulus clouds form on a hot day. All of these examples of convection are governed by the fact that a heated fluid, either liquid or gas, expands and rises because it becomes less dense than the surrounding cooler and heavier material. Thus instead of heat being transferred slowly by conduction, it is transported more rapidly upward by the moving heated material. Colder material flows in to take the place of the rising fluid, is in turn heated, and rises to continue the cycle. The regular flow circuit of rising warm fluid and sinking cold fluid shown in Figure 13-3 is called a **convection cell.**

Up to now we have been discussing convection as a phenomenon of fluids, but under certain conditions solids can also "flow" (Fig. 13-5). Over short terms, like seconds to years, the Earth's mantle behaves as a rigid solid, transmitting seismic waves efficiently and responding elastically to the tidal pull of the Moon. But when stresses are applied over millions of years, the mantle is weak, and we will see direct evidence for this when we discuss "floating" mountains in Chapters 17 and 19. Thus under long-enduring conditions of high pressure and temperature, the mantle "creeps" and behaves as an extremely viscous substance, so that convection is indeed a possibility.

Now for the key question—one that had been debated by geophysicists for years. Is convection an important process of heat transfer within the Earth? Is convection occurring at the present time or has it occurred at any time in the past? The debate hinged on the numerical values of the factors that inhibit and foster convection (see Box 13-1). Since most of these quantities were unknown for the conditions of the mantle and could only be estimated indirectly, it was difficult to resolve the debate on this basis. With the discovery of sea-floor spreading and plate tectonics, the surface manifestations of convection have, in a sense, been directly detected, although the flow pattern in the mantle is still unknown (Fig. 13-6). The rising hot matter under mid-ocean ridges builds new lithosphere, which cools as it spreads away, eventually to sink back into the mantle where it is resorbed. This *is* convective transport, in that heat is delivered from the interior to the surface by the motion of matter. The process is enormously more complicated than is indicated by the simple convection cells shown in Figure 13-3. It involves melting, upwelling, solidification, horizontal movement, sinking, and resorption. The motion may be jerky as a result of sticking and slipping at plate boundaries.

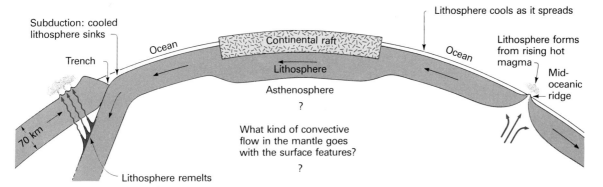

Figure 13-6
The motion of plates, spreading from mid-ocean ridges and sinking in subduction zones, is the surface manifestation of convection currents in the interior. The nature of the flow in the interior is uncertain.

For most geophysicists the debate over convection no longer concerns its existence as much as its scale and periodicity. Does convection involve the entire mantle or only the upper few hundred kilometers? Is it continuous—that is, repetitive, cycle after cycle—or transient in nature, occurring once every few hundred million years when the internal temperature builds up to a critical value? We don't know the answers, but some possible models will be discussed later in this chapter. In any case, convection in connection with the creation and spreading of the sea floor is an important mechanism for the transfer of heat from the mantle under the ocean.

The British geologist Arthur Holmes was among the first to propose convection as the driving mechanism of continental drift. When he did so in the 1930's, Holmes was 30 years ahead of his time, because corroboration had to wait for the extensive exploration of the sea floor that began after World War II and the massive gathering of data that led to the concept of sea-floor spreading.

THERMAL STATE OF THE INTERIOR

Heat Flow Observations. Except for the heat received from the Sun, the heat flow from the interior is the most important terrestrial energy source. About 2×10^{20} calories, or 10^{28} ergs, of energy per year reaches the surface from the interior. This averages out to 1.5 microcalories (μcal) per square centimeter of surface area per second. This exceeds by a factor of about 1000 the annual energy release of earthquakes and by a factor of about 10 all of the energy used by man. It is more than a thousand times the energy required to lift the Rocky Mountains by 1 centimeter (0.4 inch). Although internal heat energy is more than enough to raise mountains and make earthquakes, it is a puny amount compared to the energy received from the Sun. So far as controlling climate is concerned, it is the Sun, delivering five thousand times the energy from the interior, that is the significant factor. Ultimately both solar and internal heat are radiated into space. Solar heat has its geological conse-

---

Box 13-1   Convection

Lord Rayleigh, one of the great English physicists of the last century, studied the conditions under which convection would take place. He found that a fluid placed between a hot lower surface and a cool upper surface, as in Figure 13-3, would convect when certain conditions were met. Convection is fostered by a large temperature difference and a high **coefficient of thermal expansion**—a measure of how much a material expands when its temperature is raised. Because the expanded material is lighter, it tends to rise, displacing the colder, heavier material, which sinks. Increasing the distance between the hot and cold boundaries also encourages convection. Convection is inhibited by **viscosity**—the measure of a fluid's resistance to flow—and by a high thermal conductivity, which would make heat transfer by conduction more efficient, and convection, in a sense, less "necessary."

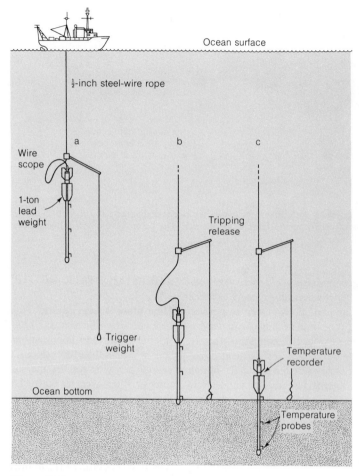

Ocean surface

½-inch steel-wire rope

Wire
scope

1-ton
lead
weight

a   b   c

Tripping
release

Trigger
weight

Temperature
recorder

Ocean bottom

Temperature
probes

Figure 13-7
Heat flowing out of the sea floor is measured by plunging a core tube into
the sediments. Thermometers on the side of the tube record the temperature
increase with depth, and the thermal conductivity of the sediments is measured when the core is retrieved. The product gives the heat flow.

An example of a heat-flow measurement: At one place in the Rocky
Mountains, the temperature increases
with depth by 25°C in 1 km (10^5 cm).
The conductivity of the rock, measured from a sample brought to the
laboratory, was 0.008 cal/cm·sec·
deg. The heat flow is given by the
product

$$\frac{25°C}{10^5 \text{ cm}} \times \frac{0.008 \text{ cal}}{\text{cm·sec·deg}}$$

$$= 2 \times 10^{-6} \text{ cal/cm}^2\text{·sec}$$

quences, however, in "driving" the atmosphere
and hydrosphere, the chief agents of erosion. In
a real sense, the Earth's internal heat engine
builds mountains, and its external heat engine,
the Sun, destroys them.

Several thousand measurements of heat flow
have been made on land and on the sea floor.
One obtains a heat flow value by first measuring
the rate of increase of temperature with depth in
the Earth (the temperature gradient). This value
multiplied by the thermal conductivity of the
rock gives the outward heat flow per unit area
and per unit time. Thermometers inserted in
boreholes measure the temperature increase with
depth. Sea-floor measurements of heat flow are

more plentiful, not only because the oceans
cover more area, but also because they are easier
to perform. Because temperatures at the land
surface undergo both diurnal (daily) and seasonal variations, deep holes are needed to remove the perturbations introduced by these
effects and by flowing groundwater, which may
cool or heat the rocks abnormally. The ocean
shields the sea floor from these effects, and this
makes it possible to obtain accurate temperature
gradients in holes only a few meters deep. Drilling is unnecessary, since the deep-sea mud can
be easily penetrated by the temperature probe as
it falls into the sea bottom under its own weight
(see Fig. 13-7).

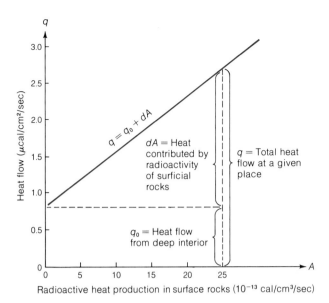

Figure 13-8
According to R. F. Roy, D. D. Blackwell, and F. Birch, heat reaching the surface includes a contribution from the higher radioactivity of surface rocks added to the heat flowing out of the deeper interior. By plotting the heat flow q, measured at many places in a region, against the radioactive heat production A of surficial rocks at each place of measurement, the two contributions can be disentangled. The intercept of the curve gives q_0 the amount of "deep heat," and the slope of the line gives d, the thickness of the surficial zone of high radioactivity.

Continental Heat Flow. The continental crust is mostly granite in the uppermost portion, and granite is radioactively the "hottest" rock, as Table 13-1 shows. We should expect, therefore, that some of the heat flowing from the continents originates in the granitic layer, but not all of it. The main problem for the specialists in the field is to determine the heat budget—that is, to assess how much heat originates in the granite, how much comes from the deeper mantle, and how this all relates to the geologic history of a region.

Geophysicists have recently developed a remarkably simple way to unscramble the diverse factors. They took all of the North American continental data, separated the heat-flow values according to geological province, and for each province plotted heat flow against the radioactive heat production of the surface rocks measured in microcalories per cubic centimeter per second. For each province, the data show a straight-line fit, and all the straight lines are nearly parallel but have different intercepts (Fig. 13-8). The straight lines represent the equation

or

$$q = q_0 + d \times A$$

The intercept of the straight line, q_0, is the heat originating in the deeper crust and underlying mantle. The slope of the line is d, the thickness of the radioactively "hot" surficial granitic layer. The value of d measured from the slope of the line turns out to be about 10 kilometers (6 miles), which shows the remarkable extent to which differentiation has concentrated these radioactive elements at the top of the crust. The value of q_0 for the east-central United States is about $0.7 \ \mu\mathrm{cal}/\mathrm{cm}^2/\mathrm{sec}$, which is to be compared with the average heat flow reaching the surface in this region of $1.0 \ \mu\mathrm{cal}/\mathrm{cm}^2/\mathrm{sec}$. We see that 30 percent of the heat flux originates in the granitic layer of this geologically old province and 70 percent comes from below. Because of the low radioactivity of the basalts and peridotites underlying the granitic layer in the lithosphere, most of this deep heat must be intro-

surface heat flow	=	deep heat	+	depth of granite	×	granitic heat production
(μcal/cm^2/sec)		(μcal/cm^2/sec)		(cm)		(μcal/cm^3/sec)

duced from below the lithosphere—that is, from regions deeper than about 100 kilometers. The quantity q_0 could include heat delivered by convection in the mantle.

The average surface heat flow, q, for the Basin and Range province (Arizona, New Mexico, Utah, and Nevada) is about $2 \, \mu\text{cal/cm}^2/\text{sec}$, of which $1.4 \, \mu\text{cal/cm/sec}$ is contributed by deep heat, q_0. Here too, in this geologically young and active region, some 70 percent of the heat has a deep source. But twice as much deep heat is being delivered here as in the geologically inactive east-central part of the country. Consequently, some geologists believe that the rising plume of a convection current lies under the Basin and Range province, which would account for such observations as the excess heat flux, the thin crust, which shows evidence of recent fracturing, the recent volcanism, and the earthquake activity. Does this mean that California will one day split from the rest of the country, with an ocean basin opening somewhere in Utah and New Mexico? At the rate of divergence—a few centimeters per year—we need not worry about the political consequences.

The Sierra Nevada, near the California-Nevada boundary, shows a surprisingly small deep-heat flux, $q_0 = 0.4 \, \mu\text{cal/cm}^2/\text{sec}$, about half the total heat flow for this mountain region. Some geophysicists have speculated that the Sierra Nevada block, because of an ancient plate collision, is underthrust by an old and still cool plate, reducing the flow of deep heat (Fig. 13-9).

The first two examples seem typical of the rest of this planet: low heat flow ($\sim 1 \, \mu\text{cal/cm}^2/\text{sec}$) in geologically old and inactive areas, such as the large area of exposed Precambrian rocks in central and eastern Canada; high heat flow ($\sim 2 \, \mu\text{cal/cm}^2/\text{sec}$) in regions of more recent mountain-building or volcanism, such as the Alps or the western United States. Special cases like the Sierra Nevada, however, require unique explanations.* In each region the highly radioactive rocks at the top of the continental crust account for less than 50 percent of the total outward flow of heat. The mantle contributes the remainder, the amount being about twice as much in regions of recent orogeny (mountain-building) and volcanism than in geologically old and stable provinces. Combining all of the regions, the average heat

High heat flow   Low heat flow

Figure 13-9
To account for the small heat flow found in the Sierra Nevada Mountains, K. E. Torrance and D. L. Turcotte propose that because of an ancient plate collision this block rests on an old and still cool plate, reducing the heat flow from the deep interior.

---

*Heat flow is also low in regions of rapid sedimentation, such as along the Gulf Coast of the United States. The sediments blanket the heat from the interior, in effect temporarily insulating the surface from the heat sources below.

flow is about $1.5 \, \mu\text{cal/cm}^2/\text{sec}$ for the continents.

The separation of continental heat flow into contributions from near-surface granites and deeper mantle sources and the identification of different geological provinces as "hot" or "cold" are new approaches to the understanding of intracontinental geology that are just beginning to be used.

Heat Flow from the Sea Floor. The continents may be likened to rafts embedded in large plates. The rafts have grown through geological time, and the oldest rocks found on Earth have been preserved on continents for nearly 4 billion years. Continents are difficult to destroy; they may be deformed, but they survive plate convergence because they are light and keep floating. In marked contrast, the sea floor is created at mid-ocean ridges and destroyed in subduction zones on a time scale of 100 to 200 million years. Furthermore, sea-floor crust and lithosphere are made of rocks like basalts and peridotites, which show far less radioactivity than the continental granites. From these considerations we should expect the sea floor and continents to show completely different heat-flow characteristics. Yet the average heat flow from the sea floor does not differ significantly from the average heat flow from the continents. When the first results emerged in the early 1950's, they produced quite a shock in geophysical circles. Could this puzzle be explained?

Like the heat-flow observations made on land, the oceanic observations show a pattern, and from them a correlation with the geology of the sea floor has been found. Oceanographers tell us that although there is some variability in the observations, the average heat flow for the major oceanic provinces is as follows: ocean ridges, >2; ocean basins, ~ 1.3; ocean trenches, $<1.0 \, \mu\text{cal/cm}^2/\text{sec}$. The reader should be able to anticipate the explanation of the decrease in heat flow from ridge crest to ocean basin to deep-sea trench. Mid-ocean ridges sit atop the rising plume of hot rock and magma that carries heat from the deeper mantle. This "mush" cools, solidifies, and becomes attached to the oceanic lithosphere. As the lithospheric plate spreads away from the ridge, it loses its heat by conduction to the sea floor and gradually cools (Fig. 13-10). For this reason, heat flow should decrease with the age of the sea floor, hence with distance from a mid-ocean ridge. The oldest parts of the sea floor should have the lowest heat flow, and these parts should be found farthest from ridges and closest to deep-sea trenches,

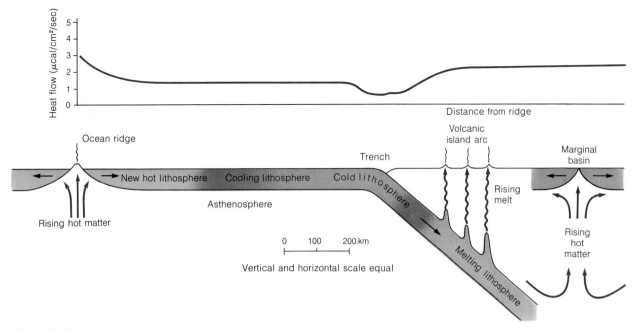

Figure 13-10

The pattern of heat flowing out of the sea floor. High values are observed over mid-ocean ridges. As the sea floor spreads and cools, less heat reaches the surface. On the side of deep-sea trenches where the lithosphere plunges into the asthenosphere, rising magma from the melting lithosphere produces higher heat-flow values. A small region of secondary spreading may develop in a marginal basin behind the subduction zone. An example is the Sea of Japan, which separates the Japanese Island Arc from the Asian continent.

where the cold slabs sink back into the mantle.

Oceanic heat flow is thus dominated by the process of cooling of the recently created oceanic lithosphere. Geophysicists believe that this process may account for as much as 45 percent of the total heat flow from the Earth, and that this may represent a major mode by which the Earth has cooled. The percolation of sea water into the many fissures associated with mid-ocean ridge spreading zones may serve to dissipate a major portion of the heat of the oceanic lithosphere. Cold water could percolate into the rift zone to depths up to 10 kilometers, extract heat, and return to the sea floor as hot water, enriched in dissolved minerals leached from the rising hot mush. The detection of this *hydrothermal circulation* was a major result of project FAMOUS, the 1974 French-American Mid-Ocean Undersea Study.

We return to the puzzle of the equality of average heat flow for the continents and oceans despite the entirely different thermal regimes. Remember that on the continents some 30 percent of the heat flow originates in the radioactively "hot" granitic crust, which is absent on the sea floor. An early explanation was offered by Sir Edward Bullard, who proposed that the subcrustal rocks of the sea floor contain more radioactivity than their subcontinental counterparts; this would provide a heat source that would compensate for the absence of a heat-producing granite layer on the sea floor. Until the uranium content of such mantle rocks as peridotites can be studied in more detail after being dredged or drilled from the sea floor, this hypothesis remains in the running. Alternatively, we could take the easy way out and explain the phenomenon as a coincidence or as part of some grand scheme of things that still eludes us.

Temperatures in the Earth. The average increase of temperature with depth, as measured in bore holes or mines, is about 2 or 3°C per 100 meters (300 feet). How can we infer temperatures in the Earth at depths greater than those we can reach with a thermometer—that is, below about 8 kilometers (5 miles)? The problem is not an easy one, and the experts need all the help they can get, especially for the lower mantle and core.

Temperatures in the continental crust are fairly well known from measurements of surface heat flow, which can be separated into heat contributions from the radioactive surficial rocks and from the underlying region by means of graphs like the one in Figure 13-8. A knowledge of these two sources of heat is sufficient to fix the temperatures with some assurance for the continental crust. **Geotherms,** or temperature-depth profiles, typical of such geologically old and stable regions as the eastern United States and of

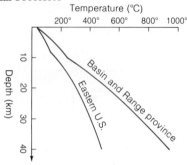

Temperature (°C)

Figure 13-11
Temperature variation with depth in different regions, according to the ideas of R. F. Roy, D. D. Blackwell, and F. Birch. The higher heat flow in the Basin and Range province implies higher temperatures at depth in this young and active region. The temperature rises to almost 1000°C at 40 km. In the geologically older and more stable eastern United States, the temperature reaches only 500°C at this depth.

such young and active regions as the Basin and Range province, are shown in Figure 13-11. The higher heat flow in the tectonically active region shows up in the more rapid increase of temperature with depth. Forty kilometers below the surface, temperature rises to almost 1000°C in the active region. This is close to the point of initial melting of such deep crustal and mantle rocks as basalt and peridotite. In contrast, temperature under the stable region reaches the relatively low value of about 500°C at a depth of 40 kilometers (25 miles). The association of tectonic activity and volcanism with subcrustal temperatures near the melting point, and of long-term geological stability with relatively cool regions of the crust, is an important discovery. For example, it supports the speculative notion that the Basin and Range province may overlie the rising plume of a convection current.

Temperatures in the suboceanic lithosphere are dominated by the process of cooling down from the high temperature of the magma that builds the slab in the first place. Referring again to Figure 13-10, we could make a good guess that the temperature under the ocean would be close to 0°C (the temperature of the bottom water) at the top of the slab, and close to 1200°C (the melting point) at the bottom of the slab, where it is in contact with the partially molten asthenosphere. Where the slab plunges deep into the mantle, we would expect it to warm up gradually to the high temperatures of the material surrounding it.

One of the important tasks of the next generation of geophysicists is to find a method for directly determining the temperature in the deep interior. Until this is done we can only use indirect evidence to speculate on the nature of convection within the Earth. We know that we

can't simply extrapolate the temperature curves for the crust (Fig. 13-11) by straight-line extension all the way to the depth of the Earth's core, at 2900 kilometers (1800 miles), for that would give a temperature of at least 25,000°C, which would mean that most of the Earth would have to be molten. This impossible situation shows once again that the important radioactive elements are concentrated in the outermost layers, and that the rate of temperature increase with depth (temperature gradient) must lessen below this radioactively "hot zone." More efficient heat transfer in the deeper layers will also decrease the temperature gradient so as not to give impossibly high values.

At present all we can do is sketch a possible geotherm, showing temperatures as they might occur all the way down to the center of the Earth (Figure 13-12). In order to "anchor" the geotherm at a few points to keep it from drifting too far from reality, the following data are used:

1. Seismology tells us that the asthenosphere is partially molten. We therefore "fix" the temperature at a depth of 100 km (60 miles) at the **solidus,** or point of incipient melting, which laboratory geologists tell us is about 1100 to 1200°C. This is just about the temperature at which lavas issue from oceanic volcanoes, which provides a nice check.

2. At depths greater than 300 kilometers (200 miles) in the mantle, the temperatures must be below the solidus, since seismic shear waves cannot pass through a partially molten region without being severely attenuated, and this is not observed below the asthenosphere. We use an estimate of the solidus recently inferred from laboratory studies as an upper limit for mantle temperatures below the asthenosphere.

3. The two rapid increases in seismic wave velocities at depths of about 400 and 700 kilometers (250 and 450 miles) are important clues, which we will discuss in Chapter 17 on Seismology. They are caused by a more dense packing of the atoms of a major mineral constituent of the mantle—olivine. The sudden densification, or **phase change,** occurs when critical pressures and temperatures are reached. A few years ago the phase change at 400 kilometers (250 miles) was actually verified in the laboratory when rocks were squeezed and heated to duplicate the pressures and temperatures at these depths. Therefore, we know the pressure and temperature at which the phase change takes place. The conditions for the phase change at

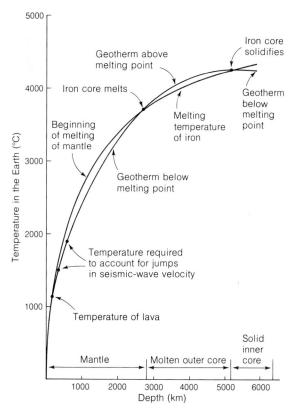

Figure 13-12
A geotherm showing how temperatures may increase with depth from
the surface to the center of the Earth. Temperatures in the central
region may reach 4000° to 4500°C. The geotherm reaches the point
of initial melting in the partially molten asthenosphere; it is below
the melting point throughout most of the mantle, and it exceeds the
melting point in the fluid iron core. [Data from D. L. Anderson, G.
Kennedy, and G. Higgins.]

700 km can be estimated theoretically. Geophysicists recently used seismological data and
new laboratory data to fix the temperatures at
about 1500°C and 1900°C for the depths 400
and 700 kilometers, respectively.

4. We will see in Chapter 17 that the core is
primarily iron, molten in the outer part and
solid in the inner part. Recently a new melting-point curve for iron (Fig. 13-12) has been
used by geochemists to fix temperatures at the
high pressures in the core. The temperature at
the mantle-core boundary must exceed the
melting point of iron to account for the liquid
core, and stay below that of the mantle to account for its solidity. It is an interesting and
useful coincidence that these upper and lower
bounds on temperature are close together at the
mantle-core boundary, fixing the temperature at
about 3700°C. Moreover, the geotherm must
cross over and fall below the iron melting-point

curve at 5100 kilometers (3200 miles) in order to
provide for the solid inner core insisted upon by
the seismologists. This gives a temperature of
about 4300°C. It seems unlikely that the temperature at Earth's center could be much above
this value.

The Tectonic Engine. It is widely accepted
that tectonic phenomena—that is, plate motions,
mountain-building, and earthquakes—are accounted for by internal convection currents.
Many schemes for convective flow have been
advanced. They vary somewhat in scale, some
involving the entire mantle and others limiting
the flow to the upper few hundred kilometers.

Some fascinating calculations have led to a
proposed scheme of convection in which the
flow of matter takes place in the outer several
hundred kilometers of the Earth. The model
explains many of the features summarized ear-

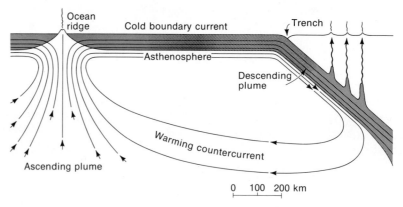

Figure 13-13
Possible convection flow in the upper mantle, according to D. H. Turcotte and E. R. Oxburgh. An ascending hot plume spreads laterally under the ocean ridges; cooling by conduction to the ocean, it solidifies to form a boundary layer, the cold, rigid lithosphere. The descending cold plume coincides with the sinking lithosphere of the subduction zone.

lier in Figure 13-10; these features are repeated in Figure 13-13, with the convective flow lines superimposed. An ascending hot plume spreads laterally, cools by conduction to the ocean and solidifies to form a cold, brittle boundary layer—the lithosphere. A descending cold plume, the subducted lithosphere, begins the return flow; the cycle of convection is completed by a counter-current several hundred kilometers below the surface, which heats up and rises again. Buoyancy forces of the light, hot ascending plume and of the heavy, cold descending plume drive the flow. The energy source is radioactivity plus perhaps some of the original heat left over from the early years of the planet. The

velocity of the flow, which is calculated for the model, agrees with the sea-floor spreading rates, and the heat coming out of the surface matches the observational data quite well. The results encourage us to believe that the men who suggested these ideas may be on the right track in the search for the mechanism that makes the tectonic engine run.

The question of the driving force behind plate tectonics has become so important that it is the basis of a new international scientific program called The Geodynamics Project. Many of the questions posed in this chapter will be attacked in a concerted, multinational research effort over the next decade.

SUMMARY

1. The internal heat of the Earth is derived from the radioactivity of uranium, thorium, and potassium. Heat left over from the early years of the planet may be an additional source.

2. Much of the internal heat reaches the surface by convective flow in the mantle; the large-scale surface manifestation of this process is the spreading sea floor. New lithosphere created from rising hot rock and magma cools as it spreads, eventually to sink back into the mantle, where it remelts. Measurements of high heat flow over mid-ocean ridges and low heat flow over deep-sea trenches are consistent with this picture. The creation of new sea floor is an important mechanism by which the Earth gets rid of its internal heat.

3. Heat flow on the continents correlates with regional geology—low values in old stable regions and high values in regions of recent rifting, orogeny, and volcanism.

4. Temperatures increase rapidly with depth in the outermost 100 kilometers (60 miles) of the Earth, reaching the solidus in the asthenosphere (100 to 300 kilometers or 60 to 190 miles). Below 300 kilometers, the geotherm must rise less rapidly or the Earth would be extensively molten. It is everywhere below the solidus until the core is reached. Here the temperature is about 3700°C—above the melting point of iron, as required for a liquid iron outer core. The temperature at the center is about 4000 to 4500°C, according to current views.

EXERCISES

1. Give some "kitchen physics" or common-experience examples of the following concepts. *Example:* Hot tea in a porcelain cup is easier to handle than in a metallic cup because porcelain is a poorer conductor of heat and will less likely burn the hand or the lip.

   a) uses of low-conductivity and high-conductivity materials,

   b) convection,

   c) materials of different viscosity,

   d) work done by heat.

2. Enlarge upon the statement "in a real sense Earth's internal heat builds mountains, and external heat from the Sun destroys them."

3. Almost twice as much heat flows out of the ground in Utah as in Massachusetts. Why?

4. If you were prospecting for geothermal energy, where would you look? If 0.1 percent of the heat reaching the surface from the interior could be used for energy would it represent a significant contribution to the world's needs? How about 0.1 percent of the solar energy reaching the surface?

5. Although the geologist has direct access only to the upper few kilometers of the Earth, he can infer temperatures at greater depths. How?

6. It is widely believed that convection currents in the mantle provide the driving forces for plate motions. What would be the connection between rising, warm convection plumes, sinking cold plumes, and sea-floor spreading and subduction?

7. If the heat flow from the ocean basin floor came solely from the radioactivity of basalt, how thick a layer of basalt would be needed to account for it? (Assume the density of basalt is 3 grams per cubic centimeter, and see Table 13-1 for basaltic heat production.)

BIBLIOGRAPHY

American Geophysical Union, *Terrestrial Heat Flow*. Geophysical Monograph Number 8, American
     Geophysical Union, 1965.
Sclater, J. G., and Jean Francheteau, "The Implications of Terrestrial Heat Flow Observations on
     Current Tectonic and Geochemical Models of the Crust and Upper Mantle of the Earth."
     Geophysical Journal of the Royal Astronomical Society, v. 20, pp. 509–542, 1970.
Turcotte, D. L., and E. R. Oxburgh, "Continental Drift." *Physics Today*, v. 22, pp. 30–39, 1969.

14

FORMATION OF IGNEOUS ROCKS

Localized heat and pressure deep in the Earth cause deep crustal and mantle materials to melt, forming magmas. Magmas crystallize to form igneous rocks of diverse composition as they intrude higher portions of the crust or erupt at the surface. Experimental studies of the crystallization behavior of melts indicate that the compositional diversity of igneous rocks is a result of partial melting of the original material and chemical differentiation. In this way, silicic magmas can be produced from originally mafic melts. Pressure and the presence of water in the melt greatly affect melting temperatures and the formation of partial melts.

The connection between the interior heat of the Earth, volcanoes, and the formation of igneous rocks (those crystallized from a molten state) seems to be straightforward. Simple observation of many volcanoes reveals how cooling and congealing of molten lava produce the rock we call basalt. More than 200 years ago, geologists drew the conclusion that ancient basalts were also of volcanic origin, even though, in many cases, all traces of the volcanoes that produced them had long since vanished. Other volcanoes produce lavas that crystallize to form rocks of different composition, ranging from andesite to rhyolite. Somehow, the composition of the melt varies from place to place, and this determines the composition of the rock (see Fig. 3-21).

GRANITE

It is not easy to demonstrate that granite, one of the commonest of coarsely crystalline materials, is a rock formed by crystallization from a hot, molten mass. It is found in high mountain

chains, such as the Sierra Nevada and the Alps, and in the cores of deeply eroded ancient mountains, such as those of the Scottish highlands, but this in itself is no great clue to its origin. The details of its relations to other rocks, however, were most important clues to James Hutton as he worked in the field in Scotland. He saw cross-cutting relations, in which sedimentary rocks were somehow fractured and invaded by the granite, as if it had been forced into them as a liquid. Even more significant were the mineralogical and textural changes in the sediments bordering the granite, which he inferred were the results of great heat.

Hutton guessed that the granite was formed by molten material rising from great depths. As it rose, it intruded the rocks of the upper part of the crust and cooled slowly to form crystals of quartz, feldspar, mica, and other minerals. The texture, a mosaic of interlocking crystals, could not be confused with the texture of a sandstone consisting of grains of the same minerals. Many of the minerals in granite show sharp crystal faces, and the crystals are interlocked and held

Figure 14-1
Cross-cutting contact of granite (below) with shales and tuffs (above). Bedding dips gently to the right. A small, nearly vertical, light-colored dike is at the right (arrow). Shasta County, California. [Photo by J. P. Albers, U.S. Geological Survey.]

Figure 14-2
Photomicrograph of a thin section of granite in polarized light. The large light crystal at lower left and the dark one above it are microcline, a variety of potassium feldspar. The more homogeneous light- and medium-gray crystals at upper right are quartz. This interlocking mosaic of crystals results from crystallization of a melt. [Photo by A. H. Koschman, U.S. Geological Survey.]

together like the pieces of a jig-saw puzzle. Sandstone, in contrast, consists of grains rounded by abrasion and bound together by a mineral cement between the grains. The minerals of granite are so insoluble in water that it would be hard to conceive of the rock having been precipitated from sea water, like an evaporite, which may have the same kind of crystalline texture. Thus granite, like basalt, came to be recognized as the product of crystallization of a **magma,** a large body of very hot molten rock.

In the second half of the nineteenth century, after the polarizing microscope had been invented and had been used for mineral identification of small crystals in rocks, geologists described the multitude of igneous rocks of the granite family, discovering in them the same range of variations as they saw in the extrusive rocks formed by volcanism. Techniques of chemical analysis, which were well advanced, were joined with microscopic examination and field study to produce a classification scheme of the sort we still use (see Fig. 3-21). The major division of igneous rocks into fine-grained (as typified by basalt) and coarse-grained (as typified by granite) was based on their differing origins. Volcanism gave rise to extrusives, which quickly cooled, at the relatively low temperature of the Earth's surface, to form glasses or fine crystals. Plutonism—the formation of a magma at depth, where temperatures and pressures were higher—gave rise to intrusives, which slowly cooled to form coarse crystals.

The explanations for the variety of compositions of the granite series, from granite to gabbro, were more elusive. Complicating the picture further were the ultramafic intrusives composed of olivine and pyroxene, which have few corresponding extrusives. What accounts for the formation of magmas of such a variety of mineralogical compositions? What temperatures were required for the formation of melts of different kinds? If these temperatures could be estimated, then we might have some idea of how deep in the Earth the magmas formed and crystallized. The effect of pressure might also prove to be important.

CRYSTALLIZATION FROM MELTS

By the early twentieth century, as all the geological data on igneous rocks accumulated, there were still no good answers to detailed questions about the origin of such rocks, either from field

Table 14-1
Chemical analysis of a granite from Cumberland, England.

Element	Formula*	Relative proportion (%)
Silicon	SiO_2	68.55
Aluminum	Al_2O_3	16.21
Ferric iron	Fe_2O_3	2.26
Magnesium	MgO	1.04
Calcium	CaO	2.40
Sodium	Na_2O	4.08
Potassium	K_2O	4.14

*Formulas are conventionally shown as oxides, though the elements are not actually present in this form.

Table 14-2
Mineralogical analysis of a granite from Cumberland, England.

Mineral	Formula	Relative proportion (%)
Quartz	SiO_2	24.4
Feldspar		
Orthoclase	$KAlSi_3O_8$	36.2
Plagioclase	$\begin{cases} NaAlSi_3O_8 \\ CaAl_2Si_2O_8 \end{cases}$	33.6
Mica		
Biotite	$K(Mg,Fe)AlSi_3O_{10}(OH)_2$	5.8

studies or from chemical analyses. These questions about where and how magmas were formed arose at a time when the young science of physical chemistry was maturing. Thermodynamics, the science of heat and energy, was then being applied to problems of crystallization from solutions and melts; by the turn of the century, it began to be applied to geological problems. The new way to approach the problem was by experimentation. Scientists mixed chemicals in the proportions in which they were known to occur in igneous rocks, melted them in high-temperature furnaces, and allowed them to crystallize, observing carefully the temperatures of melting and crystallization and the compositions of the minerals that were formed.

Igneous rocks contain many elements. In addition to the abundant elements—oxygen, silicon, aluminum, iron, sodium, potassium, magnesium, and calcium—there are a host of minor elements. The experimentalists wisely chose not to tackle the terribly complicated natural mixtures immediately but to take a few very simple compositions and to work them out first. One of those is the plagioclase feldspar system, a group of feldspars ranging from albite, a sodium aluminosilicate ($NaAlSi_3O_8$), to anorthite, a calcium aluminosilicate ($CaAl_2Si_2O_8$). Plagioclase is a major mineral component of igneous rocks, and its systematic change of composition is basic to the classification of the range of the intrusives, from granite to gabbro, and the range of extrusives, from rhyolite to basalt. The results of the experiments with plagioclase were most instructive.

The experiments showed that melts of various plagioclase compositions, if allowed to crystallize very slowly, would form crystals through a

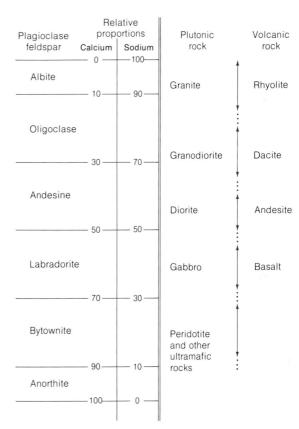

Figure 14-3
Igneous rock types are classified according to the relative proportions of the feldspars albite (sodium plagioclase) and anorthite (calcium plagioclase). The boundaries between rock types are gradual; the divisions between the feldspars are arbitrarily defined.

Box 14-1 Crystallization of Plagioclase Feldspars

The results of many crystallization experiments with melts of compositions corresponding to those of various members of the plagioclase series are shown in the accompanying figure. The chemical composition is shown on the horizontal axis of the graph as the percentage of the two components, albite and anorthite, in a simple mixture of the two. Natural plagioclases are a solid-solution series; that is, there is a continuous range of compositions from one side to the other, the basic crystal structure remaining the same throughout (see Table 3-3). Just as the solid minerals are, the melts of albite and anorthite are completely miscible in all proportions.

Because we are interested in temperatures of crystallization, we have plotted temperature, in degrees centigrade, on the vertical axis. The graph tells us what to expect if a melt of composition X (about 30 percent anorthite), heated to about 1500°C, is allowed to cool slowly. There is no change as the liquid cools until a temperature of about 1370° is reached, at which point the first crystals of plagioclase form. These crystals are very different in composition from the liquid; they turn out to be a little over 70 percent anorthite. As the first crystals form, because the proportion of anorthite to albite being taken out of the melt is much higher than the original composition at X, the liquid be-

comes a little depleted in anorthite and starts to move down the upper curve.

As more crystals grow, they form from a liquid of slightly changed composition, and so are a little less rich in anorthite. In the meantime, the first-formed crystals are no longer in equilibrium with the liquid, because the melt is now more albitic. If crystallization is very slow, these first crystals will continuously react with the changing liquid; and, as new crystals form, the composition of all of the crystals will travel down the lower curve. This process continues—the liquid moving down the upper curve and the solid moving down the lower curve—until, at a temperature of about 1190°C, the last drop of liquid (by now containing only about 5 percent anorthite) forms crystals of the original composition, X. After that, the entire crystalline mass continues to cool without further change. The melt has crystallized into a plagioclase of the same composition as the original melt, but by a complicated route. When a solid plagioclase is melted, it follows exactly the same route in reverse. The first liquid formed is of the same composition as the last drop of liquid in the crystallization process, and liquid and crystals move up their respective curves until the last crystal is melted, when the liquid attains the composition X.

Crystallization diagram for the cooling of a plagioclase feldspar melt. The original melt at composition X_0 (about 30 percent anorthite) cools to a temperature of about 1370°C (X_1), at which point the first crystal of composition C_1 is formed. As successive crystals are formed, the liquid changes in composition to that indicated by point X_2, at which time all crystals have reacted to form crystals of composition C_2, the last liquid forming a crystal with the composition of the original melt. If crystals of composition C_2 are withdrawn at that point, the liquid will change to composition X_3 and the final crystal will be of composition C_3.

complicated path of crystallization (see Box 14-1). The first crystals to form started out with more of the calcium component, anorthite, and slightly depleted the calcium present so that the melt became relatively richer in sodium. As crystallization proceeded, the earlier crystals were gradually transformed to crystals containing relatively more and more sodium, until the final homogeneous mass had the same composition as the original melt. The key to the process was the continuous transformation of the composition of earlier crystals, by a reaction with the remaining melt, to new compositions, so that, at any point in the course of crystallization, all of crystals present would have the same composition.

Figure 14-4
Drawing of a zoned plagioclase crystal formed during the fractional crystallization of a silicate melt in which crystallization was too rapid to permit continuous reaction of already formed crystals with the changing melt composition. As the melt congeals, the layers of the crystal become more albite rich.

MAGMATIC DIFFERENTIATION

When N. L. Bowen published his pathfinding experimental work on feldspars in 1913, he had natural geologic processes very much in mind. He focused on the course of crystallization in situations in which the feldspars did *not* continuously react with the liquid to change their compositions. This would occur, for example, if a magma cooled so rapidly that there was time only for the outer surface of the earlier-formed crystals to react with the changing liquid, so that only the outer rim of each crystal would change composition during the crystallization, each successive layer being covered by another layer more rich in albite. The result of such a process is a mass of **zoned crystals,** which have anorthite-rich interiors and gradually grade to albite-rich material toward their exteriors. The zoning of plagioclase has another implication. If the anorthite-rich cores of the growing crystals are unable to react with the liquid, the liquid will be more albite-enriched than it would be in a slow, continuous reaction. If, for example, at any stage of crystallization, the crystals already formed were to be withdrawn somehow, the solution at that point, already albite-enriched, would behave as though it had just started to crystallize, and the next crystals to form from it would be more albitic. Then, if there were a slow, continuous reaction thereafter, the remaining liquid would ultimately form crystals with an anorthite content much lower than the original liquid would have, had it cooled slowly in a continuous reaction from the outset.

Bowen proposed a theory of **chemical differentiation** based on this idea. If the early

crystals formed deep in the crust in a large opening filled with melt, a **magma chamber,** the crystals might settle to the bottom and thus be withdrawn from further reaction. Another possibility is that structural deformation midway in the crystallization process might squeeze the remaining liquid from the crystal mush into other places, where it would continue to crystallize. Whatever the exact details of the process, **fractional crystallization** of the melt—that is, crystallization in which crystals do not continuously react with the melt—could account for albite-rich plagioclases forming from an originally anorthite-rich melt. Basaltic magmas are anorthite-rich melts, and granites contain albite-rich plagioclases. Magmatic differentiation relates the two in the sense that the basaltic magma is the starting material that gradually differentiates to a more silicic melt by a fractional crystallization process that, if carried far enough, forms granite.

Mafic Minerals. Magmas do not just crystallize to form plagioclase feldspars; they also produce such mafic minerals as olivine, pyroxene, amphibole, and black mica (biotite). Melting-crystallization relations among those minerals are a little more complex, but their order of crystallization can produce differentiation too. In a process in which slow cooling allows all crystals to react completely with the liquid, olivines crystallize first; then, when the liquid reaches a certain point, pyroxene starts to form and all the olivine is converted to pyroxene. In

a

Fractional crystallization

Magma

Crystals form from cooling magma and settle to floor of chamber

Accumulation of crystals formed early in cooling

b

Deformational squeezing out of remaining fluid from crystal mush

Veins and dikes

Magma migrates to a secondary magma chamber where it continues to crystallize

Differentiated mass of early formed crystals forms separate intrusive body

Figure 14-5
Two stages in the evolution of a differentiated magma. In the first stage (a), crystals formed early settle to the floor of the magma chamber. During cooling, structural deformation may squeeze remaining liquid from the chamber and separate the early-formed crystals as a distinct intrusive body (b), while the liquid migrates elsewhere to form veins, dikes, and other magma chambers, where it continues to crystallize.

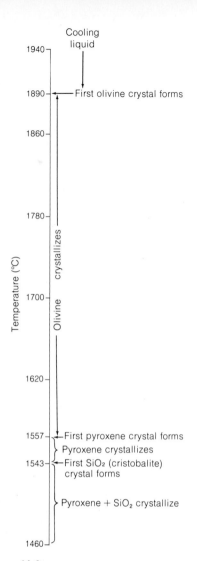

Cooling liquid

First olivine crystal forms

Olivine crystallizes

First pyroxene crystal forms
Pyroxene crystallizes
First SiO$_2$ (cristobalite) crystal forms
Pyroxene + SiO$_2$ crystallize

Temperature (°C)

1940
1890
1860
1780
1700
1620
1557
1543
1460

Figure 14-6
Sequence of events in the crystallization of a cooling liquid of magnesium and silica. This sequence forms one part of the discontinuous reaction series by which different mafic minerals are successively crystallized from a melt.

such a **discontinuous reaction** series, reactions take place between minerals of two definite compositions at a particular temperature (a little over 1550°C for magnesium olivine and pyroxene), rather than over a continuous range of compositions and temperatures, as with the plagioclase series. Just as in the continuous reactions of plagioclase formation, the first-formed crystals of olivine may settle out or become coated by later-formed pyroxene crystals, and so be withdrawn from further reaction. Then the melt becomes enriched in silica and finally crystallizes to form the high-temperature silica mineral cristobalite (or, at lower temperatures, tridymite or quartz).

Facing the city of New York on the west bank of the Hudson River is the Palisades, a massive cliff some 50 miles long and in places more than 1000 feet from top to bottom. The Palisades is a formation of basalt that was intruded almost horizontally into nonmarine sedimentary rocks as a melt. The variation in mineral composition from top to bottom of this formation makes it a classic example of how laboratory experiments serve to explain field observations. After it was emplaced at a temperature near 1200°C, which is the melting temperature of a rock of this composition, the parts of the intrusion within a few feet of its upper and lower contact cooled rapidly to become a fine-grained rock, preserv-

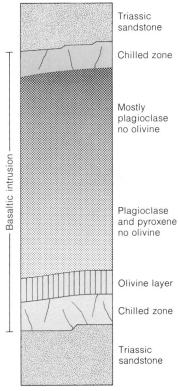

Figure 14-7
Diagrammatic section of the Palisades, on the west bank of the Hudson River. The formation is a basalt that intruded sediments as a melt some 200 million years ago. The interpretation of the vertical variation in texture and mineral composition in this formation is a classic example of fractional crystallization of the discontinuous reaction series. [After F. Walker, 1940.]

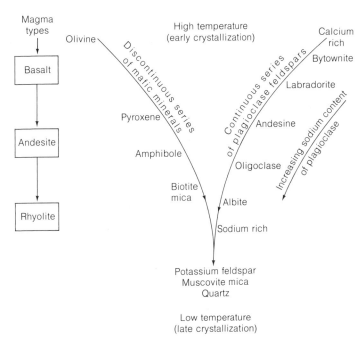

Figure 14-8
Bowen's reaction series, showing how the sequence of fractional crystallization of a melt leads to the formation of differentiated magmas.

ing or "quenching in" the chemical composition of the original magma. The molten interior cooled more slowly, so that large crystals could form. The first mineral to crystallize was olivine, which was heavy and sank through the melt to the bottom of the intrusion, where it can be found today in the olivine-rich layer just above the chilled, or fine-grained, basalt zone. The reaction proceeded to the stage of pyroxene crystallization in some parts of the intrusion, and the pyroxene accumulated in the lower third, probably by gravity-settling. After the olivine crystals settled out, changing the composition of the remaining magma, the reaction proceeded to the stage of plagioclase feldspar in the cooling of the melt. This explains the enrichment of plagioclase feldspar found in the upper third of the intrusion.

The Reaction Series. Bowen combined the continuous and discontinuous fractional crystallizations of the major minerals of igneous rocks into a general scheme for magmatic differentiation that is now called the **Bowen reaction series.** A high-temperature magma of basaltic composition starting to cool and crystallize will gradually differentiate by fractional crystallization along two paths—the continuous plagioclase-feldspar series and the discontinuous mafic-mineral series. The melt converges toward a final low-temperature granitic composition of orthoclase and albite feldspar, muscovite mica, and quartz. After the early crystallization and separation of olivine crystals, the magma corresponds to a diorite intrusive in composition—or to its fine-grained relatives, andesite volcanics, if the magma reaches the surface at that stage. At

One of the other phenomena associated with the reaction series is the tendency for the structures of the discontinuous series to become increasingly complex as temperature drops. Olivines are made of isolated silica tetrahedra, pyroxenes of single chains of tetrahedra, amphiboles of double chains, and micas of continuous sheets (see Chapter 4). Fractionation of minor chemical elements also accompanies the series.

later stages, the magma becomes more silicic, ending with granite and its extrusive equivalent, rhyolite. By the time this has happened, so many crystals have formed that only about 10 percent of the original liquid is left.

The Bowen differentiation theory accounted for many field relations and for the range of compositions of igneous rocks, and it was consistent with the known temperatures of magmas of different compositions. A number of layered intrusive bodies, such as the Palisades sill, are known in which the bottom layers are olivine and successively higher layers contain lower-temperature minerals arranged in order of the reaction series. Rhyolite volcanics erupt at times from large basaltic volcanoes toward the end of an eruption episode. Zoned plagioclase crystals are common in granites and granodiorites, as one would expect. In addition, there are very

few extrusive equivalents of the most mafic intrusives of olivine and pyroxene, which suggests that most mafic plutonic bodies are not formed from a magmatic liquid—which might be expected to erupt somewhere—but are accumulations of crystals in a magma chamber. As discussed in Chapter 15, the temperatures of basaltic lavas are much higher than those of more silicic compositions and are approximately in harmony with the experimental results.

Bowen's theory was elaborated and extended by much work in the field and laboratory. As more elements and minerals were added to the scheme and various crystallization histories of magmas were worked out, it proved to be a workable and encompassing theory that explained the diverse facts of the occurrences of many igneous rocks, particularly those of the continents. More than any earlier theory, it had integrated field observation, experimental evidence, and sound physical-chemical theory and so set the stage for further work on the origin of igneous rocks.

Many of the facts, however, were difficult to reconcile with simple differentiation as the major mechanism for silicic magma generation. Huge batholiths—enormous bodies of granite, such as those found in California or Idaho—seem to require the existence of vastly more voluminous bodies of basaltic magma from which they would have differentiated. Hence, many believe that these granites did not originate by differentiation from basalt. Oceanic basalts, typically those formed by upward movement of the asthenosphere at mid-ocean ridges, do not show differentiation. Great areas of granite in regionally metamorphosed areas merge into gneissic metamorphosed bodies of the same composition; there, much of the granite seems to be of metamorphic origin (see Chapter 16). Large granitic bodies associated with plate-convergence zones are now thought by many to have been formed by melting of some combination of sediments, igneous rocks, and metamorphic rocks that would give a melt of granitic composition. We will consider further the origin of the many kinds of granite after we turn to the origin of the magmas themselves.

Figure 14-9
Major Mesozoic (mostly mid-Cretaceous) granitic batholiths (solid black) of western North America. Enormous volumes of granite are included in these large plutons. [From *Petrologic Phase Equilibria* by W. G. Ernst. W. H. Freeman and Company. Copyright © 1976.]

ORIGIN OF MAGMA

Up to this point, we have taken for granted that magma occurs deep in the Earth, but we have not asked where, when, and how. We must reject the older notion that all of the interior of the

Table 14-3
Compositions of average oceanic crust and average continental crust.
Averages include compositions of sedimentary, granitic, and basaltic layers.

Crust	Composition (%)							
	SiO_2	Al_2O_3	Fe_2O_3	FeO	MgO	CaO	Na_2O	K_2O
Continental	60.2	15.2	2.5	3.8	3.1	5.5	3.0	2.9
Oceanic	48.7	16.5	2.3	6.2	6.8	12.3	2.6	0.4

Source: Data from Ronov and Yaroshevsky, 1969.

Earth is molten, because the data we have used to infer its nature tell us that it is solid for thousands of kilometers down to the boundary of the core (see Chapter 17). Magma chambers under active volcanoes have been surveyed by geophysical methods, and it is clear that magma occurs as discrete liquid segregations in the otherwise solid interior.

Mid-ocean ridges and rises are major zones of basaltic magma generation: **flood basalts** flow intermittently from their rifts and fissures. The same kind of flood basalts are spread extensively over continental tectonic belts and over some stable shield areas as well. Granite, granodiorites, and other silicic intrusives are essentially restricted to the continents, accompanied in places by silicic extrusives. The differences in the distribution of rock types are reflected in the more silicic composition of average continental crust (including sedimentary, granitic, and basaltic layers) as contrasted with the more mafic composition of average oceanic crust.

The differences in composition can be related to melting temperatures. All magmas must form deep in the Earth where temperatures are high. Basaltic magmas form at temperatures well over 1000°C. In contrast, granitic melts may form at temperatures several hundred degrees lower. Some idea of the depths of formation of these magmas can be obtained from the geothermal gradient in Figure 13-12. To get a better picture, we must consider other factors that influence melting and crystallization, including pressure and the presence of water in the melt.

At atmospheric pressure, pure albite in the presence of small amounts of water remains solid up to temperatures a little over 1000°C. Above that temperature, the albite melts to form a liquid containing much water, an aqueous melt. If more water is present, the melting temperature of the albite is lower (see Fig. 14–10, in which the relative amount of water present is indicated by the pressure of water vapor).

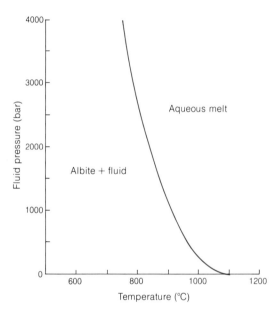

Figure 14-10
The melting curve for albite in the presence of water, as measured by fluid pressure in bars (1 bar equals 0.987 atmosphere). As fluid pressure increases, the melting temperature is lowered. These lowered melting temperatures are characteristic of silicate materials in the presence of water. [After *Earth Materials* by W. G. Ernst. Copyright © 1969 by Prentice-Hall, Inc.]

In the same way, the melting temperatures of all of the feldspars and other silicate minerals drop considerably if there are large amounts of water present. Thus, melting can occur in some places in the lower parts of the crust, both because temperature and pressure are higher there than in the upper parts of the crust and because there is more water present than in the relatively dry mantle below. Pressure alone also

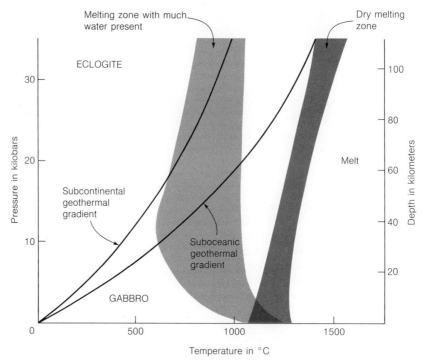

Figure 14-11
The melting temperatures or rocks of the same chemical composition as basalt vary greatly with pressure, temperature and the amount of water present. The melting region for rocks of these compositions is at much lower temperatures than for dry melts. These are shown in relation to subcontinental and suboceanic geothermal gradients. It can be seen that basalt melting can take place in water-rich melts at much lower pressures—and hence at shallower depths—under the oceans than under the continents. The solid rocks shown are gabbro, the course-grained equivalent of basalt (at low pressures), and eclogite, one of the presumed materials of the mantle (at high pressures). [Simplified and modified from *Petrologic Phase Equilibria* by W. G. Ernst. W. H. Freeman and Company, Copyright © 1976.]

has an important effect. Figure 14–12 shows the melting of dry basalt as a function of pressure and temperature, plotted together with geothermal gradients. The effect of increased pressure is to raise the melting points of basalt and the silicate minerals. At a depth of several hundred kilometers, we can expect some melting of relatively dry mantle material. This is consistent with the location of the asthenosphere, the partially molten zone found at these depths by seismological methods. This partial melting would account for the widespread occurrence of basaltic magma.

Geologic field evidence long ago provided evidence that the role of water in granitic melts is important. Numerous **hydrothermal veins** branch off from the sides and tops of many intrusive bodies. Such veins are filled with minerals that contain much chemically bound water, which, together with a variety of other evidence, shows that abundant water was associated with the magma. Hydrothermal ("hot water" in Greek) veins are of great importance in the geology of many metal ores, which are found as rich deposits in such veins. Some of the most valuable deposits of mercury, gold, silver, lead, and copper are mined from them (see Chapter 22). The hot-water solutions percolating upward from the intrusives carried these metals with them, and the metals were precipitated from them along the walls of joints and cracks as they rose and cooled.

Water-rich silicic magmas, such as those that produce hydrothermal veins, cannot be produced by simple differentiation of deep mantle material that has been melted into basalt. Such magmas are likely produced by partial melting of a mixture of quartz-rich, water-rich portions

Figure 14-12
Calculated geothermal gradients under continents and ocean basins (some-what speculative). The melting of basalt in the absence of water has been experimentally investigated only in the pressure-temperature region indicated by the solid line. [After *Earth Materials* by W. G. Ernst. Copyright © 1969 by Prentice-Hall, Inc.]

of the crust—sedimentary rocks, in particular. Sediments are richer in silica and aluminum than the parent rocks from which they were eroded, and have lost their mafic minerals by chemical weathering.

This leads to the conclusion, amply suggested by field evidence, that many large granite intrusions originate as silicic melts deep in the crust. At depths of 35–40 kilometers, temperatures of about 600°C, and water pressures of about 10,000 atmospheres, such melts would form from mixtures of sedimentary and metamorphic rocks that are compositionally equivalent to granodiorite. This seems likely to happen in deeply subsiding geosynclines, in which sediments, partly metamorphosed by heat and pressure, move down into the melting region.

In the 1960's, experimental studies of the melting behavior of mantle materials at extraordinarily high pressures (well over 30,000 atmospheres) were made possible by newly developed high-pressure equipment. The results led many geologists to propose an additional mechanism for the origin of batholiths—that of partial melting of mantle materials. This mechanism

also explained many of the facts about the voluminous andesite volcanics that occur in the same active tectonic belts, such as the western North American Cordillera; the average composition of the batholiths in that tectonic belt come close to that of andesite. A silicic melt forming in the deep crust, however well it may explain some granite batholiths, fails to provide a mechanism for the extensive andesite volcanics, which must have come from a magma of that composition; but partial melting of such mantle materials as eclogite and peridotite (pyroxene-olivine-garnet rocks), if it occurs in the presence of some water, does give a reasonable explanation for andesite magmas. The attractiveness of the notion of partial melting of mantle rocks is that it may explain both granitic batholiths and andesite volcanics.

With the development of the idea of plate tectonics, partial melting in the upper mantle has assumed new significance: it has been linked to the downward movement of lithospheric plates at subduction zones associated with volcanic island arcs. As a lithospheric plate moves down, carrying with it the oceanic crust, some

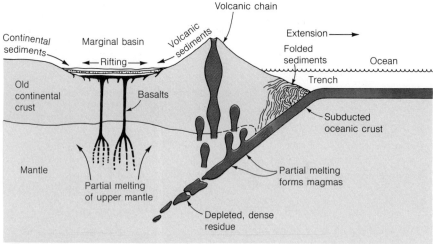

Figure 14-13
Marginal basin often opens behind volcanic island arcs where oceanic crust is being subducted under a continental margin. Some of the subducted crust melts, forming a magma. Most of the magma solidifies near the base of the continental crust, but some of it overflows as lava from volcanoes. As subduction ceases, a basin opens up behind the volcanic arc and becomes filled with lavas and sediments. [From "The Oldest Rocks and the Growth of Continents" by Stephen Moorbath. Copyright © 1977 by Scientific American, Inc. All rights reserved.]

sediment, and water, partial melting occurs as it sinks into the asthenosphere. This melting produces magmas of various compositions in or above the descending plate at various depths, depending on the amount of water, the temperature, and the pressure. These magmas are then intruded or extruded in the mountain belts associated with crustal deformation near the subduction zone. This theme will be further explored in the next chapter and integrated with a general view of magmatism and volcanism in relation to plate tectonics.

SUMMARY

1. Intrusive igneous rocks are formed by emplacement of silicic magmas in the crust.

2. Slow crystallization of plagioclase feldspars involves continuous reaction of already formed crystals with the surrounding melt until complete crystallization results in all of the crystals having the same composition as the original melt.

3. Magmatic differentiation may occur as a result of fractional crystallization, in which earlier-formed crystals do not continuously react with the melt. This differentiation can produce silicic magmas from originally mafic ones. The Bowen reaction series describes how the feldspars and mafic minerals successively crystallize during differentiation.

4. Magmatic differentiation can explain some occurrences of granite and silicic volcanics, but it is probable that many granites are formed by metamorphism or by partial melting of a mixture of sediments and earlier granitic crust, either in the crust or in a subduction zone in the upper mantle.

5. Differences in the composition of melts and the places in which they originate in the crust or mantle are accounted for by the effects of pressure and water content on the melting temperatures of basalt and the silicate minerals.

EXERCISES

1. Compare those aspects of the mineralogical composition of granites that suggest an origin from a melt with evidence from field relations.

2. What evidence could you use to decide which of two intrusions formed at different temperatures might have been crystallized from the hotter magma and which from the cooler?

3. What kinds of intrusive igneous rocks would you expect on a hypothetical planet of the same crustal composition as Earth, on which all magmas cooled extremely slowly and always maintained equilibrium between crystals and remaining melt?

4. Why would you not generally expect basaltic magmas to be generated in the upper 10 kilometers of continental crust?

5. What is the evidence for appreciable quantities of water being included in some magmas?

BIBLIOGRAPHY

Bowen, N. L., *The Evolution of the Igneous Rocks.* Princeton, N.J.: Princeton University Press, 1928. (Reprinted by Dover Publications, Inc., 1928.)

Ernst, W. G., *Earth Materials.* Englewood Cliffs, New Jersey: Prentice-Hall, Inc., 1969. (Chapters 2 and 5.)

Ernst, W. G., *Petrologic Phase Equilibria.* San Francisco: W. H. Freeman and Company, 1976.

Wyllie, P. J., "Experimental Petrology: An Indoor Approach to an Outdoor Subject." *Journal of Geological Education,* v. 14, no. 3, June, 1966.

Wyllie, P. J., *The Dynamic Earth: Textbook in Geosciences.* New York: John Wiley and Sons, Inc., 1971. (Chapters 7 and 8.)

15

VOLCANISM

Volcanoes can be beautiful, informative, and both beneficial and dangerous. They serve as windows through which we can dimly perceive the interior. Volcanism occurs in many different styles, principally in the vicinity of plate boundaries.

For decades geologists have argued about the source of magma, the hot, mobile material that is generated within the Earth and which solidifies into igneous rock. There is now little doubt, so the seismologists tell us, that the asthenosphere, which extends from depths of about 75 to 250 km, is the one large region in the mantle that is partially molten (see Chapter 17). It is reasonable, therefore, to identify this layer as a major source of magma. Remelting of sections of the lithosphere may provide another source of magma. At certain places, perhaps where the lithosphere is fractured or otherwise weakened, the magma rises, squeezed up by the weight of the overlying crust, some of it eventually reaching the surface where it erupts as **lava.** Lava differs from the parent magma to the extent that the volatile constituents (gases) are partially lost to the atmosphere or ocean and other chemical components are gained or lost en route to the surface. Despite these differences, lava provides important clues to the chemical composition and physical state of the upper mantle.

The 500–600 active volcanoes of the world are not randomly distributed, but show a definite pattern that correlates strongly, though not exclusively, with the positions of plate boundaries, where lithosphere is created or destroyed (Fig. 15-3). Not long ago our views of volcanism were for the most part colored by the grandeur and the spectacular nature of visible eruptions.

We now think that the creation of the sea floor is volumetrically the most important volcanic process, one that is hidden almost entirely from direct observation by the overlying ocean. At the end of this chapter, we will return to the question of the global pattern of volcanism: the different compositions and eruptive styles of lavas and their association with plate boundaries and other geologic features.

VOLCANIC DEPOSITS

Volcanic rocks are important not only for what they reveal about the interior but also because the chemical-mineralogical composition of lavas affects eruptive styles and the kinds of landforms they build upon freezing. To understand the variety of shapes of volcanoes—why some eruptions are explosive and others gentle—we must begin with the rocks themselves.

Figure 15-4 gives a brief review of volcanic rock types. In Chapter 3, igneous rocks were classified into four major groups on the basis of silica content and mineralogy: felsic, intermediate, mafic, and ultramafic. The major minerals associated with these rocks were listed (see Fig. 3-21). Texture is also important in rock classification. Very slow cooling gives rise to large-sized mineral grains; faster cooling results in a fine-grained rock, and very rapid cooling results

Figure 15-1
Cerro Negro, photographed in 1968. This volcano, near Managua, Nicaragua, is a cinder cone built on an older terrane of lava flows. [Photo by Mark Hurd Aerial Surveys.]

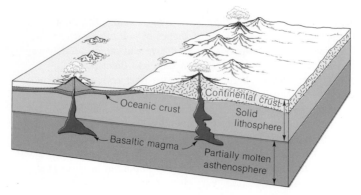

Figure 15-2
Basaltic magma, originating in the partially molten asthenosphere, rises through the lithosphere to erupt as basaltic lava on the surface.

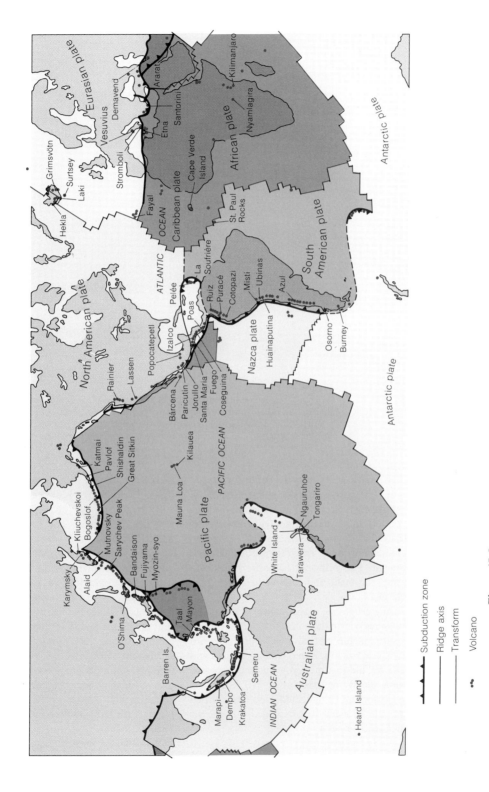

Figure 15-3
The principal active volcanoes of the world are not distributed randomly on Earth's surface; they tend to be associated with plate boundaries.

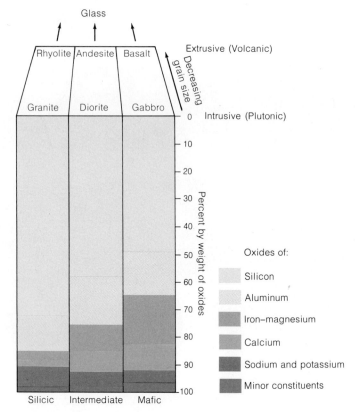

Figure 15-4
Average composition of the major types of lava (basalt, andesite, and rhyolite) and their intrusive counterparts (gabbro, diorite, and granite). Note the systematic increase in silica and the decrease in iron-magnesium oxides in going from basalt to andesite to rhyolite.

in glass, since no time is available for crystal growth. The coarse-grained, or intrusive, analogs of lava, which will be important in discussing the origin of magma, are: rhyolite-granite, andesite-diorite, and basalt-gabbro. Ultramafic magmas almost never reach the surface through volcanism. The principal lavas are basalt and andesite, the mafic and intermediate types, respectively.

During eruptions, magma moves in response to pressures within the volcano, and is effusively deposited on the surface as lava flows or violently ejected as ash. Rapid cooling follows and indeed we find that most volcanic rocks are fine grained, glassy, or pyroclastic. We recall that pyroclastics are fragmented deposits formed from material ejected or exploded into the air from a volcanic vent.

Lava Flows. As do all liquids, lavas flow downhill. Basaltic melts are highly fluid and are known to maintain their fluidity longer than the more silicic lavas; basalt can flow fast and far (Figs. 15-5, 15-20). Flow velocities as high as 100 kilometers/hour (60 miles/hour) have actually been observed, but velocities of a few kilometers/hour are more common. Lava streams extending more than 50 kilometers (30 miles) have been witnessed in historic times. On flat terrain, basaltic lava spreads out in thin sheets, successive flows often piling into immense lava plateaus. The great Columbia Plateau of Oregon and Washington is one example; the lunar maria* also formed in this way. Such sheets can sometimes be confused with sedimentary strata. In one sense they are like sediments, for they obey the laws of original horizontality and superposition. Basaltic magma erupts with temperatures in the range 1000 to 1200°C.

Rhyolite, the most silicic magma, has a lower melting point and erupts with temperatures of

---

*Plural of *mare*, from the Latin for "sea"; pertaining to the large dark areas on the Moon.

Figure 15-5
Basaltic lava flowing from a fissure on the east flank of Kilauea volcano and cascading across fault scarps. [Photo by Agatin T. Abbott, Hawaii Institute of Geophysics.]

800 to 1000°C. It is much more viscous than basalt and flows very slowly, forming thick, bulbous deposits. Andesite, with intermediate silica content, shows intermediate properties.

Lava flows can be distinguished by a variety of interesting and sometimes bizarre surface and internal features. The basaltic flows on Hawaii fall into two categories according to their surface forms: **pahoehoe** (pronounced pahoyhoy) and **aa** (ah ah). These euphonic terms are among the few Hawaiian words in the scientific vocabulary. Pahoehoe is a highly fluid lava that spreads in sheets. A thin, glassy elastic skin that forms at the surface is dragged into ropy, filamented folds as flow continues below the surface (Fig. 15-6). Aa is a slower-moving lava flow whose thick skin is broken into an indescribably rough, jagged, clinkery surface (Fig. 15-7). The blocks ride on the viscous, massive interior, advancing as a steep front of angular boulders in the manner of a tractor tread. Many is the mainland haole (non-native) who, "site" unseen, has paid dearly for an acre of Hawaiian aa. His shoes would be cut to ribbons if he tried to walk on his own land. Aa may differ in behavior from pahoehoe because it has lost its volatiles and

consequently its fluidity. Single flows commonly grade from pahoehoe near their source into blocky aa "downstream." The scale of the blockiness varies from small, football-sized blocks (as at Mt. Etna, Italy) to house-sized blocks (at Hekla, Iceland). The blocks, regardless of scale, are loose and unstable, and their surfaces are covered with gas cavities, and hence are jagged. The local topographic relief on blocky aa flows is commonly 10 feet or more. They are truly treacherous to cross. A good pair of boots has a mean lifetime of about a week, and the traveler or geologist can count on cut knees and elbows. The instability of house-sized blocks makes some flows downright hostile and sufficiently dangerous to be treated with respect, like rattlesnakes!

Pillow lavas, piles of ellipsoidal, sack-like blocks about a meter in dimension, are characteristic of underwater eruptions of basalt and andesite (Fig. 15-8). Apparently, tongues of lava, chilled by contact with water, develop a tough, plastic skin, convex upwards, filled with liquid. On cooling, the skin becomes glassy and the interior crystalline, and often radially cracked. The identification of pillow structure in

Pahoehoe in Hawaiian means "ropy"; *aa* is what it says—or what a bare-footed Hawaiian says while walking on it: "ah . . . ah . . . oh . . . ah."

Figure 15-6
Pahoehoe lava from the 1970 eruption of Kilauea, Hawaii. Trees defoliated by hot ash falls.
[Photo by H. -U. Schmincke, Ruhr-University, Bochum, Germany.]

Figure 15-7
An aa lava flow in the saddle between Mauna Kea and Mauna Loa, Hawaii.
[Photo by T. McGetchin, M.I.T.]

a geological section is a sure indication of underwater deposition. It has also been a valuable guide as to which is top and bottom in deformed sequences.

Dr. James Moore of the U.S. Geological Survey and some colleagues performed the remarkable feat of swimming up to an advancing underwater lava flow and observing the formation of pillows. This is their report:

"A team of five divers from the U.S. Geological Survey, the University of Hawaii, and the Lockheed Aircraft Company dived on the lava flow from Kilauea Volcano on the south coast of the Island of Hawaii on April 19th (1971). This is the lava flow that has been going on for six weeks and is presently flowing into the sea. The flow is advancing under water as a wall of rubble which is some 300 to 500 feet seaward of the new sea cliff. The front of the rubble wall is at the angle of repose of about 45°, and the base of it is covering over the old ocean floor to a depth of about 100 feet. Tongues of lava, circular in cross section, extend down the front of this rubble slope. Some of these are as long as 200 feet and they are 3 to 4 feet in diameter, generally. Budding off of them are typical pillows. We could approach one of these elongated lava tongues, in which lava was actually flowing inside and whose surface was too hot to touch on the outside. Generally, the surface was dark, but periodically it would crack and bright incandescence could be seen inside for a few seconds until the crack solidified and then it would crack in some other place. There was a continuous loud mixture of noises: hissing, cracking, small explosions, and rumbling noise as the lava went down through these tubes. General water temperature was slightly elevated around the flowing lava tongues from a normal of 76°F to about 80°F, but in cracks and around behind these lava tubes the water was boiling, and many bubbles were coming up out of cracks in the tubes. One surprising feature was the concentration of marine life including fish, lobsters, and eels which were crowded ahead of the advancing rubble flow at the base of the rubble, apparently having been displaced from their normal habitats along the coast. Underwater visibility was better than expected."

Lavas show many other features. They can be glassy, fine grained, or even coarsely crystalline, depending on the rate at which they cooled. When water vapor or other gases are released, ovoid gas cavities, or **vesicles,** can form (Fig. 15-9). **Pumice,** an extremely vesicular, generally rhyolitic lava, occasionally has so much void space that it is light enough to float. **Xenoliths,** foreign inclusions picked up by a magma, pro-

Figure 15-8
Pillow lava, characteristic of underwater volcanic eruptions, photographed at an ocean depth of 3300 m off Hawaii. Area of photograph approximately 1.25 by 1.25 m. [Photo by J. G. Moore, U.S. Geological Survey.]

Figure 15-9
A chunk of vesicular lava, Newberry Caldera, Oregon. [From *Volcanic Land Forms and Surface Features* by J. Green and N. M. Short, Springer-Verlag, New York. Photo by J. Green.]

362

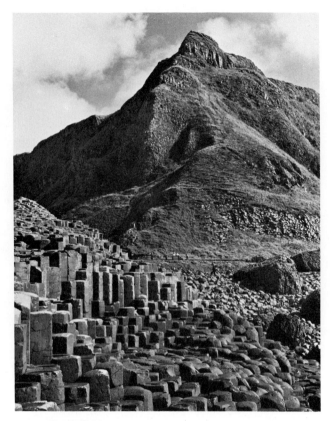

Figure 15-10
Giants Causeway, an example of columnar jointing in lava.
[Courtesy of Northern Ireland Tourist Board.]

Figure 15-11
Lava fountain building a cinder and spatter cone during the 1960 eruption of Kilauea, Hawaii. [Photo by T. McGetchin, M.I.T.]

vide important clues about the source region and also the rock formations through which lava passed en route to the surface. When lava cools and contracts, shrinkage cracks **(joints)** often form. Some flows develop impressive **columnar jointing** perpendicular to the cooling surface (Fig. 15-10). Where flows are thin and cool rapidly, the joints may be highly irregular. On Hawaii one can walk into **lava caves,** or **tubes.** These form when the source of an enclosed stream of lava is cut off and the remaining lava drained from the channel. Some geologists think the deep valley named Hadley Rille, where Apollo 15 landed, was formed by the collapsed roof of a lunar lava tube. **Spatter cones** are steep-sided, conical hills built from the spatter of **lava fountains** spewed out of vents (Fig. 15-11).

Pyroclastic Deposits. Water and dissolved gases are important constituents of magma; before eruption, the confining pressure of the overlying rock keeps these volatiles from escaping. When the magma rises close to the surface and the pressure drops, the volatiles may be released with explosive violence, shattering the lava into fragments of various sizes, shapes, and textures. This is more common in the highly silicic, volatile-rich, viscous rhyolitic and andesitic lavas than in basalts, which are more fluid and release volatiles more quickly.

Pyroclasts are the fragmentary volcanic rock materials that are ejected into the air. The particles, whether rocks, minerals, or glass, are classified according to size; the finest are called **dust,** fragments up to about 2 millimeters (generally the same as sand) are called **ash,** and chunks larger than about 6 centimeters are called **bombs** (Fig. 15-12). Bombs have several characteristic shapes: ellipsoidal, discoidal, and irregularly rounded; typical dimensions range from baseball to basketball size. Some volcanic bombs, however, can be blockbusters. Blocks as heavy as 100 tons are known to have been thrown more than 10 kilometers in violent eruptions. Volcanic ash, and especially dust, can be carried great distances (Fig. 15-22). Dust from the great Krakatoa eruption of 1883 reached the upper levels of the atmosphere and was dispersed throughout the world. More recently, in 1965, the eruption of Agung on Bali gave rise to large amounts of dust, which meteorologists measured from the violet color the particles produced in the stratosphere.

Sooner or later pyroclasts must fall, mostly near the source, building up deposits. When the fragments become cemented together (lithified), the rocks formed from the smaller fragments are called **volcanic tuffs;** those formed from the larger ones are called **volcanic breccias** (Fig. 15-13). There is as much variety in volcanic deposits as there is in sedimentary ones, and there are many similarities between the two. Some volcanic deposits show graded bedding, not unlike that of certain sedimentary rocks, because the coarse fragments settle first, followed by the finer debris. Volcanic beds often show lateral sorting, a gradation from coarser material near the vent to finer material with increasing distance from the vent. Even dune structures and cross-bedding are found, having been formed by winds blowing at the time of fallout and also by the vigorous radial (sidewise) expansion of the volcanic eruption cloud. Similar bedded and dune-like deposits were observed around some of the sites at which atomic bombs were exploded; from details of the forms of those deposits, it is possible to estimate the wind velocities produced by the blasts.

A spectacular and often devastating form of eruption occurs when hot ash and dust fragments and gases are ejected in a glowing cloud that rolls downhill with amazing speed. The solid particles are actually buoyed up by the hot gases, so that there is little frictional resistance to this incandescent, fluidized avalanche, or **nuée ardente** (Fig. 15-14). In 1902 a nuée ardente with an internal temperature of 800°C flowed down from Mont Pelée on Martinique at a speed of 100 kilometers per hour (60 miles per hour). In one minute, and with hardly a sound, it enveloped the town of St. Pierre and killed 28,000 people. Deposits left behind by a nuée ardente are poorly sorted, without much indication of bedding, as would be expected. Typically, the fragments are still hot, hence soft, when deposited and become compacted and stuck together to form **welded tuffs** or **ignimbrites** (Fig. 15-15). The welding agent that makes the fragments stick together is glass. Vast

Figure 15-12
A field of volcanic bombs and other ejecta. Haleakala volcano, Maui, Hawaii. Source cone is in the background. [From *Volcanic Land Forms and Surface Features* by J. Green and N. M. Short, Springer-Verlag, New York. Photo by J. Green.]

Figure 15-13
Volcanic breccia, Augustine Volcano, Alaska. [Photo by H. -U. Schmincke, Ruhr-University, Bochum, Germany.]

Figure 15-14
Nuées ardentes (glowing avalanches, or ash flows) plummeting down the slopes of
Mount Mayon in the Philippines during the eruption of 1968. [Photo by W. Melson,
Smithsonian Institution.]

Figure 15-15
Hand specimen of welded tuff from an ash-flow sheet. The dark lenses are collapsed pumice fragments enclosed in a light-colored matrix composed mostly of
welded glassy shards. Laboratory experiments indicate that welded tuffs form at
temperatures in the range 700–900°C. [Photo from R. G. Schmidt and R. L.
Smith, U.S. Geological Survey.]

ignimbrite sheets, also called ash flow deposits, more than 100 meters thick, covering tens of thousands of square kilometers, are known on the continents. These pyroclastic deposits represent the high-silica counterpart of the plateau basalts.

ERUPTIVE STYLES

Now that we have discussed something of the several types of volcanic deposits that have poured out or been blown out from the interior, it is natural to consider the different ways in which eruptions occur, and the different results produced. Eruptions do not always produce the majestically symmetrical cone of a Fujiyama, which has become a symbol to a nation. The hundreds of thousands of square kilometers of monotonous **flood basalt,** such as that of the Columbia Plateau, represent another variant. Eruptions such as those of Hawaii's Kilauea have been heralded by warning events that were followed by relatively quiet outpourings of lava, which move slowly and predictably, destroying property but not lives. Pyroclastic eruptions, such as the one at Mont Pelée, or **phreatic explosions** (violent steam blasts), such as that of Krakatoa in 1883, can wipe out entire populations (Fig. 15-16). Teams of archeologists and marine geologists have pieced together the story of the volcano Thera (formerly called Santorin), situated in the Aegean Sea. It appears that the eruption of Thera in the fourteenth century B.C. was an event of super-Krakatoan proportions. The volcanic debris and sea waves that were produced caused destruction in coastal settlements over a large part of the eastern Mediterranean. The mysterious disappearance of the Minoan civilization has been attributed to this cataclysm, and it is thought that the legend of the lost continent of Atlantis may have its origin in this event.

Fissure Eruptions. Either lava or pyroclastic materials may emanate from long, narrow fissures or a group of such fissures (Fig. 15-17). The lavas are usually basaltic; the pyroclastics originate from more silicic magmas. The rather fluid basaltic lavas flow away from the fissures rather than build volcanoes, and often flood extensive areas, building lava plains or piling up into lava plateaus—hence the names "flood basalts" and "plateau basalts" (Fig. 15-18). The basalt flows that made the Columbia Plateau buried 130,000 square kilometers (50,000 square miles) of the pre-existing topography, which had

Figure 15-16
A phreatic explosion on the volcano Surtsey in the Atlantic Ocean off the coast of Iceland. [Copyright by Solarfilma, Reykjavik, Iceland.]

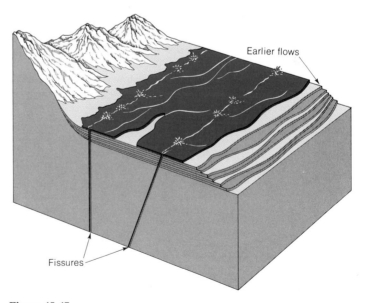

Earlier flows

Fissures

Figure 15-17
Schematic diagram of a fissure eruption of highly fluid basalt. Lava rapidly flows away from fissures and forms widespread layers, rather than building up into volcanic mountains. [After R. S. Fiske, U.S. Geological Survey.]

Figure 15-18
Map showing area covered by the
Columbia River flood basalts. [After
R. S. Fiske, U.S. Geological Survey.]

Figure 15-19
View across Imnaha River Canyon, and part of the Columbia Plateau in Oregon. Flood
basalts form the layered rocks. [Photo by H. -U. Schmincke, Ruhr-University, Bochum,
Germany.]

a relief of about 1.5 kilometers (1 mile). Some individual flows were more than 100 meters (300 feet) thick, and some were so fluid that they spread more than 60 kilometers (40 miles) from their source. The total volume of basalt poured out in this Miocene volcanic episode has been estimated at more than 100,000 cubic kilometers (25,000 cubic miles)! An entirely new landscape with new river valleys has since been created on top of the old surface. Other famous examples of continental plateau or flood basalts are the Deccan of India, which has an areal extent of more than 500,000 square kilometers (200,000 square miles), and the Parana of Brazil and Paraguay, covering more than 750,000 square kilometers (300,000 square miles).

When rocks are dredged from a mid-ocean ridge or samples are collected from such occasional oceanic ridge peaks as the Azores, which stick out above water, they always seem to turn out to be basalt. The basalt originates in fissure eruptions in connection with sea-floor spreading. The process is seemingly unspectacular because it is mostly unseen, but volumetrically it dwarfs all of the continental outpourings combined. The fissures are coincident with the ridge crests and often are marked by median **rift valleys** and seismic belts (see Fig. 1-15). The global oceanic ridge-fissure system can be traced

over distances totaling some 50,000 kilometers (30,000 miles) (see inside front cover). Enormous amounts of basalt have poured out of this world-encircling sequence of cracks, enough to build the crust of all of the present sea floor in the past 200 million years.

Iceland, an exposed segment of the mid-Atlantic ridge, provides an unexcelled opportunity to view the process of fissure eruption and sea-floor spreading directly. The island is composed mostly of basalt, with small amounts of the more felsic lavas. Repeated geodetic surveys show that Iceland is in a state of tension, literally being pulled apart, one half moving eastward with the Eurasian plate, the other westward with the American plate. Tensile cracks develop, magma flows in from below, and overflows onto the surface. Evidence of basalt flooding from great fissures has been found in the geologic record at many places, but actual flooding has been witnessed by man only on Iceland. In a single eruption in 1783, a crack 32 kilometers (20 miles) long, called the Laki fissure, opened and spewed out some 12 cubic kilometers (3 cubic miles) of basalt. At the conclusion of such an episode the lava solidifies to form a nearly vertical **dike** in the fissure and near horizontal beds on the adjacent surface. With the next episode of lateral spreading, a

Figure 15-20
The volcano Surtsey was born in the sea south of Iceland in 1963. Some 300 million m³ of lava and 600 million m³ of ash poured out of the sea floor to build this new island. [Copyright by Solarfilma, Reykjavik, Iceland.]

new crack forms, and another flow pours out over the old one. This is the way Iceland grows, by repeated fissure eruptions, as sketched in Figure 15-21. Although the details may differ under water, it is reasonable to expect the sea-floor crust to grow in a similar fashion. The upwelling basalt frequently produces ridges centered on the deep valleys of the fissures rather than Icelandic plateaus. The ridges gradually subside into ocean basins as they move away from the zone of spreading, to be replaced by fresh ridges. This is discussed further in Chapter 19, which summarizes what we know about plate tectonics.

Fissure eruptions of pyroclastic materials rather than lavas are more likely when the parent magma is more silicic than basalt. Such eruptions have produced extensive ignimbrite sheets, although man has never witnessed one of these spectacular events. The early Tertiary ignimbrites of the Great Basin in Nevada and adjacent states cover an area of about 200,000 square kilometers, and are as much as 2500 meters thick in some places. In Yellowstone National Park, successions of forests were buried by broad ignimbrite sheets (Fig. 15-22).

Central Eruptions. Unlike the linear sources of fissure eruptions, central eruptions are much like point sources of magma. The extrusive

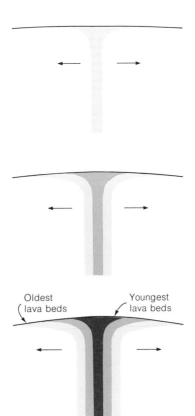

Oldest
lava beds

Youngest
lava beds

Figure 15-21
Iceland is an exposed part of the mid-Atlantic ridge. This schematic diagram shows the mechanism of its growth, by repeated fissure eruptions and lateral spreading.

Figure 15-22
Ignimbrites, or ash-flow sheets, are deposited when intensely hot, gas-charged volcanic dust, ash, and pumice spread swiftly over the surface to settle and cool as flat sheets. The example shown is on the Pajarito Plateau, near Los Alamos, New Mexico. Source of the ash lies beyond the mountains in the background. [Photo from R. G. Schmidt and R. L. Smith, U.S. Geological Survey.]

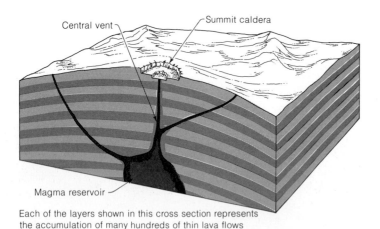

Central vent

Summit caldera

Magma reservoir

Each of the layers shown in this cross section represents the accumulation of many hundreds of thin lava flows

Figure 15-23
Schematic diagram showing how a shield volcano is built up from the accumulation of thousands of thin basaltic lava flows that spread widely and cool as gently sloping sheets. [After R. G. Schmidt, U.S. Geological Survey.]

materials issue from a **central vent,** or **pipe,** and give rise to the most familiar of all volcanic features—the **cone.**

Lava cones are built by successive lava flows. Basaltic lava is relatively free flowing and spreads widely. If there is a large supply, a broad **shield-shaped** volcano can be built up, many tens of kilometers in circumference and more than one or two kilometers in height. The slopes are relatively gentle, 6 to 12°. Mauna Loa, on Hawaii (Fig. 15-24), is the classic example of a **shield volcano.** Although it rises 4 kilometers (2.5 miles) above sea level, its actual size is hidden by the ocean. Measured from the sea floor, Mauna Loa rises 10 kilometers (6 miles) and has a basal diameter of 100 kilometers (60 miles)! It grew to this enormous size by the accumulation of individual lava flows, each only a few meters thick. The island of Hawaii is actually formed by the overlapping of a group of shield volcanoes. When the lava supply is less plentiful, a smaller lava cone is the result. Most basaltic volcanoes probably begin as fissures and develop central vents later, since it is easier for the magma to ascend as a column rather than as a sheet.

Silicic lavas are so viscous that they can just barely flow, as is shown by the shapes of the **volcanic domes** they produce (Fig. 15-25). The domes give every appearance that the lava had been squeezed out of a vent like cold toothpaste,

Figure 15-24
The shield volcano Mauna Loa on Hawaii, the giant among the active volcanoes of the world. Smaller craters lead upward to Mokuaweoweo caldera, the large depression at the summit. [U.S. Air Force photo.]

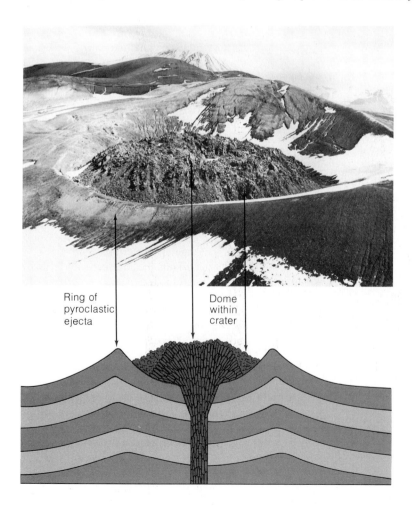

Ring of
pyroclastic
ejecta

Dome
within
crater

Figure 15-25
Volcanic domes are bulbous masses of lava. The lava masses are so viscous that they do not flow, but pile up over the vent. Shown here is Novarupta Dome in the Katmai region of Alaska. [After A. Chidester and R. G. Schmidt, U.S. Geological Survey.]

Figure 15-26
Ejecta building a cinder cone on the flank of Mt. Etna, Sicily, during the 1969 eruption. Fragments with dimensions of 0.1 to 1 m³ were thrown out of the crater with a velocity of about 50 m/sec. [Bernard Chouet, M.I.T.]

Central vent filled with rock fragments

Successive layers of ejected material

Figure 15-27
Diagrammatic representation of the structure of a cinder cone. Ejected material is deposited as layers that dip away from the crater at the summit. The vent beneath the crater is filled with fragmental debris.

with very little lateral spreading, to form a bulbous steep-sided mass. Some silicic lavas are so viscous that no spreading occurs; instead, a cylindrical, or spine-like, shape is retained.

Cinder cones are built of fragmental material, explosively ejected from a vent (Fig. 15-26). The profile of the cone is determined by the angle of repose (Fig. 5-3)—that is, the maximum angle at which the debris remains stable and does not slide downhill (Figs. 15-27 and 15-1). The larger fragments, which fall near the summit, can form stable slopes exceeding 30°. Finer particles are carried farther from the vent and form gentle slopes of about 10° at the base of the cone. The classic, aesthetically pleasing, concave-shaped, volcanic cone reflects this variation in the angle of repose. Parícutin in Mexico erupted in a farm field in 1943 and built a cinder cone 150 meters high in its first six days of activity. It is now a dormant (sleeping) volcano about 400 meters (1300 feet) high (Fig. 15-28).

When a volcano emits lava as well as pyroclasts, a **composite cone** or **strato-volcano** is built of alternating lava flows and beds of pyroclasts (Fig. 15-29). This is the most common form of the large continental volcanoes, represented by such famous examples as Fujiyama, Vesuvius, Etna, and Stromboli (Fig. 15-30).

If the central vent of a volcano grows too high or becomes plugged, the lava may find an easier route by opening a subsidiary vent and building a small cone on the flanks of the main volcano. Hundreds of subsidiary cones pimple the slopes of Etna, Mauna Loa, and Mt. Newberry (central Oregon), to cite a few examples. Flank eruptions can also originate from fissures.

Craters form the summits of most volcanoes, and are usually centered over the vent. During the eruption of a lava volcano, the upwelling lava overflows the crater walls; when eruption ceases, the lava that remains in the crater sinks back into the vent. When pyroclastic cones erupt, the material is literally blasted out of the crater, which later becomes partially filled by debris falling back into it. Because crater walls are steep, they may cave in or retreat by erosion after an eruption, becoming enlarged to several times the vent diameter. Etna, for example, has a central vent 300 meters (1000 feet) in diameter and at least 850 meters (2800 feet) deep.

Calderas are large, basin-shaped depressions of volcanic origin. Most calderas are collapse features that form after a magma chamber becomes drained and no longer supports part of the overlying cone. The subsidence can occur catastrophically or gradually, leaving a steep-

Figure 15-28
Parícutin in eruption. This volcano was born in the field of a Mexican farmer in 1945. It is now a dormant (temporarily inactive) volcano 400 m high. [Photo by Tad Nichols, Tuscon, Arizona.]

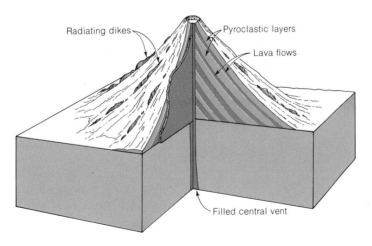

Figure 15-29
Structure of a composite volcano built up of layers of pyroclastic material and lava flows. Lava, solidified in fissures, forms rib-like dikes that strengthen the cone. [After R. G. Schmidt, U.S. Geological Survey.]

Figure 15-30
Mt. Fuji, symbol of many things to the Japanese nation and one of the most majestic mountains of the world, is a composite volcano. [Photo by S. Aramaki, The University of Tokyo.]

Figure 15-31
The evolution of the caldera at Crater Lake, Oregon. (a and b) Eruptions from the summit of the vanished former Mount Mazama deplete the magma chamber below. (c) Caldera results from collapse of the mountain summit into the empty magma chamber. (d) Lake forms in the caldera; minor eruptions into the lake continue until the magma below the surface finally solidifies. [After H. Williams, 1942.]

walled, flat-floored depression. Later activity can lead to the growth of new cones in the caldera floor. Figure 15-31 diagrams the evolution of a caldera. Some famous examples are the still-active Kilauea (Hawaii), the dormant Crater Lake (Oregon), and the newly active Krakatoa (Indonesia) (Fig. 15-32). Perhaps the largest and most spectacular caldera known is the one on Olympus Mons, a huge volcano photographed on Mars from the Mariner 9 spacecraft (Fig. 21-18).

At one time it was thought that a caldera was formed by a huge explosion, as if the volcano had "blown its top." Geologic mapping of the debris around volcanoes, however, has shown that more volcanic rock subsided than was blasted out. The pattern of down-faulting was consistent with a different explanation—that "the roof caved in."

This is not to say that volcanic explosions have not left their mark on the Earth's surface. Hot, gas-charged magma encountering groundwater or sea water results in a highly explosive mixture. Vast quantities of superheated steam are generated with disastrous consequences, in the form of phreatic explosions. The destructive eruptions of Krakatoa and Taal (Philippines) are two of the many examples of such cataclysmic events. Another is Bandai-san (Japan), which blew out in 1888 and left an amphitheater 2.5 kilometers (1.5 miles) across with walls 350 meters (1200 feet) high.

Figure 15-32
Crater Lake, Oregon, fills the caldera in the stump of the vanished Mt. Mazama. [From U.S. Geological Survey.]

Diatreme is the term given to a volcanic vent, or pipe, filled with breccia as a result of the explosive escape of gases from the deep interior. Shiprock, which towers 515 meters (1700 feet) over the surrounding, flat-lying sedimentary rocks of New Mexico, is an excellent example of a diatreme exposed by the erosion of its enclosing sedimentary rocks. It has been viewed by thousands of transcontinental air travelers, and looks like a gigantic black skyscraper in the red desert (Fig. 15-33). The eruptive mechanism that produces diatremes has been pieced together in much detail from the geologic record to be found in the ejecta and the diatremes. Rock and mineral data tell us that some diatremes are produced by the upward movement of materials from great depths—well within the upper mantle. The evidence indicates that they are formed by gas-charged magmas that melt their way to the surface, finally ejecting gases, lava fragments from the vent walls, and fragments from the deep crust and mantle—all with explosive energy and sometimes with supersonic velocity. One can imagine such an eruption to look much like the exhaust jet of a Saturn 5

Figure 15-33
Shiprock is a diatreme, or volcanic pipe, exposed by erosion of its enclosing rock. It towers 515 m above the surrounding, flat-lying sediments of New Mexcio. [From U.S. Geological Survey.]

Diamond, the hardest substance known, is formed when carbon is subjected to high pressures, corresponding to depths of about 125 km in the Earth's mantle. Gem-quality diamonds only occur naturally, whereas small industrial diamonds are now produced synthetically.

In 1938 two Russian volcanologists, V. F. Popkov and I. Z. Ivanov, made measurements of lava temperatures and collected gas while floating down a river of lava on a raft of colder lava for a distance of 2 kilometers. The surface temperature of their raft was 300°C, and the lava river showed a temperature of 870°C! The occasion was the eruption of Biliukai on Kamchatka. Pliny the Elder may have been the first scholar to lose his life studying a volcano. He was killed in the great eruption of Vesuvius, which destroyed Pompeii in A.D. 79.

rocket placed upside down in the ground, blowing rocks and gas into the air. This was observed by a Chilean Air Force pilot when the volcano Nilahue erupted in 1955. The jets lasted for about 30 minutes, each blast followed by periods of quiescence of about the same duration. Activity stopped after about a month, presumably after the volcano literally ran out of gas.

The underground workings of the fabled Kimberley diamond mines of South Africa penetrate diatremes, which contain mantle materials (including diamonds) and fragments of rock encountered en route to the surface. Geologists view this pipe in much the same way they would a 300-kilometer (180-mile) long drill core in which the rocks were scrambled by eruption. Careful field and laboratory work on such scrambles of rock has enabled geologists to unravel their mysteries and deduce something of the layering of the Earth's crust and mantle well beyond the reach of the deepest drill hole.

Other Volcanic Phenomena. When a nuée ardente meets a river, it can be transformed into a landslide or mudflow of volcanic debris called a **lahar.** Lahars can also be produced when a crater lake is breached, or when glacial ice is melted by lava flows or nuées ardentes. One formation in the Sierra Nevada contains 8000 cubic kilometers (2000 cubic miles) of material of lahar origin. Lahars have been known to carry huge boulders for tens of kilometers. When Kelut (Java) erupted in 1919, the crater lake containing 380,000 cubic meters (14 million cubic feet) of water was displaced, and the resultant lahar rushed down the flanks and killed some 5500 people.

Volcanic gases have been studied by courageous and occasionally foolhardy volcanologists. Water vapor is the main constituent (70 to 95 percent), followed by carbon dioxide, sulfur dioxide, and traces of nitrogen, hydrogen, carbon monoxide, sulfur, and chlorine. Enormous amounts of volatiles are released. Parícutin emitted some 18,000 tons of water in a single day.

Both the nature and origin of volcanic gases are of considerable interest and importance because they formed the oceans and the atmosphere. Some volcanic gas may be derived from deep within the Earth and may be making its way to the surface for the first time **(juvenile gas);** some may be recycled groundwater and ocean water or atmospheric gas or gases that had been trapped in rocks.

Emissions of gas and vapor that are unaccompanied by the eruption of lava or pyroclastic ejecta often mark the late stages of volcanic activity. Circulating groundwater can reach and be heated by buried magma (which retains heat for a long time), producing **hot springs** and **geysers.** A geyser is a hot-water fountain that spouts intermittently with great force, frequently accompanied by a thunderous roar. The best known example is *Old Faithful* in Yellowstone Park, which erupts irregularly, about every 65 minutes, sending a jet of hot water as much as 60 meters (200 feet) high. **Fumaroles** are vents that emit gas fumes or steam. All of these volcanic emanations contain dissolved materials that precipitate as the water evaporates and cools, forming various sorts of encrusting deposits (for example, travertine), some of which are valuable mineral deposits.

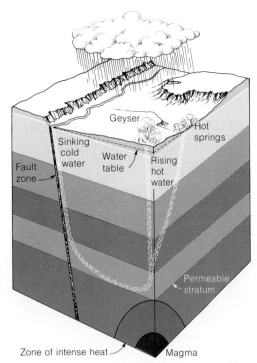

Figure 15-34
Surface water percolating down along fractures occasionally reaches the vicinity of a magma chamber. The heated fluid rises through other channels to erupt as steam and hot water in geysers and hot springs. [After D. E. White, U.S. Geological Survey.]

Figure 15-35
Old Faithful Geyser, Yellowstone National Park.
Hot water and steam are violently ejected about
once every 65 minutes. In between eruptions hot
water presumably fills underground cavities. Further
heating converts some of the water into steam, generating the pressure that forces the discharge. [From
U.S. Geological Survey.]

CASE HISTORIES
OF VOLCANOES

The stories of individual volcanoes make fascinating reading, not only for their phenomeno-
logical content but also for their human interest
value. Some volcanoes have changed the course
of ancient history—for example, Thera and Vesuvius.

Kilauea—An Instrumented Volcano. The
giant shield volcano Mauna Loa and the smaller
Kilauea on its eastern flank make up the southern half of the island of Hawaii. Because the
U.S. Geological Survey operates a volcano observatory on the rim of Kilauea caldera, this
volcano is perhaps the best studied in the world,
and what has been learned from its study has
influenced our notions of volcanic processes
profoundly. A modern network of seismographs
has been installed to provide information on the
internal structure and activity of Kilauea. Tiltmeters (instruments that measure tilting of the
ground) were emplaced to observe the swelling
and deflation of the volcano due to the accumulation and underground movement of magma. A
geochemical laboratory was established to study
the systematic variations in the chemistry and
petrology of the lavas and the chemistry of the
emitted gases.

The U.S. Geological Survey used these new
techniques to monitor the Kilauea eruption of
1959-1960. The following material is taken
from one report. Between the 14th and 19th of
August, 1959, the seismographs detected a
swarm of small earthquakes at a depth of 55
kilometers beneath Kilauea caldera. This
marked the entrance of magma into the conduits
leading from the asthenosphere, through the
lithosphere, to the surface. The upward migration of the magma could be traced by weak
seismic disturbances originating at depths of 5
to 15 kilometers. Between August and October,
the tiltmeters showed that the volcano was beginning to swell as the magma rose and filled a
shallow reservoir below the caldera.

The first sign of an outbreak occurred in
September, when seismographs picked up a
series of small earthquakes near the northeast
rim of Halemaumau, a deep pit within the
caldera. By November this swarm of tremors
exceeded a thousand per day. At this time the
summit of Kilauea was swelling three times
more rapidly than in prior months. Then on
November 14 the quakes increased tenfold in
number and intensity, signifying that the eruption fissure was splitting its way to the surface.
That evening the lava broke out of a kilometer-
long fissure in the wall of Kilauea Iki, a crater
just east of the caldera. The earthquakes
stopped, but the seismographs recorded an almost continuous tremor that typically accompa-

Kilauea Iki

Kapoho

Channelway through which magma rises
from asthenosphere about 60 km down

Shallow chamber in
which magma accumulates

Figure 15-36
Schematic diagram of the 1960 eruption on the flank of Kilauea, which destroyed
the village of Kapoho on Hawaii. In an earlier stage, lava filled Kilauea Iki crater on
the summit, forming a lake 125 m deep, but more than half drained back into the
vent. Following the cessation of activity at Kilauea Iki, the flank eruption at Kapoho,
45 km away, covered about 10 km^2 with lava. [After J. P. Eaton and R. G.
Schmidt, U.S. Geological Survey.]

Figure 15-37
View of St. Pierre toward steaming Mont Pelée, after it was destroyed by a nuée
ardente in the eruption of May 8, 1902. [Copyright 1902 by Underwood and Underwood. Library of Congress.]

nies lava outpouring. In the next seven days
about 30 million cubic meters (1 billion cubic
feet) of lava poured into Kilauea Iki, accompanied by spectacular lava fountains. The tiltmeters showed the volcano to be deflating as the
reservoir emptied its contents. There were repeated cycles of swelling and eruption until
December 21, when Kilauea Iki became dormant. The Geological Survey scientists expected
more trouble, however, because the volcano
began to inflate even more than it had in November. More lava was in the shallow reservoir
below the caldera than when the eruption began.
The pressure would have to force open new
rifts, and dikes of lava would split their way to
the surface, signalled by earthquakes. In early
January of 1960, a new swarm of earthquakes
was detected, this time not far from the village
of Kapoho, about 40 kilometers (25 miles) east
of the caldera. Then on January 13, as expected,
a flank eruption broke out (Fig. 15-36). It came
through a crack about a kilometer long, a few
hundred meters north of the village. Within the
next four weeks, more than 100 million cubic
meters (3.5 billion cubic feet) of lava poured out
of the fissure, destroying Kapoho, but causing
no casualties. A new landscape was created as
the lava flowed to the sea. Twenty-foot walls
were built in a futile attempt to divert the lava
and save a seashore community. When it was all
over, the tiltmeters showed that the reservoir
under the caldera had been drained in supplying
lava for the Kapoho eruption. Confirmation was
given by the fact that the amount by which the
summit subsided was volumetrically equal to the
lava erupted.

Geologists believe that the basaltic magma in
the partially molten asthenosphere is lighter
than the rock in the overlying lithosphere. The
magma could therefore be squeezed to the surface by the weight of the lithosphere, if an
escape route were available. A fracture under
Hawaii taps this source of magma, and the lava
rises to fill the shallow chamber under the
caldera. The rest of the story is as given above.

Mont Pelée. The term **peléan** is an adjective
that is taken from the name of this volcano, and
is used to describe violent eruptions and explosions of gas-charged and very viscous magmas.
It is an aptly chosen word, for on May 8, 1902,
at 8:02 A.M., the Caribbean coastal town of
St. Pierre, below Mont Pelée on Martinique,
was destroyed by a nuée ardente, and all but two

of its 28,000 inhabitants perished within minutes. Once the nuée ardente exploded laterally out of the mountain with very little warning, nothing could be done to save the panicked victims. The hot-gas hurricane avalanche plunged down the slopes at a speed of about 100 kilometers per hour and engulfed the town with a searing 800°C emulsion of gas, glass, and dust (Fig. 15-37). The gas was mostly CO_2. It is sobering to scientists who render advice to others to recall the statement of Professor Landes of St. Pierre's College, issued the day before the cataclysm: "The Montagne Pelée presents no more danger to the inhabitants of Saint Pierre than does Vesuvius to those of Naples." Professor Landes perished with the others.

The following is an account of an officer aboard a ship in the harbor, quoted by K. Wilcoxon:

"I saw St. Pierre destroyed. The city was blotted out by one great flash of fire. Nearly 40,000 people were killed at once. Of eighteen vessels lying in the roads, only one, the British steamship *Roddam* escaped and she, I hear, lost more than half of those on board. It was a dying crew that took her out. Our boat, the *Roraima*, arrived at St. Pierre early Thursday morning. For hours before entering the roadstead we could see flames and smoke rising from Mt. Pelée. No one on board had any idea of danger. Captain G. T. Muggah was on the bridge, and all hands got on deck to see the show. The spectacle was

---

Box 15-1   Earth Scientists' Hotline

Scientists who study short-lived natural phenomena such as volcanic eruptions, earthquakes, meteorite falls, and tsunami waves require immediate notification that an event has occurred in order not to lose valuable data. Such a service is rendered by the Smithsonian Institution's Center for Short-Lived Phenomena. The Figure shows an event notification report issued in connection with the Kilauea eruption of 1972.

Specialists are notified by telephone or cable of specific events of particular significance to them so that expeditions can reach the site in the crucial early hours. Interested individuals can subscribe and receive these event cards routinely by writing to the Smithsonian at the address shown. A fee is charged to cover mailing and preparation costs, but these cards constitute the best "newspaper" of current natural history events now available.

EVENT	9-72	KILAUEA VOLCANIC ERUPTION-1972	14 FEBRUARY 1972	1354.

"The Mauna Ulu vent on Kilauea's east rift is erupting again after more than 3 months of inactivity. A new lava lake was discovered in Mauna Ulu's summit crater about 0900, February 5. It may be that the eruption began sometime between February 2 and 4, as shown by a slight increase in tremor on a nearby seismograph, but a severe storm and lack of visibility prevented earlier inspection of the area. The level of the lava lake progressively rose from the bottom of the crater, formerly about 150 m deep, and when discovered it was 80 m below the crater rim. It continued to rise, and on February 7, at a level 25 m below the rim, lava spilled over a notch at the east end of the crater and flowed into a collapsed trench about 450 m long that extends down Mauna Ulu's east flank. At the east end of the trench, lava drains into a tube, travels SSE about 250 m, and emerges at the north edge of the subsidence bowl that marks the site of old Alae crater. Thin flows have spread across about a quarter of the floor of the depression. The surface of the lava lake in Mauna Ulu crater is presently characterized by vigorous fountains that reach as much as 25 m in height. The entire surface is continually agitated by fountains and bursts of escaping gas. A prolonged period of tumescence of Kilauea's summit preceded this eruption, which is 11 km ESE of the summit. The outbreak is mild, and only slight deflation has occurred to the present. Harmonic tremor is weak, and only a few small earthquakes, none strong enough to be felt, have accompanied the eruption."

EVENT NOTIFICATION REPORT

TYPE OF EVENT	GEOPHYSICAL
DATE OF OCCURRENCE	FEBRUARY 5, 1972 AND CONTINUING
LOCATION OF EVENT	ISLAND OF HAWAII
	U.S.A.
REPORTING SOURCE	U. S. GEOLOGICAL
	SURVEY
SOURCE CONTACT	DR. DONALD W.

PETERSON, HAWAIIAN VOLCANO OBSERVATORY
HAWAII NATIONAL PARK, HI 96718, USA

This report is based on notifications received from the center's correspondents and is disseminated for information purposes only. The Smithsonian Institution bears no responsibility for its accuracy.

SMITHSONIAN INSTITUTION
CENTER FOR SHORT LIVED PHENOMENA
60 Garden Street
CAMBRIDGE, MASSACHUSETTS 02138
UNITED STATES OF AMERICA
CABLE: SATELLITES NEW YORK
TELEPHONE: (617)-864-7910

sao-slp-5

magnificent. As we approached St. Pierre we could distinguish the rolling and leaping of red flames that belched from the mountain in huge volumes and gushed into the sky. Enormous clouds of black smoke hung over the volcano. . . . There was a constant muffled roar. It was like the biggest oil refinery in the world burning up on the mountain top. There was a tremendous explosion about 7:45, soon after we got in. The mountain was blown to pieces. There was no warning. The side of the volcano was ripped out and there was hurled straight toward us a solid wall of flame. It sounded like a thousand cannon.

"The wave of fire was on us and over us like a flash of lightning. It was like a hurricane of fire. I saw it strike the cable steamship *Grappler* broadside on, and capsize her. From end to end she burst into flames and then sank. The fire rolled in mass straight down upon St. Pierre and the shipping. The town vanished before our eyes.

"The air grew stifling hot and we were in the thick of it. Wherever the mass of fire struck the sea, the water boiled and sent up vast columns of steam. The sea was torn into huge whirlpools that careened toward the open sea. One of these horrible, hot whirlpools swung under the *Roraima* and pulled her down on her beam end with the suction. She careened way over to port, and then the fire hurricane from the volcano smashed her, and over she went on the opposite side. The fire wave swept off the masts and smokestacks as if they were cut by a knife.

"Captain Muggah was the only one on the deck not killed outright. He was caught by the fire wave and was terribly burned. He yelled to get up the anchor, but before two fathoms were heaved in, the *Roraima* was almost upset by the boiling whirlpool and the fire wave had thrown her down on her beam ends to starboard. Captain Muggah was overcome by the flames. He fell unconscious from the bridge and overboard. The blast of fire from the volcano lasted only a few minutes. It shrivelled and set fire to everything it touched. Thousands of casks of rum were stored in St. Pierre, and these were exploded by the terrific heat. The burning rum ran in streams down every street and out into the sea. This blazing rum set fire to the *Roraima* several times.

"Before the volcano burst, the landings of St. Pierre were covered with people. After the explosion, not one living soul was seen on the land. Only twenty-five of those on board were left after the first blast.

"The French cruiser *Suchet* came in and took us off at 2 P.M. She remained near by, helping all she could, until 5 o'clock, then went to Fort de France with all the people she had rescued. At the time it looked as if the entire north end of the island was on fire."

In 1976 the volcano La Soufrière on the Caribbean island of Guadeloupe erupted with a series of worrisome phreatic explosions. Fearful of another Mont Pelée catastrophe, the French government ordered the evacuation of some 70,000 people at a cost of many tens of millions of dollars. A peléan eruption did not occur, however, and the inhabitants were permitted to return after several weeks. La Soufrière is being watched closely for signs of a dangerous turn.

Krakatoa. The 1883 explosion of Krakatoa, in the strait between Java and Sumatra, was one of the greatest witnessed by man. Krakatoa was an island formed from nested volcanic cones in an ancient caldera. The caldera, 6 kilometers (4 miles) across, was a remnant of a prehistoric andesitic stratovolcano. On August 27, following numerous smaller explosions, Krakatoa blew its top in a phreatic explosion with a TNT equivalent of about 100 megatons (million tons) (2×10^{11} pounds). The sound of the explosion was heard in Australia, nearly 2000 kilometers away. The atmospheric pressure waves were recorded on weather barographs on the other side of the Earth. Nearly 20 cubic kilometers (5 cubic miles) of debris was discharged into the air, much of it falling as ash over an area of some 700,000 square kilometers (300,000 square miles). Almost total darkness settled on Jakarta, 150 kilometers (100 miles) away when the dust blotted out the Sun. Fine dust rose to the stratosphere and drifted around the Earth, producing brilliant red sunsets for several years and lowering Earth's mean annual temperature by a few degrees by partially blocking solar radiation. The explosion generated a giant sea wave that reached a height of almost 40 meters (130 feet) and drowned 36,000 people in nearby coastal towns. The sea waves were recorded on tide gauges as far away as the English Channel. After the eruption, most of Krakatoa had disappeared, leaving in its place a water covered basin 300 meters (100 feet) deep. It is believed that much of the energy was provided by the violent expansion of hot steam after the walls of the volcano were initially ruptured, permitting sea water to pour into the magma chamber. The result can be viewed as one of the biggest steam-boiler explosions in recorded history.

Following forty-four years of quiescence, another cycle of volcanic activity began in 1927. A new island, *Anak Krakatoa* (Child of Krakatoa), is now building up by repeated eruptions and has reached a height of more than 100 meters (330 feet).

THE GLOBAL PATTERN OF VOLCANISM

At the outset of this chapter, we mentioned the correlation of active volcanism with present-day plate margins. As can be seen from Figure 15-3 most volcanoes occur in connection with plate boundaries, 15 percent in belts of tension, where plates diverge, and 80 percent in belts of compression, where plates converge. To a lesser extent, volcanoes are also found within plates. Examples are Hawaii, which lies within the Pacific plate, and the eastern rift zone, which lies within the African plate. The global pattern of volcanism in association with plate boundaries also extends to the types of lavas that erupt and consequently to the styles of eruptions. Most lavas that issue from vents in oceanic divergence zones and from intraoceanic volcanoes are derived from basaltic magma. Where ocean plate collides with ocean plate, basalts and andesites predominate (see Fig. 15-4 as a reminder of the classification of lavas). Adjacent to the zone along which an ocean plate converges against a continental margin, rhyolitic ignimbrites are found as well as basalt and andesite. If we are allowed to present heuristic arguments (reasonable ones, but without proof), make some broad generalizations, and not try to account for all details at this early stage of the theory of plate tectonics, this worldwide pattern can be understood in a consistent and insightful manner. But first we must say something about mafic, intermediate, and silicic magmas and their possible modes of origin.

Magmas—Where Do They Come From? Our current views of the principal zones of the upper few hundred kilometers of the Earth are summarized in Fig. 1-14. The continents float like rafts on the rigid plates of the lithosphere. The continental crust is made up mainly of granite and other felsic rocks. Such rocks are almost entirely missing from the sea floor, the oceanic crust consisting mostly of the mafics basalt and gabbro. The crust is separated from the rest of the lithosphere by an abrupt change in chemical composition called **M discontinuity.** Beneath this discontinuity the lithosphere consists of ultramafic rock (even less silica and more ferromagnesian minerals than mafic), underlain by the weak, partially molten asthenosphere, which is also ultramafic. We will give more details about these zones in later chapters.

Basalt amounts to about 40 percent of all the rock types in the Earth's crust, and is the principal rock produced by volcanism. We surmise that basalt must be the molten component of the asthenosphere for several reasons. Recalling the case history of Kilauea on Hawaii, we know from seismic evidence that the magma taps the asthenosphere and that basalt is the eruptive result. Peridotite is our best guess for the ultramafic rock that makes up most of the upper mantle. When peridotite is heated in the laboratory to the temperature at which melting begins, basalt is the first liquid to form.*

The felsic lavas at the silicic end of the scale of volcanic rocks, such as rhyolite, must have another origin. The compositional contrast with basalt is so great that the location and nature of the parent rocks or the evolution of the magma must be different. That rhyolites are found on continents and on some islands, such as Iceland and the Azores, but not on the sea floor (where a felsic crust is absent) is an important clue. One way to make rhyolite is obvious—by completely remelting granitic continental crustal rocks to produce silicic magma. Alternatively, sediments derived from these rocks and deposited on the sea floor adjacent to continents could, if reheated, yield silicic magma. One favorable environment for the formation of silicic magma would therefore be a convergence zone where the leading edge of one of the colliding plates is a continental margin. All the ingredients for "cooking up" silicic magmas are present: heat, deformation, and an abundance of parent materials of the proper composition (see Fig. 1-18).

Fractional crystallization of a basaltic magma is another way to make felsic lavas. Suppose a basaltic magma cools in a magma chamber until crystals begin to form. The first mineral to appear is olivine, which sinks to the bottom, leaving a more silicic magma. This process of gravitational settling of heavy crystals can continue as long as new minerals crystallize; at each stage the residual liquid, or differentiate, would have a different composition, depending on which minerals were formed and separated from it. In principle, the differentiation series represented by the transformation from basalt to andesite to rhyolite is possible, and has been observed on some oceanic islands. It is doubtful whether rhyolite, the ultimate differentiate, commonly originates from a parent basaltic

---

*Basalts are highly variable, a subject we will not go into except to say that composition can depend on such factors as local composition of the parent rock, depth of melting, amount of water present, degree of partial melting, and assimilation of other rocks en route to the surface.

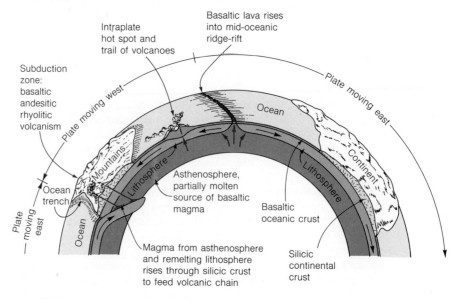

Figure 15-38
Schematic representation of volcanism on a global scale, showing the association with plate boundaries, particularly the regions of formation and destruction of the lithosphere.

magma, but an intermediate differentiate, andesite, is found on oceanic islands, where it undoubtedly formed as a differentiate from the much more abundant basalt. In fact, Icelandic geologists have shown that the longer the period of repose between eruptions, the more silicic is the eruptive, since there is more time for fractional crystallization and settling to occur (see Chapter 14 for a discussion of fractional crystallization).

As was mentioned in the preceding chapter, andesite might also be the product of partial melting of mantle materials in the presence of water, perhaps derived from the uppermost layers of a subducting plate.

Because andesites are roughly intermediate in composition between basalt and rhyolite, they can also result from a mixture of mafic and silicic magmas or by assimilation of surrounding granitic rock by a mafic magma. Nevertheless, the occurrence of large volumes of andesite in conjunction with subduction zones argues for still another source, perhaps the most important one. In recent years it has been suggested that a downgoing, cold oceanic plate begins to remelt when it plunges diagonally into the asthenosphere. Heat flowing in from the hotter asthenosphere and the heat generated by friction along the contact between the upper surface of the

descending plate and the overriding plate would supply the thermal energy needed for melting. Thus the basaltic crust of the old sea floor, chemically enriched with silica by its clinging veneer of wet ocean-bottom sediments, could melt into andesitic magma, which would rise buoyantly to erupt from volcanoes in the overlying volcanic arc. We are now in a position to summarize some of the major features of volcanism on a global scale (Fig. 15-38).

Ocean-Ridge Volcanism. A worldwide system of fissures, along which basalt erupts, coincides with the ridge-rifts depicted on the inside of the front cover and in the schematic section of Figure 15-38. The fracture between the separating plates extends to the asthenosphere. A mush of peridotite and basaltic magma rises buoyantly into the fracture to form new lithosphere. As the hot peridotite from the asthenosphere rises in the gap between the separating plates, the reduced pressures induce further melting, adding to the supply of basalt. The overflow forms ocean ridges, volcanoes, and the basaltic sea floor crust. Basaltic plateaus such as Iceland can also build up.

Intraplate Volcanism. Although most volcanic activity is concentrated at plate bounda-

Figure 15-39
If hot spots are stationary, the "tracks" of the Hawaiian Island chain and the parallel Tuomotu and Austral chains would trace movement of the Pacific plate over the hot spots marked by the active volcanoes on Hawaii, Pitcairn Island, and MacDonald Seamount. All three chains would indicate the same motion of the Pacific plate; the bends in the chains formed 40 million years ago record a change in direction of plate motion at that time. Broken segments indicate inconclusive evidence of progressively older age sequence. [After "Hot Spots on the Earth's Surface" by K. C. Burke and J. T. Wilson. Copyright © 1976 by Scientific American, Inc. All rights reserved.]

ries, volcanoes within plates can produce enormous volumes of lava. An example is the island chain that begins with the active volcanoes on Hawaii and continues as a string of progressively older, extinct, eroded, and submerged volcanic ridges and mountains (Figure 15-39). Except for Hawaii itself, where earthquakes are triggered by volcanic activity, the chain is essentially aseismic (without earthquakes) and is called an **aseismic ridge,** different from the seismic mid-ocean ridges where sea-floor spreading takes place. Aseismic ridges, which also occur elsewhere in the Pacific and in the other large oceans, have been difficult to incorporate into the framework of plate-tectonic theory.

Jason Morgan of Princeton and J. Tuzo Wilson of Toronto have introduced the controversial concept of **hot spots** to explain aseismic ridges and other volcanic centers within continents. They propose that hot spots are the surface manifestations of jets or plumes of hot

material that rise from deep within the mantle, drill through the lithosphere, and emerge as volcanic centers. These jet-like columnar currents are supposedly fixed in the mantle and do not move with the plates. As a result, the hot spot leaves a trail of extinct, progressively older volcanoes as the plate moves over it. If hot spots are indeed fixed in the mantle, they provide a powerful method of measuring the velocity and direction of plate motion from the trail of volcanoes carried away from the hot spot (Figs. 15-38 and 15-39). The assumption that hot spots are immobile is now being examined very carefully by geophysicists.

Extinct undersea basaltic volcanoes, rising kilometers or more above the sea floor, are common intraplate volcanic features. More than 10,000 are known in the Pacific Ocean alone. They are thought to have originated as active volcanoes near spreading centers and to have become extinct as the plate carried them away.

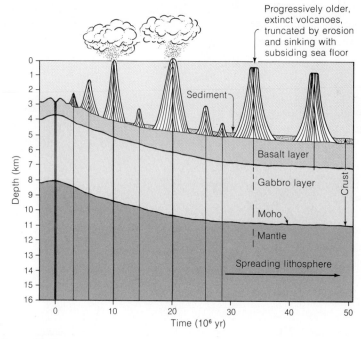

Figure 15-40
Guyots probably began as undersea volcanoes that grew near spreading centers. Many projected above sea level, became extinct, and were eroded down to flat-topped cones by wave action. The volcanoes rode along on the moving plate as they grew, were then truncated, and finally sank beneath the sea surface as the plate that carried them subsided. [After "The Deep Ocean Floor" by H. W. Menard. Copyright © 1969 by Scientific American, Inc. All rights reserved.]

Some initially projected above sea level but were eroded down to flat-topped cones by wave action. As the oceanic lithosphere spread, cooled, and contracted, the sea floor subsided, dropping the truncated volcanoes below sea level. These are the guyots mentioned in Chapter 10 and depicted in Figure 15-40.

Volcanic centers within continental plates take different forms. Fissure eruptions of basalt, like those in the Pacific Northwest of the United States, imply that a fracture penetrated the continental lithosphere and that the basalt spurted rapidly to the surface without much contamination from the silicic crust. Perhaps tensile fractures developed in the early stages of an abortive spreading episode. Eruptions of basalt, marking the initial stages of continental rifting, or breakup, can be documented in several parts of the world. For example, basalt flows found today in fault-bounded troughs in eastern North America erupted at the beginning of the breakup of Pangaea some 200 million years ago. Basalt is found in association with the rift valleys of East Africa—a feature that some geologists interpret as representing an abortive stage in the breakup of that continent.

The vast ignimbrite sheets, which are the rhyolitic counterpart of flood basalts, have no easy explanation. Perhaps magma rising slowly from the upper mantle assimilates large quantities of the granitic or sedimentary crust and in this way is transformed into a rhyolitic magma.

Convergence-zone Volcanism. The many phenomena that occur where plates converge are now being sorted out by Earth scientists. One of the main features of a region of plate collision is the chain of volcanoes that stands subparallel to the adjacent deep-sea trench and marks the edge of the overriding plate. Where two oceanic plates converge, an island arc builds up from the sea floor, typically by the extrusion of basalts and andesites. The basalts probably derive from the asthenosphere above the descending plate, and the andesites might come from the partial melting of the basaltic crust and the ocean-bottom sediments attached to the descending plate, as was mentioned earlier. The Philippine arc and the Marianas Arc are examples of this type of convergence zone. The growing island arc contributes erosion products and volcanic debris to the offshore region and beyond into the trench. In a later stage this pile can be compressed, heated, intruded, and uplifted to form new continental crust and mountains. Japan is a prototype of this process, and Fujiyama is an example of an andesitic cone rising within a growing arc. Another example is Mt. Pelée on Martinique, which squeezes out viscous silicic lavas and explosive nuées ardentes, which are deposited as ignimbrites.

When an oceanic plate is overridden by a plate carrying a continent on its leading edge, as in Figure 15-38, an arcuate mountain chain is thrown up in the zone of compression near the continental margin. The Chilean trench and the adjacent Andes Mountains are examples of such arcuate mountains, and the magmatic activity is typically manifested by the ejection of huge quantities of ash and the eruption of andesitic and basaltic lavas. Basalt would occur if magma from the asthenosphere could reach the surface without being contaminated by sediments or the intervening felsic crust. But the more felsic eruptives seem to imply remelting of the subducted plate or contamination by sediments or actual melting of continental crust. Parícutin (Mexico), Cosequina (Nicaragua), Irazu (Costa Rica), Cotopaxi (Equador), and Calbuco (Chile) are examples (see Fig. 15-3).

The Growth of Continents. It is basic to the theory of sea-floor spreading that the sea floor is ephemeral: it is created by spreading at ridge-rifts and destroyed by subduction. Furthermore, continents and island arcs can be eroded but not destroyed, since they are too light to sink back into the mantle. Continents grow on their leading edge by sedimentation and magmatism of the kind just described. Island arcs build up from the sea floor. According to the theory, ocean basins eventually close up; continents run into continents, trapping arcs and sediment-filled troughs between them. Perhaps this also contributes to continental growth. Even the erosion products may eventually be recycled back to the continents after spending some time on the sea floor (see Fig. 1-18).

VOLCANISM AND HUMAN AFFAIRS

Can volcanic eruptions be predicted? This question is of real concern. Some 200,000 people have been killed by volcanoes in the past 500 years. With the increased concentration of population, the toll could go higher. The geologic record shows that ignimbrite sheets have been deposited on a vast scale—something that humans have not yet recorded. If the Katmai (Alaska) eruption of 1912 had been centered in New York (chosen only to show the scale of the event), the city would have been destroyed, one foot of ash would have covered Philadelphia, and fumes would have reached Denver.

Volcanoes kill and destroy in several ways: lava flows, nuées ardentes, and phreatic explosions and their consequences, such as tsunamis, ash falls, and lahars. A shield volcano like Kilauea, whose eruptive style is the release of basaltic lava, provides the best chance of successful prediction. The premonitory phenomena are many: earthquakes, ground tilt, seismic tremor. There may be no way to prevent Kilauea from damaging property, but it need not be a killer. Erupting basaltic lava usually flows slowly enough for people to get out of the way, and in some situations the lava streams might be diverted from property.

Volcanoes situated at plate boundaries, erupting gas-charged, silicic (hence viscous) magma and pyroclasts, are particularly dangerous; they explode, and the instant of the explosion is almost impossible to predict. The beginning of a period of dangerous activity might be foretold by seismographs, tiltmeters, temperature monitors, gas detectors, or changes in gravity and magnetic fields. The eruption of pyroclasts containing fresh magmatic glass rather than altered, reworked old material is a danger signal. At the first indication of activity, a local population, especially downwind of the volcano, might at least be alerted for possible evacuation. This, however, would be more like long-range or climatological forecasting than a weather report for the next day. Phreatic explosions must be treated similarly, for the danger zone can extend over hundreds of kilometers, especially if the volcano has a history of generating tsunamis. Krakatoa is the prime example.

Lahars occur in conjunction with eruptions near ice fields or bodies of water. The paths of lahars should be predictable, both from topography and recent history. Even though some minutes or hours of warning might be possible after an eruption has occurred, it seems better to prevent habitation of possible lahar paths below volcanoes.

Although it will be difficult, it may soon be possible to predict future eruptions of known active or temporarily dormant volcanoes. But what of the long-extinct volcanoes? Will they come to life suddenly—as Vesuvius did? Some

Perhaps the most successful attempt to control volcanic activity was made on the Icelandic island of Heimaey during the eruption of January 1973. By spraying the advancing lava with sea water, Icelanders cooled and slowed the flow, preventing the lava from destroying homes and blocking the port entrance.

currently inactive but potentially dangerous volcanoes are Mt. Baker and Mt. St. Helens in Washington, Mt. Hood in Oregon, and Mt. Shasta in California. An even more difficult problem of prediction is posed by Parícutin, which rose up from a flat farm field. Finding out how to sense the movements of deep lava in relation to possible new outlets to the surface will be a real challenge.

Beneficial Aspects of Volcanism. We have seen something of the beauty of volcanoes and also something of their destructiveness. Volcanoes contribute to our well-being in numerous ways. The atmospheres and the oceans originated in volcanic episodes of the distant past.

Soils derived from volcanic materials are exceptionally fertile. Emissions of volcanic rock, gas, and steam are also sources of important industrial materials and chemicals, such as pumice, boric acid, ammonia, carbon dioxide. The thermal energy of volcanism is being harnessed more and more. Most of the houses in Reykjavik, Iceland, are heated by hot water tapped from volcanic springs. Geothermal steam is exploited as a source of energy for the production of electricity in Italy, New Zealand, the United States, Mexico, Japan, and the U.S.S.R. Exploration for new geothermal energy concentrations is actively underway in the United States and Mexico.

SUMMARY

1. Volcanism occurs because molten rock inside the Earth rises to the surface, squeezed up by the weight of the overlying layers.

2. The classification of lavas into felsic, intermediate, and mafic is based on the decrease in silica content and the increase in iron-magnesium mineral content. The chemical composition and gas content of lava are important in determining the form an eruption takes.

3. Basalt can be highly fluid and erupt in sheets from fissures, often building lava plateaus. Shield volcanoes grow from repeated eruption of basalt from vents. Silicic magma is more viscous and, when charged with gas, tends to erupt explosively. The pyroclastic debris piles up into cinder cones or covers extensive areas with ignimbrites or ash-flow sheets. Stratovolcanoes are built of alternating layers of lava flows and pyroclastic deposits.

4. Oceanic volcanoes are almost entirely basaltic. The formation of the sea floor from basaltic magma rising from the asthenosphere into fissures of the ocean ridge-rift system is volumetrically the most significant form of volcanism. The more intermediate and silicic eruptives tend to occur on islands and continental margins, in regions where plates collide. They may originate by remelting of the sinking lithosphere or by assimilation of silicic sea-bottom sediments or silicic continental crust into rising magma.

EXERCISES

1. It seems reasonable to identify the asthenosphere as a major source of magma. Why? What forces magma to rise to the surface?

2. What is the difference between magma and lava? Give some examples of types of lava and their coarse-grained, intrusive counterparts.

3. Describe the principal styles of volcanic eruptions and the deposits and landforms they produce.

4. What is the association between plate boundaries and volcanism? Can the eruptive style and composition of volcanic deposits be correlated with plate boundaries?

5. About 6 cubic kilometers of basalt pours out on the sea floor each year (3 times the amount of lava that spews out on continents). Assuming constant outflow and a uniform spread over all the present oceans, how thick a layer would be laid down on the sea floor over 200 million years? Obtain area of oceans from Appendix III.

BIBLIOGRAPHY

Burke, K. C., and J. T. Wilson, "Hot Spots on the Earth's Surface: *Scientific American,* August 1976.

Green, Jack, and N. M. Short, *Volcanic Landforms and Surface Features.* New York: Springer-Verlag, 1972.

Herbert, Don, and Fulvio Bardossi, *Kilauea: Case History of a Volcano.* New York: Harper and Row, 1968.

U.S. Geological Survey, *Atlas of Volcanic Phenomena.* U.S. Geological Survey, Washington, D.C. 20242.

U.S. Geological Survey, *Volcanoes of the United States* (a pamphlet), U.S. Geological Survey, Washington, D.C., 20242.

Wilcoxon, K. H., *Chains of Fire—The Story of Volcanoes.* Philadelphia: Chilton Books, 1966.

16

PLUTONISM AND METAMORPHISM

Evidence of the processes of igneous intrusion and metamorphism by heat and pressure is found in the structure and form of plutonic bodies and the metamorphic rocks that are associated with them. Plutons take a variety of shapes and sizes, depending on the kinds of rocks intruded, the volume of magma, and the deformation accompanying emplacement: dikes, sills, laccoliths, lopoliths, and batholiths are all geological expressions of intrusion. Metamorphic rocks, associated with mountain belts and igneous activity, are of three main kinds. Cataclastic rocks are mechanically broken and ground up rocks produced by high deformational pressures. Contact metamorphic rocks are produced in baked zones of high temperature bordering intrusions. Regionally metamorphosed rocks are made by the combination of pressure and temperature operating over wide areas. As is true in igneous rocks, texture and mineralogy are the pressure gages and thermometers of metamorphism.

Much is known of the mechanisms by which extrusive rocks are formed, because the eruption of volcanoes and the ejection of lava have been open to direct study in many places at the Earth's surface. This is not true, however, of the mechanisms by which igneous and metamorphic rocks are formed at depth; indirect evidence has to be relied upon in the study of their formation, long after the rocks have cooled. The forms that molten igneous masses take when they intrude the crust are deduced from direct evidence gained through geological field work done millions or billions of years after the rocks were emplaced. Similarly, metamorphism, the geological effects of regional increase of heat and pressure, has to be studied in the same way, long after the fact. The biologist dissects his specimen to see what goes on inside, but the geologist must, in a sense, wait for Earth to dissect itself. Field study of igneous and metamorphic rocks can proceed only where the crust has been uplifted and subjected to deep erosion. Thus the study of these kinds of rocks is indissolubly linked with structural geology and the history of mountain belts.

Holes have been drilled into the Earth's crust in various places where heat flow and seismic activity indicate active igneous and metamorphic processes are now operating. One of these is under the Salton Sea, in Southern California, where the North American lithospheric plate abuts the Pacific plate along the San Andreas transform fault. The temperatures in the drill hole are so high that superheated steam and water are produced, along with a great quantity of unusual chemical substances, including many metallic elements, all of which are dissolved in water. From the chemical composition of the waters, geochemists have inferred that a magmatic body at depth is metamorphosing the sediments around it. Drill holes and mine workings are of chief importance, however, not in regions of current igneous activity, but in regions where they extend the eyes of geologists to older rocks that are now cooled but still buried. In such places, the details of structure and form are mapped as a guide to further exploration for metal ores, for many of the great economic mineral resources of the Earth are formed by igneous and metamorphic activity.

Figure 16-1
Block diagram of plutonic and volcanic structures.
[After R. G. Schmidt and H. R. Shaw, U.S. Geological Survey.]

PLUTONS

Igneous bodies that have congealed from magma underground are called **plutons.** When uplift and erosion expose them to study, or when they are examined in mines and boreholes, they are found to be variable in size and shape and in their relationship to the **country rock**—that is, the invaded rock surrounding them. Plutons include **laccoliths, lopoliths, stocks,** and **batholiths.** Figure 16-1 depicts some of these different kinds of plutons as well as **dikes** and **sills.**

Magma rising through the crust makes space for itself in several ways. It can heat its way upward by breaking off blocks of the invaded rock, which sink and are assimilated at depth (**stoping,** the name of the process, is borrowed from the mining term for the removal of ore by working upwards); it can heat the invaded rock enough to make it flow plastically out of the way; and it can forcibly split rocks apart or bow them up. The structure of overlying rocks often gives the clue to the process of intrusion.

Sills, Laccoliths, and Dikes. There are probably few open voids or cavities at depths much greater than 8 or 10 kilometers. The pressure due to the weight of the overlying rock would tend to close them. Since there are no vacant spaces for sills, laccoliths, and dikes to fill, these intrusions must make their own space by wedging open and penetrating cracks, joints, or planes of weakness, the force coming from the pressure that drives the magma. A **sill** is a tabular pluton that has been formed by injection of magma between beds of layered rock in a **concordant** fashion; that is, its boundaries are parallel to the layering. Sills range in thickness from a mere centimeter to as much as hundreds of meters, and can extend laterally over considerable areas (Fig. 16-2). The Whin Sill in northern England is the type example. It averages about 25 meters (80 feet) in thickness and has an area of some 4000 square kilometers (1550 square miles). The 300-meter (1000-foot) thick Palisades Sill, which overlooks the Hudson River in New York and New Jersey, is another example.

Figure 16-2
Diabase sills in Victoria Land, Antarctica. The concordant sill in the center of the mountain face sent discordant tongues into its floor and turned abruptly into a thick dike toward the left side. [Photo by W. B. Hamilton, U.S. Geological Survey.]

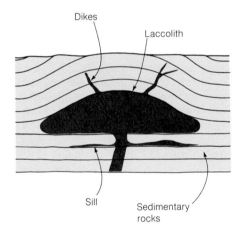

Figure 16-3
Diagrammatic cross section of a laccolith intruded between sedimentary rock layers, bowing up overlying rocks in a dome-like structure.

Figure 16-4
Map and cross section of laccoliths and stocks in the Judith Mountains, Montana. [After W. H. Weed and L. U. Pirsson, U.S. Geological Survey.]

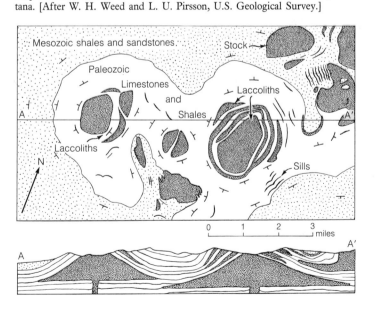

Sills can be distinguished from sheets of extrusive rock because they lack the ropy, blocky, vesicular or pillow structure of lava flows. Moreover, sills are typically coarser grained, and the rocks above and below them show thermal effects, such as baking or bleaching.

Like sills, **laccoliths** are formed by the injection of magma along bedding planes of flat, layered rocks, but instead of being tabular they typically have a mushroom shape (Figs. 16-3, 16-4). Unlike sills, laccoliths dome the overlying layers upward. Sills and laccoliths are both injected at high enough pressures to overcome the

Figure 16-5
Dikes of dark igneous rock cutting across biotite gneiss. Gunnison County, Colorado. [Photo by W. R. Hansen, U.S. Geological Survey.]

weight of the overlying rocks, which are uplifted to accommodate the magma.

Dikes are tabular plutons that are discordant; that is, they cut across the layering of the country rock. Dikes can force open pre-existing fractures, but more often their channels follow cracks opened by the pressure of magmatic injection. Some individual dikes can be traced across country for tens of kilometers. Widths vary from centimeters to many meters (Fig. 16-5). When country rock is deformed by intrusion, many cracks are formed, all of which are possible channels for the invading magma. For this reason, dikes rarely occur alone; more typically, large numbers, or **swarms,** of hundreds or thousands of dikes are found in a region.

Some dikes crop out roughly in the form of circles or ellipses. Called **ring dikes,** these features are thought to be erosional remnants of intrusions that filled cylindrically shaped fractures. Supposedly, a fracture of this sort forms when a crustal block with roughly circular section sinks into a depleted magma chamber. The resulting ring dike bounds a circular area of subsidence. Ring dikes have been found with diameters ranging up to 25 kilometers.

Lopoliths and Batholiths. These are more massive intrusions, generally formed deeper in the crust than the plutons discussed in the preceding section. A **lopolith** is a large, floored intrusive whose center has sagged downward, both roof and floor, to form a bowl-shaped body. The Duluth lopolith, the type example, is a huge intrusion of gabbro. It crops out on both sides of Lake Superior's western end, and is inferred to continue beneath the lake. It is estimated to be 250 kilometers across, 15 kilometers thick, and to have a volume of about 200,000 cubic kilometers. Geophysical data suggest that, buried beneath younger rocks, it extends all the way to Kansas. If so, it is enormously more voluminous than estimated above.

Batholiths, the largest of plutons, are discordant intrusives that are, by definition, at least 100 square kilometers in area. Similar, but smaller, discordant plutons are called **stocks.** The bottoms of most batholiths are unexposed and hence unplumbed by the field geologist. Whether they remain constant or increase in cross section with depth is known only by geophysical inference, but many are estimated to extend perhaps 10 to 30 kilometers into the crust. Some batholiths seem to be less thick; the Boulder batholith, for example, is no more than 15 kilometers deep, and may be much less.

Lopoliths and batholiths are generally coarse-grained—a consequence of the slow cooling that deeply buried bodies experience. Most lopoliths are differentiated, showing conspicuous zones or bands of contrasting minerals. During the slow process of crystallization that takes place in these igneous masses, crystals become segregated; the heaviest and first to form sink through the melt under gravity to a level governed by their density (Fig. 16-7; see also Chapter 14). Convection currents in the cooling magma might also influence the mineral stratification by sorting out groups of minerals.

Some batholiths have sharp contact with country rock, and show flow structures in which elongated, needle-shaped crystals are arranged

Figure 16-6
Generalized geological map of the Sierra Nevada and adjacent areas, showing the extent of this large batholith, now exposed at the surface by subsequent erosion. [After P. C. Bateman and J. P. Eaton, *Science*, v. 158, p. 1407, 1967. Copyright 1967 by the American Association for the Advancement of Science.]

Younger volcanic rocks

Mesozoic and Paleozoic rocks intruded by Batholith

Batholith

Pre-Cenozoic rocks of unknown age

Figure 16-7
Banded structure, or layering, in granitic intrusion, possibly due to gravity settling. Sierra Nevada batholith. [From P. C. Bateman, L. D. Clark, N. King Huber, J. G. Moore, and D. Rinehart, U.S. Geological Survey.]

Figure 16-8
Contact metamorphism displayed by a limestone intruded by a sill. The hammer lies along the contact of the sill, the dark gray rock below. The limestone above the sill is bleached to a light and moderate gray in contrast to the darker unmetamorphosed limestone above. Gallatin County, Montana. [Photo by I. J. Witkind, U.S. Geological Survey.]

Figure 16-9
Photomicrograph in polarized light of a cataclastically deformed rock, a gneiss taken from a fault zone. Bands of coarse, granulated gneiss with large, light crystals alternate with darker bands of finely granulated mylonite. Gilpin County, Colorado. [Photo by W. A. Braddock, U.S. Geological Survey.]

in parallel alignment, like logs aligned parallel to the flow of a river. These features imply that the batholiths were formed by injection of an igneous magma. Other batholiths grade into country rock without sharp contacts, and exhibit structures that vaguely resemble those of sedimentary rocks. Such features imply that preexisting sediments were **granitized**—converted in place to granite by hot solutions and gases percolating up from great depths. The origin of batholiths, linked with the origin of granite (Chapter 14), is one of the most durable of controversies; it is still a hotly debated subject. Geologists today subscribe to various combinations of two views: that plutons are the result of igneous intrusions, and that they are produced by granitization of pre-existing rocks in place.

As we will see, batholiths form in the cores of many mountain ranges (see Fig. 14-9). Moreover, immense regions of exposed Precambrian rocks in continental interiors are made up of successions of overlapping batholiths, many of which show the characteristics of roots of ancient mountains long since removed by erosion. All of this implies a connection between large-scale plutonism and the mountain-making process—a connection that will be further explored in Chapter 20.

METAMORPHISM

What happens to a rock when it is baked and squeezed in the Earth? The change in mineral composition and texture may be ever so slight or it may be so great that the rock is completely altered in appearance. The degree of change depends mainly on the pressures and temperatures to which the rock was subjected. One good place to see the effect of heat alone is in an outcrop where a shale has been intruded by a dike or sill. At some distance from the intrusion, the shale begins to show a loss of bedded structure, and its clay minerals have recrystallized to micas. At the contact with the igneous rock, the shale has lost all of its original texture, and is now a coarsely grained, crystalline, **contact metamorphic** rock containing pyroxenes and anhydrous (lacking water) aluminosilicate minerals like andalusite (Al_2SiO_5). The conclusion is inescapable that the high temperature of the intrusion caused the disappearance of clay minerals, which were originally formed by low-temperature weathering processes, and the appearance within the rock of new minerals, such as pyroxenes, that are characteristic of high temperatures.

The transforming effect of pressure and tectonic movement alone on rocks is obvious along fault planes, where rock is sheared and ground up to a paste. The mineralogy may be unaffected even though the rock has become pulverized. These **cataclastic** rocks, the mechanically fragmented metamorphic products of intense folding and faulting, are associated with a variety of tectonic structures.

The great bulk of metamorphic rocks are those that have been subjected to both high temperature and pressure over large regions, with the consequent destruction of original igneous or sedimentary structures and the growth of new minerals. These rocks are the products of **regional metamorphism** rather than the products of localized reactions along fault planes or the borders of igneous intrusions, with which cataclastic and contact metamorphic rocks are associated. Regionally metamorphosed rocks are found in the cores of deeply eroded, folded, and intruded mountain belts in company with granitic batholiths. The formation of new minerals goes hand in hand with structural deformation, and both produce characteristic textures.

METAMORPHIC TEXTURES

The ways in which the crystals in a metamorphic rock have been rearranged are guides to the processes that produced the new rock from its original sedimentary or igneous parent. The grain and bedding textures in detrital sediments are mainly the products of fluid flow regimes, and the crystalline textures of igneous rocks and some chemical sediments are the result of primary crystallization from a melt or solution; in contrast, the textures of metamorphic rocks are the result of recrystallization of conversion of one mineral to another in the solid state.

Foliation and Fracture Cleavage. Most conspicuous in a large variety of deformed metamorphic rocks are parallel planes that generally cut the rocks at an angle to the bedding of the original sediment, though it may coincide with it in some places. This **foliation** may be so weak as to be barely seen, or it may so dominate that it is the only visible structure. Many shales part fairly easily along bedding planes, a property called **fissility.** As many such shales are traced into structurally deformed mountain belts, they

Figure 16-10
Structurally deformed and complexly metamorphosed Paleozoic rocks in Eastern Massachusetts. [Photo by R. Siever.]

Figure 16-11
Slaty cleavage in a schist. [Photo by W. B. Hamilton, U.S. Geological Survey.]

Original bedding best shown by thin sandy layers

New foliation of slate, best developed in original layers of shale

Sandy layer with imperfect foliation

Foliation plane is a shear plane

Original bedding

Sand grains

0   5 cm

Figure 16-12
Fragments of slate (left) showing foliation (vertical lines) and relics of original bedding. The enlargement shows small offsets of the bedding along the surfaces of foliation of the cleavage. [From *Principles of Geology* (4th ed.) by J. Gilluly, A. C. Waters, and A. O. Woodford. W. H. Freeman and Company. Copyright © 1975.]

Figure 16-13
Intricately folded veinlet of quartz cutting across planes of schistosity in a mica schist. [Photo by J. C. Reed, U.S. Geological Survey.]

become transformed into **slates,** harder rocks that typically show a **fracture cleavage.** This variety of foliation is named from a tendency to cleave or break into moderately thin sheets at more or less regular intervals. The cleavage is not only at an angle to the bedding but sometimes can be seen to offset it by a small amount at each fracture. The cross-cutting relationship is evidence of the deformational origin of the foliation. The almost perfect cleavage of some slates makes them ideal for us as roofing tile. Others that cleave into thicker sheets are more suitable for flagstones. The cleavage is sound textural evidence of metamorphism.

If the slate can be traced into an even more deformed region, the foliation is found to become finer and more all pervasive, the rock showing the lineation of **flow cleavage,** characterized by very thin sheets along which platy minerals, such as mica, have grown parallel to the foliation planes. Further growth of crystals to larger size, visible to the naked eye, accompanied by some segregation of minerals into lighter and darker bands produces **schistosity,** the coarse foliation of **schists.**

The coarsest foliation is shown by **gneisses,** in which coarse bands of segregated light and dark minerals are prominent throughout the rock. There is little or no tendency to part or split along these bands, and there are relatively few platy minerals parallel to the bands.

Amphiboles form needle-like crystals in many metamorphic rocks. In some the needles show a marked **lineation,** or parallel alignment. Lineation can also be formed by the intersection of cleavage and bedding planes. In schists this

Figure 16-14
A banded gneiss of metamorphosed sandstone and schist. The darker beds are a mixture of flattened lenses of dark biotite schist and lighter gray quartz-feldspar rock similar to the lighter metamorphosed sandstone layers. Great Smoky Mountains, South Carolina. [Photo by J. B. Hadley, U.S. Geological Survey.]

Figure 16-15
Lineation is a metamorphic texture formed by parallel orientation of prismatic or needle-shaped crystals of such minerals as pyroxenes or amphiboles. Viewed end on, the needles appear as dots.

texture is oriented parallel to foliation. Where foliation is not well developed, the lineation may be the most prominent textural feature. Good foliation is most common in the mica-bearing slates and schists formed from shales. Good lineation is best developed in rocks of mafic composition, which metamorphose to form large amounts of elongate amphibole crystals.

Foliation, lineation, and other metamorphic textures are the product of **preferred orientation** of crystals, the pronounced tendency toward parallel alignment of crystals. The orientation is related to the directions of the compressional forces of deformation responsible for crystallization or recrystallization. In simplest relation to folded structures, mica flakes grow with their shortest dimension (the crystallographic *c*-axis) perpendicular to the major compressional force. The plane of the flake or sheet is parallel to (and is the main cause of) the cleavage or foliation, which is itself parallel to the plane of the folding, as shown in Figure 16-16 (see also the section "Axial Plane" in Chapter 20). Preferred orientation probably results from a combination of crystal growth in the preferred direction, some plastic deformation or flowage of an existing crystal, and the physical rotation of a crystal during deformation.

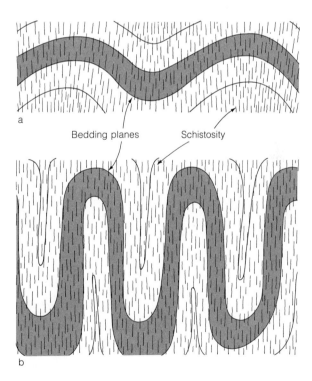

Bedding planes   Schistosity

Figure 16-16
(a) In moderately folded, bedded rocks, the angle between schistosity and bedding planes varies from the limbs to the apex of a fold. (b) In tightly folded rocks, the schistosity is essentially parallel to bedding over most of the fold.

Figure 16-17
A hornfels breccia. Darker fragments of hornfels were broken during the intrusion and recemented with a lighter hornfels. Both kinds show a granular texture and absence of foliation. [Photo by H. C. Granger, U.S. Geological Survey.]

Mineral Textures. Because most contact metamorphic rocks have undergone little or no deformation, they lack foliated structures. Their texture is nondirectional; platy or elongate crystals are randomly oriented. Contact rocks of this type are called **hornfels,** and the texture is **hornfelsic.**

In both contact and regionally metamorphosed rocks, new minerals may grow into large crystals surrounded by a much finer-grained matrix of other minerals. These **porphyroblasts** form in the solid state from the chemical ingredients of the rock, and they grow at the expense of the matrix surrounding it. Porphyroblasts look something like phenocrysts, the large crystals in predominantly fine-grained igneous rocks, but the textural relations are the opposite. Prophyroblasts grew after the main rock matrix was formed, whereas phenocrysts formed first, after which the matrix crystallized around them.

Some metamorphic rocks have developed an interlocking mosaic of crystals with no outstanding preferred orientation or foliation. **Marbles,** metamorphosed limestones, may develop this texture together with some dark mineral banding. Similarly altered silicate rocks are called **granulites.**

Cataclastic Textures. The shearing and grinding associated with faulting and intense folding produce a broken, granulated texture in which pre-existing crystals are pulverized and strung out in bands or streaks. Coarse-grained rocks of this type, **friction breccias,** consist of particles ranging from a millimeter to a meter in diameter. The finer-grained, more pulverized variety, **mylonite,** is composed of grains 0.01 to 0.1 millimeter in diameter. A distinctive texture, **augen** (from the German for "eye"), is formed by the shearing and abrasion of large porphyroblasts. They give the name to strongly banded, sheared **augen gneiss.**

All of these textural details serve as evidence of the pressure changes that took place during or after heating and of the rapidity of heating during metamorphism. Though our knowledge of the mechanisms by which all of the many textures are formed is still far from complete, the textures themselves nevertheless constitute some of the best information that the field geologist has for interpreting the extent to which pressures and/or temperatures were increased and in what sequence. They are also indispensable tools of the trade for the structural geologist as he unravels the patterns of folding and faulting.

Figure 16-18
Feldspar porphyroblasts and thin quartz veins in biotite schist. The light-colored feldspar crystals have grown large at the expense of the surrounding fine-grained matrix. [Photo by J. E. G. W. Greenwood, U.S. Geological Survey.]

Figure 16-19
Augen gneiss. The augen (eyes) are large white or light-gray potassium feldspar
crystals that grew as porphyroblasts and were then sheared and abraded as the rock
was structurally deformed. [Photo by H. L. Foster, U.S. Geological Survey.]

REGIONAL METAMORPHISM

Geologists have learned to use minerals as pressure gages and thermometers. This has been well developed in the study of metamorphism. By mapping characteristic **index minerals** in the field, geologists were able to define broad zones or belts of metamorphism, ranging from least to most intense. On a typical traverse from weakly to strongly metamorphosed shales, slates, and schists, one may go from detrital micas and other unchanged sedimentary minerals in the shale toward the metamorphic rocks and encounter the first new mineral, chlorite, in the slates. Moving in the direction of increasingly intense metamorphism, one may successively meet biotite and garnet in the schists, then staurolite, kyanite, and finally sillimanite, the schists becoming progressively more coarsely foliated. Lines on a map connecting points where an index mineral first appears are **isograds,** signifying a change in metamorphic grade (Fig. 16-20). The isograds are rough measures of pressure and temperature. They are calibrated by reference to laboratory experiments. Metamorphic minerals do not everywhere appear in ex-

actly the same sequence as metamorphic grade increases, because pressure and temperature may not increase at the same rate as metamorphism becomes more intense. Thus, in some areas, high pressure may have built up with relatively little increase in temperature; in other places, temperature may have increased greatly with relatively little pressure increase. Most common are the regionally metamorphosed rocks that have formed by a combination of moderately high temperatures and pressures. This kind of metamorphism is a more severe extension of the mild changes caused in sediments by diagenesis after burial. The dividing line between diagenesis and metamorphism is thus more or less arbitrarily drawn at low temperatures and pressures (see Chapter 11). Metamorphic rocks formed at high temperature and pressure may later be subjected to another set of metamorphic conditions, perhaps as a part of a second orogeny. If the second episode is at a lower temperature and pressure, the rocks will be lowered in metamorphic grade, a process called **retrograde** metamorphism.

The course of metamorphism is partly determined by the chemical (and thus mineralogical) composition of the original rock. The examples

The Body of the Earth:
Internal Processes

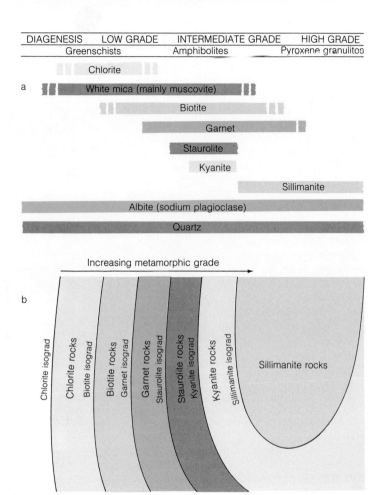

Figure 16-20
(a) Changes in mineral composition of shales metamorphosed under conditions of intermediate pressure and temperature. (b) Idealized map view of a regionally metamorphosed terrain in which shales have been metamorphosed under the same conditions. The isograd lines mark the first appearance of the index mineral.

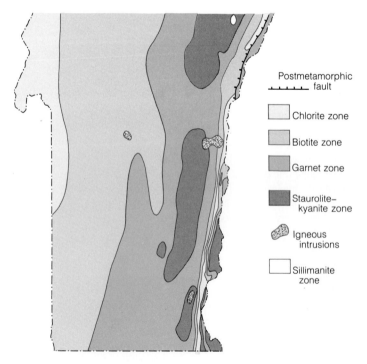

Postmetamorphic
fault

Chlorite zone

Biotite zone

Garnet zone

Staurolite–
kyanite zone

Igneous
intrusions

Sillimanite
zone

Figure 16-21
Metamorphic zones in the southern part of Vermont. The trend of those zones generally parallels the structural lineaments of the terrain. [Simplified from "Centennial Geologic Map of Vermont." Copyright © 1961, State of Vermont.]

given above were drawn from shales. Volcanic rocks rich in mafic minerals show a different progression of associated minerals with increasing metamorphic grade. The lowest-grade rocks contain a variety of **zeolite** minerals, complex hydrous aluminosilicates formed by the alteration of mafic volcanic glasses. The next higher grade, called **greenschist,** contains chlorite (a sheet silicate), epidote (an aluminosilicate), and actinolite (an amphibole)—all minerals containing much iron, magnesium, and calcium—plus albite (sodium plagioclase feldspar). Following the greenschists in grade are the **amphibolites,** characterized by hornblende (an amphibole), sodium-calcium plagioclase feldspar, and garnet. The highest metamorphic grade of mafic volcanics includes the **pyroxene granulites,** containing pyroxenes and anorthitic plagioclase. This metamorphic mineral assemblage does not differ greatly from the mineral composition of gabbro, the intrusive equivalent of basalt, though the textures are different.

If a mafic volcanic is subjected to high temperatures but relatively low pressures, pyroxene granulites are the common product. In metamorphic belts where pressures are high and temperatures low, the typical metamorphic rock is a **blueschist,** characterized by glaucophane, a blue amphibole. At extremely high pressures and variable moderate to high temperatures **eclogites** form. These rocks, which many geologists think are characteristic of many parts of the earth's mantle, are pyroxene-garnet rocks.

Many of the same mineral groups are represented in all of these varied metamorphic rocks. The amphiboles, pyroxenes, and garnets are divided into many species of variable chemical composition, each more or less characteristic of a different rock type. It is this range of compositions that is so useful in applying the results of experimental synthesis of metamorphic rocks at controlled temperatures and pressures, for the mineral compositions are strongly affected by pressure and temperature as well as by the total chemical composition of the rock. The experimental work gives the basic pressure-temperature data. The metamorphic geologist first obtains samples of rocks in the field, noting carefully where they were collected, and then takes them to the laboratory, where he analyzes the exact compositions of the minerals by a number of methods. The most powerful techniques makes use of the electron microprobe to give the chemical analysis of a small area of a single crystal only a few thousandths of a millimeter in diameter. From this field and labora-

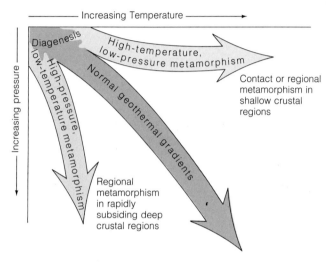

Figure 16-22
Different metamorphic routes of pressure and temperature increase may be induced by combinations of tectonic and igneous activity that produce different groups of metamorphic rock types.

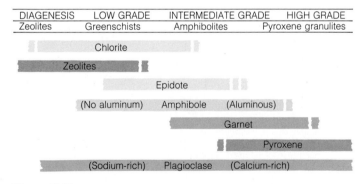

Figure 16-23
Changes in mineral composition of basalts and the other mafic rocks metamorphosed under conditions of intermediate pressure and temperature. Compare with mineral assemblages of shales metamorphosed under the same conditions (Fig. 16-20) to see the effect of original composition on mineralogy.

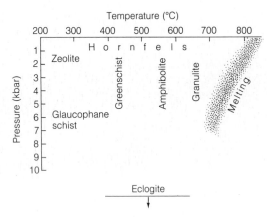

Figure 16-24
Generalized and simplified metamorphic facies diagram, showing the distribution of metamorphic rock types in relation to the temperature and pressure fields in which they are formed. There are no sharp boundaries between any of these facies. [Modified and simplified from various sources.]

Figure 16-25
A veined gneiss of migmatite origin. The darker layers are strongly metamorphosed sedimentary rocks. The lighter layers are quartz-feldspar rock introduced by invasion of partly molten material. [Photo by J. B. Hadley, U.S. Geological Survey.]

tory information, the geologist is able to plot pressure-temperature lines on a map to show the direction in which the intensity of metamorphism increased or decreased.

All of this work on pressures and temperatures of metamorphic rock formation resulted from a concept enunciated in 1920 by a great Finnish metamorphic geologist, Pentti Eskola. He drew a chart on which the different metamorphic rocks could be related to pressure and temperature; a modified version of his chart is shown in Figure 16-24. There are no exact boundaries, because the rock types depend partly on the total, or bulk, chemical composition of the rock. This idea has been one of the most durable in metamorphic geology, and remains the cornerstone of modern interpretation.

Extreme Metamorphism. The most far-reaching effects of metamorphic transformation can be seen where erosion has cut deeply into the crust in such ancient mountains as the Adirondacks of New York. The rocks are badly deformed, stretched, and contorted, and show much evidence of having flowed as plastic solids. In addition, the rocks are shot through with veins and intrusions of igneous rock. In such country it is difficult to say which rocks are metamorphic and which are igneous, particularly for a kind of veined gneiss frequently called **migmatite.** This is used for rocks of mixed origin. Such a rock is partly metamorphic in having been converted to its present condition largely as a solid, but it is also partly igneous in that parts of it have at times been molten. Arguments have raged over the origin of these rock types for 50 years, for many of them look remarkably like intrusive granites.

Some veined gneisses are truly intrusive, formed by the injection of magma in veins that show contact metamorphic margins or evidence of having forced the surrounding rock apart. Others seem to have been transformed at high temperatures in the solid state by the diffusion of elements, an exchange process in which individual atoms or ions migrate slowly through the crystalline material. In this process elements like sodium and potassium replace others like calcium and magnesium and convert the rock to a granitic composition. The rocks may exhibit original textures, and there may be no evidence that they have disrupted the surrounding rock, which suggests that they are products of recrystallization rather than melting. More problematic gneisses seem to have formed by partial melting, and others seem to be extreme examples of the kind of mineral segregation into bands that is typical of lower-grade schists and gneisses. Many geologists believe that large volumes of batholithic granites are migmatites rather than true intrusives. Careful, detailed mapping coupled with analysis of the pressures and temperatures of mineral formation is needed to evaluate the origin of these rocks in any particular area.

CONTACT METAMORPHISM

Igneous intrusions are surrounded by margins of altered rock called **aureoles.** The width and nature of an aureole depends on the temperature of the intrusive magma and on the depth in the crust at which the intrusion took place, which determines the pressure and temperature of the rocks being intruded. Aureoles are most prominent around plutons injected at temperatures of about 1000°C in shallow crustal rocks only a few kilometers from the surface. In such a situation, there is a strong change in temperature away from the magma contact. Magmas intruded deep in the crust are not that much hotter than the surrounding rocks, and aureoles are obscured by general regional metamorphism.

Contact aureoles display sequential zones of index minerals in the same way as regional metamorphic isograds. The particular minerals formed by recrystallization are strongly influenced by both temperature and the bulk chemical composition of the rock. Thus limestones show patterns that differ greatly from those of shales, because their compositions are so different. Pressures are generally low to moderate. The thickness of the zones may be as little as a few centimeters adjacent to small dikes and sills and as much as several kilometers wide bordering a large granite pluton.

The metamorphism of limestone to marble in aureoles leads to a number of changes in the mineralogy of the rocks, many of them involving the clay or silica impurities in the calcite or dolomite of the sediment. One of the minerals formed by such metamorphism is wollastonite (calcium silicate), a product of the reaction between silica impurities (in the form of quartz silt or chert) and the calcium carbonate of the limestone:

calcite + silica → wollastonite + carbon dioxide
$CaCO_3$ SiO_2 $CaSiO_3$ CO_2

This reaction produces carbon dioxide gas, which generally escapes. Though silica and calcium carbonate have no tendency to react at low temperatures, we know from experiments at near-surface pressures that at around 500°C they will combine. As is true of many other reactions, the temperature at which these substances begin to react rises as the pressure increases.

If the rock contains dolomite, the mineral diopside (calcium-magnesium pyroxene) will form in the same way as wollastonite. If diopside forms near the contact, it gives way farther out to tremolite (calcium-magnesium amphibole), a mineral that contains the same elements but which crystallizes at lower temperatures. Different patterns of zones form from the interplay of compositional and temperature factors. A common pattern shows a gradation from the unaltered dolomite to a tremolite zone a few hundred meters wide, then to a somewhat narrower diopside zone, and finally to an inner contact zone of wollastonite that may be only a few meters wide.

Contact metamorphism of silicate rocks produces similar patterns but with different minerals. Outer zones contain micas, amphiboles, and calcite. Inner zones are characterized by pyroxenes, including wollastonite and the aluminosilicate andalusite (Al_2SiO_5). The general nature of contact aureole patterns illustrates the tendency for the minerals that contain **volatiles,** the easily escaping elements or compounds (for example, carbon dioxide bound chemically in calcite), to be found in outer zones and for dry, gas-free minerals to be found in inner, hotter zones.

Figure 16-26
Skarns are banded rocks produced by contact metamorphism of limestones and dolomites. Grading from unaltered rock toward the contact, they change progressively from pure carbonate marble to bands composed of different calcium-magnesium silicate minerals, finally to a carbonate-free silicate rock.

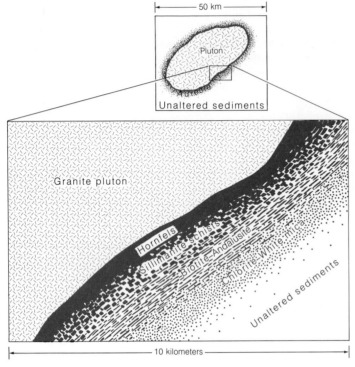

Figure 16-27
A contact aureole in sandstones and shales intruded by a granite pluton is a series of zones characterized by mineral assemblages formed at progressively lower temperatures with greater distance from the intrusive.

METAMORPHIC CHEMICAL CHANGES

The mineral transformations of regional and contact metamorphism illustrate the general tendency for systematic chemical changes that accompany increased temperature and pressure. One of the major processes affecting sediments is the loss of volatiles, mainly water and carbon dioxide. The opposite is true of the metamorphism of some continental mafic volcanics, many of which may erupt as relatively dry, volatile-free lavas and become hydrated and carbonated (combination with carbon dioxide to form carbonate minerals). Organic materials containing carbon and hydrogen (such as the hydrocarbons in petroleum) lose their volatile gas, hydrogen.

The high solubility of silica and two of the alkali metal elements, sodium and potassium, in hot aqueous fluids associated with metamorphism can lead to solution and transportation of these elements from deeper to shallower zones in the crust, forming the granite-like veined gneisses called migmatites.

Even though these chemical transformation processes are known to take place, a great deal of regional and contact metamorphism seems to have taken place with little or no bulk chemical change—excluding losses of water and carbon dioxide. It is this fact that enables metamorphic geologists to "look through" the metamorphic mineral assemblage to reconstruct the original mineralogy of the sediment or igneous rock that was transformed. Knowing the total mineral composition of the rock, he can recast it, using his knowledge of experiments on mineral reactions, such as the conversion of calcite and silica to wollastonite, to infer the former presence of a mineral assemblage that would have been stable at lower temperatures and pressures. In this way, former rock patterns, including sedimentary facies, can be reconstructed even though almost all direct evidence has been obliterated. The study of metamorphism illustrates again how knowledge of process—how things happen—is inextricably tied to the history of the Earth, how things *did* happen.

It is the link between rock formation and the history of the Earth, combined with questions about the ultimate nature of the forces causing regional metamorphism and their association with mountain-building, that is causing metamorphic geologists to use plate-tectonic theory as a new conceptual framework for their ideas. Greenstones, metamorphosed basalts, have been dredged from such zones of plate divergence as the mid-Atlantic ridge. At these active zones of basalt upwelling, localized heating transforms newly extruded basalts into low-grade metamorphic rocks. Blueschists, metamorphosed sediments whose minerals indicate that they were formed under very high pressures but relatively low temperatures, were recognized for years as the result of rapid and deep subsidence of geosynclinal sediments into the crust, with little heating. Metamorphism at a subduction zone is now seen as the explanation. The subducted plate, carrying deepwater marine sediments, such as turbidites and cherts, moves down so rapidly that its great mass heats up very slowly while the pressure increases rapidly. Just the opposite pair of conditions, high tempera-

Figure 16-28
Schematic diagram of a convergent plate margin. Partial melting of pre-existing rocks occurs in three distinct regions: (a) the metamorphosed basaltic oceanic crust at the top of the downgoing plate, consisting of amphibolite at shallow levels and eclogite at deeper levels; (b) the stable, nonsubducted (hanging wall) asthenosphere through which volatiles (carbon dioxide and water) are presumed to be migrating above the adjacent descending plate; and (c) the basal, thickened portions of the sialic, H_2O-rich crust. The first two magma types are shown in black, and include both tholeiitic and calc-alkaline compositions; whereas the third, indicated by a checked pattern, represents a relatively silicic, largely plutonic series. The width of the zone of active igneous activity at any one time is somewhat less than the composite field shown. Fields of alkali olivine basalt lie toward the interior of the stable, nonsubducted continental-crust-capped lithospheric plate, and have been derived from great depths by very minute degrees of partial fusion of the mantle. Large arrows indicate directions of material transport. [After W. G. Ernst, *Petrologic Phase Equilibria.* W. H. Freeman and Company. Copyright © 1976.]

tures and low pressures, characterizes the metamorphic rocks of volcanic island arcs at plate convergences. Here the igneous rocks that are generated by melting at plate margins come close to the surface and transform shallowly buried volcanics and sediments. Recognition of these broad metamorphic zones along ancient continental margins can thus be used to reconstruct something of the pattern of ancient plate motions. We discuss the full story of the relationships between the theory of plate tectonics and igneous and metamorphic processes in Chapter 19, after the stage has been set by exploring how seismological and other geophysical investigations led to the theory.

SUMMARY

1. The forms of igneous intrusions, such as plutons, dikes, and sills, are a guide to their method of emplacement at depth. Such bodies may intrude by stoping, by heating surrounding rock so that it gives way by plastic flow, or by fracturing or bowing up.

2. Sills and laccoliths are concordant; dikes are discordant.

3. Lopoliths and batholiths are very large plutons. Some batholiths appear to be granitized sediments.

4. Metamorphic rocks are of three kinds: contact, cataclastic, and regional. Contact metamorphism is produced by heat at the borders of an igneous intrusion. Cataclastic rocks are mechanically fragmented by folding and faulting. Regionally metamorphosed rocks are the product of generalized heat and pressure associated with orogeny.

5. Metamorphic textures include foliation, the general term for parallel planes, fracture cleavage, flow cleavage, schistosity, and lineation. These textures are formed by the preferred orientation of platy and needle-shaped crystals of new minerals grown during metamorphism. Hornfelsic textures form in contact metamorphic rocks. Porphyroblasts are large crystals formed at the expense of a fine-grained matrix. Granulites have little or no preferred orientation.

6. Cataclastic rocks include friction breccias, mylonites, and augen gneiss.

7. Regional metamorphism produces a series of mineral assemblages that may be used to map isograds that are indications of pressure and temperature conditions. Metamorphic facies are a grouping of rock types by their mineral assemblages in relation to pressure and temperature of formation.

8. Extreme metamorphism can produce migmatites, which may be a major component of some batholiths.

9. Contact metamorphic aureoles are altered margins around plutons in which zones of index minerals appear in definite sequences.

10. Systematic chemical changes normally accompany regional metamorphism, mainly the loss of volatiles, carbon dioxide, and water.

11. Metamorphic belts are now being interpreted in the framework of plate tectonics.

EXERCISES

1. What differences in the modes of formation of sills and lava flows account for their differing texture and general appearance?

2. What properties of some granitic batholiths are difficult to reconcile with formation by the simple emplacement of a large body of differentiated magma?

3. Which kind of pluton would you expect to have produced the most intense contact metamorphism of surrounding rocks, and why—a granite intrusion very deep in the crust or a gabbro intrusion at moderate depths?

4. What properties of a group of metamorphic rocks of medium and high grade would you use to infer the nature of the rocks before metamorphism?

5. Would you choose foliation or chemical composition as the better property to use in determining metamorphic grade? Why?

6. Why might you characterize weathering and metamorphism as opposites with respect to volatile elements or compounds?

BIBLIOGRAPHY

Billings, M. P., *Structural Geology* (3rd ed.). Englewood Cliffs, New Jersey: Prentice-Hall, Inc., 1972. Chapters 16, 17, 18, and 19.

Ernst, G., *Earth Materials.* Englewood Cliffs, New Jersey: Prentice-Hall, Inc., 1969.

Harker, A., *Metamorphism.* London: Methuen, 1932.

Turner, F. J., *Metamorphic Petrology.* New York: McGraw-Hill Book Company, 1968.

Turner, F. J., and J. Verhoogen, *Igneous and Metamorphic Petrology.* New York: McGraw-Hill Book Company, 1960.

Winkler, H. G. F., *Petrogenesis of Metamorphic Rocks* (3rd ed.). New York: Springer-Verlag, 1976.

17

SEISMOLOGY AND THE EARTH'S INTERIOR

The basic causes of earthquakes are strains induced by plate motions. In fact, by their locations and the nature of the ruptures they produce, earthquakes define the plate boundaries. Analysis of seismic waves, together with laboratory studies of rocks, helps us to infer the composition and state of the Earth's interior.

Seismology deals primarily with earthquakes and seismic waves. Because earthquakes are among the scourges of mankind, seismologists are concerned with minimizing their destructiveness. They do this by assessing seismic risks in different geographic regions, so that sensible building and zoning codes can be written, and by researching the problems of **tsunamis*** and earthquake prediction, and even earthquake control. But reducing the hazards of earthquakes is not the only job of seismologists.

By studying the pattern of earthquake occurrence, seismologists have provided one of the essential clues to the development of the concept of plate tectonics: earthquake belts demark plate boundaries, the zones along which plates collide, diverge, or slide past one another (Fig. 17-1). The modern seismograph, which records the waves generated by earthquakes and explosions,

provides the most important means of probing the deep interior, a region that would otherwise be closed off from observation.

SEISMOGRAPHS

The seismograph is to the Earth scientist what the telescope is to the astronomer—a tool for peering into inaccessible regions. The ideal seismograph would be a "skyhook," a device fixed to a frame outside of the Earth, so that when the ground shakes, the seismic vibrations could be measured by the changing distance between the fixed device and the ground. Because this is impossible to achieve, a compromise is struck by loosely coupling a mass to the Earth so that the ground can vibrate without causing appreciable motion of the mass. The mass is coupled to the Earth by means of a pendulum (Fig. 17-2) or by suspending it from a spring (Fig. 17-3). When the ground moves, the mass tends to remain stationary because of its inertia, and the displacement of the Earth relative to the stationary mass is used to sense the

---

***Tsunamis** are potentially destructive sea waves generated by earthquakes and volcanic explosions. They can cross oceans in a matter of hours, traveling with a velocity of 700 to 800 km/hr (440 to 500 mi/hr), and can reach heights of 10 to 20 m (30 to 60 ft) when they impact on a coast.

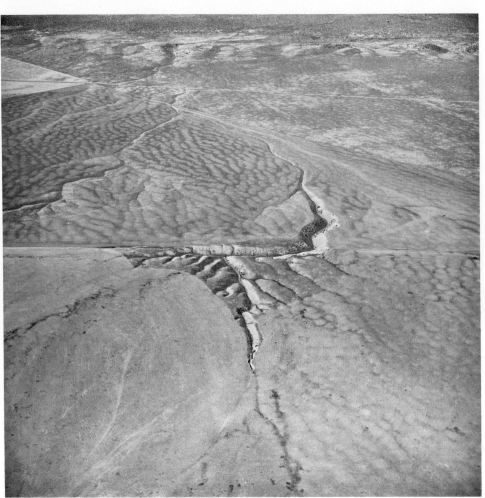

Figure 17-1
The San Andreas fault—the boundary between the American and Pacific plates. The block in the background is being displaced to the right relative to the block in the foreground, as evidenced by the stream offset. Carrizo Plains, California. [Photo by R. E. Wallace, U.S. Geological Survey.]

Figure 17-2
Schematic diagram illustrating the principle of the seismograph. Because of its inertia, the mass does not keep up with the motion of the ground. The pen traces the difference in motion between the mass and the ground, in this way recording vibrations that accompany seismic waves. The instrument schematized here records horizontal ground motion.

Figure 17-3
Schematic diagram depicting a seismograph that records vertical ground motion.

ground movement. The most advanced electronic technology* has been employed to magnify this motion, so that modern instruments can detect ground displacements as small as 10^{-8} centimeter ($\frac{1}{4}$ inch $\times 10^{-8}$)—an astounding feat, considering that such small displacements are of atomic size. Actually this is more sensitivity than can even be used on Earth, because the ground moves in a continual state of unrest, shaken by the action of the winds, ocean waves, and man's machinery: in most places such sensitive seismographs would be driven off scale by Earth's "noise." The Moon is the place for man's most advanced seismograph; there, no winds, no ocean sounds, no mechanical vibrations can overload it. The lunar seismographs left behind by the astronauts can detect the seismic waves generated by a 1-kilogram (2.2 pound) meteor striking anywhere on the Moon's surface. A modern seismograph is shown in Figure 17-4.

The strain seismograph shown schematically in Figure 17-5 was developed by H. Benioff, a leader in the design of electronic musical instruments and seismographs. By electronic measurement of the change in distance between two concrete piers placed about 30 meters (100 feet) apart, this instrument is capable of detecting extensional and compressional responses of the ground during seismic vibrations and the pull of the Moon on the solid Earth (body tides, just like those to which the ocean responds, but much smaller). A photograph of an actual installation is shown in Figure 17-6. A record made by a strain seismograph is shown in Figure 17-7.

EARTHQUAKES

What Is an Earthquake? The rupture of the San Andreas fault that resulted in the devastation of San Francisco in 1906 also provided the evidence that led H. F. Reid, one of the official investigators of that catastrophe, to advance his **elastic rebound theory** of earthquakes. Earthquakes are associated with large fractures, or faults, in the Earth's crust and upper mantle. Consider the fault between the two hypothetical

---

*For the electronics hobbyist, we might mention that the magnification of a seismograph is achieved by means of moving-coil and variable-reluctance transducers, like those on phonograph pickups, and low-noise, ultra-high-gain, solid-state amplifiers. The output is recorded photogalvanometrically on film, on paper with direct-recording pen motors, on AM, FM, or digital magnetic tape.

Figure 17-4
The Press-Ewing seismograph, an example of a modern instrument. Airtight cover, electronics, and recording system not shown.

Figure 17-5
Schematic diagram of the Benioff strain seismograph. The distance between two piers attached to the ground changes due to tides in the solid Earth and the passage of seismic waves. These variations are measured by placing an electronic motion detector in the gap.

Figure 17-6
Example of an actual strain seismograph installation in an underground tunnel. This system is so sensitive that it could detect a change of 1 mm in the distance between New York and California.

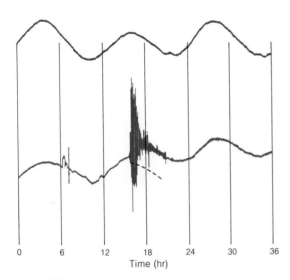

Figure 17-7
Record made by a strain seismograph. The slow periodic movements are the Earth tides; the more rapid vibrations are the seismic waves from an earthquake. [From "Resonant Vibrations of the Earth" by Frank Press. Copyright © 1965 by Scientific American, Inc. All rights reserved.]

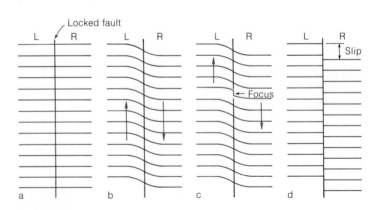

Figure 17-8
Sketch illustrating the elastic rebound theory of an earthquake. The two simulated crustal blocks L and R are being forced to slide past one another (a). Friction along the fault prevents slip (b), but the deformation builds up until the "frictional lock" is broken (c) and an earthquake slip occurs (d).

Figure 17-9
The earthquake of 1906 was caused by slip along the San Andreas fault. The offset fence shown here shows a slip of nearly 3 m. Scene is near Bolinas, California. [Photo by G. K. Gilbert; courtesy of R. E. Wallace, U.S. Geological Survey.]

Figure 17-10
Diagram showing the focus and epicenter of an earthquake. The focus is the site of initial slip on the fault. The epicenter is the point on the surface above the focus. Also shown are seismic waves radiating from the focus.

crustal blocks in Figure 17-8. Suppose that surveyors had located lines running perpendicular to the fault from block L to block R, as shown in part a of the diagram. Blocks L and R are moving in opposite directions, but because they are pressed together by the weight of the overlying rock, friction locks them together, just as a brake can lock the wheel of a car if enough force is applied. Instead of slipping taking place along the fault, the blocks are deformed in the vicinity of the fault, and the surveyors' lines are bent as shown in Figure 17-8b. As the rock is strained, elastic energy is stored in it in the same way that it is stored in a wound-up watch spring. The movement continues, the strain builds up until the frictional bond that locks the fault can no longer hold at some point on the fault, and it breaks, as in Figure 17-8c. The blocks suddenly slip at this point, which is the **focus,** or **hypocenter,** of the earthquake. Once the rupture is initiated it will travel at a speed of about 3.5 kilometers per second (2 miles/ second), continuing for as much as 1000 kilometers (600 miles). In great earthquakes, the **slip,** or offset, of the two blocks can be as large

as 15 meters (50 feet). Figure 17-8d shows the two blocks after the earthquake, displaced by the amount of slip. Once the frictional bond is broken, the elastic strain energy, which had been slowly stored over tens or hundreds of years, is suddenly released in the form of intense seismic vibrations—which constitute the earthquake. The vibrational waves are propagated large distances in all directions away from the fault. Near the focus the waves can have large, destructive amplitudes. The process may be likened to storing elastic energy by slowly drawing out the rubber band of a sling shot, and then releasing it suddenly to propel a pebble.

Strictly speaking, the elastic rebound theory is an incomplete one. The reason for this is that the pressure holding the blocks together is so great that the frictional bond is actually stronger than the rock itself. In other words, the block would prefer to fracture elsewhere rather than slip along the fault. Yet faults do exist, and movement occurs along them periodically. To complete the theory, we need a means of "lubricating" the fault or reducing the locking pressure. Geologists working in the field of rock

410

Figure 17-11
Determination of earthquake magnitude from a seismograph recording. Dividing A, the maximum trace motion, by the magnification of the seismograph gives the maximum ground motion a, measured in micrometers (10^{-4} cm). T is the duration of one oscillation, or the period of the seismic wave in seconds. Magnitude $m = \log(a/T) + B$, where B is a factor that allows for the weakening of seismic waves with increasing distance from the earthquake. *Example:* An earthquake 10,000 km away ($B = 6.8$ from the table of data) produced a ground motion $a = 10$ micrometers with period $T = 1$ sec. Thus $m = \log 10 + 6.8 = 7.8$. The correction factor B is found empirically, so that a seismograph located any place in the world would give the proper magnitude of an earthquake, regardless of distance to it.

mechanics are currently trying to remove some of the mystery of the mechanics of faulting.

Earthquakes—How Big and How Many?
The time between great earthquakes is about 50 to 100 years in California and somewhat less in more active seismic regions, such as Japan or the Aleutians. Thus the time required to build up the elastic strain energy in the rocks adjacent to a fault is enormous compared with the time that elapses during the release of stored energy, for earthquakes last only a few minutes. The amount of stored energy can be gauged in several ways: perhaps the two most common methods are to measure the distortion of surveyed lines, as in the example just discussed, or to measure the energy of the released seismic waves. About 10^9 ergs (a unit of energy) of elastic strain energy is released from each cubic meter (1.3 cubic yards) of rock at the time of an earthquake—the equivalent of a fire cracker per cubic meter. This may not seem very impressive until one adds up the cubic meters affected by a great earthquake: suppose the fault is 1000 kilometers (600 miles) long, extends 100 kilometers downward, and distorts surveyed lines as far as 50 kilometers on either side of the fault. This amounts to a strained volume of 10^{16} cubic meters, each cubic meter contributing 10^9 ergs, which gives a total of 10^{25} ergs. This is one big

fire cracker indeed—about the equivalent of 1000 nuclear explosions, each with a strength of 1 megaton (1 million tons) of TNT!

Energy release gives the most precise measure of the size of an earthquake, but it is a long, complicated process to determine the fault dimensions, the slip, and the other factors needed to compute it. Seismologists have therefore adopted the **Richter magnitude scale,** which is based on the amplitude of seismic waves recorded by seismographs. Actually, magnitude is based on the logarithm of the maximum amplitude plus an empirical factor that takes into account the weakening of seismic waves as they spread away from the focus. Thus seismologists all over the world can study their records and in a few minutes come up with nearly the same value for the magnitude of an earthquake. Seismographs are sensitive enough to detect earthquakes of magnitude less than 1 quite easily. The largest earthquakes yet recorded show Richter magnitudes of about 8.5. Because these magnitudes are based on a logarithmic scale, an increase in magnitude of 1 unit corresponds to a tenfold increase in the size of an earthquake as measured by the amplitude of seismic waves. An earthquake of magnitude 8 would be 10,000 times larger than one of magnitude 4. Figure 17-11 shows how the magnitude of an earthquake is determined in practice.

Table 17-1 shows how magnitude and energy can be related in a rough way to earthquake effects, and also indicates the number of earthquakes each year. The table demonstrates the fortunate fact that most earthquakes are small. Each year, 800,000 little tremors are recorded by instruments, but not felt by humans. Great earthquakes, with magnitudes exceeding 8, occur about once every 5 to 10 years. Damage begins at magnitude 5 and increases to nearly total destruction in nearby settlements for earthquakes with $m > 8$ ($>$ means "greater than"). The San Fernando (Los Angeles) earthquake of 1971 was only of magnitude 6.6, yet the damage bill amounted to a billion dollars. It is no wonder that Californians worry about the great shock that should visit them about every 50 to 100 years!

The report in Figure 17-12 from the Smithsonian Institution's Center for Short-Lived Phenomena was issued a few days after the San Fernando earthquake. The description is in the dry language of the specialist, with no hint of the fear or personal tragedy that accompanies these catastrophes. As damaging as the earthquake was, the seismic energy release was about

Table 17-1
Earthquake magnitudes, energies, effects, and statistics.

Characteristic effects of shallow shocks in populated areas	Approximate magnitude	Number of earthquakes per year	Energy (ergs)
Damage nearly total	≥ 8.0	0.1–0.2	$>10^{25}$
Great damage	≥ 7.4	4	$\geq .4 \times 10^{24}$
Serious damage, rails bent	7.0–7.3	15	$0.04–0.2 \times 10^{24}$
Considerable damage to buildings	6.2–6.9	100	$0.5–23 \times 10^{21}$
Slight damage to buildings	5.5–6.1	500	$1–27 \times 10^{19}$
Felt by all	4.9–5.4	1,400	$3.6–57 \times 10^{17}$
Felt by many	4.3–4.8	4,800	$1.3–27 \times 10^{16}$
Felt by some	3.5–4.2	30,000	$1.6–76 \times 10^{15}$
Not felt but recorded	2.0–3.4	800,000	$4 \times 10^{10}–9 \times 10^{13}$

Source: Data from B. Gutenberg.

EVENT 17-71 SAN FERNANDO EARTHQUAKE 26 FEBRUARY 1971 1139.

EVENT INFORMATION REPORT : 4

TYPE OF EVENT GEOPHYSICAL

DATE OF OCCURRENCE 9 FEBRUARY 1971

LOCATION OF EVENT LOS ANGELES

COUNTY, CALIFORNIA, U.S.A.

REPORTING SOURCE SEISMOLOGICAL LAB

CALIFORNIA INSTITUTE OF TECHNOLOGY PASADENA, CALIFORNIA, 91109, U.S.A.

SOURCE CONTACT NATIONAL CENTER

FOR EARTHQUAKE RESEARCH, U. S. GEOLOGICAL SURVEY

MENLO PARK, CALIFORNIA, USA.

This report is based on notifications received from the Center's correspondents and is disseminated for information purposes only. The Smithsonian Institution bears no responsibility for its accuracy.

SMITHSONIAN INSTITUTION
CENTER FOR SHORT-LIVED PHENOMENA
60 Garden Street
CAMBRIDGE, MASSACHUSETTS 02138
UNITED STATES OF AMERICA

CABLE: SATELLITES NEW YORK
TELEPHONE: (617)-864-7911

"The San Fernando earthquake of 6:01 a.m., Feb. 9, 1971 was responsible for 62 deaths and an estimated property damage of one billion dollars. The main shock was located 14 kilometers east of Newhall; 42 aftershocks were located in the region between the main shock and the zone of surface faulting in the northernmost San Fernando Valley. The earthquake was associated with oblique-slip, reverse faulting along the southern front of the San Gabriel Mountains, thrusting the mountains relatively to the southwest over the northern San Fernando Valley. The aftershock pattern, the focal plane solution and the surface ruptures in the San Fernando Valley are all consistent with faulting on a plane striking east-west and dipping at 50-60° beneath the San Gabriel Mountains.

"The extensive damage to buildings in San Fernando is closely linked to the location of the zone of ground breakage. Preliminary estimates of the length of faulting at the surface give at least 11km with horizontal compression of 1 m and locally, left lateral slip of as much as 1.7m.

"The main shock had a magnitude of 6.6 on the Richter scale with the largest aftershock having a magnitude of 5. Over 1000 aftershocks greater than Richter magnitude 2 were recorded in the first 3 days following the main shock. Faulting at the time of the earthquake was either on a plane that (i) strikes east-west with dip 60° N, or (ii) strikes N152°E with dip 50°W. For the most probable fault plane, the E-W north-dipping nodal plane, slip is in a southwesterly direction. The slip has approximately equal components of reverse and left lateral displacement on this nodal plane."

sao-slp-2

EVENT 17-71 SAN FERNANDO EARTHQUAKE 26 FEBRUARY 1971 1140.

EVENT INFORMATION REPORT : 5

TYPE OF EVENT GEOPHYSICAL

DATE OF OCCURRENCE 9 FEBRUARY 1971

LOCATION OF EVENT LOS ANGELES

COUNTY, CALIFORNIA, U.S.A.

REPORTING SOURCE SEISMOLOGICAL LAB

CALIFORNIA INSTITUTE OF TECHNOLOGY, PASADENA, CALIFORNIA, 91109, U.S.A.

SOURCE CONTACT NATIONAL CENTER

FOR EARTHQUAKE RESEARCH, U. S. GEOLOGICAL SURVEY

MENLO PARK, CALIFORNIA, U.S.A.

This report is based on notifications received from the Center's correspondents and is disseminated for information purposes only. The Smithsonian Institution bears no responsibility for its accuracy.

SMITHSONIAN INSTITUTION
CENTER FOR SHORT-LIVED PHENOMENA
60 Garden Street
CAMBRIDGE, MASSACHUSETTS 02138
UNITED STATES OF AMERICA

CABLE: SATELLITES NEW YORK
TELEPHONE: (617)-864-7911

SURFACE FAULTING
"The most intense surface faulting associated with the San Fernando earthquake occurred in an E-W trending zone about 130 meters wide. The zone trends eastward to the hills from central San Fernando turning southward from about 500 meters south of Lopez dam. The fault zone runs south to the San Fernando Industrial Park and the Foothill Nursing Home and thence eastward along the base of the hills north of the town of Tujunga for about 8 kilometers.

"The deformation is characterized by compression normal to the surface trace. Asphalt, concrete and sod are buckled into compression ridges 30 cm or more in height and horizontal shortening normal to the zone locally exceeds 1m. In the western part of the zone, linear features such as curbs, white lines, etc., are locally offset as much as 1.7 meters in a left-lateral sense. The zone of faulting is closely correlated with one major zone of damage. In another major zone of extensive structural damage near the Olive View Sanitarium and Veterans' Hospital careful investigation revealed no tectonic rupture but whether tectonic deformation other than surface faulting has taken place is being investigated.

FREQUENCY OF EARTHQUAKES
"During the first three days after the main shock, thousands of aftershocks occurred. We counted more than 1,000 events which were clearly recorded at our SBLG station (Δ=70km) with local magnitude greater than 1.5 (or possibly 2). The counted earthquakes were plotted on a histogram of two-hour intervals. Within three days, aftershocks decreased from about 40 per hour to less than 5 per hour. Such exponential decrease of the number of aftershocks is normal."

sao-slp-2

Figure 17-12
Event-information report issued on the occasion of the destructive San Fernando, California, earthquake of 1971. [From Center for Short-Lived Phenomena, Smithsonian Institution.]

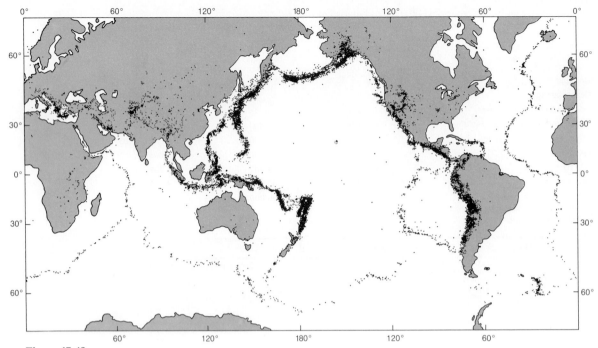

Figure 17-13
Epicenters of some 30,000 earthquakes recorded in the years 1961–1967, with focal depths between 0 and 700 km. [Epicenters by the U.S. Coast and Geodetic Survey. Computer plot by M. Barazangi and J. Dorman, Columbia University.]

a thousand times smaller than some truly great earthquakes, such as those in San Francisco (1906), Tokyo (1923), Chile (1960), Alaska (1964), and China (1976).

Table 17-1 also points up the interesting fact that the few large earthquakes each year release more seismic energy than the hundreds of thousands of small shocks combined. This should put to rest the notion that small earthquakes act as a safety valve, gradually releasing strain in harmlessly small amounts and thus forestalling a big shock. About 10^{26} ergs of seismic energy are released each year. This is about 1 percent of the heat energy reaching the Earth's surface from the interior, which is equivalent to about 2 percent of the electrical energy produced by man.

Earthquakes—Where Do They Occur? A **seismicity** chart showing the map locations, or **epicenters,** of almost 30,000 earthquakes that occurred between 1961 and 1967 is reproduced in Figure 17-13. The seismologists who prepared the map placed all of the epicenters in the memory of a computer so that statistical studies

on distribution and timing could be made and also to make use of automatic plotting machines linked to the computer. Seismologists have known for decades that earthquakes tend to occur in belts—for example, the "ring of fire" surrounding the Pacific Ocean. In recent years, however, it has become possible to detect the more numerous, smaller earthquakes and to improve methods of locating epicenters, so that seismic belts can now be defined more accurately. Interestingly, the increase in the number of seismic observatories and the use of computers that made this possible were stimulated by research done in the 1960's, during the negotiations for a nuclear test-ban treaty; the purpose of the research was to determine whether small underground nuclear explosions could be detected and distinguished seismically from earthquakes.

The high-quality seismicity maps showed that narrow belts of epicenters coincide almost exactly with the crest of the mid-Atlantic, the east Pacific, and other oceanic ridges, where plates separate. Earthquake epicenters are also aligned along transform faults, where plates slide past

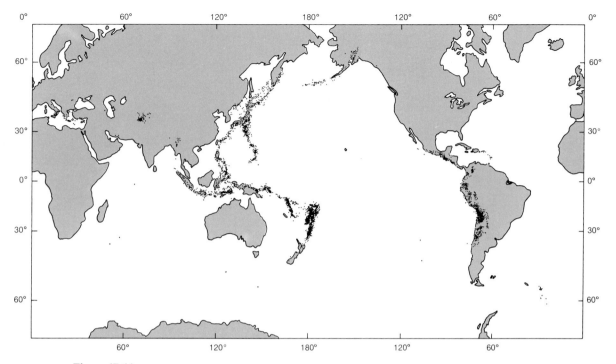

Figure 17-14
Subset of earthquakes from preceding figure with focal depths greater than 100 km. These deep earthquakes typically originate near margins where plates collide, and thus serve to identify such plates. [Computer plot by M. Barazangi and J. Dorman, Columbia University.]

each other. But earthquakes that originate at depths greater than about 100 kilometers (60 miles) typically occur near margins where plates collide (Fig. 17-14). The foci of these earthquakes are distributed on well-defined planes that dip into the mantle, and these occur in close association with deep-sea trenches, island arcs, young mountains, and volcanoes. It is a basic tenet of the theory of plate tectonics that these deep earthquakes actually define the positions of subducted plates which are plunging back into the mantle beneath an overriding plate (Fig. 17-15). This global correlation between topography, geology, and seismicity provided the essential data for defining the boundaries of the lithospheric plates. It may seem like a simple matter now to draw a line through the seismic belts and so define the plates depicted on the inside of the front cover, but this important advance could not have been made without the "knowledge explosion" in seismic data and the imaginative, uninhibited, and synthesizing minds of about ten workers who sifted through those data in the years following 1967.

Although most earthquakes are recorded at

plate boundaries, the seismicity map shows that a small percentage originate within plates. Some of these have been quite destructive, as is indicated by these examples: New Madrid, Missouri (1812), Charleston, South Carolina (1886), Boston, Massachusetts (1755), T'ang-shan, China (1976). Apparently, stresses can exceed the strength of rock within lithospheric plates, albeit infrequently.

A brief digression on how earthquake epicenters are located is in order. The principle is quite similar to deducing the distance to a lightning bolt from the time interval between the flash and the sound. Later in this chapter we will describe the two types of seismic waves which travel through the body of the Earth—the first-arriving P and the slower-traveling S waves, which take almost twice as long to reach the seismograph. Surface waves, a third type, skirt along the surface. The lightning flash may be likened to the P waves of earthquakes and the thunder to the S waves. The time interval between the arrival of P and S waves therefore increases with the distance traveled by the waves, and with each S-P time interval there is

Figure 17-15
Diagram illustrating the association of earthquakes with three types of plate boundaries: ocean ridges, transform faults, and trenches.

Figure 17-16
The time it takes *P*-, *S*-, and surface waves to travel a given distance can be represented by curves on a graph of travel time against distance over the surface. To locate an earthquake epicenter, the time interval observed at a given station is matched against the travel-time curves for *P*- and *S*-waves until the distance is found at which the separation between the curves agrees with the observed $S - P$ time difference. Knowing the distance from the three stations *A*, *B*, and *C*, one can locate the epicenter, as in Figure 17-17.

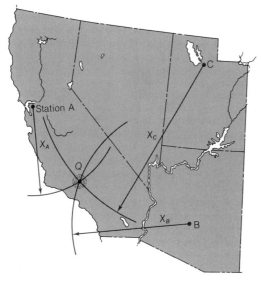

Figure 17-17
Knowing the distance, say X_A, of an earthquake from a given station, as by the method of the preceding figure, one can only say that the earthquake lies on a circle of radius A, centered on the station. If, however, one also knows the distances from two additional stations B and C, the three circles centered on the three stations, with radii X_A, X_B, X_C, intersect uniquely at the point Q, the epicenter.

a

b   Normal fault

c   Thrust fault

d   Lateral slip fault

Figure 17-18
Summary of types of fault movement and the stresses that cause them: (a) situation before movement takes place; (b) normal fault due to tensile stress; (c) thrust (or reverse) fault due to compressive stress; (d) lateral slip (or strike slip) fault due to shearing stress.

associated a definite distance to the epicenter. This is indicated on the travel-time chart for P and S waves in Figure 17-16, which shows diagrammatically how the travel times of P and S waves depend on distance and how the $S - P$ interval increases with distance. To get an approximation of the epicenter, the seismologist simply reads off the $S - P$ interval on the seismogram from a given station and uses a nomogram* like that in Figure 17-16 or a table to get the distance to the epicenter. Knowing the distances from three or more stations enables him to pinpoint the epicenter (Fig. 17-17). He can also deduce the time of the shock at the epicenter because he knows the arrival time of the P waves at each station, and from a nomogram or a table he can tell about how long the waves took to reach the station. Once an approximation has been made, the exact location can be found by making refinements. The estimated location of the epicenter is used to predict the arrival time of P waves at each station. These predicted times are compared with the observed values, and the discrepancies are used as a guide to improving the estimated distance to epicenter

*A nomogram is a graph used to determine an unknown quantity from two or more known quantities, saving the time to solve an equation or look up the answer in a table.

and time of origin. For example, if all of the predicted times exceed the observed arrival time for P waves, then the estimated time of the earthquake is too late. If all of the stations on the east show earlier predicted times and the stations on the west are late, then the estimated epicenter is moved west. All of this is done in a computer, and the procedure is iterated—that is, repeated with corrections—until the discrepancies are reduced to small values, signifying that a precise location has been found.

Obtaining Stress Patterns. When an earthquake occurs, one block slips relative to an adjacent one along a **fault plane** (Fig. 17-18a), as has already been indicated. The orientation of the fault plane and the slip direction are of great interest because they provide information about what happens at plate boundaries.

If the concept of plate tectonics is correct and seismicity is primarily associated with boundaries along which plates separate, collide, or slide past each other, then the fault orientations and slip directions should be different for each type of plate junction. Earthquakes in divergence zones should occur in response to tension, as if the plates are being pulled apart, and **normal faults,** in which the overlying block moves down the dip of the fault plane, should charact-

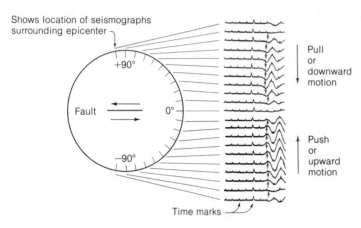

Shows location of seismographs
surrounding epicenter

+90°

Fault   0°

−90°

Pull
or
downward
motion

Push
or
upward
motion

Time marks

Figure 17-19
The initial motion of seismic waves shows a characteristic movement, a push away from the
source or a pull toward the source, depending on the orientation of the fault, the direction of
slip along the fault, and the direction of the seismograph from the earthquake. In this example, taken from a laboratory simulation, the stations located between 0° and +90° show a
pull toward the source, because the slip along the fault is in a direction away from these
stations. The fault orientation can be obtained from the direction 0°, which separates the
stations into two groups, one showing an initial push (0 to −90°) and another showing an
initial pull (0° to +90°). Because most earthquakes originate below the surface, seismologists
must use this principle in analyzing their records in order to find the orientation of the fault
and the direction of slip.

erize the earthquake mechanism, as in Figure
17-18b. Many earthquakes in convergence
zones, where plates collide, should show a compressive mechanism—for example, **thrust
faulting,** in which the overlying block moves
up the dip of the fault plane (Figure 17-18c).
Where plates slide past each other along transform faults, the earthquake mechanism should
be simple lateral (sideways) slip along nearly
vertical planes (Fig. 17-18d). Faults will be
discussed further when we take up structural
geology in Chapter 20.

Seismologists have discovered how to deduce
these earthquake mechanisms from their seismograms. This is especially convenient, since
very few earthquake faults break through to the
surface, where the slip direction and fault orientation can be observed directly, and many small
faults are not always clearly and unambiguously
displayed in the field (contrary to our beautiful
illustrations). How seismologists do this is
shown in Figure 17-19, taken from a laboratory
experiment in which an "earthquake" was in-

duced under controlled conditions so that the
pattern of seismic waves radiated from the fault
could be studied. Although the scale is reduced
by about a millionfold from that of nature, the
simulation is valid. The experiment models a
vertical fault plane along which the slip is lateral. The "seismographs" are positioned on a
circle surrounding the fault; the motion recorded after the "laboratory earthquake" is
shown at 10° intervals from −100° to +100°.
Note that in the quadrant 0 to −90°, the **first
motion** on the seismic trace is upward, which is
consistent with the slip on that side of the fault
being a push to the right. The first motion from
0 to +90° is downward, indicating a pull to the
left. Thus these positive and negative first motions help define the orientation of the fault
plane and the directions of slip.* Although the
model simplifies nature somewhat and real seismograph stations are not situated in simple
circles surrounding faults, seismologists know
how to allow for natural complexities and can
uncover the true source mechanism of an earthquake from the radiation pattern of *P* waves.
This is what they find.

When the topography of mid-ocean ridges is
examined in detail, the ridges are often found to
be segmented, the segments being offset by
transform faults (Fig. 17-15). Earthquake epicenters coincide with the ridge crests and with
the transform faults between the offset ridge
segments, as shown in the figure. In 1967, seismologists at Columbia University found that the
pattern of *P*-wave motions radiated from earthquakes on ridge crests indicated that they originate in normal faults that run parallel to the
ridge crest. This means that the axis of tension is
perpendicular to the trend of the fault, as we
have seen in Figure 17-18, just as predicted by
the plate-tectonics concept, which specifies that
the ridge crests mark the boundary between
separating plates. Furthermore, it was found
that earthquakes in transform faults between
ridge crests show lateral slips, just as would be
expected for a region where plates slide past
each other in opposite directions. What elegant
support seismology gives to the notion that
plates spread from ridge crests! Outside the

*Actually, a fault perpendicular to the one shown in
the figure would produce the same pattern of up and
down motions if the slip directions were ↑↓ rather than
⇆. Fortunately, however, the correct orientation of
the fault plane can be deduced either from field evidence, if there is any, or from the aftershocks that
follow the main event, for they originate in the fault
plane, and their positions define the true orientation of
the fault.

Figure 17-20
Oblique airview of structures that collapsed during the San Fernando, California,
earthquake of 1971. [Photo by R. E. Wallace, U.S. Geological Survey.]

region between the ridge crests, the transform fault becomes **aseismic**—that is, produces no earthquakes. This is to be expected, since there is no differential slip in this region, where the plates move in the same direction on both sides of the fault. In a sense the fault has healed, and is evidenced only by topography, usually by a scarp (cliff or steep slope), as shown in Figure 17-15.

So much for the receding edges; what about the leading edges on the other side of the moving plates, where collisions occur? Seismologists have found that many of the deep earthquakes that originate within the subducted plate show the predicted compressive mechanism, in the direction of the dip of the downgoing plate (Fig. 17-15). They have also devised methods of mapping the downgoing plate by tracking the seismic waves, which are guided more efficiently up the cold plate from the earthquake focus to the surface.

Earthquake Destructiveness—Can It Be Controlled? Earthquakes cause destruction in several ways. Ground vibrations can shake structures and stress them to the point of failure and collapse. The ground accelerations caused by great earthquakes can approach and even exceed that of gravity near the epicenter, and very few man-made structures can survive without severe damage. Certain kinds of soil lose their rigidity and "liquefy" when subjected to repeated seismic shocks. The ground simply slides away, taking man's creations with it (Fig. 17-21). As was mentioned earlier, coastal earthquakes on occasion generate the awesome waves called "tsunamis," which can form walls of water as much as 20 meters high as they sweep over low-lying coastal areas (Figs. 17-22, 17-23). Avalanches, mudflows, and fire may accompany earthquakes and take their toll (Fig. 17-24). Of the 99,000 fatalities in the Tokyo earthquake of 1923, 38,000 were due to fire. Table 17-2 lists

Figure 17-21
Foundation failure as a result of soil liquefaction caused these buildings in Niigata, Japan, to topple during the earthquake of 1964. The structures themselves were built to withstand earthquakes; they toppled intact. [Photo by G. Housner, California Institute of Technology; National Science Foundation.]

Figure 17-22
Destruction at Seward, Alaska, caused by the tsunami generated during the earthquake of 1964. Although a warning system exists to alert people on distant coasts to the danger of tsunamis, it cannot yet function rapidly enough to help residents in the epicenter region. [Photo by F. Press.]

Figure 17-23
The tsunami from the great Alaskan earthquake of 1964 reached California, where several people perished and some coastal damage resulted from the waves. A tide gauge at Crescent City, California, which usually serves to record ocean tides, made this record of the tsunami, showing sea-level changes of almost 2 m more than normal.

Figure 17-24
Monument standing atop the debris of an avalanche that buried the town of Khait in the Tadzhik Republic of the USSR following the earthquake of 1949; 12,000 people were killed. The slide, more than 30 m thick, moved over the town with a velocity of 100 m/sec. No sprinter could have outrun it. Pamir Mountains in distance. [Photo by F. Press.]

the human losses of historical earthquakes. A seismic-risk map of the United States, based on the earthquake history of the country, is shown in Figure 17-25. Many readers may be surprised to find that they live in a zone where there is risk of earthquake damage.

Can anything be done about reducing earthquake hazards? Seismologists in the United States, Japan, the Soviet Union, and China are working hard to find answers to this question. Even though no major scientific breakthroughs have been made so far, damage and loss of life can be mitigated by encouraging sound building practices. Figure 17-26 shows something that should not be allowed—a residential area built in an active fault zone, the San Andreas, the most dangerous in the United States. Construction on unstable soils or in avalanche-prone areas should be prohibited. Engineers know how to design anti-seismic structures that will withstand most earthquakes, and building codes should require that this be done in high-risk areas.

Ten years ago only astrologers, mystics, and religious zealots were concerned with earthquake prediction. Today seismologists in many countries are actively working on this problem and can claim important initial successes. In February 1975 an earthquake was predicted five hours before it occurred near Haicheng in northeast China. Several million people, prepared in advance by a public education campaign, evacuated their homes and factories in the hours before the shock. Although many towns and villages were totally destroyed, only a few hundred lives were lost. Western scientists who have since visited the region estimate that tens of thousands of lives were saved. The Chinese have successfully predicted other earthquakes, but unfortunately were only able to provide a long-term warning (within 5 years) of the great T'ang-shan earthquake of August 1976—not enough accuracy to save the 700,000 people estimated to have lost their lives. Smaller earthquakes have been predicted in the United States and the Soviet Union, in connection with the research programs in those countries.

The scientific basis of earthquake prediction rests on a combination of laboratory and field experiments carried out in recent years. When a rock is squeezed, it deforms and eventually breaks. Just before it breaks, it swells because of

Figure 17-25
Map shows expected level of earthquake-shaking hazards. Levels of ground shaking for different regions are shown by contour lines that express in percentage of the force of gravity the maximum amount of shaking likely to occur at least once in a 50-year period. Damage begins to occur at about 10 percent g. An acceleration of 0.1 percent g or more is perceptible to people. [Modified from U.S. Geological Survey Chart.]

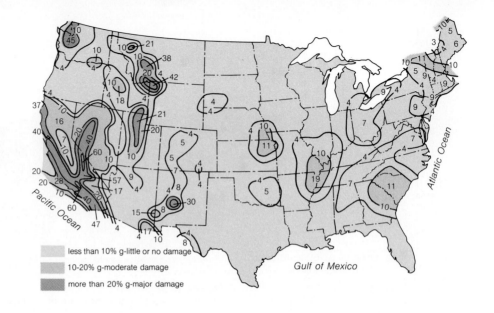

less than 10% g-little or no damage

10-20% g-moderate damage

more than 20% g-major damage

Table 17-2
Some of the world's worst earthquakes (in lives lost).

Year	Place	Deaths (est.)	Year	Place	Deaths (est.)
856	Corinth, Greece	45,000	1908	Messina, Italy	160,000
1038	Shansi, China	23,000	1915	Avezzano, Italy	30,000
1057	Chihli, China	25,000	1920	Kansu, China	180,000
1170	Sicily	15,000	1923	Tokyo, Japan	99,000
1268	Silicia, Asia Minor	60,000	1930	Apennine Mountains, Italy	1,500
1290	Chihli, China	100,000	1932	Kansu, China	70,000
1293	Kamakura, Japan	30,000	1935	Quetta, Baluchistan	60,000
1456	Naples, Italy	60,000	1939	Chile	30,000
1531	Lisbon, Portugal	30,000	1939	Erzincan, Turkey	40,000
1556	Shen-shu, China	830,000	1948	Fukui, Japan	5,000
1667	Shemaka, Caucasia	80,000	1949	Ecuador	6,000
1693	Catania, Italy	60,000	1949	Khait, U.S.S.R.	12,000
1693	Naples, Italy	93,000	1950	Assam, India	1,500
1731	Peking, China	100,000	1953	Northwestern Turkey	1,200
1737	Calcutta, India	300,000	1954	Northern Algeria	1,600
1755	Northern Persia	40,000	1956	Kabul, Afghanistan	2,000
1755	Lisbon, Portugal	30,000–60,000	1957	Northern Iran	2,500
1783	Calabria, Italy	50,000	1957	Western Iran	1,400
1797	Quito, Ecuador	41,000	1957	Outer Mongolia	1,200
1819	Cutch, India	1,500	1960	Southern Chile	5,700
1822	Aleppo, Asia Minor	22,000	1960	Agadir, Morocco	12,000
1828	Echigo (Honshu), Japan	30,000	1962	Northwestern Iran	12,000
1847	Zenkoji, Japan	34,000	1963	Skopje, Yugoslavia	1,000
1868	Peru and Ecuador	25,000	1968	Dasht-e Bayaz, Iran	11,600
1875	Venezuela and Columbia	16,000	1970	Peru	20,000
1896	Sanriku, Japan	27,000	1972	Managua, Nicaragua	10,000
1897	Assam, India	1,500	1976	Italy	900
1898	Japan	22,000	1976	Guatemala	23,000
1906	Valparaiso, Chile	1,500	1976	T'ang-shan, China	700,000
1906	San Francisco	500	1976	Philippines	3,100
1907	Kingston, Jamaica	1,400	1976	New Guinea	9,000

Figure 17-26
Housing tracts constructed within the San Andreas fault zone, San Francisco peninsula. The white line indicates the approximate fault trace, along which ground ruptured and slipped about 2 m during the earthquake of 1906. [Photo by R. E. Wallace, U.S. Geological Survey.]

the opening and extension of tiny cracks. This increase in volume, called *dilatancy*, begins when the stress reaches half the value needed to break the rock. When rocks become dilatant, other measurable physical changes occur—for example, in their electrical resistance, and the propagation speed of seismic waves (Fig. 17-27). The idea is to detect these physical changes in a region of the Earth's crust that has become dilatant just before an earthquake and issue a warning. For a great earthquake some of these changes (seismic velocity, uplift) can begin to occur 10 to 15 years before the shock, so that long-term preparations can be initiated (Fig. 17-28). Such changes as a reduction in the number of small tremors, followed by a rapid in-

crease, can occur days or hours before the shock and can serve notice that it is time to evacuate weak structures, close down nuclear power plants and gas lines, and take other last-minute precautions.

If earthquake prediction has just become respectable, earthquake control continues to boggle the imagination. Yet some chance discoveries have opened this intriguing possibility. In 1966, a dramatic correlation was found between the rate of high-pressure injection of waste fluids into a deep well and the frequency of earthquakes in the vicinity of Denver, Colorado (Fig. 17-29). Apparently the earthquakes were triggered by reduction of frictional resistance to faulting. The pressure exerted by the injected

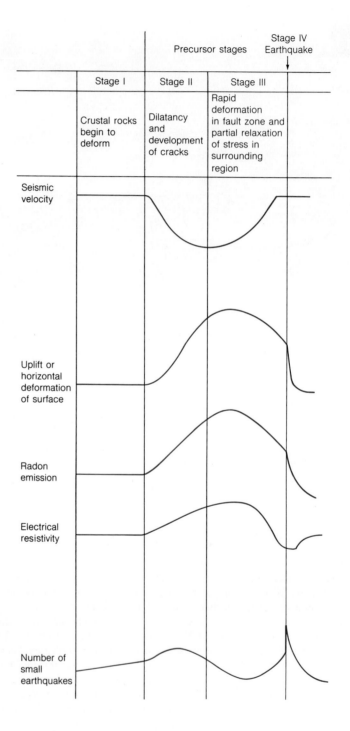

Figure 17-27
Earthquake precursors and their relation to dilatancy. When rocks are stressed by crustal forces, they are deformed elastically (stage I). Before faulting occurs, cracks open up, the rocks become dilatant and expand (stage II). This expansion is manifested as uplifting or tilting of the surface. The opening of cracks also results in a reduction in seismic velocity and an increase in the transfer of radioactive radon gas to water percolating through the rock. Small earthquakes increase in number. Stage II can serve for long-term predictions, years in advance of a great earthquake. In the third stage, rapid deformation occurs along portions of the fault that will break, relaxing the stress in the surrounding rock, so that cracks close. Uplift or tilting would decrease or reverse in direction, seismic velocity would increase, and small earthquakes would decrease in number. Days or hours before the fault breaks, the number of small earthquakes increases rapidly, signalling the imminence of the earthquake. [Modified from the work of V. I. Myachkin and G. A. Sobolev of the USSR.]

Figure 17-28
Contours of uplift that has taken place in the vicinity of Los Angeles since
1960. Some seismologists are concerned that this extraordinarily large and
rapid uplift is indicative of precursory stage II, signalling a major earthquake. [After U.S. Geological Survey.]

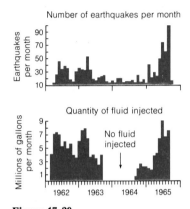

Figure 17-29
Correlation found by D. M. Evans
between quantity of waste water injected into a deep well and number of
earthquakes per month in the vicinity
of Denver, Colorado. This unplanned
"experiment" opens the distant possibility of earthquake control by fluid
injection.

fluids "unlocked" a pre-existing fault and strains
that had built up earlier were released. Perhaps
someday earthquake-control wells will be spotted every few miles along the San Andreas fault,
and fluid injected so as to cause the fault to
creep continuously and slip frequently in controlled earthquakes rather than allowing strain
to build up over periods of 50 to 100 years and
be released in a large, damaging shock. Much
research will be needed to achieve this important (and perhaps impossible) goal; the first steps
have already been taken.

EXPLORING THE INTERIOR
WITH SEISMIC WAVES

To appreciate the importance of seismic waves
in revealing the properties of the interior, one
need only reflect on what the state of knowledge
would be in the absence of this key tool. We
might surmise the existence of a crust from the
observation that most surface rocks are generally
light and felsic or mafic compared to the more
dense ultramafic intrusions that seem to invade
the surface layers from below, but we could only
speculate on its thickness. The sea-floor crust
would of course be terra incognita. We probably
would have guessed the mantle to be composed
of ultramafic rocks, but could only wonder
about its physical state, structure, and thickness.
From the clues provided by iron meteorites, the
large relative abundance of iron in the cosmos,
and our efforts to explain the Earth's density and
magnetic field, we might have been led to hypothesize the existence of a molten iron core,
but this would have been argued extensively. Its
depth would be uncertain, and the inner solid
core would be unknown. Continental drift and
sea-floor spreading would be debated, but the
overall concept of plate tectonics—especially the
fate of plates in subduction zones—would probably have escaped us.

Types of Seismic Waves. As early as the
1800's, mathematicians proved with pencil and

Compressional (P) waves

Shear (S) waves

Figure 17-30
Stages in the deformation of a block
of material with the passage of compressional, or P-waves, through it.
The undeformed block is shown at
the top. In the sequence from top to
the bottom, a crest of compression,
marked by an arrow, moves through
the block with the P-wave velocity. It
is followed by an expansion, and any
small piece of matter, like the marked
square, shakes back and forth in response to alternating compressions
and expansions as the wave train
moves through. A sudden push (or
pull) in the direction of wave propagation, indicated by the hammer
blow, would set up P-waves. [After
O. M. Phillips, *The Heart of the
Earth*, Freeman, Cooper & Co.]

Figure 17-31
Stages in the deformation of a block
of material with the passage of shear,
or S-waves, through it. A wave crest,
marked by an arrow, moves through
the block with the S-wave velocity as
vertical planes shake up and down.
Any small piece of matter, like the
marked one, shakes up and down and
experiences a shearing deformation
(from a square to a parallelogram in
the figure) as the shear wave passes
through. A sudden shear displacement, indicated by the hammer blow
at right angles to the direction of
wave propagation, would set up S-
waves. [After O. M. Phillips, *The
Heart of the Earth*, Freeman, Cooper
& Co.]

paper the existence of compressional and shear
waves in elastic bodies. Not until the close of the
nineteenth century, however, did seismologists
devise instruments sensitive enough to detect
such waves in the Earth—the P waves and S
waves generated by sudden slip along a fault.
Figure 17-30 shows the faster-traveling P wave
as the propagation of a volume change—a
squeezing and unsqueezing of the medium; the
individual particles vibrate to and fro in the
direction of wave propagation. In Figure 17-31,
the S wave is shown as a traveling shearing
disturbance, the material distorting in shape
rather than changing in volume; the particles
vibrate back and forth at right angles to the
direction of propagation.

Figure 17-32 depicts the trajectory of P waves
as they travel from the source of an earthquake
or explosion into the interior, emerging again at
distant points. These wave paths and their travel
times have been determined empirically from
the seismographic records of earthquakes all
over the world. Note particularly the **shadow
zone** and its geometrical relationship to the
focus and the core. The Earth's core deflects the
waves and in effect casts a shadow where very
little P-wave energy reaches the surface. The
existence of shadow zones suggested that the
core is molten, because compressional waves
decrease sharply in velocity when they pass from
a solid into a liquid of the same composition.
The suggestion became a firm pronouncement
when seismologists found that shear waves
could not penetrate this region. Liquids transmit
P waves but not S waves, since the fluids elastically resist and recover from squeezing, but do
not resist shearing.

When P and S waves encounter a boundary
such as that between the core and the mantle,
they are in general reflected back as well as
transmitted across it, just as light may be partly
reflected and partly transmitted at a water surface. If in the new medium the wave velocity is
different, the waves are bent, or **refracted.**
Because of all of these possibilities of reflection,
transmission, and refraction, P and S waves
break up into several types as they travel
through the Earth, as shown in Figure 17-33.
Follow the wave PcP in the figure as it bounces
in radar-like fashion from the Earth's core and
yields its depth from the round-trip time. The
wave PKP, which penetrates the core, is useful
for exploring that region. Many of the P-wave
trajectories and travel times are sketched in
Figure 17-32.

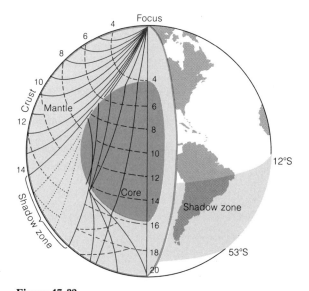

Figure 17-32
Cutout showing the pattern of *P*-wave paths through the Earth's interior. The numbers show the travel time in minutes for the waves to reach the associated broken line. Note the shadow zone, a region not reached by *P*-waves (for this hypothetical earthquake at the north pole) because they are deflected by the Earth's core. [After *Internal Constitution of the Earth* by B. Gutenberg (ed.), Dover Publications, 1951.]

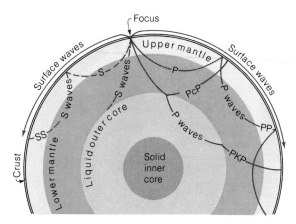

Figure 17-33
P- and *S*-waves radiate from an earthquake focus in many different directions. Waves reflected from the Earth's surface are called *PP* or *SS*. *PcP* is a wave that bounces off the core, and *PKP* is a *P*-wave transmitted through the liquid core. *S*-waves cannot travel in a liquid.

In addition to *P* and *S* waves, another category of seismic wave is the surface wave, guided in its propagation by the Earth's surface. These waves travel only through the outer layers of the Earth, just as the motion of ocean waves is mostly surficial. Figure 17-34 shows seismograms in which many of these seismic waves are labeled.

Pluck a violin string and a tone is emitted; strike a bell with a hammer and it rings. The Earth also rings when it is disturbed by a great earthquake that causes the entire globe to vibrate like a bell for as long as several weeks. The tones of Earth's vibrations are pitched too low for the human ear to hear, but modern seismographs are sensitive enough to detect these low-frequency oscillations. The Earth can vibrate in different modes, actually an infinite number of them. Some are shown in Figure 17-35. The mode with the lowest pitch is the "football," or **spheroidal**, mode, which takes 53 minutes to execute one vibration. For our musician-readers, we add that in terms of what one might call music of the spheres, that vibration corresponds to E flat in the twentieth octave below middle C. The "balloon," or **radial**, mode has a frequency of one

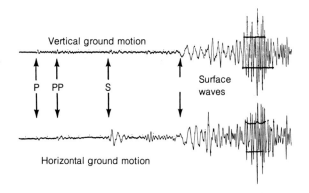

Figure 17-34
Seismograph recording of *P*-, *S*-, and surface waves from a distant earthquake.

vibration in 20 mintues; and the twisting, or **torsional**, mode, a frequency of one in 44 minutes.

Finding Earth Models from Travel Times and Vibration Frequencies. The basic experiment with seismic waves is to measure precisely the travel times of *P*, *S*, and surface waves

In the decade of the 1960's, seismologists worked to develop a method to distinguish underground nuclear explosions from earthquakes. They found that explosions excite surface waves with less efficiency than do earthquakes—a discovery that may stimulate statesmen to agree to an underground nuclear test-ban treaty.

and the frequencies of the vibrations of the Earth. The tools used to make these measurements are thousands of sensitive seismographs and highly accurate clocks distributed throughout the world. From these measurements we can plot travel-time curves for the different kinds of seismic waves (Fig. 17-36). The travel times depend on how the velocities of compressional and shear waves change as they pass through materials having different elastic properties. The vibration frequencies of the Earth depend on the velocities of these waves as well as the density of different parts of the interior, just as the tone of a bell depends on its elasticity and density. Once all the seismological data are accumulated, the next step is to find Earth models whose *P*-wave and *S*-wave velocities and internal densities explain the data.

A general method employed in many different scientific fields has been used to find Earth models; it has some similarity to gambling with dice. In fact, it is called the Monte Carlo

Box 17-1

The use of seismic waves in exploring for oil is an important application of seismology. In offshore prospecting, a ship tows a sound source and underwater phones. Sound waves are generated by a pneumatic device that works like a balloon burst. The sounds bounce off rock layers below the sea floor and are picked up by the phones. In this way subsurface sedimentary structures that trap oil, such as faults, folds, and domes, are "mapped" by the reflected waves. This technique is used extensively to explore the submerged continental shelves and shallow seas for oil and gas deposits. Oceanographers use this method to study the sedimentary layers on the continental slope and rise and on the floor of the deep sea.

A section of the Gulf of Mexico, 30 km long and 10 km deep, in which folded sedimentary layers are revealed by reflected seismic waves. [From Petty Geophysical Engineering Co.]

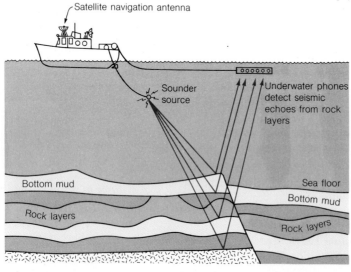

Seismic method of prospecting for oil and gas offshore. [After U.S. Dept. of Interior.]

"Balloon" mode   20.5 minutes

Football mode   53.9 minutes

Twisting mode   40.0 minutes

Figure 17-35
Three of Earth's vibrational modes. The schematic illustration shows how the planet changes shape, and gives the time it takes to complete the sequence of vibrations shown. The actual movements are only a small fraction of a millimeter.

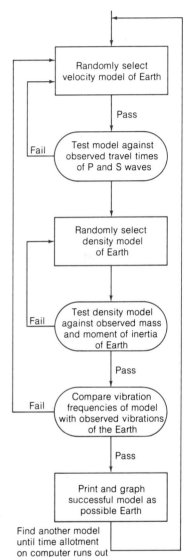

Figure 17-36
A computer must be told what to do, step by step. It makes up for this weakness by having an enormous memory and an ability to follow instructions at fantastic speeds. This illustration shows a "flow diagram" of instructions to a computer programmed to find models of the Earth that fit the observed travel times of seismic waves, the Earth's vibration frequencies, and mass.

method, named after the gambling casino. Imagine throwing dice to obtain a value for the density at some depth in the Earth. If the number 5 came up, it would be the density assigned to that depth in a trial model. Velocities of P and S waves can be randomly selected and tested in the same way. Actually, all this selecting and testing is done in a computer, which generates millions of random numbers instead of throwing dice. Follow the flow diagram of the computer program shown in Figure 17-36 to see the steps. The computer first randomly selects a velocity model of the Earth. The travel times of the P and S waves for this model are compared with the observed travel times from nuclear explosions. If the model fails, it is discarded, and the program loops back to the beginning; this happens repeatedly until a successful model is found. A density model is then sought until one is found that fits the known mass of the Earth. If this test is passed, the so-far successful velocity and density model is used to compute vibration frequencies for this trial Earth, and these are compared with about 100 observed ones for the real Earth. If this last test fails, the model is rejected, and the search begins again from the start. Millions of models are created and rejected in the search for a successful one. This may

seem wasteful, but modern computers are so fast that a million Earth models can be created and tested every hour. Scientists, after all, are human, and despite their efforts to keep an open mind, they may be prejudiced in favor of certain ideas about what the Earth is like inside. The Monte Carlo method, being a random one, helps us guard against bias and preconceived notions in building Earth models. A computer that has been honestly programmed should not throw loaded dice.

If a model passes all the tests—that is, if it fits the observed data—we have a possible Earth model. Unfortunately, it is not necessarily a description of the real Earth, because the data currently available are somewhat incomplete and imprecise, and therefore many possible models fit the same set of data. Thus a model that uniquely describes the interior of the real Earth in all details still eludes us; we need more complete and more precise data for its specifications. Nevertheless, the close similarities shown by the various possible models accepted by the computer clearly indicate that modern seismology has made considerable progress: densities and P-wave and S-wave velocities can now be specified to within several percent of the true value for most of the Earth's interior.

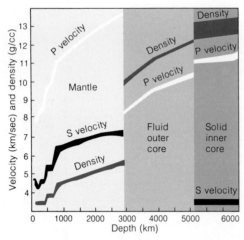

Figure 17-37
The variation of density and *P*- and *S*-wave velocity in the Earth's
mantle and core probably lies within the narrow bands shown in the
illustration. As data become more precise and plentiful, the bands of
uncertainty will become narrower. Nevertheless, even today we can
specify the density throughout most of the interior with an uncertainty of only a few percent of the actual value.

A computer plot of the ranges of internal
densities and *P*-wave and *S*-wave velocities for
all possible Earth models is given in Figure
17-37. It is quite likely that within the rather
narrow bands shown by these data there is a
model that would accurately describe the real
Earth. As more complete and more precise data
become available, these bands should become
narrower, perhaps someday converging to give
us a perfect model of the real Earth. But what
can we say *now* about the interior?

**Composition, Structure, and State of the
Interior.** To know these properties of the
interior is the main goal; velocity and density
models represent only a means to this end. We
use laboratory experiments to make the connection between seismology on the one hand and
petrology and geochemistry on the other.
High-pressure equipment and shock waves generated by explosives are employed, as described
in Box 17-2, to learn how velocity and density
would vary in different rocks, either in the solid
or in a partially molten state, and either near the
surface or in the deep interior. With this information the band of Earth models shown in

Figure 17-37 can be interpreted so that we can
make some statements about the materials and
their state.

The major divisions into crust, mantle, and
core (Fig. 17-33) were discovered from the
analysis of reflected and refracted *P* and *S*
waves, and have been known for more than 60
years. The boundary between the crust and the
mantle is called the **Mohorovičić discontinuity (M,** or **Moho,** for short) after the Yugoslavian seismologist who discovered it in 1909.
It separates rocks in which *P* waves have velocities of about 6 to 7 kilometers per second (3.8 to
4.4 miles per second) from underlying mantle
rocks, in which P waves have a velocity of about
8 kilometers per second (5 miles per second).
The field method of measuring these velocities
is described in Box 17-3. From geological sampling to find all possible crustal and mantle
materials and from laboratory measurements of
the properties of these materials, we have
learned to associate *P*-wave velocities with composition, as indicated in Table 17-3. We con-

Table 17-3
Correspondence between composition and
P-wave velocity in igneous rocks.

Composition	*P*-wave velocities (km/sec)
Silicic (granitic)	6
Mafic (gabbro)	7
Ultramafic (peridotite)	8

clude from these measurements that the continental crust consists mostly of granitic rocks,
with gabbro appearing near the bottom, and that
no granite occurs on the floor of the deep ocean,
the crust there being entirely basalt and gabbro.
The mantle below the M discontinuity is almost
certain to consist primarily of the dense ultramafic rock peridotite. The crust is a distillate of
the mantle, and therefore differs chemically
from its parent. In this sense, the Moho is a
chemical boundary located by seismic waves.

Nowadays seismologists are excited by the
finer details, the variations within the crust,
mantle, and core. Consider the lateral variations
in crustal thickness in a section extending from
continent to ocean, as shown in Figure 17-38; it
is one of the most important recent seismological results. The thickness of the crust varies
from about 35 kilometers to 10 kilometers in a
section extending from continent to ocean.
Under a high mountain the crust thickens to as

much as 65 kilometers. If Figure 17-38 suggests to the reader that the continental crust floats on the denser mantle like an iceberg on the ocean, he has made a good observation. Icebergs float because they are less dense than sea water; flotation comes from the large volume of ice that lies below the sea surface. When Archimedes' principle of buoyancy is applied to the flotation of continents and mountains, it becomes the **principle of isostasy,** which holds that the relatively light continents float on a more dense mantle; most of a continent's volume lies below sea level for the same reason that most of an iceberg lies below the ocean surface. Nature has contrived that large topographic loads like

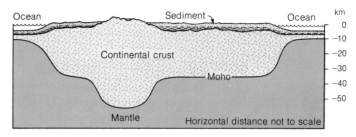

Figure 17-38
The lithosphere is topped by a relatively lightweight crust. Seismology reveals that the crust varies in thickness; it is thin under oceans, thicker under continents, and thickest under high mountains.

Box 17-2 High Pressure and Shock Experiments

Even if we knew in detail how density and seismic velocities change with depth in the Earth, we would still want to identify the materials and describe their physical conditions. To do this we also need information on the densities of different materials and the velocities with which seismic waves travel through them under the high pressures and temperatures that exist in the interior of a planet. The pressure at the center of the Earth is nearly 4 million times greater than atmospheric pressure,* and temperatures range in several thousands of degrees. Using a hydraulic press, geophysicists can squeeze rocks in the laboratory to pressures of about 100 kilobars, heat them to temperatures of about 1000°C, and at the same time measure many of their properties. This procedure, however, only duplicates the conditions at depths of about 300 kilometers—far short of our goal, the very center of the planet. Fortunately a new technique is available for compressing rocks to the necessary pressures; it happens to be the very same method used

to compress uranium when triggering an atomic explosion. An ordinary chemical explosive, such as dynamite, is wrapped around the rock. When the dynamite is detonated, the shock wave squeezes the rock, raising the pressure and temperatures to the high values needed to duplicate conditions at great depths. The rock is destroyed in the process, but in the few millionths of a second before it falls apart, data needed to calculate the density, pressure, and shock velocity (which is simply related to the seismic wave velocities) are obtained electronically from sensors on the rock. Other types of experiments are used to determine such things as strength, thermal, electrical, and elastic properties at elevated pressures and temperatures.

---

*Pressure is measured in atmospheres (atm), bars, or pounds per square inch (p.s.i.). 1 atm = 1.01 bars = 14.7 p.s.i. Geologists tend to use bars, kilobars (10^3 bars) and megabars (10^6 bars).

The Bridgman "squeezer," a device for subjecting minerals to pressures of a few tens of thousands of atmospheres and temperatures of several hundred degrees. The low pressure of the hydraulic press is amplified by concentrating the total force on the small area of the anvil. A furnace surrounding the anvil supplies heat. This apparatus simulates environments deep in the Earth's crust.

Box 17-3   Seismological Sounding of the Earth's Crust and Upper Mantle

Seismologists have developed a field procedure for measuring the thickness of the crust and the velocity of P waves in the crust and at the top of the mantle. Small seismographs are placed on the surface in a line extending away from a "shot point," where an explosion is set off to generate P waves. The waves leave the explosion in all directions—some traveling along the surface, others along the top of the mantle, as shown in the upper figure. A travel-time curve can be plotted on which each point represents the travel time required for the waves to reach the seismograph. The waves that travel along the surface plot on a straight line that passes through the origin of the graph and has a slope of $1/V_1$. The slope of the line is measured to obtain the speed V_1 of P waves in the crust. The waves traversing the mantle plot on a line with slope $1/V_2$ and with intercept T.

Values of V_1, V_2, and T obtained from the graph are used to calculate the thickness from the formula

$$D = \frac{T}{2} \frac{V_2 V_1}{\sqrt{V_2^2 - V_1^2}}$$

A student familiar with trigonometry and Snell's law might try his hand at deriving this simple but important equation.

An example is shown (see lower figure) of seismic waves recorded at a distance of 163 kilometers from an explosion of TNT. The traces are recorded from 6 seismometers placed 100 meters apart. The waves that have traveled through the crust and mantle are indicated by P_1 and P_2, respectively.

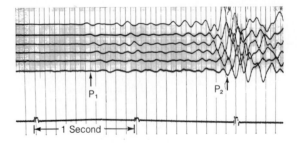

mountains and continents are compensated—that is, supported primarily by buoyancy rather than by the strength of the crust. Rocks, which we know to be solid and strong over the short term (seconds or years), are weak and flow like a viscous fluid when loaded over the long term (thousands to millions of years). When continents grow or mountains are pushed up, a supporting root must develop as part of the process to provide buoyancy and keep the new load from sinking. One variant should be mentioned. If for some reason—for example, regional heating—a part of the upper mantle becomes less dense than the adjacent mantle, it will also exert a buoyant force that can support elevated topography above it without the need for a crustal root. In a sense, the lower-density mantle serves as a root. This mode of isostatic compensation seems to be operating in the Basin and Range province (Utah, Arizona, Nevada) of the United States. The fact that this is also a region of high heat flow is consistent with the explanation. We shall see later that isostatic compensation does not operate in many places on the Moon, where the outer layers seem to be colder and thicker and, for this reason, stronger and able to support loads. Isostasy was actually discovered from variations in gravity, as we will see in the next chapter, where we take up the subject again. Seismological studies of crustal thickness have provided quantitative corroboration for the mechanism of isostasy.

In the years 1965 to 1970, geologists and geophysicists the world over concentrated their research efforts on the upper thousand kilometers of the Earth as part of the International Upper Mantle project. This concerted attack led to many exciting discoveries about a region that had previously been poorly known. We can illustrate the more important of these by discussing one of the shear-wave velocity models found in the Monte Carlo search. The model is divided on the basis of shifts in velocity into zones *a* to *g*, as shown in Figure 17-39.

Zone *a* is the **lithosphere,** a slab about 70 kilometers (45 miles) thick in which the continents are embedded. Crust forms the uppermost part of this outer shell of the Earth. Its lower boundary is marked by an abrupt decrease in shear-wave velocity. The lithosphere is characterized by high velocity and efficient propagation of seismic waves, both of which imply solidity and strength. We have already discussed in several places how the Earth's lithosphere is made up geographically of about ten distinct plates, created along mid-ocean ridges and destroyed in subduction zones.

Figure 17-39
A modern view of the structure of the outermost 700 km of the Earth is illustrated by a plot of *S*-wave velocity against depth. Note how velocity changes mark the important zones: lithosphere, partially molten asthenosphere, transitions to more dense molecular structures.

Zone *b* is the **asthenosphere,** or zone of weakness. It is also called the **low-velocity zone** for the obvious reason that the shear-wave velocity takes on low values. Seismic waves are attenuated more strongly in the asthenosphere than anywhere else in the Earth. Because laboratory experiments show that seismic waves are slowed and absorbed in a crystalline-liquid mixture, most geophysicists and petrologists think that these features of the asthenosphere indicate partial melting, perhaps 1 to 10 percent melt. Velocity and density in both the lithosphere and asthenosphere would fit a peridotitic composition. These two zones, therefore, do not differ so much chemically as they do in physical state; the boundary at 70 kilometers marks the solidus (where melting begins), separating the solid lithosphere from the not-so-solid asthenosphere. In Chapter 15 it was proposed that the melt of the asthenosphere is the primary source of basaltic magma, which fits the picture nicely. A solid slab underlain by a weak layer might be

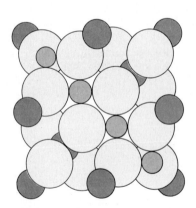

Figure 17-40
Olivine (Mg₂SiO₄, with Fe₂SiO₄) is a major mineral in the Earth's mantle. The figure at the top shows olivine in its low-pressure form. The large pale-brown atoms are oxygen, the medium-brown atoms are silicon, and the dark-brown ones are magnesium (or iron). When the pressure reaches a critical value, corresponding to a depth of about 400 km in the Earth, the molecule collapses into a more dense form (lower figure). Note the decrease in void space in the high-pressure form, in which the oxygen atoms are more closely packed. Seismologists have found where this transition occurs in the Earth, and petrologists have observed the transition in high-pressure laboratory experiments.

more easily movable, and perhaps this accounts for the mobility of the lithospheric plates.

The asthenosphere ends at a depth of about 250 kilometers (155 miles), and the rocks become solid again in zone *c*. The velocity increases slightly with depth in this region because of the effect of increasing pressure.

Zone *d*, about 400 kilometers (250 miles) below the surface, is thin but very important. Note the rapid increase in velocity, which correlates with the rapid increase in density in Figure 17-37. This transition is too rapid to be accounted for by a composition change. A change of phase—that is, a closer repacking on the atomic level—is required. The theoretical explanation was beautifully checked in 1969 when E. A. Ringwood and S. Akimoto squeezed olivine in their laboratories and found that at critical pressures and temperatures its atoms take up a more compact arrangement, changing into the spinel structure (Fig. 17-40). Olivine is the principal mineral in peridotite, and at a depth of about 400 kilometers in the Earth, conditions are just right for it to change phase. This is an excellent example of how the collaboration of specialists with different backgrounds (seismologists and petrologists) can, little by little, remove some of the mystery of Earth's interior.

Zone *e* is one of small change with depth, but zone *f*, near 700 kilometers, shows another rapid transition. This one had been verified by explosion-shock-wave experiments, but since the samples are destroyed in this method the transition had not been identified. In 1974, however, experimenters in Japan and the U.S. reached the required pressures by squeezing samples in the laboratory and found that olivine breaks down into dense, simple oxides like FeO, SiO₂, and MgO at this depth. The entire region from 400 to 700 kilometers, containing zones *d*, *e*, and *f*, is sometimes called the **transition zone.**

The lower mantle, zone *g*, extending from 700 kilometers (435 miles) to the core at a depth of 2898 kilometers (1800 miles), is a region that changes little in composition and phase with depth. Density and velocity increase gradually, again due to increasing pressure.

The Earth's core is far away, but not out of the reach of seismic waves. We know that its outer region is fluid and its inner one solid (Fig. 17-33). To obtain its composition, we use the same approach that has already proved so useful—comparison of laboratory experiments and seismological data. Look at Figure 17-41 to see how this is done. A band of Monte Carlo solutions for the density in the core is plotted. Also

Figure 17-41
Density in the Earth's fluid core plotted against depth below the surface and against pressure. The true density is not precisely known, but probably lies within the colored band. Despite this uncertainty, comparison with the densities for iron, nickel, and iron-silicon mixtures found in laboratory studies enables seismologists to conclude that the core is mostly iron, but slightly less dense than pure iron, as if a small amount of a "lightening" element like silicon were present.

shown are the densities of nickel, iron, and a mixture of iron and silicon, determined by "shocking" these materials in the laboratory with explosives, as was described in Box 17-2. We see that nickel is too dense, iron is better but needs to be lightened by adding perhaps 15 percent silicon. Would other shocked elements fit the data? Perhaps, but our choice is limited by the relative abundance of elements; the core accounts for one-third of the mass of the Earth, and must therefore contain relatively abundant elements. Iron is the only abundant element that approaches the required density under the pressure of millions of atmospheres at these great depths. It is a little too dense, as Figure 17-41 shows, so a plentiful "lightening" element like silicon must be added. Oxygen or sulfur might also be possible lightening elements.

In this way seismological observations and laboratory measurements of the properties of materials combine to give an incomplete but nevertheless good approximation of the Earth's interior. A zoned, differentiated Earth is found in which the major components are a metallic iron core and a rocky mantle consisting primarily of iron-magnesium silicates. The mantle includes a transition zone in which atoms are forced into closer packing, a partially molten asthenosphere, and most of the outer lithosphere. A thin, lightweight crust—the end-product of the differentiation process—caps the mantle.

SUMMARY

1. Most earthquakes originate in the vicinity of plate boundaries. The mechanism of earthquakes is governed by the kind of plate boundary: fracture under tensile stress at boundaries of divergence, fracture under compressive stress at boundaries of convergence, and lateral slip along transform faults.

2. Great earthquakes release in a few minutes huge amounts of elastic strain energy that had been slowly stored in the rocks of the fault zone over tens or hundreds of years. The source of this strain is plate motions.

3. Richter magnitudes are determined from the size of the ground motions, as measured when seismic waves are recorded on seismographs. The three types of seismic waves are P waves, S waves, and surface waves. The entire Earth can be set into global vibration by great earthquakes.

4. From a study of the travel times of seismic waves and the frequency, or pitch, of the global oscillations, seismologists have found that the earth is divided into shells—that is, it is a zoned, differentiated planet, with

   a) A slab-like, mostly ultramafic lithosphere, broken into large, mobile plates.
   b) A partially molten asthenosphere, the primary source of basaltic magma, as evidenced by reduced velocity and high absorption of seismic waves.
   c) A transition zone, where atoms are forced into a closer packing due to the high pressures.
   d) A lower mantle, predominantly iron-magnesium silicate.
   e) A fluid outer core, mostly iron but with one or more "lightening" elements.
   f) A solid iron central core.

   The continents with their lightweight silicic crusts—the end-products of the differentiation process—are embedded in the lithosphere.

EXERCISES

1. What is an earthquake? How is its magnitude measured? How many earthquakes cause serious damage each year?

2. How does the distribution of earthquake foci correlate with the three types of plate boundaries?

3. Seismograph stations report the following data for an earthquake: Dallas, $S - P = 3$ minutes; Los Angeles, $S - P = 2$ minutes; San Francisco, $S - P = 2$ minutes. Use a map of the U.S. and travel time curves (Fig. 17-16) to obtain a rough epicenter.

4. Taking into account the possibility of mass hysteria and economic depression following an earthquake prediction, false alarms, reduction of casualties, and other possible consequences, do you think the objective of predicting earthquakes is a worthwhile goal?

5. You wish to determine the depth to the water table before drilling a well. Using small explosions and seismographs you find that the P-wave velocity in the surface sediment is 600 meters/second and the velocity in a subsurface layer, presumably the water table, is 1500 meters/second. The intercept time, T, is 0.8 second. How deep is the water table? (See Box 17-3.)

6. Draw a cross section of the Earth, showing, to scale, the crust, lithosphere, asthenosphere, transition zone, core-mantle boundary, fluid outer core, solid inner core. What are the major characteristics of each region?

BIBLIOGRAPHY

Anderson, D. L., "The San Andreas Fault," *Scientific American,* November 1971. (Offprint No. 896.)

Bolt, B. A., "The Fine Structure of the Earth's Interior," *Scientific American,* March, 1973.

Isacks, B., J. Oliver, and L. R. Sykes, "Seismology and the New Global Tectonics," *Journal of Geophysical Research,* vol. 73, pp. 5855–5899, 1968.

Office of Earth Sciences, National Research Council, *Trends and Opportunities in Seismology.* Washington, D.C.: National Academy of Sciences, 1976.

Press, F., "Earthquake Prediction," *Scientific American,* May 1975.

Richter, C. F., *Elementary Seismology.* San Francisco: W. H. Freeman and Company, 1958.

Tectonophysics, "Forerunners of Strong Earthquakes," *Tectonophysics,* vol. 14, pp. 177–344, 1972.

18

THE EARTH'S MAGNETISM AND GRAVITY

Earth's magnetic field originates in the fluid iron core. Many rocks "remember" the direction of the magnetic field that existed at the time of their formation, and this remanent magnetization provides not only a history of the magnetic field but also a history of the movements of the lithosphere. Variations in the gravity field over the surface correlate with subsurface geological changes. Mountain roots, an example of isostatic compensation or buoyant support of mountains, were inferred from the gravity anomalies they produced.

The Earth, like any body, is surrounded by a gravitational field that attracts other bodies through interaction with their gravitational fields. Just why this occurs is unknown, yet, since Newton's time, we have been able to calculate the effects of gravity—such as the acceleration of an apple falling from a tree, the orbits of planets, the trajectories of spacecraft, the gravitational attraction of a mountain, and so on. Similarly, without knowing its basis, we observe and use the fact that magnetism is associated with moving electric charges, such as an electric current in a wire, or electrons spinning around the nucleus of an atom, as depicted in Figure 18-3. In this chapter, we will see how a planet's magnetic and gravity fields can be used to infer conditions and processes in its interior. For instance, just a few years ago, the Earth's magnetic field provided the key that unlocked the secret of sea-floor spreading.

EARTH'S MAGNETIC FIELD

The Earth as One Big Magnet. Twenty-five hundred years ago, the Greeks discovered the magnetic properties of lodestone, one of the naturally occurring ores of iron, the mineral called magnetite. It took about another thousand years for the Chinese to invent the first crude magnetic compass, which was simply a piece of lodestone suspended on a string. Travelers of the fourteenth century brought news of this discovery back to Europe, where it was adopted as a navigational aid, making possible the great feats of such men as Columbus and Magellan during the Age of Exploration. It remained for William Gilbert, physician to Queen Elizabeth I, to explain in his book *De Magnete*, published in 1600, how the magnetic compass works. He offered the proposition that "the whole Earth is a big magnet" whose field acts on the small magnet of the compass needle to align it in the north–south direction.

The Earth's magnetic field can be fairly well described by postulating a small but powerful permanent bar magnet located near the center of the Earth and inclined about $11\frac{1}{2}°$ from the geographic axis, as shown in Figure 18-4. The "lines of force" of the magnetic field, shown in the figure, imply the presence of a magnetic force at each point in space. A magnetic needle that is free to swing rotates under the influence of this magnetic force into a position parallel to

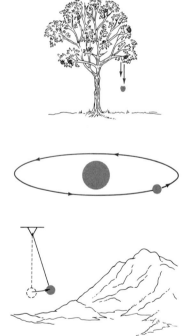

Figure 18-1
Three examples of gravitational attraction: an object falling in Earth's gravity field, a planet held in orbit by the Sun's gravity, a pendulum deflected by the gravitational attraction of the mass of a mountain.

Figure 18-2
Magnetic fields of a bar magnet and of a wire carrying an electric current, made evident by the alignment of iron filings on paper. The filings are aligned parallel to the direction of magnetic field lines. [From *PSSC Physics*, 3rd edition, D. C. Heath and Co. Reprinted by permission of the publisher.]

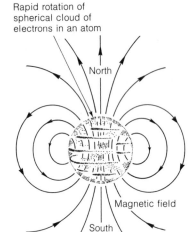

Rapid rotation of spherical cloud of electrons in an atom

North

Magnetic field

South

Figure 18-3
Moving electrons are equivalent to electric currents and create magnetic fields as they whirl around the nucleus of an atom. [After *Magnets* by F. Bitter, Doubleday Anchor Books. Copyright © 1959 by Educational Services, Inc.]

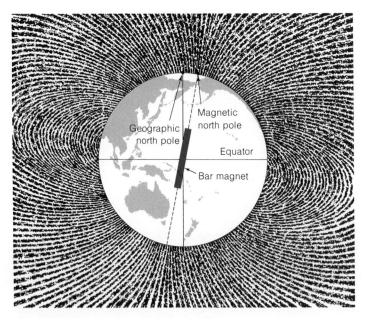

Geographic north pole

Magnetic north pole

Equator

Bar magnet

Figure 18-4
Earth's magnetic field is much like the field that would be produced if a giant bar magnet were placed at the Earth's center and slightly inclined (11°) from the axis of rotation.

the local line of force, approximately in the north–south direction. The north-seeking end of the needle points to the **magnetic north pole.** A compass needle that is free to swing in a horizontal plane does not point to true geographic north, but deviates slightly, east or west, depending on where the observer is, as Figure 18-4 implies; the angle of east or west deviation from true north is called the **declination.** In New York, the compass points about 10° west of geographic north; in California, the declination is about 20° east. The declination would be zero everywhere, making a navigator's life simple, if the magnetic north pole coincided with the geographic north pole in Figure 18-4—that is, if the hypothetical bar magnet at the center of the Earth lined up perfectly with the axis of rotation.

A magnetized needle free to pivot in a vertical plane (called a **dip needle**) measures the **inclination** of the magnetic field—that is, the angle the field makes with the surface of the Earth. At the magnetic poles, the dip needle swings into a vertical position, as shown in Figure 18-5, which is how some early explorers located these two points on the Earth's surface. Near the equator, where the inclination is zero, the dip needle takes a horizontal position. For the configuration shown in Figure 18-5, where the magnetic pole coincides with the geographic pole, the angle of inclination i is related to the latitude θ by the simple formula $\tan \theta = \frac{1}{2} \tan i$.

The compass and dip needle together give the direction of the geomagnetic field. To characterize the field fully, one must also measure its intensity or strength with a device called a **magnetometer,** which, in some versions, simply measures the force exerted by the Earth's field on a small, standard magnet. The unit of magnetic field strength is the gauss (named after the great mathematician Karl Friedrich Gauss). Ordinary horseshoe magnets have fields of about 10 gauss. The Earth's field is about 0.5 gauss near the surface.

The Puzzle of the Earth's Magnetism.

Unfortunately, though a good description of the field can be given assuming a permanent magnet at the center of the Earth, this idea has a fatal defect: heat destroys magnetism, and magnetic materials lose their permanent magnetism when the temperature exceeds a certain value called the **Curie point** (named after Pierre Curie). For most magnetic materials, the Curie point is about 500°C, a temperature exceeded below depths of about 20 or 30 kilometers in the Earth.

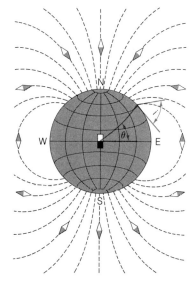

Figure 18-5
A suspended magnet needle aligns itself in the direction of the Earth's magnetic field. This diagram shows that the inclination i of the needle would vary with latitude from vertical over the pole to horizontal at the equator. [After *Continental Drift* by D. and M. Tarling, Doubleday Anchor Books. Copyright © 1971 by G. Bell and Sons, Ltd.]

In other words, the Earth cannot be permanently magnetized below this depth, so the notion that there is something like a bar magnet near the center of the Earth is eliminated, even though it represents the field nicely.

Another way to make magnetic fields is with electric currents, as the sketch in Figure 18-2 shows. About a billion amperes of current would be needed to produce the Earth's magnetic field, and this is nearly as much electric current as the total amount generated by man. Dynamos in power plants make electricity using an electrical conductor, propelled by steam or falling water, rotating in a magnetic field. Where inside the Earth is there a dynamo with the capacity to generate this much current?

The obvious place to look is the Earth's fluid iron core, because fluids can move readily and iron is a good conductor. Walter Elsasser and Edward Bullard proposed that a dynamo actually exists in the Earth's core—a **self-exciting dynamo,** which generates its own magnetic field. Figure 18-6 shows the principle of such a dynamo. No one believes that a rotating disk

Figure 18-6
Simple dynamo generates an electric current (colored arrows) when a copper disk is turned through the magnetic field of a bar magnet. If the bar magnet is replaced by a coil of wire, the same electric current creates a magnetic field in the coil, which keeps the system going. As long as the disk keeps rotating, the current will flow, and the magnetic field will remain in this "self-exciting dynamo." The Earth's magnetic field is thought to originate in a self-exciting dynamo, but one that is enormously more complicated. [From "The Earth as a Dynamo" by W. M. Elsasser. Copyright © 1958 by Scientific American, Inc. All rights reserved.]

1580
11° east of north

1660
Due north

1820
24° west of north

1970
7° west of north

Figure 18-7
A compass needle does not remain fixed in direction for all time, but drifts gradually in response to slow changes in the Earth's magnetic field. The example above shows how a compass in London varied in direction between 1580 and 1970.

30,000 years ago

Today

Figure 18-8
Earth's magnetic field 30,000 years ago was reversed from that of today's. We know this from the discovery of reversely magnetized rocks found in the fireplace of an ancient campsite. The rocks, cooling down after the last fire, became magnetized in the direction of the ancient magnetic field, leaving a permanent record of it, just as a fossil leaves a record of ancient life.

like the one in the figure actually exists in the core; what is proposed is that the fluid iron is stirred into convective motion by heat generated from residual radioactivity in the core. A small, stray magnetic field would interact with the moving fluid iron to produce electric currents, which would then create their own magnetic field, starting up a self-exciting dynamo. This sounds vague because it is: the dynamo theory for the core is exceedingly difficult to spell out in detail—in fact, the mathematical equations have never been completely solved. We do know enough, however, to show (1) that the mechanism is feasible; (2) that the magnetic pole and the geographic pole (about which the Earth rotates) must nearly coincide, as they do today; and (3) that the polarity of the magnetic field is a matter of chance—that is, that the north magnetic pole could just as easily be a south magnetic pole. Large-scale fluid motions in the core seem to offer the best possibility for explaining the Earth's magnetic field.

Changes in the Earth's Magnetic Field.
The fact that the magnetic compass was a key factor in navigation led governments to subsidize the science of geomagnetism. As a result, magnetic observations have been made since the sixteenth century. This historic documentation of the geomagnetic field over the last 400 years shows that declination, inclination, and field strength vary gradually the world over—a phenomenon called **secular variation.** For example, the compass needle in London has swung from 11° east of true north in 1580, to due north in 1660, to 24° west of north in 1820, and back to 7° west of north in 1970, as Figure 18-7 shows. This amounts to a drift of about 0.1° per year, a rapid rate of change compared to most

geological processes. The solid parts of the Earth, even when they creep plastically, change much more slowly. Because fluid motions can occur this fast, however, again we resort to the fluid core as the likely source of the secular variation. Thus fluid motions in the core not only account for the origin of the main field, but also for its fluctuations, which originate perhaps in small eddies superposed on the large-scale convective motion.

Fossil Magnetism. Not too long ago, an Australian graduate student found a fireplace in an ancient campsite where the aborigines cooked their meals. He carefully removed several stones that had been baked by the fires, first noting their orientation. Then he measured the direction of magnetization of the stones, and he found that they were magnetized exactly opposite to the present geomagnetic field. He proposed to his disbelieving professor that, as recently as 30,000 years ago, when the campsite was occupied, the geomagnetic field was reversed from the present one—that is, that magnetic north was south.

Surprisingly enough, Earth scientists have discovered how to find out what the geomagnetic field was like in the past, not just thousands but millions of years before man developed instruments and started keeping records. The Curie point was mentioned earlier as the temperature at which permanent magnetism is lost when a magnet is heated. An important property of many very hot magnetizable materials is that, in cooling below the Curie point, they become magnetized in the direction of the surrounding magnetic field. This is **thermoremanent magnetization,** magnetization "remembered" by the rock long after the a　Above the Curie point, atoms take random directions

b　Below the Curie point, atoms become parallel within domains

c　Below the Curie point, in the presence of an external magnetic field, domains line up

Figure 18-9
Magnetic properties of magnetizable material. (a) At temperatures above the Curie point, heat "agitates" the atoms; they take random directions, and their randomly oriented magnetic fields cancel. (b) Below the Curie point, domains form in which the atoms line up, giving each domain a definite magnetization, represented by the larger arrows. (c) If the material cools below the Curie point, in the presence of an external magnetic field, the domains line up parallel to the external field, and the material becomes permanently magnetized.

magnetizing field has disappeared. Thus the Australian student was able to determine the direction of the field when, after the last meal was cooked in that ancient fireplace some 30,000 years ago, the stones cooled down and took on the magnetization of the surrounding geomagnetic field (Fig. 18-8). One might also think of an ancient volcano in eruption, say 100 million years ago. When the lava solidified and cooled below the Curie point, it became magnetized, leaving us with a permanent record of the geomagnetic field in mid-Cretaceous time, just as a fossil leaves a record of ancient life (Fig. 18-10).

Some sedimentary rocks can also take on a remanent magnetization. Recall that marine sedimentary rocks are formed when sedimentary particles that have settled through the ocean to the sea floor become lithified. Magnetic grains among the particles—chips of the mineral magnetite, for example—would become aligned in the direction of the Earth's field while falling through the water, and this orientation would be incorporated into the rock with lithification. The **depositional remanent magnetization** of a sedimentary rock would then be due to the parallel alignment of all of these tiny magnets, as if they were compasses pointing in the direction of the field prevailing at the time of deposition (Fig. 18-11).

With this important tool of **fossil magnetism** or **paleomagnetism** for exploring the ancient magnetism of the Earth, scientists roamed the surface of the planet, in the 1950s and 1960s, collecting old rocks on every continent and determining their magnetism and ages in order to reconstruct the history of the geomagnetic field. This worldwide effort led to the

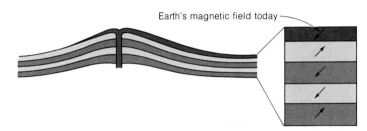

Earth's magnetic field today

Figure 18-10
Schematic illustration of how lava beds preserve the record of reversals of the Earth's magnetic field. The modern flow at the top shows the direction of the field today. Earlier flows record the directions of ancient fields that existed when the lavas cooled.

discovery of three startling phenomena: (1) **polar wandering,** (2) **reversals of the geomagnetic field,** and (3) **the sea floor as a magnetic "tape recorder."**

Polar Wandering. Once the direction of remanent magnetism in a rock is measured, it is possible to determine the position of the magnetic pole at the time the rock was magnetized. For example, suppose a formation 600 million years old is found whose remanent magnetic inclination is zero; that is, $i = 0°$. This means that regardless of the present location of the land mass in which the formation is situated, it was close to the equator 600 million years ago; that is, $\theta = 0$, as Figure 18-5 shows. Knowing the remanent magnetic inclination of a formation, one can use the formula given earlier in this chapter to deduce the latitude it occupied at the time it became magnetized. It is assumed, of

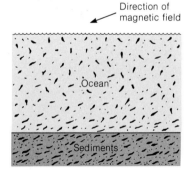

Direction of magnetic field

Ocean

Sediments

Figure 18-11
Schematic illustration of how a sedimentary rock can take on a magnetic field. Magnetic mineral grains, transported to the ocean with other erosion products, become aligned with the Earth's magnetic field while settling through the water. The initial orientation is preserved in the lithified rock, which thus "remembers" the field that existed at the time of deposition.

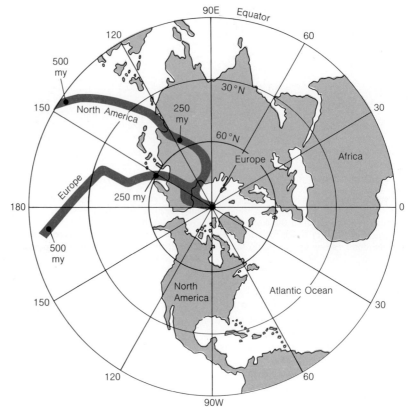

Figure 18-12
Apparent polar-wandering curves based on North American and European paleomagnetic data showing positions of the magnetic pole from the present to 500 million years ago. Most geophysicists believe that the pole didn't actually wander, as
the figure implies; it remained fixed, close to the geographic pole, while the
"map"—that is, the outer layers of the Earth—drifted over the interior. If the Atlantic had not opened and continental drift had not occurred, the European and
North American polar wandering curves would coincide prior to Triassic time. The
polar wandering curve, though fictitious, is a convenient way of summarizing paleomagnetic data.

course, that (1) the formation hasn't been folded
or magnetically disturbed and (2) that the geomagnetic field was always of the same simple
configuration shown in Figure 18-5, with coincident magnetic and geographic poles. The first
assumption can be checked for each sample. The
second assumption is generally accepted on theoretical grounds, but also because, even though
the magnetic pole has deviated slightly from the
geographic pole over the past 5 million years (as
today), the average position seems to center on
the geographic pole.

Unfortunately we cannot recover the original
longitude of the sample, since the magnetic
inclination for a given latitude is the same for all
longitudes. If the remanent declination of the
sample differs significantly from zero, however,
it indicates that the landmass rotated in addition
to moving in a north–south direction.

Using these assumptions, ancient pole positions can be plotted for remanent inclinations
and declinations found in rock formations of
different ages, and the movement of the magnetic pole for hundreds of millions of years can
be charted as in Figure 18-12. The magnetic
pole (and presumably the geographic pole)
seems to have wandered extensively in the past.
Some 600 million years ago, it was in the mid-
Pacific equatorial region. It moved to its present
position gradually, following the path shown in

Figure 18-13
Coal outcrop below sandstone, Victoria Land, Antarctica. The presence of coal implies tropical or subtropical conditions, suggesting that the Antarctic continent was closer to the equator at one time. [Photo by W. E. Long, Ohio State University.]

the figure. In the absence of any external influences, however, the direction of the Earth's axis of rotation (which defines the geographic pole) cannot shift but remains fixed in space for all time. This is a requirement of the law of conservation of angular momentum, which was mentioned in Chapter 1. The only way out of this dilemma is for the "geography" to move relative to the axis of rotation. To an observer in space, the geographic pole would remain fixed, and polar wandering would show as a movement of the surface features of the Earth over the globe. The continents would appear to "wander" about 90° to the north in some 600 million years, and not the magnetic pole, as Figure 18-12 implies. The sites of Denver and Paris would have been south of the equator 600 million years ago. Actually, it is the plates of the lithosphere that "wander" with respect to the axis of rotation, "carrying the geography along." The apparent polar-wandering curve of Figure 18-12, though fictitious, is a convenient way of summarizing paleomagnetic data. Paleoclimatic data—that is, the rock record of ancient climates—such as the occurrence of coal beds (which indicate humid climates) in polar regions and glacial deposits near the equator, may be taken as additional evidence for the movement of continents, as implied by the polar-wandering curve.

Polar wandering is really a manifestation of the mobility of the plates of the lithosphere. An observer in space would not simply see the map slip over the globe, he would also see it distorted, with the continents colliding and drifting apart and the oceans closing and opening. In a sense, paleomagnetism enables the geologist to view continental movements like the fictitious observer in space.

Reversals of the Geomagnetic Field. Imagine the state of shock and consternation if navigators and hikers the world over were to see their compass needles flip around with the north-seeking pole pointing south. A reversal of the Earth's magnetic field will take place in the next few hundred thousand years, except not as rapidly as the preceding sentence implies. Erratically, but roughly every half-million years, the Earth's magnetic field changes polarity, taking perhaps a few thousand years to reverse its direction.

The reversals are clearly indicated in the fossil magnetic record of layered lava flows, as shown in Figure 18-10. In the sequence of rocks, each layer represents a progressively earlier period of geological time whose age can be determined by radiometric methods. The direction of remanent magnetism can be obtained for each layer and, in this way, the time sequence of flip-flops of the field—that is, the **magnetic**

The polar wandering curve based on European paleomagnetic data is roughly parallel to the North American curve in Figure 18-12, but separated by about 30° in longitude for much of Paleozoic and Triassic time. This is because the Atlantic Ocean opened by this amount after the Triassic, that is, after the Paleozoic and Triassic rocks were magnetized. The two polar wandering curves become approximately coincident if the paleomagnetic pole directions are rotated so as to close the Atlantic and bring the continents together. This observation, as well as similar results for other continents, buttressed the case for continental drift in the middle 1950's before sea floor data became available.

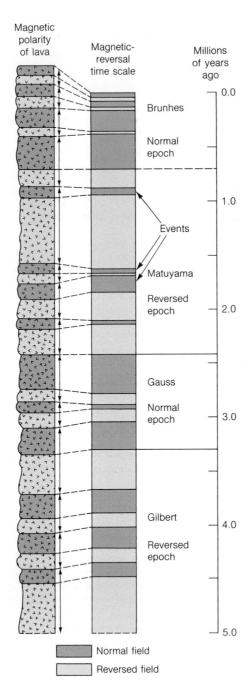

Magnetic polarity of lava

Magnetic-reversal time scale

Millions of years ago

— 0.0

Brunhes

Normal epoch

— 1.0

Events

Matuyama

Reversed epoch

— 2.0

Gauss

Normal epoch

— 3.0

Gilbert

Reversed epoch

— 4.0

— 5.0

Normal field

Reversed field

Figure 18-14
Schematic illustration of how magnetic polarities of lava flows are used to construct the time scale of magnetic reversals over the past 5 million years. In no one place is the entire sequence found; the sequence is worked out by patching together the ages and polarities from lava beds all over the world. The radiometric-magnetic time scale has recently been extended to 7 million years.

stratigraphy—can be deduced. The history of reversals going back almost 7 million years has been worked out in this way (Fig. 18-14). It has been found that about half of all rocks studied are magnetized opposite to the Earth's present magnetic field, which implies that the field has flipped frequently over geologic time and that normal and reverse fields are equally likely. Although normal and reverse **magnetic epochs** (each of which is named after a famous magnetician) seem to last on the order of one-half million years, superimposed on the major epochs are transient, short-lived flips of the field, known as **magnetic events,** which may last anywhere from several thousand to 200,000 years. The Australian graduate student mentioned earlier apparently found a new reversal event within the present Brunhes normal epoch.

Just why the field reverses is unknown. We are even uncertain whether the field dies down and builds up again in the opposite direction or simply tilts over. The simple self-exciting dynamo can have either polarity, and perhaps this indicates that the Earth's internal dynamo is easily changeable.

Some specialists on the microfossils of the sea floor have reported a curious correlation between extinctions of certain faunal types and reversals of the field. It is a matter of some concern if the disappearance of certain organisms is related to polarity changes. One explanation that has been advanced is that penetration to the Earth of lethal cosmic rays may be increased when the geomagnetic field is near zero. Most cosmic rays, however, are absorbed by the atmosphere rather than deflected by the magnetic field, so that the effect on life is likely to be small. Perhaps the constituents of the microfauna somehow depend on the magnetic field in their internal biochemical reactions. Perhaps an external common cause, like a large meteorite impact, affects both the fauna and the field. Perhaps the correlation is spurious.

Although the cause of reversals remains for future scientists to explain, their occurrence has made possible an important discovery about the sea floor.

The Sea Floor as a Magnetic "Tape Recorder." During World War II, extremely sensitive airborne magnetometers were developed to detect submarines by their magnetic fields. With slight modification, these same instruments were adopted by oceanographers for towing behind their research ships. Used in this way, the magnetometers measure two things: the main planetary or geomagnetic field (see Fig. 18-5) and the local magnetic disturbance, or **magnetic anomaly,** due to magnetized rocks on the sea floor. The general, broad geomagnetic field could easily be subtracted, leaving a record of a highly variable magnetic anomaly originating in the magnetized rocks beneath the sea. Rocks strongly magnetized in the normal direction would show as a positive anomaly; reversely magnetized rocks would show as a negative anomaly.

Steaming back and forth across the ocean, sea-going scientists discovered amazing magnetic anomaly patterns like the one shown in Figure 18-15. In many areas, the bands of positive and negative magnetic anomalies are linear over hundreds of miles and show an almost perfect symmetry with respect to the central magnetic anomaly. The axis of symmetry coincides with the crest of the mid-ocean ridge. If one folds a map of such anomalies along the ridge axis, he will find that the magnetic bands on one side fall nearly on top of those on the other side, almost like the ink-blot pattern of a Rorschach test. Figure 18-16 shows a magnetic profile across a ridge, which illustrates these features in greater detail. Note the amazing correspondence of the sequence of peaks and troughs of the magnetic-anomaly curve on both sides of the ridge.

This peculiar magnetic pattern puzzled scientists for several years until 1963, when two Englishmen, F. J. Vine and D. H. Mathews, and, independently, two Canadians, L. Morley and A. Larochelle, made a startling proposal. They reasoned that the positive and negative magnetic zones correspond to bands of rock on the sea floor that were magnetized during ancient episodes of normal and reversed magnetism of the Earth's field, and that the magnetic stripes could be used as evidence in support of the theory of

Figure 18-15

Magnetic anomaly pattern associated with the Reykjanes Ridge, a part of the mid-Atlantic ridge southwest of Iceland. The white spaces correspond to rock formations on the sea floor that are reversely magnetized. The strips shown in tones of brown or gray correspond to normal magnetization—that is, similar to the present-day direction. The almost perfect symmetry with respect to the ridge axis is emphasized by the matching tones on opposite sides; the youngest rock is brown and the oldest black, in accordance with the hypothesis of sea-floor spreading. [After "The Origin of the Oceanic Ridges," by E. Orowan, Copyright © 1969, by Scientific American, Inc. All rights reserved.]

Figure 18-16

Symmetry of the magnetic anomaly of sea floor rocks on both sides of the ridge axis is demonstrated by reversing a record covering about 900 km of both flanks (brown) and superposing it on the record as ordinarily shown (black). [After "Sea Floor Spreading" by J. R. Heirtzler. Copyright © 1968 by Scientific American, Inc. All rights reserved.]

Figure 18-17

The succession of normal and reversed magnetic anomalies on the sea floor provides strong support for the concept of sea-floor spreading. Rocks of normal, or present-day, polarity are shown in shades of brown; rocks of reversed polarity are in shades of gray. The symmetry of the magnetic stripes and the correlation with the time scale of reversals worked out from lava flows on land suggests that molten rock upwelling along the ridge axis became magnetized as it cooled, was pushed out on both sides, and gradually moved outward with the separating plates. The separation of the two blocks represents a transform fault. The diagram is based on the studies of many scientists. [After "The Confirmation of Continental Drift" by P. M. Hurley. Copyright © 1968, by Scientific American, Inc. All rights reserved.]

sea-floor spreading (Fig. 18-17). They argued that the ocean progressively widens as new sea floor is created along a crack that follows the crest of mid-ocean ridges. Lava flowing up from the interior solidifies in the crack and becomes magnetized with either normal or reversed magnetization, depending on the direction of the Earth's field at the time. As the sea floor spreads away from the ridge, approximately half the newly magnetized material moves to one side and half to the other, forming two symmetrical, magnetized bands. Newer material fills the crack, continuing the process. In this way, the sea floor acts like a tape recorder that encodes, by magnetic imprinting, the history of the opening of the ocean in terms of the history of reversals of the geomagnetic field. By discovering how to "replay the tape"—that is, by dating the magnetic bands on the sea floor using the magnetic stratigraphy of Figure 18-14 worked

out from lavas on land—geophysicists showed that the magnetic data could indicate how fast the ocean opened up. We would expect the rocks on the crest of the ridge to be normally magnetized, because they were extruded during the present normal magnetic epoch. Reversely magnetized rocks corresponding to a magnetic epoch of about one million years ago have been displaced some distance from the ridge—say, about 15 kilometers on each side of the ridge crest if the spreading rate is 1.5 centimeters per year. The reversal time scale can actually be followed through many oscillations of the Earth's field, and the corresponding magnetic bands extend out to many hundreds of kilometers from the ridge crest (Fig. 18-18).

The magnetized strips of sea floor provided a powerful tool to extend the history of magnetic-field reversals back in time almost 200 million years into the Jurassic Period. Precise dating of reversals (and therefore of spreading rates) goes back only about 5 million years, because the radiometric method of dating lava flows on land loses accuracy beyond this time. By simply assuming the spreading rate determined for the past 5 million years to be representative of a much longer period, the older normal and reversed magnetic epochs could be correlated over all the oceans and assigned dates. Figure 18-19 shows the sequence of 171 reversals, extending back 76 million years to the Cretaceous Period, as they were worked out by this method. The magnetized strips on the sea floor are shown schematically below the observed magnetic anomalies. Note that the spacing of the strips differs in the several oceans because the sequence of reversals can be compressed or stretched out according to slower or faster spreading.

After geologists study a region, they often present the sequence of rock layers extending back in geological time as a stratigraphic section. Magnetic anomalies on the sea floor enable geophysicists to plot a "magnetic-stratigraphic"

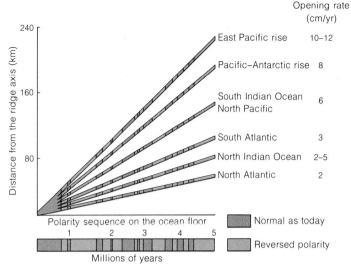

Figure 18-18
The rate of ocean spreading from magnetic anomaly patterns. The same magnetic polarity zone may be encountered at various distances from different ridges in different oceans, depending on the rate of spreading. Since the ages of the polarity zones are known from the magnetic-reversal time scale, the spreading rates can be calculated. The spreading rate of the Pacific Ocean along the East Pacific rise is the most rapid, amounting to 10–12 cm/yr. The North Atlantic shows the slowest rate, 2 cm/yr. [After *Continental Drift* by D. and M. Tarling, Doubleday Anchor Books. Copyright © 1971 by G. Bell and Sons, Ltd.]

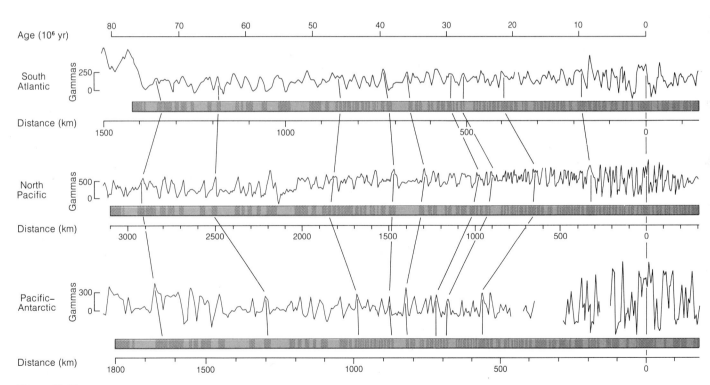

Figure 18-19
Magnetic anomalies recorded over the oceans reveal the same succession of magnetized lava formations on the seafloor, depicted by the dark and light stripes. The spacing may differ because the spreading rates vary, but each ocean shows the same sequence of some 171 reversals over the past 76 million years. The illustration shows the correlation of the anomalies from ocean to ocean. [After "Sea Floor Spreading" by J. R. Heirtzler. Copyright © 1968 by Scientific American, Inc. All rights reserved.]

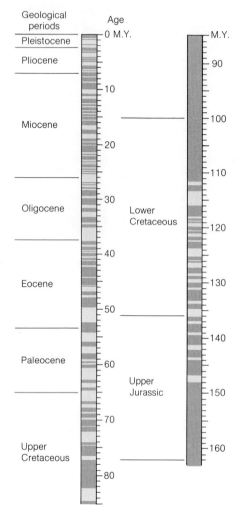

Figure 18-20
Geomagnetic reversal time scale from the present to the base of the Upper Jurassic 162 million years ago. Shaded intervals are normal; white intervals are reversed field directions. [After J. R. Heirtzler, R. L. Larson, and W. C. Pitman III.]

section, as in Figure 18-20, showing the historical sequence of worldwide magnetic reversals back in geological time to the Jurassic Period.

The power and convenience of the new magnetic stratigraphy in working out the history of ocean basins cannot be overemphasized. Simply by steaming back and forth, measuring the magnetic field of the magnetized rocks of the sea floor, and correlating the pattern of reversals with the sequence shown in the preceding two figures, ages can be assigned to different regions of the sea floor without even examining rock samples! All one needs is a good magnetic record, and these have already been obtained and interpreted for large sections of the world's oceans.

Isochrons (contours of the age of the sea floor) obtained in this way show the time that has elapsed and the amount of spreading that has occurred since the magnetized rocks were injected as lava into a mid-ocean rift. Note how the isochrons in Figure 18-21 show progressively older sea floor on both sides of the major ocean-ridge rifts, the more widely spaced isochrons of the east Pacific signifying a faster spreading rate than those of the Atlantic. We will see in the next chapter that these "magnetic ages" were verified when the deep-sea drilling project brought back rock samples from the sea floor that could be dated in the laboratory using fossils and radiometric methods. What a coup for the scientists who discovered this tool!

Magnetized Moon Rocks—A Puzzle. Unlike the Earth, the Moon has no planet-wide magnetic field. There is no question about this. Soviet and American spacecraft have been unable to detect such a field after several efforts. Yet magnetized rocks have been found lying on the lunar surface. Discordant data are the stuff of great discoveries, and planetary scientists are vying to explain these seemingly contradictory results. The leading hypothesis at this time proposes that the Moon rocks, in their remanent magnetism, "remember" an earlier period of lunar history some 3–4 billion years ago (the age range of the rocks), when the Moon did have a planetary magnetic field. This implies also the existence, at this early time, of a small liquid iron core that has since cooled and solidified. Is there a better way to manifest the power of modern geological and geophysical methods than to return a rock from the lunar surface, date it, measure its magnetic field, and then describe the physical state at the center of the Moon billions of years earlier?

Figure 18-21
Isochrons derived from magnetic-anomaly patterns for the oceans around South America. Isochrons are numbered from 1, the youngest, located at the axis of a mid-ocean ridge spreading center. Dots show that most earthquakes originate at plate boundaries, where spreading and subduction are underway. They outline the Peru-Chile trench subduction zone along the west coast of South America. [From map by Walter C. Pitman III, Roger L. Larson, and Ellen M. Herron, Lamont-Doherty Geological Observatory; drawn by Mildred M. Alvarez, Hester Cason, 1974. Geological Society of America.]

EXPLORING THE EARTH WITH GRAVITY

The Indian Puzzle. Some 150 years ago, during the great land survey of India, a curious discrepancy was uncovered by the British surveyors. The distance between Kaliana, some 100 kilometers (60 miles) south of the Himalaya range, and Kalianpur, 600 kilometers (375 miles) farther south, was determined in two precise ways—by measurement over the surface and by reference to astronomical observations—and the results disagreed by some 150 meters (500 feet) in 600 kilometers. This may seem like a small amount, but it was an intolerable surveying error even by nineteenth-century standards. The astronomical method of measuring distance uses the angles of stars with respect to the vertical, which is defined by a plumb line (a weight suspended on a string). To account for the difference, it was proposed that the plumb line was tilted toward the Himalayas because of the gravitational attraction of the mountains on the plumb bob, causing an error in the distance measurement. When the calculation was actually made, it was found that the mountains should

Figure 18-22
Worldwide pattern of sea-floor spreading is revealed by the age of the sea floor, as determined from magnetic data. Mid-ocean ridges, along which new sea floor is extruded, coincide with the youngest sea floor. The dating of magnetic anomaly stripes makes it possible to establish isochrons (shown by different colors and textures) that give the age of the sea floor in millions of years since creation at the ridges. The Atlantic Ocean is symmetrical about the mid-Atlantic ridge. Asymmetry of the pattern in the Pacific is partly caused

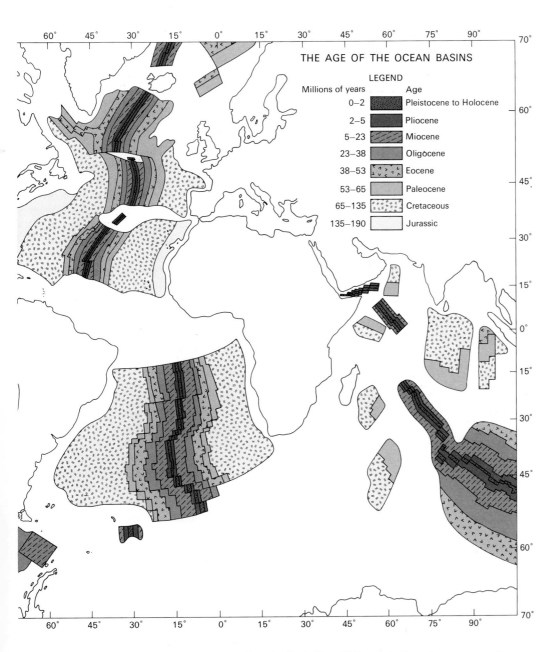

THE AGE OF THE OCEAN BASINS

LEGEND

Millions of years	Age
0–2	Pleistocene to Holocene
2–5	Pliocene
5–23	Miocene
23–38	Oligocene
38–53	Eocene
53–65	Paleocene
65–135	Cretaceous
135–190	Jurassic

by subduction in the Aleutian trench south of Alaska, in the Peru-Chile trench along the west coast of South America, and in many trenches in the Western Pacific. [After map by Walter C. Pitman III, Roger L. Larson, and Ellen M. Herron, Lamont-Doherty Geological Observatory; original drawn by Mildred M. Alvarez, Hester Cason, 1974. Geological Society of America.]

Figure 18-23
A plumb line ordinarily occupies a vertical position. Near a mountain system, we would expect the plumb bob to be deflected toward the mountains because of the gravitational attraction of their mass. The observed deflection is typically less than expected, a discrepancy whose explanation led to an important discovery. The diagram exaggerates the amount of deflection, which is small but readily measurable.

Figure 18-24
Examples of buoyancy. Icebergs and ship hulls float because the volume submerged is lighter than the volume of water displaced. Similarly, the volume of relatively light crustal rock projecting into the denser mantle provides a buoyant force that supports the mountain mass above.

Figure 18-25
The discrepancy between the observed and expected deflection of the plumb bob in Figure 18-23 can be reconciled if the excess mass of the mountain is compensated by a deficiency of mass in a "light" crustal root below. The root provides buoyant support for the mountain, which otherwise would sink into the mantle.

have introduced an even larger error—one of about 450 meters (1500 feet)—thus compounding the puzzle (Fig. 18-23).

In 1865, no less a figure than the Astronomer Royal, Sir George Airy, came forward with an explanation for this discrepancy that contained the basis of the principle of isostasy (already discussed in Chapter 17). Airy proposed that the enormously heavy mountains are not supported by a strong, rigid crust below, but that they "float" in a "sea" of denser rock. Stated otherwise, the excess mass of the mountains above sea level is **compensated** by a deficiency of mass in an underlying root. This root provides the buoyant support, in the manner of all floating bodies, just as a ship with a deep hull is buoyed up (Fig. 18-24). The plumb bob "feels" both the excess mass on top and the deficiency of mass below, hence the reduced deflection (Fig. 18-25). The resolution of the "Indian puzzle" not only led to the concept of isostasy but also introduced **gravity surveying** as a method for detecting mass variations in the interior by their corresponding gravity variations.

Gravimeters. The local value of gravity, g, can be obtained from the period* of a swinging pendulum or the acceleration of a falling weight—an experiment performed in every elementary physics course. Pendulums have been used in gravity surveys, but they have mostly been supplanted by the modern gravimeter. This is a device no more complex than a weight on a spring that stretches or contracts as gravity increases or decreases from place to place (Fig. 18-26). Although the principle is simple, the engineering of the gravimeter is most elegant: This device, not much larger than a thermos bottle, can detect gravity variations as small as 0.00001 centimeter per second per second. Thus, because the average value of gravity is 980 centimeters per second per second, this instrument can measure variations as small as $10^{-8}g$! The standard unit of acceleration used in gravity surveys is the milligal, which is 0.001 centimeter per second per second. A modern gravimeter can easily measure the difference in gravity between a table top and the floor, even though the table top is only 1 meter farther from the center of the Earth!

Gravity Surveying. The millions of dollars required to develop the sensitivity achieved by the modern gravimeter were underwritten by the

---

*Time required for one complete oscillation.

oil industry. This was the direct result of the recognition, made some forty years ago, that the buried geologic structures in which oil is trapped (such as folds, faults, and salt domes) often produce **gravity anomalies** that are detectable by sensitive instruments. A gravity anomaly is a perturbation in the normal gravity field caused by a change in subsurface mass due to a mountain root, a salt dome, or any other lateral geological change. The idea is to find and describe the mass anomaly from its gravity effect, and thus to explore the subsurface geology by making gravity surveys. An example of a gravity anomaly is given in Figure 18-27. Before such a profile can be produced, however, three important corrections must be applied to the value of g from each station at which the gravimeter is read; otherwise, the most interesting anomalies would be obscured.

1. If the Earth were spherical and nonrotating, the gravitational attraction of the planetary body would be the same everywhere on the surface. Because of centrifugal force, however, things tend to fly outward from a rotating body; hence, gravity is less at the equator, or things weigh less there than at the poles. The same centrifugal force makes the Earth bulge outward at the equator and flatten at the poles. Remember that g is proportional to $1/R^2$, in which R is the distance to the center of the planet. Because R decreases by 21 kilometers going from the equator to the pole of our flattened or spheroidal planet, g increases with latitude. An International Formula has been adopted that best describes g everywhere on the Earth's surface, taking into account the Earth's shape and rotation.* This formula value is subtracted from the gravimeter reading in the search for anomalies, which could otherwise be masked by the big effects of rotation and flattening.

2. Because of topographic variations, gravity stations generally differ in elevation—that is, in distance R from the center of the Earth. In our search for anomalous subsurface masses, we must remove the obvious effect of elevation on the local gravity value (using the fact that g varies as $1/R^2$ to get the correction), and all readings are corrected as if they were made at sea level. This is called a **free-air correction,**

---

*By international agreement, the value of $g = 978,049 \ (1 + 0.0052884 \ \sin^2\phi - 0.0000059 \ \sin^2 2\phi)$ milligals, in which ϕ is the latitude. Thus, gravity is about 0.5 percent stronger at the north pole where $\phi = 90°$ and $\sin\phi = 1$, than at the equator, where $\phi = 0°$ and $\sin\phi = 0$.

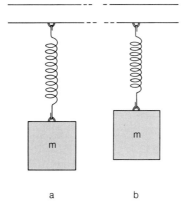

Figure 18-26
The gravimeter is simple in concept but elegant in implementation. A mass attached to a spring experiences a larger or smaller pull as gravity varies. The corresponding extensions or compressions of the spring are measured very precisely, so that small changes in gravity can be observed.

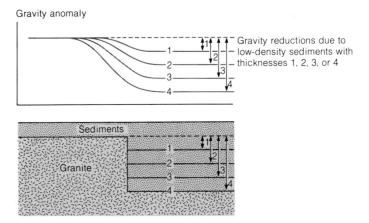

Figure 18-27
Schematic illustration of a gravity anomaly. The value of gravity changes across the structure shown because the less-dense sediments contain less mass than an equal volume of granite. The thicker the sedimentary deposit, the greater the decrease in gravity, as the curves show.

and it amounts to adding 0.31 milligals for each meter of elevation above sea level.

3. Finally, in order to highlight subsurface effects, it is important to account for all obvious near-surface masses that affect gravity. The free-air correction reduces the reading to sea-level only partially, because it allows for the distance to the center of the Earth but not for the attraction of the mass of rock between the station and sea level. The correction that com-

B

A

Gravity observed at
stations A and B

B

A

Free-air correction
places B at same
distance from center
of Earth as A

B

A

Bouguer correction
removes gravitational
attraction of mountains

Figure 18-28
Gravity is measured at *A* and *B* to see if there is a difference in subsurface mass.
To emphasize subsurface effects, corrections are made to the value of gravity at *B*,
as if to bring *B* to the same elevation as *A*, and also to remove the obvious gravita-
tional attraction of the mountain. Any remaining gravity difference between *A* and
B is ascribed to a change in subsurface geology.

pletes the subtraction of the local topography is
called the **Bouguer correction.** It amounts to
subtracting about 0.1 milligals for each meter of
rock above sea level. For gravity surveys on the
ocean, where *g* is measured at sea level, the
Bouguer correction corrects for the low density
and, therefore, the low gravitational attraction of
water by increasing the gravimeter reading by
an amount necessary to "convert" the ocean to
rock. In this way, the obvious gravity deficiency
of the ocean is removed in order to emphasize
anomalous suboceanic masses. The free-air and
Bouguer corrections are depicted diagrammatically in Figure 18-28.

If there were no lateral variations in mass in
the interior, the sum of all these corrections and
the gravimeter reading would be close to
zero—there would be no gravity anomaly, because everything would have been taken into
account. However, if the sum were to differ
from zero, we would have found an anomalous
mass—that is, something more or less dense
than the average rock: an ore body, an intrusion,
a sedimentary basin, or a mountain root. The
shape and magnitude of such a gravity anomaly
can help us define the dimensions and density of
the anomalous rock mass.

Imagine driving across the United States,
stopping every mile to measure gravity. You
would thereby produce a gravimetric profile of
the country crossing many geological provinces,
and it might be interesting to see how the gravimeter can aid us in interpreting these contrasting features. This has actually been done,
and the resultant gravity-anomaly profile is
shown in Figure 18-29, which includes an extension into the Atlantic Ocean made with a
shipboard gravimeter. The top and middle sections of the figure show the gravity profile and
the topography and identify the major geological provinces. All the corrections have been
applied to the gravity curve—that is, all the land
mass above sea level and all of the *lack* of land
mass in the oceans have been accounted for—so
this wiggly curve should reflect subsurface mass
variations. The bottom section of the figure
gives an interpretation of the gravity-anomaly
profile in terms of changes in the crust and
mantle. Note the negative values—that is, the
deficiency in gravity—across the Sierra Nevada,
the Rocky Mountains, and the Basin and Range
province. The anomaly is close to zero in the
low plains, becomes slightly negative under the
Appalachian Mountains, approaches zero again
in the coastal plains and continental shelf, and
zooms to large positive values over the deep
Atlantic.

The striking feature of the gravity-anomaly
interpretation shown in the bottom section of
Figure 18-29 is the way the Mohorovičić discontinuity mirrors the topography (except in the
Basin and Range province). The gravity anomaly is strongly negative where the crust thickens
to provide buoyant support for mountains. What
causes the negative anomaly in these topographically high places is the mass deficiency due to
the displacement of denser mantle by the less
dense crustal root. The high positive gravity
values over the ocean basin signify the presence
of excess: dense mantle rock is much closer to
the surface here. This feature has been called an
antiroot, and it mirrors the "negative" topography (water instead of rock) of the ocean basin.
The Appalachians show a modest negative
anomaly, which indicates that they have a shallow root. This is appropriate for an old mountain system: its root (and *g* anomaly) is disap-
pearing as its topography erodes away. One
might have expected the structurally high Basin
and Range province, with its average elevation
of about one kilometer, to have a slightly thickened crust to go along with its negative anomaly.

Figure 18-29
Transcontinental gravity survey from the Pacific Ocean to the Atlantic Ocean. The negative gravity anomalies over the mountainous regions, the near-zero values at low elevations, and the positive values over deep oceans, mirroring the topography, demonstrate the role of isostatic compensation in shaping Earth's surface features.

Actually, many geophysicists thought this to be the case until experiments with seismic waves revealed the thin crust. Because the seismic information reveals that there is no crustal root for the Basin and Range province, it is necessary to assume that the mass deficiency there is a result of the area being underlain by mantle material of relatively low density, as shown in the figure.

Many of these results were anticipated in Chapter 17, in which we discussed isostasy in the context of the structure of the crust and upper mantle as determined by seismic methods. Actually, the concept of isostatic compensation with its notions of "floating" continents and still higher floating mountains was discovered from gravity observations such as these. But, the seismological data mentioned in Chapter 17 contributed much to our understanding by clearing up such questions as where the mass deficiencies were located and whether compensation involving crustal roots or compensation via low-density mantle was the isostatic mechanism responsible for them. Low-density mantle seems to go with a tectonic setting that includes recent volcanism, high heat flow, and low seismic velocities—which implies, perhaps, a partially molten mantle directly below the Moho. Some geologists suggest that these features, as they occur in the Basin and Range province, indicate that tension-producing forces, perhaps due to a spreading or divergence zone, are active within a continent. Compensation involving crustal roots is the predominant isostatic mechanism for continents as a whole, as well as for high mountains.

In this way, gravimetry and seismology combine to reveal the importance of isostasy to the study of geology on a regional and continental scale. The kinds of insights that emerge are given by the following examples. Mountains eroding down will be pushed up by the excess buoyancy of the root, until both root and mountain range nearly disappear. Such loads as ice caps or sediments filling a basin can depress the crust. Where gravity studies indicate that a positive or negative load (a depression, for example) is not compensated, some force must be present that helps support it and keeps it from subsiding or rising. Continents are unlikely to be destroyed by subduction; their ability to float allows them to "ride out" repeated episodes of splitting and collision.

Figure 18-30
Map showing the amount of uplift in meters in Fennoscandia in the past 5000 years, according to M. Sauramo. The crust, depressed by the weight of the ice cap of the last "ice age," is still rebounding some 10,000 years after the ice disappeared.

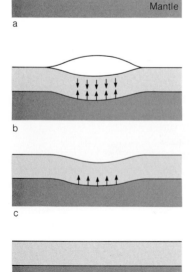

Figure 18-31
Schematic diagram of the mechanism of postglacial uplift. (a) Continental glacier grows, loading the crust. (b) Crust sags, and root develops to support ice load isostatically. (c) Glacier disappears, but root remains because of viscosity of mantle. Root evidenced by negative gravity anomaly. (d) Buoyancy of root leads to slow uplift. Root disappears, surface assumes original level, and gravity anomaly disappears. Arrows depict direction of forces due to ice load and root. Fennoscandia today is between stages c and d. Figure not to scale. Crust is about 40 km thick; a 3-km thick glacier would produce a root about 1 km thick—less if the strength of the crust supported part of the weight.

The Fennoscandian Uplift—Nature's Experiment with Isostasy. If you depress a cork floating in water with your finger, and then release it, it pops up almost instantaneously. A cork floating in molasses would rise more slowly; the drag of the viscous fluid would slow down the process. If we could perform a similar experiment on the Earth, much could be learned about the viscosity of the mantle and how it affects rates of uplift and subsidence. How convenient it would be if we could push the crust down somewhere, remove the force, and then sit back and watch it rise.

Nature has been good enough to do this experiment for us. The load is a continental glacier—an ice sheet 2 to 3 kilometers thick that can appear, with the onset of an ice age, in the geologically short period of a few thousand years. The crust is depressed by the ice load, and a downward bulge develops on its underside to provide buoyant support. With the onset of a warming trend, the glacier melts rapidly. With the removal of the load, uplift of the depressed crust begins. The rate of uplift can be documented by dating ancient beaches that are now well above sea level (see Fig. 10-7). Such raised beaches can tell us how long ago a particular stretch of land was at sea level. The presence of a negative gravity anomaly can tell us how much of a relic root remains and how much more uplift will occur before the root disappears.

Such depression and uplift has occurred in Norway, Sweden, and Finland, as well as elsewhere in glaciated regions. The ice cap retreated from these regions some 10,000 years ago and the land has been rising since. For example, Figure 18-30 shows how much upwarping took place in the past 5000 years. The most intense upwarping has occurred near west-central Sweden, which is believed to have been overlain by the thickest ice. Some 200 meters of uplift has occurred in 10,000 years, indicating an average rate of 2 centimeters per year. There is a remaining negative gravity anomaly of -50 milligals, which implies that part of the root still remains and that about 200 meters more uplift must occur before isostatic compensation is complete. The region shows minor seismicity, additional evidence, perhaps, that stresses due to too much buoyancy are still present. Geophysicists have used these data to show that the weak zone (which "flows" so that the crustal root could develop) coincides with the asthenosphere, the partially molten zone discussed in earlier chapters. This region is not only an important factor in the mobility of the lithospheric plates and as the source of basaltic magma; its ability to "yield" makes it the key factor of isostatic compensation.

No human could have designed a better experiment to demonstrate the isostatic mechanism than nature's demonstration with the Fennoscandian postglacial uplift.

SUMMARY

1. Motions in the fluid iron core somehow set up a dynamo action that generates the Earth's magnetic field. The field can be fairly well described by a hypothetical bar magnet located near the center of the Earth and approximately aligned with its axis of rotation.

2. Many rocks become magnetized in the direction of the geomagnetic field that prevailed when they were formed. If the rocks are dated radiometrically, the history of the magnetic field can be recovered from this remanent magnetization.

3. The remanent magnetization of old rocks shows that the Earth's magnetic pole occupied different positions in the past. Actually, the magnetic pole probably did not wander, but stayed fairly close to the geographic pole. Thus polar wandering is probably an indication that the lithospheric plates have been moving, changing the geography of the surface. Paleoclimatic evidence, such as coal in Antarctica and glacial till near the equator, support this idea.

4. Remanent magnetization has also led to the discovery of reversals in the magnetic field, and the history of reversals since Cretaceous time has been worked out. Although unexplained, these reversals have become a very important tool in dating the sea floor. When the sea-floor crust is formed at mid-ocean rifts, it becomes magnetized. This magnetic imprinting stays with the crust as it spreads away from the rift. The sequence of reversals shows as positive and negative magnetic anomalies, which a surveying ship can readily detect. Using the history of reversals, we can determine the age of the underlying sea floor and the rate of sea-floor spreading.

5. Gravity changes over the surface of the Earth are due to the planet's oblateness, its rotation, its topography, and differences in its subsurface mass. The first three factors can be allowed for, so that the remaining gravitational anomalies indicate subsurface geological differences.

6. Gravity anomalies associated with continents, oceans, and mountains show that the Earth's crust is not strong enough to support topographic loads over long periods. Roots, or downward bulges of the crust, develop and provide buoyant support. This is an example of isostatic adjustment. Another example is the depression of the Fennoscandian crust by the weight of a continental glacier. Although the ice cap disappeared some 10,000 years ago, uplift is still continuing in that area and will continue until the relic root disappears.

EXERCISES

1. What evidence supports the hypothesis that the Earth's magnetic field originates in a fluid iron core? Some meteorites and Moon rocks show remanent magnetism, which has yet to be explained. Would you hazard a guess as to its origin?

2. In a region where the geothermal gradient—that is, the temperature increase with depth—is 3°C per hundred meters, at what depth would you expect the rocks to lose their magnetism?

3. A sedimentary formation is found to have remanent magnetism, with an inclination of 45° measured from the bedding plane. What was the latitude of the formation when it became magnetized? What was its longitude? Would your answer change if the bed had been tilted after it was magnetized?

4. What is the connection between the sequences of magnetic reversals worked out on land and the bands of positive and negative magnetic anomalies found on the sea floor? There are regions of the sea floor known as "magnetic quiet zones" where no reversals in magnetic anomalies occur. Can you guess the age of the crust in these regions from the magnetic reversal time scale in Figure 18-20?

5. Would the gravity anomaly (after making free-air and Bouguer corrections) show large negative values, values near zero, or large positive values at each of the following places?
   a) Rocky Mountains
   b) east coast of U.S.
   c) middle of an ocean basin
   Explain your answers.

6. You observe a near-zero gravity anomaly atop a mountain after making the free-air and Bouguer corrections. What would you conclude?

BIBLIOGRAPHY

Cox, A., (editor) *Plate Tectonics and Geomagnetic Reversals.* San Francisco: W. H. Freeman and Company, 1973.

Garland, G. D., *The Earth's Shape and Gravity.* New York: Pergamon Press, 1965.

Heirtzler, J. R., "Sea-Floor Spreading," *Scientific American,* December 1968. (Offprint No. 875.)

LePichon, X., J. Francheteau, and J. Bonnin, *Plate Tectonics.* New York: Elsevier Publishing Company, 1973.

Strangway, D. W., *History of the Earth's Magnetic Field.* New York: McGraw-Hill Book Co., 1970.

Takeuchi, S., S. Uyeda, and H. Kanamori, *Debate about the Earth* (revised ed.). San Francisco: Freeman, Cooper, & Company, 1970.

19

GLOBAL PLATE TECTONICS: THE UNIFYING MODEL

Geologists are gradually rejecting the notion of a rigid Earth with fixed continents and ocean basins. Most now believe that the Earth's lithosphere is broken into about a dozen plates, which for reasons not fully understood move over the interior. Plates are created along the crests of mid-ocean ridges and are pushed down into the mantle near deep-sea trenches. Continents, embedded in the lithosphere, drift along with the moving plates. Plate tectonics gives new life to the old ideas of continental drift and explains the distribution of many large-scale geological features and zones of activity—narrow belts of mountains, volcanic and seismic activity—in terms of their association with plate margins.

Not long ago, on the occasion of an international geophysical meeting in Moscow, an interesting exchange occurred between two western participants—a younger man who had achieved prominence because of his work on plate tectonics and a well-known older scientist. The setting was a party in the apartment of a Soviet geophysicist, and the conversation was well lubricated by vodka. The din of cocktail party chatter stopped suddenly when the younger man called out to his older colleague, "Dr. _____, everyone tells me how brilliant you were in your younger days. If that's the case why didn't you discover sea-floor spreading and plate tectonics twenty years ago?" The explosive response of the older man needn't be recorded, but the question, properly generalized, is indeed thought-provoking. Why did this concept, which unifies so much of geological thought, "arrive" so late in the history of the subject?

Actually, a key element of the concept—large-scale displacement of continents—had been around for a long time. The jigsaw-puzzle fit of the coasts on both sides of the Atlantic did not escape the attention of early natural philosophers. Francis Bacon remarked on the parallelism of the facing shores of the Atlantic in 1620. Antonio Snider published maps in France depicting continental drift as early as 1858. At the close of the nineteenth century, the Austrian geologist Eduard Suess put some of the pieces of the puzzle together and postulated the former existence of a single giant continent—Gondwanaland, made up of the combined present-day southern continents. Early in this century, Alfred Wegener, a German meteorologist, cited as further evidence of continental drift the remarkable similarity of rocks, geological structures, and fossils on opposite sides of the Atlantic. In the years following, Wegener continued to build up the case for continental drift, wherein he postulated that a supercontinent called Pangaea, once made up of all of the present continents, began to break up some 200 million years ago, with ocean filling the widening gaps. Figure 19-1 shows what Pangaea may have looked like and how it may have fragmented.

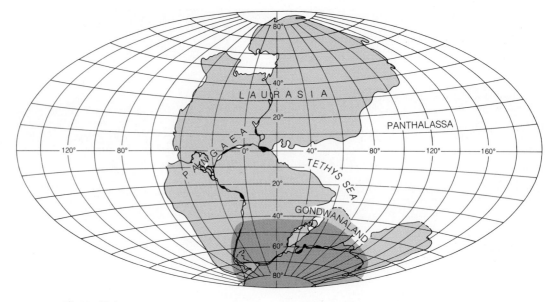

Figure 19-1
The ancient landmass Pangaea, meaning "all lands," may have looked like this some 200 million years ago. Panthalassa ("all seas") evolved into the present Pacific Ocean, and the present Mediterranean Sea is a remnant of the Tethys. Permian glacial deposits are found in widely separated areas, such as South America, Africa, India, and Australia. This distribution is simply explained by postulating a single continental glacier flowing over the south polar regions of Gondwanaland in Permian time, before the breakup of the continents. Probable extent of glacier shown by shading.

Although the theory received serious attention for about a decade, aside from a few vocal geologists in Europe and South Africa, "continental drift" never caught on. The proponents could not come up with a plausible driving force. More important, drift advocates buttressed their speculation with special pleading, selecting evidence patently favorable to their views, evidence that was far from incontrovertible. Aside from the geometrical matching of continents, their main arguments were based on fossil and climatological data. The evolution of vertebrates and land plants showed similarities in development on different continents up to the supposed breakup time, after which they showed divergent evolutionary paths. The distribution of Permian glacial deposits in South America, Africa, India, and Australia was difficult to explain in terms of separate glaciers, some close to the equator. Note, however, that if the southern continents are reassembled into Gondwanaland in the south polar region, a single continental glacier could account for the glacial deposits (Fig. 19-1). "It has always happened that after several distinguished palaeontologists have presented evidence favourable to continental drift,

some other equally distinguished ones have proceeded to point out other facts that are made more difficult to explain"—so argued Sir Harold Jeffreys in his influential book *The Earth*. Independent, diverse, corroborative evidence would be needed before the scientific establishment would abandon prevailing ideas and elevate an unorthodox speculation to the level of a generally accepted theory.

In 1928, Arthur Holmes, a widely respected British geologist, wrote an article invoking the mechanism of thermal convection in the mantle as the driving force. Holmes proposed that subcrustal convection currents "dragged the two halves of the original continent apart, with consequent mountain building in the front where the currents are descending, and ocean floor development on the site of the gap, where the currents are ascending." Holmes came close to expressing the modern notions of plates, divergence, and subduction when he speculated that a subcrustal basaltic layer serves as a conveyor belt that carries a continent along to the place where the belt turns downward into the mantle, leaving the continent resting on top. Figure 19-2, which depicts his concept, contains many

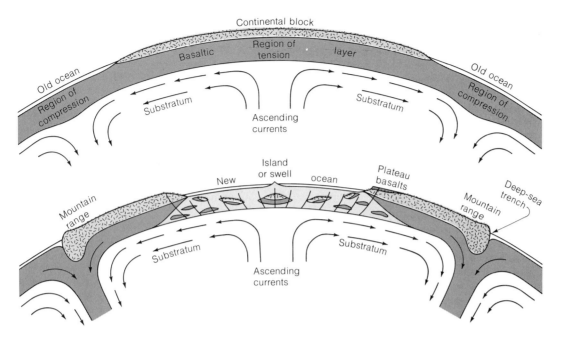

Figure 19-2
This early convection model, which remained unknown to many geologists for 30 years, was proposed by
Arthur Holmes around 1930. It shows a continent being pulled apart by rising mantle currents, with new
ocean developing from the growing rift. In the vicinity of a descending current, a mountain range and
bordering deep-sea trench develop. Holmes's theory, which has been called "sea-floor stretching," is a forerunner of the modern theory of "sea-floor spreading." The figure is modified from an illustration published
by Holmes in 1929 in the *Transactions of the Glasgow Geological Society.*

of the ingredients of the theory of sea-floor
spreading as we know it today. Nevertheless,
Holmes called attention to the tenuous nature of
his views when he wrote that "purely speculative ideas of this kind, specially invented to
match the requirements, can have no scientific
value until they acquire support from independent evidence."

Convincing evidence began to emerge as a
result of extensive exploration of the sea floor
during the years following World War II. In
particular, the mapping of the mid-Atlantic
ridge and the discovery of the deep, crack-like
valley or rift running down its center line
sparked much speculation. In the early 1960's
Harry Hess of Princeton University suggested
that sea floors separate along the rifts in mid-
ocean ridges, and that new sea floor forms by
upwelling of mantle materials in these cracks,
followed by lateral spreading (see Fig. 15-38).
The work of Vine and Mathews, mentioned in
the previous chapter, showed how the oceanic
magnetic patterns could be explained by Hess's
concept. Thus was born the theory of sea-floor
spreading. Within a few years abundant confirmation would be available from the study of

such diverse evidence as that provided by
worldwide magnetic-anomaly surveys, the observation of earthquake mechanisms, the measurement of heat flow, and the determination of
the thickness and age of the sedimentary layers
of the sea floor.

It remained for a younger generation of geophysicists to broaden the concepts of continental
drift and sea-floor spreading into the more general theory of plate tectonics. Beginning about
1967, they extended the idea of Hess and Canadian geophysicist J. T. Wilson about the mobility of the lithosphere by identifying the separate
lithospheric plates and discussing the geometry
of their relative motions and the phenomena that
occur at their boundaries. By the end of the
1960's the evidence became so persuasive that
most Earth scientists, except for a few prominent holdouts, embraced these concepts. Text-
books were revised, and specialists began to
think of the implications that the new discoveries held for their own fields.

Let us return to the question raised earlier
about why these new concepts became generally
accepted so late in the history of geology. There
are different styles among scientists. Some sci-

entists—those with particularly inquiring, uninhibited, and synthesizing minds—perceive great truths in advance of others. Although their perceptions may frequently turn out to be false, these individuals are often the first to comprehend the great generalizations of science. Most scientists, however, proceed more cautiously and wait out the slow process of gathering supporting evidence. The concepts of continental drift and sea-floor spreading were slow to be accepted simply because the audacious ideas came so far ahead of the firm evidence. The oceans had to be explored, a new world-wide network of seismographs had to be installed and used, the magnetic stratigraphy had to be painstakingly worked out, and the deep sea had to be drilled before the majority could be convinced. In a well-known European laboratory, a list is being assembled (in good humor) to record the names of Earth scientists in the order of the date of their acceptance of sea-floor spreading as a confirmed phenomenon. It is interesting that the names of scientists of distinction appear at both the top and the bottom of the list.

PLATE TECTONICS— A REVIEW AND SUMMARY

Plate tectonics forms the conceptual framework of this book, and we have already introduced the basic ideas in earlier chapters. In this chapter we draw together and review the diverse lines of evidence that support the theory of plate tectonics, using primarily illustrations rather than words for material repeated from earlier chapters. The geometry of plate motions is discussed, as well as the geological phenomena associated with plate boundaries. We will begin a discussion of rock associations and orogeny within the framework of plate tectonics. The fragmentation of Pangaea since the Jurassic will be reviewed together with some speculation about continental drift and extinct plates in the pre-Jurassic. The chapter will close with some brief remarks on the driving mechanism of plate tectonics, but the reader shouldn't expect more than vague speculations, for the subject is just beginning to receive serious study.

The Mosaic of Plates. According to the theory of plate tectonics, the lithosphere is broken into a number of moderately rigid plates whose outlines are shown in the illustration inside the front cover. The plates slide over a partially molten, plastic asthenosphere, and their relative directions of motion are shown in the figure. According to the relative motions of adjacent plates, we can define three kinds of plate boundaries, or marginal zones: (1) zones of divergence or spreading, typically ocean ridges; (2) fracture zones, or transform faults; and (3) zones of convergence (Fig. 17-15).

Zones of divergence are boundaries along which plates separate; in the process of plate separation, partially molten mantle material upwells along linear ocean ridges, and new lithosphere is created along the trailing edges of the diverging plates. Such boundaries are characterized by active basaltic volcanism, shallow-focus earthquakes caused by tensile (stretching) stresses, and high rates of heat flow. The outpouring of magma along ocean ridges and the building of the oceanic lithosphere is volumetrically the most significant form of volcanism. Figures 1-15, 1-19, 13-10, 13-13, 15-21, and 15-38 emphasize the different aspects of divergence zones.

Transform faults are boundaries along which plates slide past one another, with neither creation nor destruction of lithosphere. Occasionally marked by scarps, transform faults are characterized by shallow-focus earthquakes with horizontal slips. Examples were given in Figures 1-19, 17-15, and 18-17.

Zones of convergence are boundaries along which the leading edge of one plate overrides another, the overridden plate being subducted, or thrust into the mantle, where lithosphere is resorbed. The thrusting mechanisms that operate along these collision boundaries tend to produce deep-sea trenches, shallow- and deep-focus earthquakes, adjacent mountain ranges of folded rocks, and both basaltic and andesitic volcanism. Convergence zones were illustrated in earlier chapters (Figs. 1-18, 13-10, 13-13, and 15-38).

Each plate is bounded by some combination of these three kinds of zones, as can be seen on the inside of the front cover. For example, the Nazca Plate in the Pacific is bounded on three sides by zones of divergence, along which new lithosphere forms, and on one side by the Peru-Chile trench, where lithosphere is consumed. Continental margins may or may not coincide with plate boundaries. If they do, the continents tend to remain "floating" because continental plates are thicker and more buoyant and are not readily subducted. Where two plates with continents at their leading edges converge, the crust thickens to form great mountain ranges like the Himalayas.

Figure 19-3
Cross section of the upper mantle. The lithosphere is a plate of solidified rock that "rides" on the partially molten asthenosphere. It is approximately 70 km thick under oceans and perhaps 100 to 150 km thick under continents. The continent is embedded in the plate and moves along with it. The lithosphere forms at mid-ocean ridges from a rising plume of partially molten rock; it sinks back into the mantle in subduction zones, where it remelts. Arrows in plastic asthenosphere indicate directions of possible convective motions. Secondary convection currents may form small spreading centers in a marginal basin, a small ocean like the Sea of Japan, situated behind an island-arc volcanic chain, and separate the chain from a continent.

The global sum of plate creation and consumption is approximately zero. The Earth would otherwise change size in order to accommodate the new sea floor, and this doesn't seem to be happening; instead, the plates form and disappear and change in size and shape as they evolve.

The Structure and Evolution of Plates.
Figure 19-3 depicts some of the structural details of a rigid lithospheric slab, or what we call a plate, from its region of generation at a ridge axis to its region of subduction, where it is resorbed. Both oceanic and continental crust cap the plate; the continent, embedded in the moving plate, is carried along passively by it. Thus, in a real sense, continental drift is simply a consequence of plate movements. Underneath is the plastic, partially molten asthenosphere—source of the raw materials that build new lithosphere. Once heated and partially melted, subducted lithosphere becomes a source of magma, which rises to feed the overlying volcanic chain. A generalized heat-flow profile (see Fig. 13-10) shows a large amount of heat coming out along the ridge axis, a lesser amount from the older, cooled slab, and higher heat flow from the vol-

canic chain of the subduction zone and the marginal basin behind it, where a small region of secondary spreading occurs.

Geophysicists have made theoretical studies and computer models of the evolution of a plate, from its creation out of hot rising matter at ocean ridges, through its spreading and cooling phase to its subduction, with reheating, melting and final resorption in the underlying mantle. The models provide understanding of some important geological and geophysical observations: the major bathymetric features of the oceans, the variation of heat flow from the sea floor, the occurrence of volcanism at plate margins, and the location and mechanism of earthquakes in the subducted slab.

When ocean depths are plotted as a function of age, t, of the sea floor, a remarkably regular and simple curve results (Fig. 19-4). For the first 80 million years the data fit a curve in which ocean depth increases as $\sqrt{t}$, precisely the relationship predicted by the thermal contraction of a spreading, cooling plate. Beyond 80 million years ocean depths tend to flatten out, as would be expected if a small amount of heat is added to the bottom of the plate from the underlying hot asthenosphere.

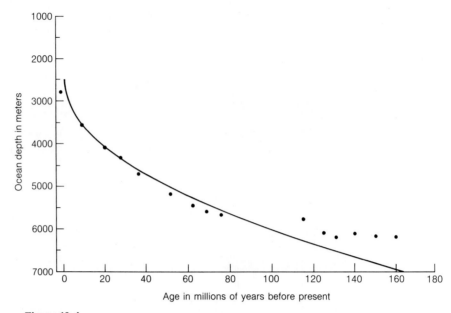

Figure 19-4
Mean ocean depths for the North Pacific plotted as a function of age of the sea floor. Theoretical curve assumes depth is proportional to the square root of age. [After B. Parsons and J. G. Sclater.]

When a cold plate is subducted it remains cooler than the surrounding hot mantle for about 12 million years, only gradually heating up as it penetrates more deeply. Slow-moving plates will of course heat up and be assimilated at shallow depths, perhaps 400 km, compared to fast-moving plates, which can penetrate to about 700 km before heating to the point of assimilation. The process of subduction involves very large forces, and in a general way these forces must be responsible for the deep-focus earthquakes that occur only in downgoing plates (see Chapter 17). The sudden failure associated with earthquakes can take place until the plates become so warm that stress is relieved by slow plastic deformation rather than faulting. This seems to be the likely explanation for the fact that earthquakes are absent below 700 km (Fig. 19-5).

Rates of Plate Motion. The velocities of moving plates are measured by dating ocean-floor magnetic anomalies (using the time scale of magnetic stratigraphy) and dividing the age of each anomaly into the distance between it and the ridge axis. The procedure was outlined graphically in the preceding chapter (Figs. 18-17, 18-18, 18-21, 18-22).

The worldwide pattern of sea-floor spreading is being worked out by using a combination of magnetic, seismic, and bathymetric data. The charts used earlier (Fig. 18-22 and inside front cover) map the world's zones of spreading, subduction, and fracture; their geographic locations were obtained from the positions of ocean ridges, deep-sea trenches, earthquake epicenters, and other indications of activity. On the basis of spreading rates determined from magnetic data, isochrons (contours that connect points of the same age) were drawn to show the age of the sea floor in millions of years. The distance from a ridge axis to a 50-million-year isochron, for example, indicates the extent of new ocean floor created in the period of time represented by the isochron. In Figure 18-21, note how the isochrons are closely spaced in the Atlantic and widely spaced in the Pacific, where the spreading rate is higher. The fracture zones offset the isochrons, so that upon crossing one of these great faults there is an abrupt change in the age of the sea floor. A summary of the rates and directions of plate motions, measured in centimeters/year relative velocity, is given in Figure 19-6. The largest spreading velocity, 18.3 centimeters/year, occurs between the Pacific and Nazca plates.

Figure 19-5
Evolution of descending slabs is described by computer models made by M. N. Toksöz. These diagrams depict the fate of a plate subducted at a rate of 8 cm/year. Contours show computed temperatures in plate and adjacent mantle. Note that temperatures in plate are several hundred degrees cooler than the adjacent mantle. After 12 million years, the plate reaches the temperature of the surrounding mantle at a depth of 600-700 km and loses its original identity. At shallow depths, earthquakes (dots) occur in the shear zone between the colliding plates and in the overriding plate. The deeper earthquakes occur in the cooler, brittle, center of the slab, but no deeper than 700 km, where the plate is assimilated.

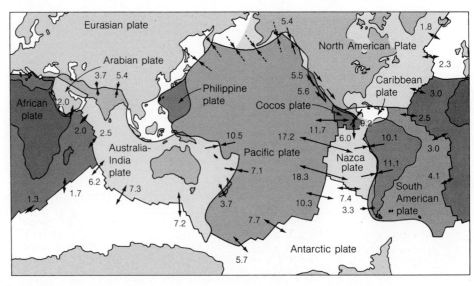

Figure 19-6
Relative velocities and directions of plate separation and convergence in centimeters per year. Opposed arrowheads indicate convergence at trenches, except for Himalayas. Diverging arrowheads indicate plate separation at ocean ridges. Parallel and opposed arrowheads, as along the San Andreas fault in California, indicate transform faults, where plates slide past each other. [From "Convection Currents in the Earth's Mantle", by D. P. McKenzie and Frank Richter. Copyright © 1976 by Scientific American, Inc. All rights reserved.]

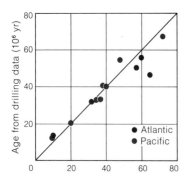

Figure 19-7
A comparison of ages of igneous rocks at different distances from mid-ocean ridges with ages obtained from fossils in the sediments immediately above the igneous rock. The igneous rocks were dated from their magnetic anomaly pattern. The sediments were recovered by deep-sea drilling operations. The 45° line is a theoretical one, implying perfect agreement between these two methods of dating the sea floor. The substantiation of the "magnetic" ages by deep-sea drilling, shown by the close fit of the experimental points to the theoretical line, lends strong support to the concept of sea-floor spreading. [After C. L. Drake.]

It was a great triumph for the magneticians, who worked out spreading rates, when the first results of the Deep Sea Drilling Project were announced. This joint project of the major oceanographic institutions and the National Science Foundation had as its primary goal to drill through the sediments of the sea floor at many places in the world's oceans. By studying the sedimentary cores, it is possible that the history of the ocean basin can be worked out directly, in contrast to the indirect methods of magnetic anomalies. Since sedimentation begins as soon as an ocean exists, the age of the oldest sediment in the core, adjacent to the basaltic bedrock, dates the ocean floor at that spot. The age is obtained from the fossils found in the cores. Sediments older than about 150 million years have not been found, attesting to the "youth" of the sea floor. The sediments become older with increasing distance from mid-ocean ridges, confirming the prediction of the sea-floor-spreading hypothesis. Figure 19-7 is a plot of the ages determined from drill cores from the Atlantic and Pacific Oceans against ages predicted from the magnetic data. It is remarkable how close the experimental points approach the straight line, with slope of 1, which is theoretical and represents perfect agreement. In our opinion, one that is generally but not universally shared, this agreement clinches the concept of magnetic stratigraphy and the hypothesis of seafloor spreading.

As an interesting aside, we have included a photograph of the drilling vessel Glomar Challenger (Fig. 19-8). It is 400 feet long, and amidships it carries a drilling derrick 140 feet high. The only ship of its kind in the world, it has the capability of lowering drill pipe several kilometers to the sea floor and of drilling thousands of meters into the sediments and underlying volcanic rock. Before the ship could accomplish such a feat, a technological breakthrough had to be made. A means had to be devised to hold the ship stationary, regardless of current, wind, or waves, during drilling. Otherwise, the drill pipe would break off. The problem was solved by developing a positioning device that uses sound waves from acoustic beacons planted on the sea floor. Any change in the ship's position is sensed by a computer that monitors the time of arrival of the sound pulses. The same computer controls bow and stern side thrusters and the ship's main propulsion to keep the vessel on station. The Glomar Challenger was the answer to those who said when lunar exploration started, "It's better to explore the ocean's bottom than the backside of the Moon." We ended up doing both.

Figure 19-8
The deep-sea drilling vessel Glomar Challenger, a unique facility capable of recovering cores of sediment and underlying igneous rock from the floor of the deepest oceans. The deep-sea drilling program was originally an American one; it is now jointly supported and operated by the United States, the U.S.S.R. and other countries. [From National Science Foundation.]

Geometry of Plate Motion. If the individual plates behave as rigid bodies, which seems to be a reasonable first assumption, several interesting and useful geometric consequences follow. By "rigid" we simply mean that the distances among three points on the same plate—say, New York, Miami, and Bermuda—do not change, no matter how the plate moves. But the distance between New York and Lisbon will of course increase because the two cities are on different plates, which are being separated along a narrow zone of spreading on the mid-Atlantic ridge. Listed here are some geometric principles, mostly self-evident, that govern the sliding of plates on a plane:

1. Along transform faults, surface area is conserved; that is, it is neither created nor destroyed. Stated simply, no overlap, buckling, or separation occurs at such boundaries; the two plates merely slide past one another. Look for a transform fault if you want to deduce the direction of plate motions, because the orientation of the fault *is* the direction of relative sliding of two plates, as Figures 1-18 and 17-15 show. Surface area is obviously not conserved at zones of convergence or divergence where plates are subducted or created. The plates can move perpendicularly or obliquely to the trend of convergent boundaries, which are therefore not as reliable indicators of directions of movement as transform faults or divergence zones.

2. Magnetic anomaly stripes and isochrons are roughly parallel and symmetrical with respect to the ridge axis along which they were "created." Look at Figure 18-17 to see why this must be so. Since each magnetic strip or isochron marks the edge of an earlier plate margin, isochrons that are of the same age, but on opposite sides of an ocean ridge, can be brought together to show the positions of the plates and the configuration of the continents as they were in that earlier time. By this means we can reconstruct, for example, the opening of the Atlantic Ocean, as shown in Figure 19-9.

3. The point at which three plates meet is called a **triple junction.** Figure 19-10 shows an example of a point at which a spreading zone, a subduction zone, and a transform fault meet. If the relative motion between two pairs of plates is known, we can solve for the third by using a simple equation (see Box 19-1).

An example of an actual triple junction is the point where the Pacific, Cocos, and Nazca plates meet (see inside front cover). Three spreading zones meet at this junction, as shown in the enlarged view in Figure 19-11. The unknown motion, found by vector addition, was that between the Nazca and Pacific plates, the motions between the Pacific-Cocos and Cocos-Nazca plates having been worked out from transform faults and magnetic-anomaly stripes. The arrows show the resultant plate movements. Note

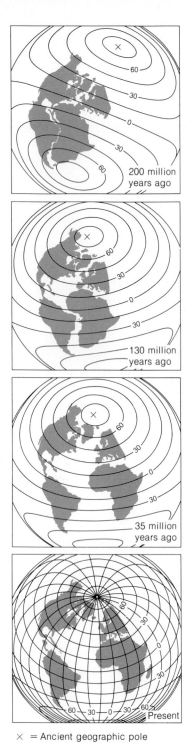

× = Ancient geographic pole

Figure 19-9
Magnetic and deep-sea drilling data are used to chart the northward drift of the continents and the opening of the Atlantic Ocean over the past 200 million years. The Central Atlantic, the Caribbean, and the Gulf of Mexico began to form about 200 million years ago in Triassic time, when Africa and South America drifted away from North America. The South Atlantic opened about 150 million years ago with the separation of South America from Africa. As the continents drifted apart, so did they migrate in a northerly direction to their present positions. Note that the equator passed through the southern parts of the United States and Europe in Triassic time. [From J. D. Phillips and D. Forsyth, *Bull. Geol. Soc. America*, v. 83, p. 1579, 1972.]

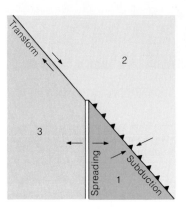

Figure 19-10
Illustration of a triple junction. Plates 1, 2, and 3 meet at the intersection of a spreading zone, a subduction zone, and a transform fault. An example of a different kind would be the intersection of the Pacific plate, the North American plate, and the Cocos plate below the mouth of the Gulf of California. Three spreading zones intersect to form a triple junction where the Pacific plate, the Nazca plate, and the Cocos plate join (see illustration inside front cover and Fig. 19-11). The arrows depict relative motion between adjacent plates.

Figure 19-11
Triple junction formed by the intersection of three spreading zones in the southeast Pacific Ocean. The schematic isochrons are parallel to the ridge axes from which they migrate as the sea floor ages and spreads. The spacing between isochrons is a measure of the spreading velocities. [After R. N. Hey, K. S. Deffeyes, G. L. Johnson, and A. Lowrie, "The Galapagos Triple Junction," *Nature*, v. 237, p. 20, 1972.]

also how the isochrons bend to become parallel to the spreading centers, where they originated, and how they are offset by the transform faults. The spacing of the isochrons reflects the spreading rates, which are largest for the Pacific-Nazca plates and least for the Cocos-Nazca plates.

Up to this point we have considered plates sliding on a plane. Although much can be learned about plate motions by making this simplification, plates actually move on the Earth's spherical surface. A theorem of spherical geometry worked out two hundred years ago by Euler has been resurrected by geophysicists to handle the real situation. Box 19-2 explains how plate movements on a sphere can be described.

With the application of these geometric prin-ciples to get spreading directions, and magnetic anomalies to deduce spreading rates, the relative motions of the lithospheric plates are being worked out on a worldwide basis. Some results have already been pictured in Figures 18-2 and 19-6. However, geophysicists are searching for ways to measure the absolute motions of indi-vidual plates rather than their motions relative to each other. If the hot spots mentioned in Chapter 15 turn out to be fixed in the mantle below plates, then the string of extinct volcanoes trailing from the hot spot would record the movement of individual plates as they glide over the mantle (Fig. 15-39). This is currently a subject of active research.

Box 19-1 Solving for the Relative Motions of Plates

Velocity is a **vector** quantity, meaning that it has both direction and magnitude. A simple example of how vectors are added is shown in the figure above. If a man walks single blocks north on Avenue A, east on 1st Street, south on Avenue B, he ends up at a place he could have reached directly by walking one block east on 2nd Street. In vector addition this direct route is equal to the sum of the segments that make up the long route.

In the figure at right (part a), let the velocities of the three plates meeting at a triple junction be V_1, V_2, V_3. The velocity of plate 2 relative to plate 1 is $V_2 - V_1$; $V_2 - V_3$ and $V_3 - V_1$ are the other possible relative plate velocities. It is clear that the sum of the relative velocities of the plates, taken in order around the triple junction, must be zero, since $(V_2 - V_1) + (V_3 - V_2) + (V_1 - V_3) = 0$, or $(V_2 - V_1) = (V_3 - V_1) + (V_2 - V_3)$. In the lower figure (part a), the transform fault and the spreading zone show

their usefulness in prescribing the directions of relative motions between plates 2 and 3 and 3 and 1, and presuma-bly magnetic stripes give the velocity of motion. This enables us to solve for $V_2 - V_1$, the direction and amount of relative motion across the subduction zone. Part b of the figure below shows the solution for $V_2 - V_1$ in terms of vector addition.

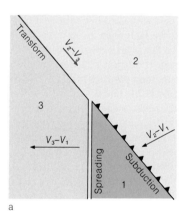

$$(V_2 - V_1) = (V_3 - V_1) + (V_2 - V_3)$$

b

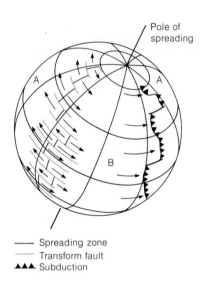

— Spreading zone
— Transform fault
▲▲▲ Subduction

Box 19-2 Plate Motions on a Spherical Earth

The above figure shows how the separation of two plates on a sphere can be described. The motion of plate *B* relative to plate *A* can be completely represented by a rotation of *B* about some pole. (For completeness a schematic subduction zone is shown where plate *B* sinks into the mantle.) Since surface area is neither created nor destroyed in slip along a transform fault, the fault must lie on what is called a *small circle* centered on this pole of rotation, which is also called a pole of spreading. If a tennis ball were sliced in two (not through the center) and put back together, one could rotate the two parts to see that this is so. The cut, which would describe a small circle, would also represent a transform fault. To locate the pole of spreading, one need only to draw a great circle (any circle whose center is also the center of the ball) perpendicular to the cut at two or more positions. The intersection of the great circles is the pole of spreading. On a model of the Earth, if great circles are drawn perpendicular to transform faults between a pair of plates, their intersection locates the pole of spreading, which together with the spreading rate completely describes the relative motion of the two plates. The spreading rate is zero at the pole of spreading and increases to a maximum 90° away at the equator of spreading, as the figure indicates. This maximum equatorial value is frequently cited as the spreading rate between plates.

To see how a pole of spreading is located in practice, refer back to Figure 1-16, which shows the zone of spread-

ing and the transform faults that are separating the African and American plates. Great circles perpendicular to the transform faults are drawn in the figure below. They intersect near the point 58°N, 36°W, off the southeast coast of Greenland. This is the pole of spreading of these two great plates. Don't bother going there, for there is nothing to be seen. The pole of spreading has no physical significance. It serves only as a construction point, a convenience for describing the relative motion of plates merely by giving the latitude and longitude of this point.

[After W. J. Morgan, "Rises, Trenches, Great Faults, and Crustal Blocks," *J. Geophysical Research*, v. 73, pp. 1959–1982, 1968.]

SEA-FLOOR SPREADING AND CONTINENTAL DRIFT— RETHINKING EARTH HISTORY

One of us (F. P.) once helped write a paper dealing with the permanence of ocean basins. If he were allowed to expunge from the scientific record the one contribution he regrets the most, this would be it. The notion of the stability of global geographic features was not only a main tenet of the old geology but seems to be firmly rooted in the human psyche. We now know that the sea floor is ephemeral on the geological time scale. The present ocean basins are being created by spreading and recycled by subduction on a time scale of about 200 million years, which is less than 4 percent of the age of the Earth. There is little likelihood of finding extensive older remnants of sea floor. Continents, on the other hand, are mobile but permanent features. They are too buoyant to be subducted. They may be fragmented, moved, reassembled, deformed, and eroded at their surfaces, but their bulk does not seem to be much diminished. Old terranes with ages of around 3.5 to 3.7 billion years can still be found. Continents grow with time by the gradual accumulation of materials along their margins. New continental strips can therefore be added on in different places at different times, depending on the history of fragmentation, movement, and reassembly.

With the emergence of these revolutionary ideas, geologists are rethinking Earth history. Most of the evidence for plate tectonics comes from the sea floor, a relatively simple place compared to the enormously complicated continents. Just how plate tectonics explains continental geology is now receiving much attention. The appearance of new developments in nearly every issue of the geological journals shows that the subject has definitely been revitalized. Rock associations, volcanism, metamorphism, the evolution of mountain chains—all are being reexamined in the framework of plate tectonics. Some of the new interpretations that we describe in this chapter may not stand the test of time. In this connection, future editions of this book may show some changes, not so much in the big picture of plate tectonics as in the details of fitting regional geology into the overall framework. The student (as well as the authors of this book) should be cautioned against calling on plate tectonics for facile explanations of everything geological. It is not clear, for example, how or if the origin of such structures as the Ozarks, the Black Hills, the Colorado Plateau, or such intracontinental, sediment-filled depressions as the Michigan Basin are related to plate movement. In what follows we draw in large part on the recent work of W. R. Dickinson of Stanford University, J. F. Dewey and J. B. Bird of the State University of New York, and R. S. Dietz, now at the National Oceanographic and Atmospheric Agency. In all fairness it should be mentioned that we are emphasizing one point of view, the one that is generally accepted. A small number of geologists, however, still believe that the continents have been fixed over geologic time.

Rock Assemblages and Plate Tectonics. The only record we have of past geologic events is the incomplete one found in the rocks that have survived erosion or subduction. In a number of previous chapters, some of the methods used to read the rock record were described. Here we explore the nature of the rock assemblages that would characterize different plate-tectonic regimes, as a first step in unraveling the history of past plate motions. Our motivation is to find ways to reconstruct the process of continent fragmentation and ocean development, to locate the sites of vanished oceans, and to recognize the sutures that mark ancient plate collisions.

Of the three kinds of plate boundaries, we might expect distinct suites (assemblages) of rocks to be associated with zones of divergence and convergence. At transform faults no distinct or characteristic rock assemblages are to be expected. Discontinuities across the fault are found, however, since rock formations formed and altered elsewhere have slipped past one another, and once-continuous formations or structural features are displaced. Within plates, where conditions are generally tectonically quiet, the relatively stable offshore margin between a continent and a deep ocean should receive an orderly sequence of undeformed sediments—the geosynclinal deposits that are the products of erosion of the adjacent land mass.

Think of everything that happens at a zone of divergence, where plate accretion and spreading occur, and you can predict the suite of rocks that would characterize the place and the process. Because there is extensive undersea volcanism, one would expect to find submarine basaltic lava, perhaps pillow lavas, the kind of volcanic rock formed when hot lava is quenched by cold sea water (Chapter 15). Suboceanic crust and mantle are created here; dredge hauls and geophysical data show these layers to consist of

Deep-sea sediments:
shales, limestones,
cherts, turbidites,
fossils of pelagic
marine organisms

Basaltic pillow lava

Gabbro, evidence of
hydrous metamorphism

Peridotites and
other ultramafic
rocks, often showing
hydrous metamorphism

Figure 19-12
Idealized section of an ophiolite suite. The combination of deep-sea sediments, submarine lavas, and mafic igneous intrusions indicates a deep-sea origin. Many geologists now believe ophiolites to be fragments of oceanic lithosphere emplaced on a continent as a result of plate collisions.

mafic rocks, such as gabbro and peridotite, often showing evidence of alteration in a water environment (hydrous metamorphism). A carpet of deep-sea sediments would cover all of this. From Chapters 10 and 11 we remember that these deposits are recognized by thin layers of shale, limestone, and chert,* often intercalated with thin, discontinuous turbidites† and containing the fossil remains of pelagic (open ocean) marine organisms. A combination of deep-sea sediments, submarine basaltic lavas, and mafic igneous intrusions like that shown in idealized section in Figure 19-12, is called an **ophiolite suite.** The presence of narrow ophiolite zones in convergence features like the Alpine-Himalayan belt and the Ural and Appalachian belts may indicate that slices of oceanic crust and mantle originally produced at accreting plate margins were thrust onto land when an ancient ocean finally disappeared as two continents converged. Some geologists believe that the Appalachians, for example, mark the site at which the ancestral Atlantic Ocean closed when North America and Africa converged about 375 million years ago. They also propose that the Atlantic reopened a few hundred kilometers east of this old suture, about 200 million years ago, in a spreading episode that is still underway.

Just as the events that take place in a convergence zone are different from divergence-zone phenomena, so do the rock assemblages have different characteristics. The main features of ocean-ocean or ocean-continent collision are shown in transverse section in Figure 19-13. Thick marine sediments, mostly turbidites, eroded from the continent or the island arc, rapidly fill the adjacent, elongate, marginal depressions. In descending, the cold oceanic slab stuffs the region below the inner wall of the trench with these sediments as well as with deep-sea materials brought in with the incoming plate. Regions of this sort are enormously complex and highly variable, as they include turbidites and ophiolitic shreds scraped off the downgoing slab by the edge of the overriding plate—all highly folded, intricately sliced and metamorphosed. They are difficult to map in detail but recognizable by their distinctive mix of materials and structural features; such a cha-

---

*A reminder: Chert is a siliceous rock; cherts derived from the siliceous ooze of the sea floor are made up largely of radiolarian (marine protozoans) or diatom (algae) skeletons.

†A turbidite is a turbidity-current deposit—the result of a sudden underwater flow of a mix of sediments and fluids, plunging downslope under gravity, settling finally on the deep-sea floor.

Arc: Magmatic belt:
volcanoes, intrusions,
and high-temperature,
low-pressure
metamorphism

Subduction mélanges:
low-temperature,
high-pressure
metamorphism

Continent or
ocean basin
behind arc

Ocean trench

Ocean

Ocean sediments

600°C

Cold lithospheric plate

Hot asthenosphere

1500°C

Melting

1500°C

Figure 19-13
Geologic features and activities associated with plate collisions and subduction: ocean trenches, mélange deposits, magmatic belts, metamorphism, volcanism, earthquakes (dots). Not to scale. Thickness of lithosphere is about 70 km, depth of ocean trench 10 km, distance from trench to arc is 300–400 km.

otic mess has been called a **mélange.** The metamorphism is characteristically the kind that takes place under high pressure and low temperature, because the material may be carried relatively rapidly to depths as great as 30 kilometers, where recrystallization occurs in the environment of the cold slab. Somehow, perhaps by buoyancy and mountain-building, the material rises back to the surface much later. Find a mélange and you can't be too far from the place of downturn of an ancient plate, long since consumed, but leaving this relic of its former existence.

Refer again to Figure 19-13. Parallel to the mélange is a magmatic belt, coincident with the island arc or a mountain chain near the continental margin as the case may be. Here the conditions are dominated by the rise of magma from the descending plate. At the interface, where the descending plate slides past the overriding one, perhaps friction is great enough to melt the upper part of the downturned slab, including the subducted wet sediments and ocean crust. The liquids rise buoyantly from depths of 100–200 kilometers to erupt and build the volcanic chains on the leading edges of plates. The characteristic igneous rocks produced are andesitic lavas and granitic intrusives. Island arcs, built up from the sea floor, may contain larger amounts of basalt; continental margins typically erupt rhyolitic ignimbrite and are intruded by granitic batholiths below. These differences were discussed in Chapter 15 on volcanism. In contrast to that in a mélange, the metamorphism in the magmatic belts is typically the result of recrystallization under conditions of high temperatures and low pressures. This is because the hot fluids rise close to the surface, delivering much heat to a low-pressure environment.

Paired belts of mélange and magmatism shown in Figure 19-13 are the signature of subduction. The details may differ from place to place, but the essential elements of these features of collision have been found in many places in the geologic record. One can see mélange in the Franciscan Formation of the California Coast Ranges and magmatism in the parallel belt of the Sierra Nevada to the east (Fig. 19-14). This paired belt marks the Mesozoic boundary between the colliding Pacific and American plates, and even shows the polarity of the convergence by the spatial order of mélange on the west and magmatism on the east: the Pacific plate was the subducted one. Other paired belts—for example, in Japan—can be found along the continen-

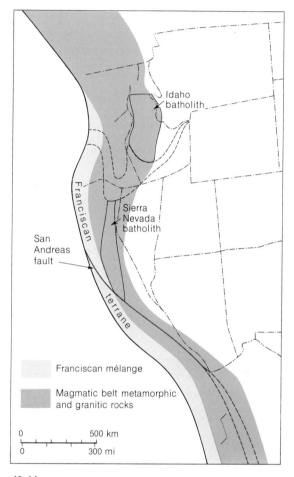

Figure 19-14
Paleogeologic map of the western United States shows the geology of the region as it was at the beginning of Tertiary time. The paired mélange and magmatic belts indicate a collision of the Pacific and American plates in Mesozoic time, the Pacific plate being the subducted one. [After W. Hamilton and W. B. Myers, "Cenozoic Tectonics," *Reviews of Geophysics,* v. 4, p. 541, 1966.]

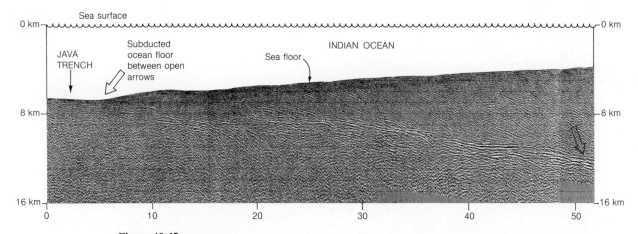

Figure 19-15
Seismic reflection profile across the Java Trench subduction zone south of Bali, along longitude 112°E. Subducted ocean floor (between double arrows) dips about 6° under overthrust wedge of highly deformed sediments. Ocean floor can be followed from the beginning of subduction at the north wall of the trench to a depth of 12 km below sea level. [Courtesy of R. H. Beck and P. Lehner, Shell Internationale Petroleum.]

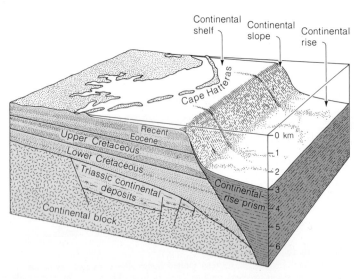

Figure 19-16
Geosynclines off the Atlantic coast of the United States. The sediments beneath the continental shelf are shallow-water, miogeosynclinal deposits that have been accumulating over the past 150 million years as the continental margin gradually subsided following the opening of the Atlantic Ocean. Under the continental rise are thick, deep-sea, eugeosynclinal deposits. Important accumulations of oil are believed to exist under the Atlantic continental shelf. [After "Geosynclines, Mountains and Continent-Building" by R. S. Dietz. Copyright © 1972 by Scientific American, Inc. All rights reserved.]

tal margins framing the Pacific basin. The central Alps, a European example, were produced by the convergence of a Mediterranean plate with the European continent.

Seismic reflection profiles (see Box 17-1) are beginning to provide "X-ray" views of layers deep within the crust. Figure 19-15, a remarkable example of this new technique, shows the Australian plate being subducted under the Eurasian plate at the Java trench.

Continental-shelf deposits are sedimentary rock assemblages that are laid down under tectonically quiet conditions in a geosyncline situated at a continental margin within a plate. Figure 19-16 shows the orderly sequence of deposits in what Dietz called the "living" geosyncline, which is still forming off the Atlantic coast of the United States. The continental margin there was formed when a rift developed in Laurasia about 200 million years ago and the American plate separated from the European plate. Resting on the offshore shelf is a wedge-shaped body composed of sediments that were eroded from the continent and deposited in shallow water. Because the trailing edge of the receding continent slowly subsides as the spreading lithosphere cools and contracts, the geosyncline continues to receive sediments for a long time. In addition, the load of the growing mass of sediment further depresses the crust isostatically, so that the geosyncline can receive still more material from land. For every three meters of sediments received, the crust sinks two meters. The result of these two effects is that the geosynclinal deposits can accumulate in an orderly fashion to thicknesses of 10 kilometers or more. At the same time, the supply of sediments is sufficient to maintain the shallow-water environment of the geosyncline, or miogeosyncline, as we called it in Chapter 11.

The deposits exhibit all of the indicators of shallow-water conditions, which were discussed in Chapter 11. At the bottom of the entire sequence are rift valleys containing basaltic lavas and nonmarine deposits formed during the early stages of continental fissuring. Subsequently, in the early stages of shelf deposition, sandy materials started to fill the depression. Much was dropped on the continental slope, only to be moved later to the eugeosyncline on the continental rise by turbidity currents. Very thick deposits can be built up in deep water in this way. As the shelf miogeosyncline builds up, deposition becomes dominated by shales and carbonate platform deposits—indicators of a decrease in the supply of detritus from the continent.

Think of what might happen to these geosynclines if the orderly, sequentially layered, gently dipping sediments were to become the leading edge of a plate in collision. In the following section we describe some of the many possibilities.

Orogeny and Plate Tectonics. Orogeny means mountain-making, particularly by folding and thrusting of rock layers. In the framework of plate tectonics, orogeny occurs primarily at the boundaries of colliding plates, where marginal sedimentary deposits are crumpled and magmatism and volcanism are initiated.

Consider first some scenarios of plate convergence. In Figure 19-17,*a*, a plate with a continent at the leading edge collides with another plate carrying a continent. In the early stage, during which the convergence is between continent and subducted oceanic lithosphere, a magmatic belt, folded mountains, and mélange deposits may be features of the overriding continental boundary. A "living" example may be found today along the Pacific coast of South America, where the American and Nazca plates are colliding. Look at the illustration inside the front cover to see the setting of the plates. The Andes, from which the name of the volcanic rock andesite is derived, lie in the magmatic belt; subduction is taking place under the Peru-Chile trench.

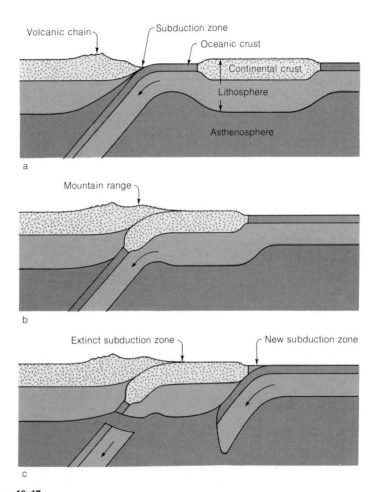

Figure 19-17
Schematic illustration of possible stages in plate collisions. (a) Convergence between plates with continental and oceanic lithosphere at leading edges. Magmatic belt, folded mountains, and mélange deposits are features of the overriding continental boundary. (b) Collision of continents, producing a mountain range, magmatic belt, and thickened continental crust. Since the continent is too buoyant to be carried down into the mantle, plate motions may be brought to a halt. (c) Alternatively, the plate may break off and a new subduction zone be started elsewhere. An extinct subduction zone may show as a scar in the form of a mountain belt within a continent. Examples are the Ural Mountains and the Himalayas. [After "Plate Tectonics" by J. F. Dewey. Copyright © 1972 by Scientific American, Inc. All rights reserved.]

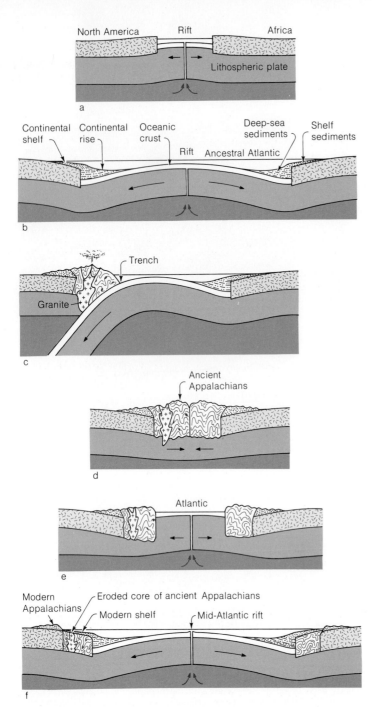

Figure 19-18
Stages in the formation of the Appalachian Mountains. According to the theory of continental drift, North America and Africa split apart more than 600 million years ago, an ancestral Atlantic opened, and sediments were deposited on the margins of the receding continents (a and b). About 500 million years ago, the Atlantic began to close, subduction was initiated, and the geosynclinal deposits were deformed, intruded, and uplifted (c). About 375 million years ago, the Atlantic closed as North America collided with Africa and Europe (d). The modern Atlantic opened about 200 million years ago with the fissuring of Pangaea, and marginal geosynclines began to develop anew (e and f). [After "Geosynclines, Mountains and Continent-Building" by R. S. Dietz. Copyright © 1972 by Scientific American, Inc. All rights reserved.]

In a later stage, continent may meet continent, as shown in Figure 19-17,*b*. Since continental crust is too light to be carried down, the plate motions could be brought to a halt. Another possibility, the one depicted in the figure, is that the plate motions continue, with subduction ceasing at the continent-continent suture but starting up anew elsewhere. Cold and dense as the descending slab is, chunks of it may conceivably break off, fall freely into the mantle, and be resorbed. As Figure 19-17,*c*, shows, the suture will be marked by a mountain range made up of either folded or thrusted rocks, or both, coincident with or adjacent to the magmatic belt, and by a much-thickened continental crust. A prime example of continent-continent collision is the Himalayas, which began forming some 25 million years ago when a plate carrying India ran into the Asiatic plate (the uplift is still going on). This may be the way in which the root underlying the Himalayas originated (see Chapter 18). The plate-tectonic cycle of the closing of an ocean basin, a continent-continent collision, and the formation of an intracontinental mountain belt has been called the Wilson cycle, after the Canadian geologist J. Tuzo Wilson, who first suggested the idea that the Atlantic Ocean closed and then reopened, which we now describe.

The Appalachian Mountains—A Case History. Some daring geologists are now attempting to reconstruct the events of a collision that began some 500 million years ago and which may have resulted in the formation of the Appalachians, an old and eroded mountain belt. Although still debated in its details, this avant-garde concept is presented here to illustrate how plate tectonics may be applied to geological problems in the years to come.

There are four chapters to the Appalachian story, as interpreted in the language of plate tectonics. The first chapter, summarized in Figure 19-18,*a* and *b*, begins more than 600 million years ago in late Precambrian time, when a continuous North American-African continent split apart, and an ocean, the ancestral Atlantic, opened. As North America receded from Africa and Europe, the newly formed North American continental shelf received sediments from the northwest under stable, intraplate conditions, and eventually developed into a miogeosyncline filled with shallow-water deposits. A thick sequence of deep-sea deposits grew in the eugeosyncline along the continental rise beyond the shelf, perhaps fed as well from Africa. The

second chapter of the story opens in Early Ordovician times some 500 million years ago,
when the ancestral Atlantic stopped opening and
began to close again in an episode of contraction
that was to last through Devonian time. The
lithosphere broke along the edge of the North
American continental margin, and plate loss
began in a subduction zone adjacent to the
continental rise (Figure 19-18,c). During the
third chapter (Figs. 19-18,c and d), the compressive stresses of convergence collapsed the
eugeosyncline of the continental rise, and the
deep-sea sediments, altered by pressure, magmatic intrusions, and volcanism, were thrust up
to form a lofty mountain range—the ancient
Appalachians. The continental shelf deposits in
the miogeosyncline to the west were subsequently folded into the series of ridges situated
between the present-day Blue Ridge of Virginia
and the Allegheny front of Pennsylvania. Sheets
of rock were thrust onto the shelf as a result of
the intense lateral compression of the continen-
tal-rise deposits. By middle Devonian times,
about 375 million years ago, the ancestral Atlantic closed as North America collided with
Europe and Africa, forming once again a single
continuous continent—Pangaea (Fig. 19-18,d).
The final chapter begins about 200 million years
ago with the fissuring of Pangaea east of the old
suture line. The modern Atlantic opened, and
geosynclines of the continental shelf and rise
developed anew (Figure 19-18,e). The modern
shelf (Figs. 19-18,f and 19-19) occupies the site
of the late Precambrian and early Paleozoic
continental rise and also the site of the lofty
mountain ranges of Ordovician and Silurian
times, now almost completely eroded down to
their roots east of the Piedmont. In this sense,
North America may have grown as a result of
the Appalachian orogeny, having added strips
from the earlier episodes. How many times such
strips may have been added in the Precambrian
is hard to know.

How are geologists able to reconstruct, or
hypothesize, such a complex sequence of events?
They know how to recognize the shallow continental-shelf deposits and the deep-sea deposits
that are the trademarks of the expansion phase
of ocean basins. They can recognize the imprints
of ocean contractions and plate convergence by
the fold belts, the thrust sheets, the magmatism
and metamorphism, and the scraped-up ophiolites that such plate movements produce. Once
these crustal features are recognized for what
they are, the events that produced them can be
pieced together to tell the story of the expansion,

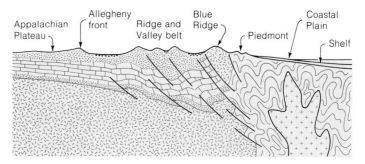

Figure 19-19
A section of the Appalachian Mountain belt. According to a plate-tectonics interpretation, the present-day basement east of the Blue Ridge is the eroded crystalline
core of Ordovician and Silurian mountain ranges that were formed from the crum-
pling of a Precambrian and early Paleozoic eugeosyncline (Fig. 19-18,c and d).
The ancient miogeosyncline was folded into the series of ridges and valleys between the Allegheny Front and the Blue Ridge. The positions of the remnants of
the ancient geosynclines to the west of the modern ones are indicative of the
growth of the continent as a result of the Appalachian orogeny. [After "Geosynclines, Mountains and Continent-Building" by R. S. Dietz. Copyright © 1972 by
Scientific American, Inc. All rights reserved.]

contraction, and re-expansion of an ocean
basin—a story that spans more than 600 million
years.

The Grand Reconstruction. As we have
seen, there is evidence, albeit controversial, that
before the present expansion of the Atlantic and
contraction of the Pacific commenced, Pangaea
had undergone an earlier episode of fragmentation and reassembly. Old mountain belts like the
Appalachians and the Urals seem to suggest
lines along which continental fragments collided
before the most recent breakup of Pangaea, some
200 million years ago. In time, geologists may be
able to sort out more details of this complex
jigsaw puzzle, whose individual pieces change
shape over geological time. But even the reconstruction of events over the past 200 million
years still involves some guesswork, because the
subject is so new and evidence is still being
gathered.

The sequence of Figures 19-1 and 19-20 to
19-23 summarizes one notion of the most recent
breakup of Pangaea. Figure 19-1 shows the
world as it may have looked in Permian times, a

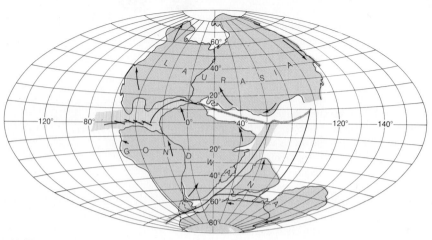

Figure 19-20
One view of world geography at the end of the Triassic Period, 180 million years ago, after some 20 million years of drift. New ocean floor is shown in color. Spreading zones are represented by dark brown lines, transform faults by black lines, and subduction zones by hatched lines. Arrows depict motions of continents since drift began. [After "The Breakup of Pangaea" By R. S. Dietz and J. C. Holden. Copyright © 1970 by Scientific American, Inc. All rights reserved.]

little more than 200 million years ago. Pangaea was an irregularly shaped land mass surrounded by a universal ocean called Panthalassa, the ancestral Pacific. The Tethys Sea, between Africa and Eurasia, was the ancestor of part of the Mediterranean. The fit of North and South America with Europe and Africa is very good in detail when taken at the outer edge of the continental shelves, and not at the present shorelines, which are some distance from the original rift. It is the fit for which we have the firmest evidence. The positions of Central America, India, Australia, and Antarctica are less certain.

The breakup of Pangaea was signaled by the opening of rifts from which basalt poured. Relics of this great event can be found today in the Triassic basalt flows of the east coast of the United States. Dating of these flows by radioactivity provides the estimate of about 200 million years for the beginning of drift.

The geography of the world after 20 million years of drift—at the end of the Triassic some 180 million years ago—is sketched in Figure 19-20. The Atlantic has opened, the Tethys has contracted, and the northern continents (Laurasia) have all but split away from the southern continents (Gondwana). New ocean floor has also separated Antarctica-Australia from Africa-South America. India is off on a trip to the north.

By the end of the Jurassic period, 135 million years ago, drift had been underway for 65 mil-

lion years. The big event at this time is the splitting of South America from Africa, which signals the birth of the South Atlantic (Fig. 19-21). The North Atlantic and Indian oceans are enlarged, but the Tethys Sea continues to close. India continues its northward journey.

The close of the Cretaceous period 65 million years ago sees a widened South Atlantic, the splitting of Madagascar from Africa, and the close of the Tethys to form an inland sea, the Mediterranean (Fig. 19-22). After 135 million years of drift, the modern configuration of continents becomes discernible.

The modern world, produced over the past 65 million years, is shown in Figure 19-23. India has collided with Asia, bringing its trip to an end. Australia has separated from Antarctica. Nearly half of the present-day ocean floor was created in this period. Figure 19-24 shows several schematic sections that summarize modern plate, ocean, continent, and island-arc relationships for the American, African, Eurasian, and Indian plates.

Most of the modern Pacific Ocean basin consists of the Pacific plate side of the East Pacific rise spreading zone, as can be seen in the front endpaper and Figure 19-24,b. This implies that an area equal to most of the Pacific Ocean has disappeared by subduction under the Americas in the past 130 million years. As much as 7000 kilometers of Pacific sea floor may have been thrust under North America!

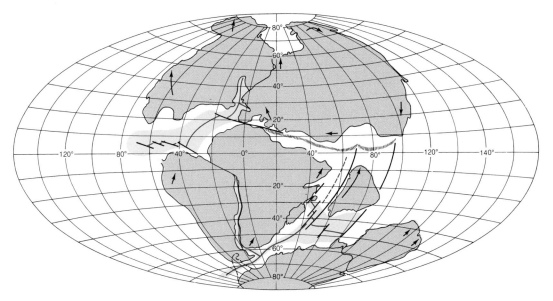

Figure 19-21
World geography at the end of the Jurassic Period, 135 million years ago, after some 65 million years of drift. Ocean floor created in the preceding 45 million years is shown in color. [After "The Breakup of Pangaea" by R. S. Dietz and J. C. Holden. Copyright © 1970 by Scientific American, Inc. All rights reserved.]

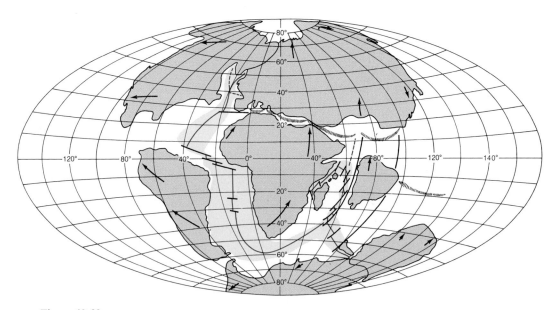

Figure 19-22
World geography at the end of the Cretaceous Period, 65 million years ago. Color indicates new ocean floor created after some 135 million years of drift. [After "The Breakup of Pangaea" by R. S. Dietz and J. C. Holden. Copyright © 1970, by Scientific American, Inc. All rights reserved.]

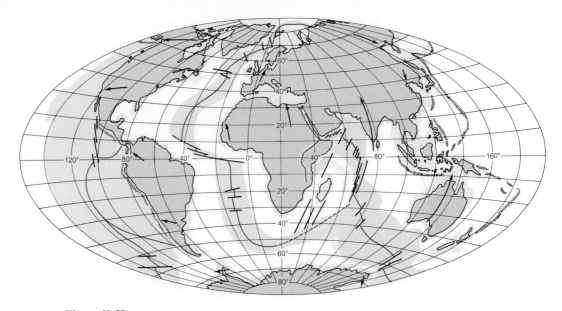

Figure 19-23
World geography today. Color shows sea floor produced during the past 65 million years, in the Cenozoic Period. [After "The Breakup of Pangaea" by R. S. Dietz and J. C. Holden. Copyright © 1970 by Scientific American, Inc. All rights reserved.]

Figure 19-24
Schematic sections showing modern plate, ocean, continent, and island-arc relationships. [After J. F. Dewey and J. M. Bird, "Mountain Belts and New Global Tectonics" *J. Geophysical Research*, v. 75, pp. 2625–2647, 1970.]

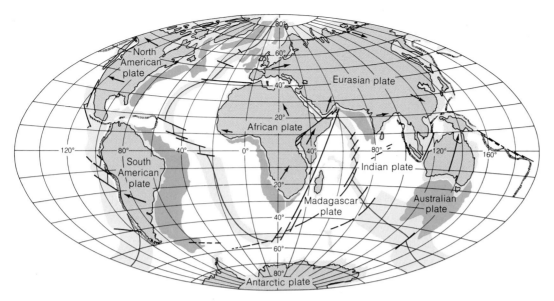

Figure 19-25
World geography as it may look some 50 million years from now if present-day plate movements continue.
[After "The Breakup of Pangaea" by R. S. Dietz and J. C. Holden. Copyright © 1970, by Scientific
American, Inc. All rights reserved.]

If the pattern of modern plate motions continues for another 50 million years, the continents of the world may have the configuration shown in Figure 19-25, but this is sheer speculation. The Atlantic and Indian oceans have expanded at the expense of the contracting Pacific. Australia is beginning to collide with Asia. A new ocean appears in its beginning stages in east Africa. Los Angeles has by-passed San Francisco's position on its northward journey to destruction in the Aleutian trench.

There is not a branch of geology that is untouched by this grand reconstruction of the continents, except perhaps crystallography. Economic geologists are using the fit of the continents to find mineral and oil deposits by correlating the formations in which they occur on one continent with their pre-drift continuations on another continent. Paleontologists are rethinking some aspects of evolution in the light of continental drift. For example, during most of the age of reptiles, the continents we know today were grouped together in two supercontinents, Laurasia and Gondwanaland. These continents were fragmented during most of the age of mammals, with faunas developing on the daughter continents under conditions of isolation from one another. Is this the reason why mammals diversified into so many more orders than the reptiles, and in a much shorter period

of time? Structural geologists and petrologists are extending their sights from regional mapping to the world picture, for the concept of plate tectonics provides the means of interpreting such geological processes as sedimentation and orogeny in global terms. For example, the Caledonian mountain belt that runs along the northwest margin of Europe is the predrift continuation of the Appalachian belt, and the trend of the Andes may be followed into Antarctica and Australia, as Figure 19-26 shows.

Oceanographers are reconstructing currents as they might have existed in the ancestral oceans, to understand better the modern circulation and to account for the variations in deep-sea sediments. Paleoclimatologists are "forecasting backwards" in time to describe temperature, winds, the extent of continental glaciers, and the level of the sea as they were in predrift times. What better testimony to the triumph of this once-outrageous hypothesis than its ability to revitalize and shed light on so many diverse topics!

THE DRIVING MECHANISM OF PLATE TECTONICS

Up to this point everything we have discussed might be categorized as descriptive plate tecton-

Figure 19-26
When the ancient continent of Pangaea is reconstructed, the Caledonian Mountains of Europe and the Appalachian Mountains form a continuous belt, indicative of a plate collision between continents antedating Pangaea. The continuity of the mountain belt that extends from the Americas across Antarctica and western Australia supports the reconstruction. The Urals and other old mountains contain ophiolite zones, marking these sutures as the sites of vanished oceans. [After "Plate Tectonics" by J. F. Dewey. Copyright © 1972 by Scientific American, Inc. All rights reserved.]

Figure 19-27
Schematic illustration of possible driving mechanism of plate tectonics. (a) Plate is pushed by the weight of the ridges at centers of spreading or is pulled by cool, heavy downgoing slab or both. (b) Plate is dragged by convection current in mantle. (c) Plate is the cooled, brittle, boundary region of a convection current in the hot, plastic upper mantle. (d) Jet-like thermal plume rises from great depth, causes hot spots at mid-ocean ridges, spreads laterally, dragging plates. Downward return flow occurs throughout remainder of mantle.

ics. The geometry and rates of plate motions, the consequences of plate separation and collision have been described. But what drives it all? Full understanding of the entire phenomenon awaits the answer to this question. The International Geodynamics Project will enlist the efforts of thousands of scientists to help find the underlying cause of plate motions.

It is generally accepted that most of the mantle is a hot solid, capable of flowing like a liquid at a speed of about a centimeter per year, about as rapidly as your finger nail grows. The lithosphere is broken into rigid plates, somehow responsive in their motions to the flow in the underlying mantle.

As is generally the case when there is an abundance of data in search of a theory, many hypotheses have been advanced. Some would have plates pushed by the weight of the ridges at the zones of spreading or pulled by the heavy downgoing slab at subduction zones. Others hold that the plates are dragged along by currents flowing in the underlying asthenosphere. Figure 19-27 shows some of these ideas. In line with the discussion in Chapter 13, we agree with those who view the process not in piecemeal but as a highly complex convective flow, involving rising, hot, partially molten materials and sinking, cool, solid materials, under a variety of conditions ranging from melting to solidification and remelting. A significant part of the mantle must be involved, since slabs are known to penetrate to depths of some 700 kilometers before being completely resorbed. Figure 19-27,*c*, which was discussed in Chapter 13, shows one of the first computer models of the process—one that neglects many of the effects just mentioned, but which nevertheless accounts for many of the observations. A rising plume of hot material, heated from below, reaches the surface at a center of spreading. It moves away from the center, cools near the surface, and the cooled boundary becomes solid, strong lithosphere. Finally becoming heavier after it has cooled, the lithospheric slab sinks back into the mantle in a subduction zone, where it is reassimilated, to be heated and to rise again in the future. Another theory (Fig. 19-27,*d*) proposes that hot, narrow, jet-like plumes rise from the bottom of the mantle, feed the growing plate, and drive it laterally away from spreading centers where the plumes mostly occur. These same plumes are evidenced at the surface by hot spots. Among the problems left to the next generation of Earth scientists are the incorporation of such important details as the shapes of plates and the history of their movements, and the formation and growth of continents, into an explanation of the distribution of convective cells in time and space.

SUMMARY

1. According to the theory of plate tectonics, the lithosphere is broken into about a dozen rigid, moving plates. Three types of plate boundaries are defined by the relative motion between plates: boundaries of divergence and convergence and transform faults.

2. In addition to earthquake belts, many large-scale geological features are associated with plate boundaries, such as narrow mountain belts and chains of volcanoes. Boundaries of convergence are recognized by deep-sea trenches, inclined earthquake belts, mountains and volcanoes, and paired belts of mélange and magmatism. The Andes Mountains and the trenches of the west coast of South America are modern examples. Divergent boundaries (for example, the mid-Atlantic ridge) typically show as seismic, volcanic, midocean ridges. A characteristic deposit of this environment is the ophiolite suite. Transform faults, along which plates slide past one another, can be recognized by their topography, seismicity, and offsets in magnetic anomaly bands. Ancient convergences may show as old mountain belts, such as the Appalachians.

3. Age of the sea floor can be measured by means of magnetic-anomaly bands, and the "stratigraphy" of magnetic reversals worked out on land. The procedure has been verified and extended by deep-sea drilling. Isochrons can now be drawn for most of the Atlantic and large sections of the Pacific, enabling geologists to reconstruct the history of opening and closing of these oceans. Using this method and drawing on geological and paleomagnetic data, the fragmentation of Pangaea over the last 200 million years can be sketched.

4. Although plate motions can now be described in some detail, the driving mechanism is still a puzzle. An attractive hypothesis proposes that the upper mantle is in a state of convection with hot material rising under divergences and cool material sinking in subduction zones. The plates, according to this notion, would be the cooled, upper boundary region of the convection cell.

EXERCISES

1. Summarize the principal geologic features of subduction zones and divergence zones.

2. Explain the following in the context of plate tectonics:
   a) Iceland.
   b) San Andreas fault of California.
   c) Ural Mountains.
   d) Aleutian trench.
   e) Earthquakes in Italy and Turkey.
   f) Andes Mountains.

3. How do we know that spreading along the East Pacific rise is faster than along the mid-Atlantic ridge?

4. What would an astronaut look for on Mars to find out if plate tectonics is an active process on the planet?

5. How would one recognize the boundaries between ancient plates no longer in existence?

6. Can you think of a way, not mentioned in the text, to measure absolute motions of individual plates rather than relative motions between plates?

BIBLIOGRAPHY

Cox, A., (editor), *Plate Tectonics and Geomagnetic Reversals.* San Francisco: W. H. Freeman and Company, 1973.

Dewey, J. F., "Plate Tectonics," *Scientific American,* May 1972. (Offprint No. 900).

Le Pichon, X., J. Francheteau, and J. Bonnin, *Plate Tectonics.* New York: Elsevier Publishing Company, 1973.

Marvin, Ursula B., *Continental Drift.* Washington, D.C.: Smithsonian Institution Press, 1973.

Meyerhoff, A. A., and H. A. Meyerhoff, "The New Global Tectonics: Major Inconsistencies," *American Association of Petroleum Geologists Bulletin,* v. 56, pp. 269–336, 1972.

Sullivan, Walter, *Continents in Motion.* New York: McGraw-Hill Book Co., 1974.

Tarling, D., and M. Tarling, *Continental Drift.* Garden City, New York: Doubleday & Co., Inc., 1971.

Wesson, P. S., "Objections to Continental Drift and Plate Tectonics," *Journal of Geology,* v. 80, pp. 185–197, 1972.

Wilson, J. Tuzo (compiler), *Continents Adrift—Readings from Scientific American.* San Francisco: W. H. Freeman and Company, 1970.

Wyllie, Peter J., *The Way the Earth Works.* New York: John Wiley & Sons, 1976.

20

DEFORMATION OF THE EARTH'S CRUST

Forces in the crust have been active throughout geologic time. Rocks respond to these forces by folding and fracturing. In a typical mountain-making (orogenic) episode, a thick section of sediments, deposited in a geosyncline along the margin of a stable block, is crumpled. Mountains are raised as the belt is deformed and the sediments are thrown into a series of folds and faults. Intrusion and metamorphism are typical. After the highlands are eroded down, a final stage of rejuvenation by uplifting often occurs. The cycle of geosyncline formation and orogeny can be integrated with the plate-tectonic concept of opening and closing oceans in a simple and natural way.

What a spectacular movie could be made if a camera could be fixed to film the Earth's surface by snapping one frame every thousand years. Replayed at standard speed, a movie made this way would condense almost 50 million years of geologic time to an hour-long feature. Geologic movements that normally are invisibly slow could be viewed and really appreciated in such a fast-motion replay. One could see the drift of continents accompanying the opening of some oceans and the closing of others. In some regions, uplift, tilting, faulting, or folding would give rise to plateaus, mountains, rift valleys, and other geologic structures, and the continuous interplay between tectonic activity and erosion would be evident. Subsidence in other places would lower portions of a continent beneath the sea. The idea is not as far-fetched as it sounds, because movies of this sort have been made in the manner of animated cartoons: the frames of such films are photographs of sketches based on interpretations of the geologic record.

When geologists examine the geologic record and make a geologic cross section showing beds in various attitudes—flat-lying, tilted, folded, faulted, perhaps intruded by igneous rocks, metamorphosed, or covered by lava flows—they do so to unravel the geologic structure of the region and then to deduce the sequence of events that we call geologic history (Fig. 20-1). They know how to recognize those features (such as lithology, bedding, subaqueous slump, ripple marks, or mud cracks) that are connected with the original formation of the sedimentary beds, using the criteria described in Chapters 2 and 11. Deformation structures, such as folds and faults, which are imposed by events subsequent to formation, can then be interpreted in terms of the sequence in which they occurred. This chapter takes up the subject of geologic structures—particularly the changes ranging in extent from meters to hundreds of kilometers that take place in rocks due to deformation of the Earth's crust.

HOW ROCKS DEFORM

Folding and faulting are the most common forms of deformation of the rocks that make up the outer layers of the Earth's crust. For years, geologists were baffled by the problem of how

Figure 20-1
Stages in the development of the Basin and Range province, as postulated by W. M. Davis. (a) Deposition of stratified sediments. (b) Folding and thrusting. (c) Development of an erosional surface. (d) Sheets of lava cover the eroded surface. (e) Block faults develop, breaking up the earlier features. A geologist sees only the last stage and attempts to reconstruct from the structural features all of the earlier stages in the history of a region. [After *The Evolution of North America* by P. B. King. Copyright © 1977 by Princeton University Press. Redrawn with permission of Princeton University Press.]

Figure 20-2
Small-scale folds in interbedded shales and cherts of the Franciscan Formation in central California. [From A. M. Johnson, *Physical Processes in Geology,* Freeman, Cooper & Company. Copyright © 1972.]

rocks, which seem strong and rigid, could be distorted by crustal forces into folds or broken along faults (Fig. 20-2). The question still does not have a complete answer, but much understanding has come from laboratory experiments in which rocks were squeezed under the conditions of high pressure and temperature that are known to occur in the crust.

Figure 20-3, for example, shows what happens to a small cylinder of marble when it is squeezed by applying **stress** at the ends. Stress is a force divided by the area over which it is applied. (For example, a weight of 4 kilograms applied over an area of 2 square centimeters exerts a stress of 2 kilograms per square centimeter. Pressure is also measured as force per unit area. One kilogram per square centimeter is approximately equivalent to atmospheric pressure.) The experiment consists of applying stress by pushing down on one end of a sample of rock with a piston, while at the same time applying pressure to all sides of the sample to simulate the confining pressure to which materials deep in the crust are subjected because of the weight of the overlying rock. Temperature can also be raised to realistic, deep Earth values, usually to

several hundred degrees centigrade. The figure shows an unstressed cylindrical sample and two samples that have been **strained** by 20 percent—that is, changed in length (in this case), shortened by 20 percent owing to the applied stress. Low confining pressures, which simulate shallow depths in the crust, allowed the middle sample to fracture; high confining pressures, which are equivalent to conditions at greater depths in the crust, made the third sample deform **plastically** under stress—that is, made it flow, without any cracking, into its shortened, bulging shape. The investigators concluded that, if a bed of this particular marble were stressed near the surface, it would tend to deform by faulting; but, if it were deeper than a few kilometers, it would behave plastically and fold. Experiments also show that, if rocks are hot when they are stressed, plastic flow will occur more readily.

Rocks, like most solids, can be classed as **brittle** or **ductile,** according to how much plastic flow they show. A brittle material ruptures, rather than flows, when stressed beyond a critical value. Ductile substances are capable of considerable plastic flow before they break.

Figure 20-3
Marble cylinder deformed in a laboratory by pushing down at one end. From left
to right: (a) undeformed; (b) 20 percent strain (shortened by 20 percent of original
length), 270 atmospheres confining pressure; (c) 20 percent strain, 445 atmospheres
confining pressure. Note how the sample deforms plastically at higher confining
pressure and fails by fracture at lower confining pressure. [Photo by M. S. Paterson, Australian National University.]

Glass, near room temperature, is a familiar example of a brittle material, and modeling clay is
obviously ductile. The marble discussed in the
previous paragraph would be brittle at shallow
depths, but it would respond to stress as a ductile substance deeper in the crust.

The graph in Figure 20-4 summarizes the
deformation behavior of many rocks under
stress. The ordinate shows the applied stress and
the abscissa shows the corresponding deformation. When the stresses are low, the strains follow **Hooke's elastic law:** strain changes in the
same proportion as the applied stress. The graph
shows this elastic behavior as a straight line
starting from zero stress and strain. In this region of low stress and elasticity, the deformation
is reversible—that is, the sample returns to its
original size and shape when the stress is removed, like the spring in a scale when a weight
is removed. If the stress is increased, the **elastic
limit** is reached, beyond which the rock begins
to deform by plastic flow. On the stress–strain
diagrams, the curve bends where this occurs,
which means that small increases in stress lead
to larger deformations. Plastic flow is a permanent distortion—the original shape of the material is not restored if the stress is removed. If the
stress increases further, the material finally
breaks when its **rupture strength** is reached.
For brittle materials, the region of plastic deformation is small or absent, and the material
breaks with little additional stress after the elas-

tic limit is exceeded. Naturally, the shape of the
curve varies for different materials. Wet clay
would show little elasticity and much plasticity,
whereas a rock like basalt would show no plasticity at near-surface conditions.

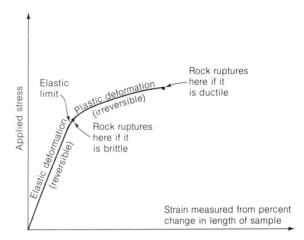

Figure 20-4
Schematic graph showing how a rock deforms when stress is applied. Initially, the
deformation is elastic and reversible, with stress proportional to strain. If stress is
increased beyond the elastic limit, the rock undergoes a permanent, plastic deformation. Brittle rocks rupture with little or no plastic deformation. Ductile rocks
undergo much plastic deformation before they break.

Figure 20-5
Rocks respond differently to forces in the Earth's crust. In this tilted section, sandstone beds were able to withstand deformation, but shales show evidence of flowage and changes in original thickness. Zumaja, Spain. [Photo by R. Siever.]

Nature is more complex, of course, than the conditions under which such simple experiments are performed. For example, stresses produced by crustal deformation may continue for thousands or millions of years, whereas laboratory geologists have never squeezed individual rock samples for much longer than a few years. Rocks may flow under stresses much lower than those required in the laboratory if the stresses are applied for long periods, and would flow more readily if wet or hot. Nevertheless, the experiments shed some light on how rocks respond to stresses, and they give us more confidence in our interpretations of field evidence. When we see folds and faults in the field, we can remember that some rocks are brittle, that others are ductile, that the same rock can be brittle at shallow depths and ductile deep in the crust, and that every rock either flows plastically if stressed beyond its elastic limit or ruptures if stressed beyond its strength. Other things being equal, laboratory experiments teach us that we should expect to find that granite is stronger than sandstone, that crystalline basement rocks are more brittle than the plastically deformable young sediments that may cover them, that sedimentary rocks increase in ductility from limestone and sandstone through clay and shale to salt and gypsum.

REGIONAL MOVEMENTS OF THE EARTH'S CRUST

Orogenic movements. A striking feature of continents is that they are marked by long, relatively narrow mountain chains made up of strongly folded and faulted rocks. The movements that produce these deformed belts are termed **orogenic,** and they are generally thought to be the result of horizontal compression. The Appalachian Mountains provide a prime example, and the case history given in the previous chapter tells the story of this orogenic belt in terms of the compression of a belt of geosynclinal sediments accompanied by episodes of intrusions and metamorphism. The Alps, the Urals, and the Rockies are other examples. We will say more about orogenic belts later in this chapter, following a discussion of folds and faults.

Epeirogenic Movements. Sedimentary rock sequences all over the world record the same kind of history of downward and upward movements of the crust that we can see in the Grand Canyon (Chapter 2). **Epeirogeny** is the term used to describe these movements. Great thicknesses of marine deposits of shallow-water origin, once buried hundreds or thousands of met-

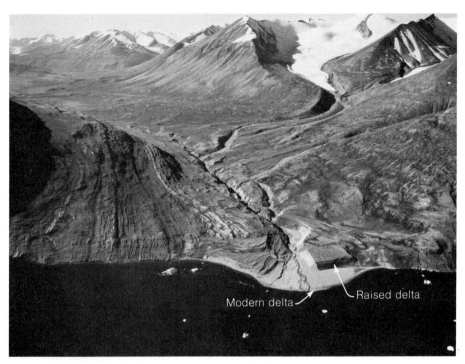

Figure 20-6
Regional uplift, evidenced by a delta raised about 30 m above sea level. An old
delta is being dissected by streams as a new delta is being deposited. Antarctic
Sund, E. Greenland. [Lauge Koch Expedition; courtesy of John Haller, Harvard
University.]

ers below the sea floor, are now found well
above sea level. These deposits give evidence of
continued slow subsidence during sedimentation. In many cases, later elevation to their
present position above the sea is due to simple
uplift. Gaps in the rock sequence represented by
unconformities (Fig. 20-16) tell of uplifts of
large regions that stopped sedimentation and
started stripping away previously deposited
rocks. Fossil trees and other plants embedded in
coal deposits now mined deep in the Earth tell
of earlier times when they grew in the sunlight
of the surface. Raised beaches and marine shells
now found at elevations of 250 meters above sea
level substantiate the postglacial uplift of Fennoscandia. Other examples that indicate vertical
movements are incised meanders, coral reefs
raised above sea level, and drowned river valleys
(see Figs. 10-7, 20-6 and Chapters 5 and 7).

Along seacoasts, the geologist is careful to
distinguish between movements in which one
portion of the crust went up or down relative to
another part of the crust and the worldwide
sea-level changes that accompanied Pleistocene

glacial and interglacial periods. Whether the
land goes up or the sea goes down (or vice versa)
makes no difference in shaping such landforms
of seacoasts as terraces or eroded headlands.

Though many of the vertical movements are
connected with orogeny, epeirogenic movements
commonly affect large regions without extensive
folding or faulting. A typical product of this
kind of downward movement, which is usually
slow and intermittent, is a **basin,** a bowl- or
spoon-shaped depression that gets filled up with
sediment. An example of gradual and intermittent downward movement of the crust in one
part of the relatively undeformed or stable broad
region between the Appalachians and the Rockies is the Michigan Basin. Covering much of the
lower peninsula of Michigan, this is a circular
area of about 500,000 square kilometers that
subsided throughout much of Paleozoic time
and received sediments more than 3 kilometers
thick in its central, deepest part. The structure
of the formations in this basin has been likened
to a pile of saucers (Fig. 20-7).

Upward movement with little or only moder-

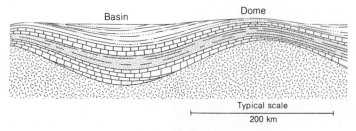

Figure 20-7
Idealized section of a dome and basin; evidence of vertical movements in the relatively undeformed interior of the United States.

Figure 20-8
The Black Hills of South Dakota, a domal uplift in the Great Plains. Erosion of the central part exposes the core of Precambrian igneous and metamorphic rocks and the succession of Paleozoic and Mesozoic sediments that slope away from the center. [After *Geology of Soils* by C. B. Hunt. W. H. Freeman and Company. Copyright © 1972.]

ate faulting or folding can produce broad uplands and plateaus. The Colorado Plateau, the Adirondack Mountains, and the Black Hills of South Dakota are examples of structures produced by general upward movements. The Black Hills structure is an oval-shaped **dome**—an area of uplift sloping off more or less uniformly in all directions from the highest point—that rises more than 2 kilometers above the Great Plains surrounding it. The larger area in which the Black Hills are located was once lower, and it subsided to receive a blanket of Paleozoic and Mesozoic sediment more than 2 kilometers thick. Sometime between late Cretaceous and Oligocene, the whole area of about 50,000 square kilometers was uplifted, as if pushed up from below by a piston, without being extensively crumpled or broken. Subsequent erosion has stripped away the sediments overlying the central part of the uplift, exposing the Precambrian igneous and metamorphic rocks below. Here is where the famous Homestake Gold Mine was discovered in the Precambrian rocks near Lead, South Dakota (Fig. 20-8). Some geologists speculate that the doming of the Black Hills was caused by an upwelling of magma from deep within the crust.

Geologists have no ready mechanisms to account for most of these slow and broad epeirogenic movements, although hypotheses exist for some of them. The Fennoscandian uplift, as mentioned in Chapter 18, represents the slow upward recovery of the crust following the removal of the glacial load that had depressed it. The sediment-filled downwarp off the east coast of the United States may be evidence of the subsidence of the edge of the continent after it drifted apart from North Africa. This subsidence may represent contraction of the newly formed lithosphere as it cools in the spreading process, as mentioned in Chapter 19 (see Fig. 20-9). Some of the broad uplifts, such as the Tibetan Plateau, may be connected with plate collisions; in general, however, warping within the continents and far from plate margins is still a puzzle.

Recent Movements. Up-and-down movements, or **warping,** of large regions are not restricted only to the geologic past, but are measurable as they occur in our own time. For example, the city of Venice is slowly sinking into the Adriatic Sea at a rate of 4 millimeters per year. The process is mostly one of coastal downwarping, though man-made subsidence due to the withdrawal of water and natural gas from

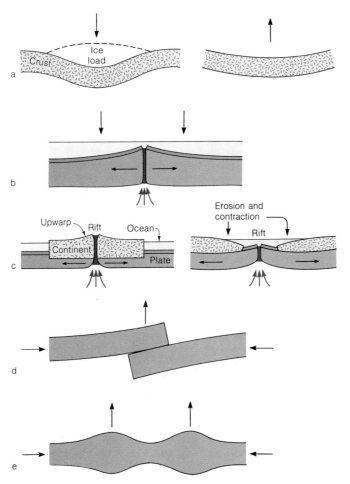

Figure 20-9
Some proposed mechanisms for vertical movements (not to scale). (a) Glacial ice
load buckles the crust; slow uplift follows removal of ice. (b) Formation of lithosphere at mid-ocean ridges. Spreading sea floor subsides as plate cools and contracts. (c) Rifting and upwarping due to heating, followed by separation of two segments of a continent; receding edges erode at the top, cool and contract within,
forming subsiding continental margin. (d) Two plates collide; overriding plate is
uplifted. (e) Crust deforms by thickening due to horizontal forces.

the underlying sediments is, unfortunately, has-
tening this beautiful city's demise (Fig. 20-10).

Precision surveys across the United States
have revealed the pattern of vertical movements
shown in Figure 20-11. Large regions are currently sinking and rising at rates of 1–15 millimeters per year. If the pattern persists for the
geologically short time of only 1 million years,
much of New England and the Gulf Coast will
have sunk to the sea floor and plateaus a few
kilometers in height will have grown in the
Midwest. These seemingly slow rates of displacement, unnoticed by the inhabitants, are all
that it takes to produce highlands and basins.

There is one type of crustal movement that
the inhabitants of an affected area do take notice
of: the sudden and large displacements along
faults that produce large earthquakes. Integrated
over thousands or millions of years, the accumulated displacements due to earthquake movements may be of the same order as the gradual
displacements depicted in Figure 20-11. The
catastrophic nature and the large size of each
impulse of displacement is what sets earthquake
movements apart in the minds of men.

As discussed in Chapter 17, earthquake displacements can be horizontal and vertical and, in
the case of a truly great shock, can amount to as

Figure 20-10
Venice is slowly subsiding into the Adriatic Sea. Water level now reaches the base of the columns of this old building. The raised sidewalk, of recent construction, will be awash in several decades if subsidence continues unimpeded. [Photo by Roberto Frassetto, National Research Council of Italy.]

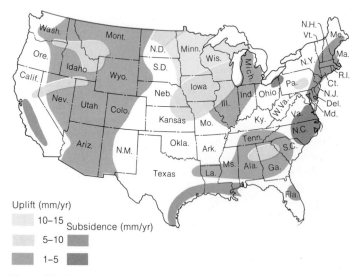

Uplift (mm/yr)
10–15
Subsidence (mm/yr)
5–10
1–5

Figure 20-11
Crustal-movement map showing areas of present-day uplift and subsidence in the United States. [Chart by S. P. Hand, National Oceanic and Atmospheric Administration.]

much as 10 or 15 meters. Horizontal displacements along the San Andreas fault at the time of the San Francisco earthquake of 1906 amounted to as much as 5 meters (Fig. 17-9). The earthquake of 1872 that devastated the Owens Valley just east of the Sierra Nevada in California produced a vertical displacement of 4 meters. At the rate of one such earthquake every few thousand years, this lofty mountain range could have been raised in but a few million years, even allowing for erosion.

The permanent displacements accompanying large earthquakes are not restricted to the vicinity of the fault. They can affect immense areas. The great Alaskan earthquake of 1964 is a well-documented example. Figure 20-12 shows the amount of uplift and subsidence that took place in an area of more than 200,000 square kilometers. The maximum uplift amounted to 13 meters, and the greatest subsidence was 2 meters. All of this occurred in a few minutes as the Pacific plate slipped a few meters deeper into the mantle beneath southern Alaska. It was not very difficult to document the pattern of vertical displacements along the Alaskan coast. Barnacles and certain other marine organisms that live permanently attached to the rocks of the shore are limited in their vertical distribution by the reach of the tides, such that they grow in horizontal bands along the shore, whose upper limits may correspond with, say, the mean high-water level. So close are such correspondences that, following the Alaskan earthquake, uplift could be measured by comparing the height of the band of dead barnacles with that of the band of new, living barnacles (Figure 20-13). Similarly, subsidence could be determined from the height to which high tide inundated land plants. Differences in the levels of pre- and post-earthquake beaches, tide-gage readings, and inland surveys of elevation along roads and railroad routes also provided data on permanent vertical displacement. The displacements accompanying earthquakes, integrated over thousands or millions of years, can be a major factor in regional deformation.

The broad, gradual uplifts described in the preceding pages almost always entail some slight undulating deformation of the rocks. Rocks that look flat-lying and horizontal prove to be slightly tilted and gently folded when careful surveys are made. Within the continent, in apparently flat terrain, there are also small faults along which very small amounts of movement occurred. Thus folds and minor faults are widely distributed in most parts of the crust. In

Figure 20-12
Permanent uplift and subsidence caused by the great Alaskan earthquake of 1964. Contours show displacements in feet—uplift to the southeast and subsidence to the northwest of a hinge line running from the vicinity of Kodiak to that of Valdez. [After G. Plafker, U. S. Geological Survey.]

Figure 20-13
Geologist measuring distance from sea level to the upper limit of barnacle growth of a sea cliff (white band). Barnacles normally grow below the level of high tide, but uplift due to the Alaskan earthquake of 1964 has raised them out of the sea. By measuring the distance from the present level of high tide to the upper growth limit on the cliff, the amount of uplift can be obtained. [Photo by G. Plafker, U. S. Geological Survey.]

Figure 20-14
Large-scale folds in lower Paleozoic graywacke, northeast Victoria Land, Antarctica. [Photo by W. B. Hamilton, U. S. Geological Survey.]

orogenic belts, strong folding and faulting are the major structural features. Folds and faults are the details of the patterns of deformation, strong and weak, that geologists map in the field as the clues to the large panorama of tectonics. We shall go on to treat the geometry of these folds and faults as they are exhibited best in strongly deformed terrains.

FOLDS

The term "fold" implies that a structure that originally was planar, like a sedimentary bed, has been bent. The deformation may be produced by horizontal or vertical forces in the crust. One type of deformation can result when large rock masses glide down an inclined bedding plane, fault plane, or unconformity under the force of gravity.

Folding is the most common form of deformation of layered rocks, and its most typical manifestation is in mountain belts. In young mountain systems, where erosion has not yet erased them, majestic, sweeping folds can be traced, some of them with dimensions of many kilometers (Fig. 20-14). On a much smaller scale, very thin beds can be crumpled into folds a few centimeters long. Folds can be gentle or the bending can be severe, depending on the magnitude of the applied forces and the ability of the beds to resist deformation. Ancient mountains, long since eroded away, have left a partial record that enables geologists to reconstruct their former grandeur—the remnants of intense folding found today in the stable Precambrian terrains of continental interiors (Fig. 20-15).

In order to characterize and interpret a deformed rock layer, a geologist must first describe it. Ideally, it would be easiest to visualize a deformed stratum if the elevation of its surface could be mapped and contoured, just as a topographic map charts the Earth's surface in terms of contours (Appendix V). Sometimes, particularly when a search for oil or minerals is involved, there is sufficient information to do just this, using such evidence about the depth of the layer as data obtained from mines, boreholes, outcrops in valleys, or perhaps the radar-like echoes of seismic waves (see Box 17-1).

More often, the geologist has to reconstruct the geometry of folds and faults from sparse surface information only (Fig. 20-16). He begins with a topographic map showing the contours of the Earth's surface. From his field observations,

Figure 20-15
Folds in Precambrian iron formation, Beresford
Lake area, Manitoba. This is a relic of an ancient
mountain-making episode in the continental interior,
a region that has remained relatively stable for approximately the past billion years. [From Geological
Survey of Canada, Ottawa.]

Figure 20-16
Geologists typically work from surface outcrops of
rock formations to reconstruct subsurface structures.
This block diagram shows schematically one example of the surface expression of a fold in a sequence
of sedimentary rocks.

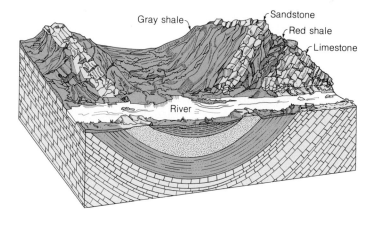

Gray shale
Sandstone
Red shale
Limestone
River

Figure 20-17
Construction of a geological section from a geological map. In this example, the formations are horizontal and therefore crop out at the same topographic level—that is, between the same elevation contours. [After *Principles of Geology* (4th ed.) by J. Gilluly, A. C. Waters, A. O. Woodford. W. H. Freeman and Company. Copyright © 1975.]

Figure 20-18
Illustration of the strike and dip of an inclined bed.

which involve much walking and surveying, he superimposes on the topographic map the pattern of outcrops of the different formations. The geologist is ever hopeful the soil cover doesn't hide all of the outcrops. If there are hills and valleys and the beds are horizontal, the outcrop of a given stratum will always fall at the same topographic level—that is, on the same contour line (Figure 20-17). More often, the beds are tilted, folded, or faulted, and the same formation will outcrop at many different elevations. Using such criteria as relative age (indicated by fossils or radiometric dating) and lithology, the geologist keeps track of the sequence of layers. In order to figure out the structure of the deformed beds, he must also keep track of the geometric attitude or orientation of the beds at outcrops. He does this by marking on his map the **dip** and **strike** of the beds wherever they outcrop. The dip is the angle of inclination of the bed from the horizontal, in the direction of steepest descent: water flows in the down-dip direction. The strike is at right angles to the dip direction.

It is the intersection of the plane of the bed with the horizontal plane. Figures 20-18 and 20-19 show how dip and strike are measured in the field and plotted on maps; topographic and geological maps are described in more detail in Appendix V.

Once the formations are mapped and the dips and strikes are recorded from many places, one can attempt to reconstruct the deformed shape of the bed, even when erosion has removed sections of it. It is like putting together a three-dimensional jigsaw puzzle with missing pieces. Figure 20-20 shows a geological map with formations, strikes, and dips indicated, and below it is a cross section inferred from the map, with eroded portions indicated by dashed lines. The up folds and down folds of the beds show in the section as they would appear if a vertical cut could be made through the Earth in the direction indicated on the map, providing the geologist was correct in his reconstruction.

Upfolds or arches of layered rocks are called **anticlines,** and downfolds or troughs are **syn-**

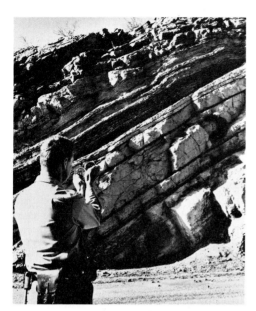

Figure 20-19
Geologists measuring the dip of inclined beds using
a clinometer. The dip is given by the angle between
the horizontal and the edge of the instrument,
which is aligned parallel to the bedding planes. The
horizontal is found by rotating a level bubble until
the bubble is centered. [From U. S. Geological
Survey.]

clines (Fig. 20-21). A steplike bend in otherwise
gently dipping or horizontal beds is a **monocline** (Fig. 20-22).

In order to discuss the different types of
folding with an economy of language, we need
to define the parts of a fold. The two sides of a
fold are its **limbs.** The **axial plane** is a surface
that divides a fold as symmetrically as possible.
The line made by the intersections of the axial
plane with the beds is the **axis** of the fold. If the
axis of a fold is not horizontal, the fold is said to
plunge by an amount given by the angle the
axis makes with the horizontal. Parts of a fold
are illustrated in Figure 20-23.

It is easy to see (Fig. 20-20) that, for a folded
sequence of layers, the oldest beds would be
found at depth in the core (or central axis) of the
anticline and the youngest rocks on the surface
over the axis of the syncline. On a geological
map or cross section, eroded anticlines would be
recognized by an axial core of older rocks, bordered on both sides by younger rocks dipping
away from the axis. In the core of a syncline, the
map would show younger rocks on the axis with
older rocks dipping inward on both sides, as in
Figures 20-20 and 20-21.

Figure 20-20
Geological map with formations, strikes, and dips indicated. Geological sections *A-A'* and *B-B'* are inferred from the map. Note how the surface features indicated on the map along the lines *A-A'* and *B-B'* are transferred to
the corresponding cross sections, and how the subsurface reconstruction is
consistent with the surface observations. [After U. S. Geological Survey.]

Figure 20-21
Upfolds, or anticlines, and downfolds, or synclines. Erosion of the folds produces parallel ridges where resistant rocks crop out and parallel valleys on the
easily eroded formations. [After U. S. Geological Survey.]

Figure 20-22
Schematic illustration of a monocline.

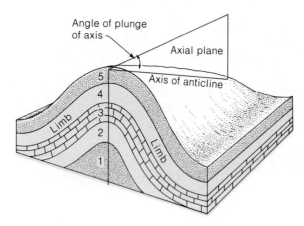

Figure 20-23
Diagrammatic illustration of parts of a fold.

Symmetrical folds

Axial plane is vertical

Overturned folds

Upper limb of syncline and lower
limb of anticline, tilted beyond
vertical, dip in same direction

Asymmetrical folds

Beds in one limb dip more
steeply than those in the other

Recumbent folds

Beds in lower limb of anticline
and upper limb of syncline are
upside down; axial plane is
nearly horizontal

Figure 20-24
Diagrammatic illustration of symmetrical, asymmetrical, overturned, and recumbent folds.

Types of Folds. We should not expect every fold to have a vertical axial plane with limbs dipping symmetrically away from the axis. When a horizontal force is applied to layers that have an initial dip or that change laterally, say, in thickness, strength, or ductility, or when the force itself is uneven, the folds can be thrown into **asymmetrical** shapes, with one limb dipping more steeply than the other. This is a common situation. When the deformation is intense, the fold can be **overturned,** with the lower limb of an anticline or the upper limb of a syncline tilted more than 90° from its original attitude. Both limbs of an overturned fold dip in the same direction, as in Figure 20-24, and the overturned limb shows an inverted sequence in an outcrop, with older beds on top of younger ones. In **recumbent** folds, the axial plane is horizontal, or nearly so, and one limb has been rotated into a completely upside-down sequence (Fig. 20-26). Figure 20-27 shows how an overturned fold might evolve. The spectacular recumbent folds of the Alps, some of the first ones to be mapped in detail, are particularly famous among geologists.

As mentioned earlier, domes and basins are folds in which beds dip radially away from, or toward, a point, respectively (Fig. 20-9). The outcrops of such formations on the surface would tend to be circular or elliptical (Fig. 20-28). Domes are very important in oil geology, because oil tends to migrate upward and become trapped against impervious rocks at the high point of a dome.

Follow the axis of any fold, and sooner or later the fold will die out. When an anticline disappears, for example, its axis descends and the folds get smaller and smaller, as in Figure 20-29. The axis of a syncline ascends as the fold disappears. The outcrops of eroded remnants of a plunging fold show a characteristic pattern like the bow of a canoe, because the limbs converge where the fold disappears (Fig. 20-29). Successions of (eroded) plunging anticlines and synclines show on geological maps or air photographs as a zig-zag pattern of outcrops (Figs. 20-29 and 20-30).

Folds tend to occur not in isolation but in elongated groups. When a geologist finds a **folded belt,** he infers that the region at one time was compressed by horizontal crustal forces. The Appalachians were mentioned earlier as an excellent example of a folded mountain belt (Fig. 20-31), and one current hypothesis, discussed in Chapter 19, invokes a plate collision to account for the wrinkling of the once flat sheets of Paleozoic sediments.

Figure 20-25
Overturned syncline in Cretaceous limestone, Lake Lucerne, Switzerland.
[Photo by W. B. Hamilton, U. S. Geological Survey.]

Figure 20-26
A recumbent fold, north of Grandjeans, Fiord, Greenland. From top of cliff to valley bottom,
the difference in altitude is about 800 m. [Lauge Koch Expedition; courtesy of J. Haller, Harvard University.]

Figure 20-27
Diagrammatic illustration of how an
overturned fold might evolve as a result of an increasing horizontal force.
In the bottom sketch the formation
has actually ruptured.

Figure 20-28
Dome in strata 6 miles east of Rawlins, Wyoming. Highway and railroad at right give scale. [From *Geology Illustrated* by John S. Shelton. W. H. Freeman and Company. Copyright © 1966.]

Figure 20-29
(Left) Schematic block diagram of plunging folds. (Right) The eroded remnants of plunging folds show a characteristic pattern in which the limbs converge like the bow of a canoe.

Figure 20-30
The erosional remnants of plunging folds show a zig-zag pattern in this view taken in the Valley and Ridge belt of the Appalachian Mountains, 30 miles northwest of Harrisburg, Pennsylvania. In the drawing below, the imaginary trench reveals the subsurface structure. [From *Geology Illustrated* by J. S. Shelton. W. H. Freeman and Company. Copyright © 1966.]

Allegheny front | Ridge and Valley belt | Great Valley | Reading Prong | Triassic lowland | Piedmont

Appalachian plateau | Newer Appalachians | Older Appalachians | Coastal Plain

Figure 20-31
Block diagram of a section of the Appalachian Mountains, an example of the remnants of a folded mountain belt. [After *Stream Sculpture on the Atlantic Slope* by D. Johnson. Columbia University Press. Copyright © 1931.]

Figure 20-32
Intersecting joints form rectangular blocks in volcanic rocks near Braintree, Mass. [Photo by J. Haller, Harvard University.]

FRACTURES

Rocks yield to deforming forces in several ways: Some layers will crumple into folds, some will break, some will fold first and then break if the applied stresses build up beyond the strength of the rock. Fractures may be divided into two categories, **joints** and **faults.** A joint is a crack along which no appreciable movement has occurred. If there is displacement of the rocks on both sides of a fracture and parallel to it, the fracture is a fault.

Joints. These are structural features found in almost every outcrop. In some places, they are randomly irregular. They are particularly interesting to the geologist if they show a regional pattern—for example, if all the cracks in a particular area are approximately parallel. Very often there are two or more sets of joints that intersect, breaking the rocks into large rectangular blocks or parallelepipeds. Regularity in a joint system often implies uniformity in the stress system that produced it. For example, the compression of sedimentary layers produced by the weight of overlying beds can produce one set of joints and the decompression of erosional unloading can establish another set. Regional stresses—compressional, tensional, or shear—that have long since vanished can leave their imprint in the form of distinct sets of joints. The contraction of layers of cooling lava can result in columnar jointing (see Fig. 15-10).

As noted in Chapter 4, joints provide channels for the flow of water through rock. Because of the greater ratio of surface area to volume, the irregular blocks formed by intersecting joint systems are more readily attacked by air and water than are massive, unjointed formations; thus, the weathering process is accelerated by jointing (Fig. 20-32). Joints also can provide underground channels for the flow of magma,

Block before faulting

Fault plane

Normal fault

Reverse fault

Strike-slip fault

Oblique-slip fault

Figure 20-33
Types of faults.

often leaving in evidence a swarm of parallel dikes, or cracks filled with igneous rock. Magma injected under high pressure can enlarge existing joints or open new ones.

Faults. Because faults have already been discussed in the chapters on seismology and plate tectonics (Chapters 17 and 19), the review here will be brief. Like folds, faults are a common feature of mountain belts, particularly where the deformation is intense. As discussed in Chapter 19, margins where plates collide, pull apart, or drift past each other are the sites of subduction zones, rift valleys, or transforms, all of which involve faults. Some transform faults—the San Andreas fault of California, for example—show such large displacements that the offset of the two plates may amount to hundreds of kilometers. The different categories of faulting are distinguished by the direction of motion along the fracture plane (Fig. 20-33). A **dip-slip** fault involves displacements up or down the dip of the plane. A **strike-slip** fault is one in which the movement is horizontal, parallel to the strike of the fault plane. A combination of dip-slip and strike-slip movements would describe an **oblique-slip** fault.

Faults need a further characterization, since the movement can be up or down, or right or left. A **normal fault** is one in which the rocks above the fault plane move down relative to the rocks below. A **reverse fault,** then, is one in which the rocks above the fault plane move up relative to the rocks below. A reverse fault in which the dip is small so that the overlying block is pushed predominantly horizontally is a **thrust fault.** Finally, if, as one faces a strike-slip fault, the block on the other side is displaced to the right, then the fault is a **right-lateral** fault; **left-lateral** faults are displaced in the opposite direction (see Figs. 1-19, 17-9, and 20-34 for some photographs of faults).

Figure 20-34
Thrust fault in limestone, Gusta, Norrland, Sweden. Offset of once-continuous bed, indicated by line, is about 0.8 m. [Photo by J. Haller, Harvard University.]

Figure 20-35
Schematic diagram of large-scale thrust sheet, modeled by
C. K. Longwell after examples in California and southern Nevada.

Figure 20-36
Block diagrams of a
graben and a horst.

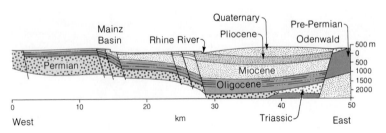

Figure 20-37
Geological cross section of the Rhine graben. [After P. Dorn.]

Low-angle thrusts or overthrusts with displacements of many kilometers are often found in intensely deformed mountain belts. These thrusts are an expression of compressive forces, which shorten the crust. The surficial layers accommodate the crustal shortening, in this case, by breaking, with one sheet overriding another. An example of thrusting from California and southern Nevada is shown in Figure 20-35.

Grabens—a term sometimes used synonymously with rift valleys—are long, narrow troughs bounded by one or more parallel normal faults. Tensional crustal forces, literally pulling the crust apart, are responsible for these down-dropped fault blocks. The East African rift valleys, the mid-ocean ridge rifts, and the Rhine River Valley are famous examples. A **horst** is the opposite, a ridge formed by parallel reverse or, more commonly, normal faults (Figs. 20-36, 20-37, and 20-38).

Because a fault implies that dislocation has occurred along a fracture, it can be recognized in the field by the disruption of formations on either side. In some places, the two segments of an offset formation can be found, and the amount of relative displacement can be measured directly (Fig. 20-34), but this becomes increasingly difficult with large offsets. In establishing the time of faulting, geologists use the simple rule that a fault must be younger than the youngest rocks it cuts and older than the oldest undisrupted formation that covers it (see Fig. 20-1).

Crushed or ground up rock is often found in a fault zone. In some places, polished and striated surfaces result from friction along a fault plane. These surfaces are called **slickensides** (Fig. 20-39); because they align in the direction of relative movement of the fault blocks, they tell the geologist what this direction was, though not with complete reliability. If movement has occurred recently, the effect on topography, drainage patterns, vegetation, and man's artifacts can often be recognized (see Figs. 17-1 and 17-9).

Several cross sections of folded and faulted belts are shown in Figures 20-31, 20-40, 20-41, and 20-42 to illustrate some of the ways rocks deform in response to crustal forces.

Figure 20-38
The Red Sea bifurcates to form the Gulf of Suez on the left and the Gulf of Aquaba on the
right. The Arabian Peninsula on the right, splitting away from Africa on the left, has opened
these great rifts, now flooded by the sea. [Photo by Apollo 7 astronauts; from National Aeronautics and Space Administration.]

Figure 20-39
Slickensides on rhyolite, Braintree, Mass.
[Photo by J. Haller, Harvard University.]

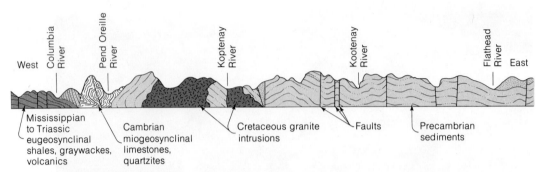

Figure 20-40
Geological cross section from the Cascade Mountain front of northeast Washington to the Rocky Mountains of northwest Montana. Deformed eugeosynclinal and miogeosynclinal deposits and granitic intrusions characterize much of this region. [After R. G. Yates, G. E. Becraft, A. B. Campbell, and R. C. Pearson, Canadian Institute of Mining and Metallurgy.]

Figure 20-41
Unconformities, folds, and thrust sheets in a section of the southern Alps. [After *Structural Geology* by L. U. De Sitter. McGraw-Hill Book Company. Copyright © 1964.]

Figure 20-42
Folds and faults in a section of the Juras, an example of a folded mountain belt. According to one hypothesis, the beds overlying the Triassic were sheared off and deformed independently of the older rocks below.

Needless to say, deformation—in the form of mountain belts with their folds and faults, plateaus, grabens, and strike-slip faults—leaves its mark on the configuration of the Earth's surface. These topographic expressions are often a guide to the structures that control them. Even with such relatively small-scale features as the shapes of hills and valleys and the courses of streams, the controlling factors are the structural elements in a complex interaction with erosion.

It should also be apparent that, the older the structure, the more likely it is that erosion has erased it and the less evident is its physiographic expression. Thus, present-day surface relief is largely due to movements that occurred during and since the Tertiary Period. These movements and earlier erosion have tended to obscure Mesozoic and Paleozoic structures. Precambrian deformation no longer shows as mountains but only as relic remnants of folds and faults in the basement rocks of the continental interior. Examples of Tertiary deformation with marked physiographic expression are the Alpine and Himalayan belts, the island arcs and deep-sea trenches of the Pacific, the great rift valleys of Africa, the rejuvenated Late Paleozoic Appalachians, the Rocky Mountains, and the Pacific Coast Ranges (see the figure in Box 20-2, p. 518).

Although most features of topography can be related to some particular structural element, one should not expect that the crests of anticlines always form ridges and that the troughs of synclines always become valleys. When stratified rocks are deformed, the resistance of the individual beds to weathering and erosion are important factors in controlling landforms, as well as whether the layers are flat-lying, tilted, folded, or faulted. In the block diagram of the Appalachians (Fig. 20-31), one can see all combinations of anticlinal and synclinal hills and valleys.

Figure 20-43
The Jura Mountains, in a view looking northeast over the town of Moutier, Switzerland. The near and distant ridges are anticlines of upper Jurassic limestone. The crest of the anticline can be seen in the water gap in the distant ridge. The town is in a synclinal valley. See previous figure. [Photo by J. Haller, Harvard University.]

MAJOR REGIONAL STRUCTURES

Up to this point, we have discussed the slow up-and-down movements of the crust, the deformation of layers by folding and faulting due to horizontal crustal forces, and the emplacement of plutons. These structural elements, in conjunction with the kinds of rocks involved—in short, the sequence in space and time of magmatic, sedimentary, and deformational episodes—determine the geological character of a region. In this section, we will discuss the broad regional characteristics of continents, using North America as an example.

The geologic fabric of a continent is not random. Similar structures tend to occur in association so as to make up distinctive mountains, fault-block mountains, stable interior platforms, marginal depressions, and so on. Moreover, the spatial relations of these regions seem to have a pattern, as we can see from Figures 20-44 and 20-46, in which the major physiographic and structural divisions of North America are indicated. A transcontinental section showing the major structural divisions schematically is shown in Figure 20-45.

Stable Interior. The extensive, flat, stable interiors of continents, which have been relatively undisturbed since Precambrian time except for gentle warping, are called **cratons.** The cratons typically include large areas of exposed, very old crystalline basement rocks called **shields,** surrounded by sediment-covered platforms. The Canadian Shield is dominated by granitic and high-grade metamorphic rocks, such as gneisses, which, together with highly deformed and metamorphosed sediments and volcanic rocks, imply a series of intense mountain-making episodes in Precambrian time before the stable conditions set in (Fig. 20-47). The shield also includes some very old sediments that were hardly touched by deformation and metamorphism. This primitive block contains one of the oldest and most complex records of geological history, much of it still unknown in detail, and it is famous for major deposits of iron, gold, copper, and nickel. Other shields are found in Fennoscandia, Siberia, central Africa, Brazil, and Australia.

South of the Canadian Shield (see Figs. 20-44, 20-45, and 20-46, regions 12 and 13) is the central stable region, a sediment-covered platform that, in a sense, is a subsurface continuation of the shield, inasmuch as it contains Precambrian basement rocks covered by a veneer of Paleozoic sediments typically less than about 2 kilometers thick. The sediments, which were laid down under quiet conditions, have remained unmetamorphosed and only slightly deformed to this day. There is abundant evidence for up-and-down movements—basins, domes, marine transgressions and regressions, and unconformities. Some examples are the Michigan Basin, mentioned earlier, and the Ozark dome, an ancient structural high that was surrounded and occasionally barely covered by mid-Paleozoic seas. The deformation is mostly in gentle tilts, folds, and faults with small displacements. The Russian platform, which includes much of European Russia, is analogous to the North American platform. Figure 20-7 shows a representative section of the stable interior.

The platform sediments were laid down under a variety of conditions. Nonmarine sediments testify to deposition in large lakes and give evidence of alluvial fans and deltas. Evaporite and limestone deposits indicate landlocked inland seas, occasionally open to the ocean, with surrounding land areas of low relief. Some deposits of sandstone and shale imply the existence of highlands near the margins of the craton, elevated perhaps by plate collisions. Much of the continent's uranium, coal, oil, and gas deposits are contained in the platform sediments. Figures 20-48 and 20-50 show paleogeographic maps for the Cretaceous and Ordovician periods, respectively, in which the distribution of ancient land areas, inland seas, coastal plains, and geosynclines are reconstructed from the sedimentary record.

Orogenic Belts. Referring to Figures 20-44 and 20-46, we see that, surrounding the great stable interior of the continent, there are **orogenic belts,** regions that were deformed by folding and faulting and were subjected to plutonism and metamorphism at various times in the Paleozoic, Mesozoic, and Cenozoic eras.

Orogenic (or folded) mountain belts usually show certain general features that enable us to say something of how they were formed. Figure

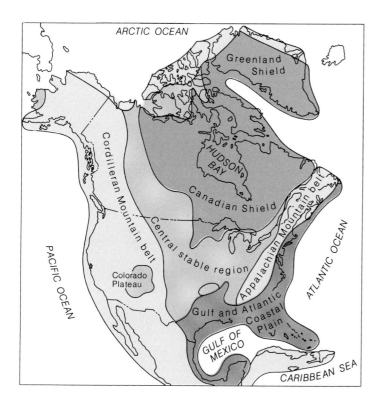

Figure 20-44
Major tectonic features of North America.

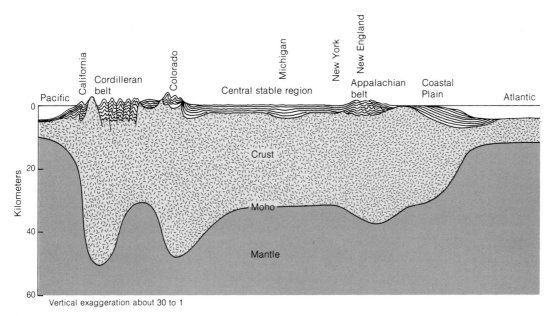

Figure 20-45
Schematic section across the United States, depicting major structural regions and variations in crustal thickness.

PHYSIOGRAPHIC REGIONS AND PROVINCES
OF THE CONTERMINOUS UNITED STATES

Appalachian
Highland
region

Atlantic Coastal Plain region

Central
stable
region

Ozark
region

Great
Plains
region

Cordilleran
Mountain
region

Figure 20-46

Physiographic regions and provinces of the conterminous United States. [After *Natural Regions of the United States and Canada* by Charles B. Hunt. W. H. Freeman and Company. Copyright © 1974.]

1. *Superior Upland.* Hilly area of erosional topography on ancient crystalline rocks.
2. *Continental Shelf.* Shallow, sloping submarine plain of sedimentation.
3. *Coastal Plain.* Low, hilly to nearly flat terraced plains on soft sediments.
4. *Piedmont province.* Gentle to rough, hilly terrain on belted crystalline rocks becoming more hilly toward mountains.
5. *Blue Ridge Province.* Mountains of crystalline rock 3000 to 6000 feet high, mostly rounded summits.
6. *Valley and Ridge province.* Long mountain ridges and valleys eroded into strong and weak folded rock strata.
7. *St. Lawrence Valley.* Rolling lowland with local rock hills.
8. *Appalachian Plateaus.* Generally steep-sided plateaus on sandstone bedrock, 3000 to 5000 feet high on the east side, declining gradually to the west.
9. *New England province.* Rolling, hilly, erosional topography on crystalline rocks in the southeastern part, changing to high mountainous country in the central and northern parts.
10. *Adirondack province.* Subdued mountains on ancient crystalline rocks rising to more than 5000 feet.
11. *Interior Low Plateaus.* Low plateaus on stratified rocks.
12. *Central Lowland.* Mostly low, rolling landscape and nearly level plains. Most of area covered by a veneer of glacial deposits, including ancient lake beds and hilly, lake-dotted moraines.
13. *Great Plains.* Broad river plains and low plateaus on weak, stratified sedimentary rocks. Rises toward Rocky Mountains, reaching altitudes above 6000 feet at some places.
14. *Ozark Plateaus.* High, hilly landscape on stratified rocks.
15. *Ouachita province.* Ridges and valleys eroded on upturned, folded strata.
16. *Southern Rocky Mountains.* Complex mountains rising to more than 14,000 feet.
17. *Wyoming Basin.* Elevated plains and plateaus on sedimentary strata.
18. *Middle Rocky Mountains.* Complex mountains with many intermontane basins and plains.
19. *Northern Rocky Mountains.* Rugged mountains with narrow intermontane basins.
20. *Columbia Plateau.* High rolling plateaus underlain by extensive lava flows; trenched by canyons.
21. *Colorado Plateau.* High plateaus on stratified rocks cut by deep canyons.
22. *Basin and Range province.* Mostly isolated ranges separated by wide desert plains. Many lakes, ancient lake beds, and alluvial fans.
23. *Cascade-Sierra Nevada Mountains.* The Sierra Nevada, in the southern part of the province, are high mountains eroded from crystalline rocks. The Cascades, in the northern part of the province, are high volcanic mountains.
24. *Pacific Border province.* Mostly very young, steep mountains; includes the extensive river plains in California.

The Body of the Earth:
Internal Processes

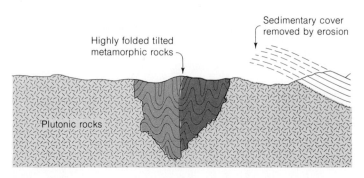

Sedimentary cover
removed by erosion

Highly folded tilted
metamorphic rocks

Plutonic rocks

Figure 20-47
Idealized section in the Canadian Shield. The highly deformed and metamorphosed rocks in this region indicate that an intense orogenic episode took place in Precambrian times, before stable conditions set in.

Figure 20-48
Paleogeographic map of the Cretaceous. Note transgression of the sea between Early and Late Cretaceous as evidenced by extension of shelf deposits. This map shows present position of continents; Figures 19-21 and 19-22 show the relative Cretaceous positions, allowing for continental drift. [From *History of the Earth* (2nd ed.) by Bernhard Kummel. W. H. Freeman and Company. Copyright © 1970.]

20-49 reviews this important concept, which was discussed in Chapter 19 in terms of plate-tectonic theory. These deformed belts occur typically on the margins of stable shields in close connection with geosynclines. A geosyncline is a subsiding linear trough that earlier received a thick succession of layered sediments, sometimes more than 10,000 meters (30,000 feet) thick—which contrasts strongly with the thin sedimentary veneer on the platform. Typically, two geosynclines are involved, an inner miogeosyncline with sandstone and limestone shelf deposits and an outer eugeosyncline with a great thickness of such deep-water sediments as turbidites, shales, and pelagic limestones, and volcanic rock (see Chapter 11). Folded mountain chains almost always seem to be the result of a wave of deformation that begins in the eugeosyncline and later extends to the miogeosyncline. Lateral forces develop that intensely compress the crust in some places by 20 percent or even more, as if it were caught in the jaws of a vise. In response to this squeezing, the overlying sedimentary cover in the eugeosyncline is deformed into great folds and thrust faults, generally trending parallel to the edge of the shield. Intrusions work their way into this compressed

Geosynclines
Shelf areas in Early Cretaceous
Shelf areas in Late Cretaceous
Nonmarine deposits
Land

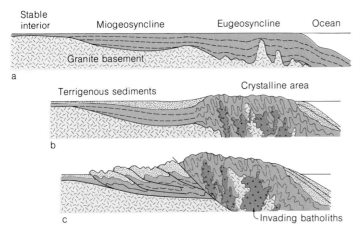

Stable interior   Miogeosyncline   Eugeosyncline   Ocean

Granite basement

a

Terrigenous sediments   Crystalline area

b

c   Invading batholiths

Figure 20-49
General features of an orogenic belt, showing its inferred development from geosyncline to
deformed belt. (a) Geosynclinal stage. (b) After deformation of eugeosyncline and deposition
of terrigenous sediments eroded from the newly formed mountains. (c) After final deformation of miogeosyncline. According to the plate-tectonics hypothesis, stage *a* would follow plate
separation and the opening of an ocean basin, with deposition on the receding margin of a
continent. Stages *b* and *c* would occur with plate collision and the closing of an ocean basin.
[After *The Evolution of North America* by P. B. King. Copyright © 1977 by Princeton University Press. Redrawn with permission of Princeton University Press.]

Box 20-1   Transgressions and Regressions of the Sea—a Plate-Tectonic Explanation

The periodic advances and withdrawals of shallow seas,
evidenced by the marine sediments of the platforms and
shelves, have perturbed geologists for a long time. Do the
transgressions and regressions represent vertical movements
of the platforms and shelves or changes in sea level? Glacial
and interglacial periods can lead to sea-level changes of 100
meters, as was the case in the late Cenozoic Era (Chapter 9).
There is no evidence, however, that a glacial-interglacial
cycle was responsible for the extensive continental flooding
of the late Mesozoic Era. A novel plate-tectonics explanation of sea-level changes has recently been proposed by
J. D. Hays and W. C. Pitman III. We have seen in the
preceding chapter that the new lithosphere that forms at a
mid-ocean spreading ridge is initially hot and elevated. As
it spreads from the ridge axis, the lithosphere cools and
contracts, and the sea floor subsides. At times when sea floor
spreading is rapid, the ocean ridge systems would be
younger, hotter, and therefore substantially increased in
volume, as the figure shows. Water would be displaced from
the oceans, spilling onto the continents. When spreading
slows down, the ocean-ridge systems would be cooler on

the average and occupy less volume, and the seas would
retreat from the continents back to the more capacious
ocean basins. Support for this novel idea comes from the
late Cretaceous transgression (Fig. 20-8), which seems to
correlate with an episode of rapid spreading between 110
and 85 million years ago. Similarly, the subsequent regression correlates with a reduction in spreading rates. Alternatively, changes in the total length of actively spreading
ocean ridges could be the agent of transgressions and regressions of the sea.

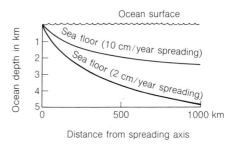

Ocean surface

Sea floor (10 cm/year spreading)

Sea floor (2 cm/year spreading)

Ocean depth in km

0   500   1000 km

Distance from spreading axis

and contorted belt. New mountains are thrown up, reversing submarine slopes, so that erosion leads to episodes of rapid deposition of terrigenous sediments toward the continent on one side, both in arms of the sea and on land, as well as toward deeper water on the other side, as Figure 20-49 shows.

In a final stage, the miogeosyncline is deformed. The deforming forces are typically directed from the ocean basins toward the interior shield. This can be seen in the frequent transition from gentle folds adjacent to the shield to severe folding and thrusting and increasing metamorphism and magmatism with increasing distance away from the shield. Also, the deformed belts are asymmetrical in other ways— the folds lean or are overturned toward the shield, and the thrust sheets have been pushed in the same direction.

Batholiths form the cores of many continental mountain ranges, which implies that they have some connection with the mountain-making process. For example, the great mountain ranges that extend for thousands of kilometers along the western margins of the North American and South American plates have cores of contiguous batholiths. Huge areas of exposed Precambrian terrain in the now stable areas within continents are made up of successions of batholiths, and many of these seem to be roots of mountains that have long since been eroded. In Chapter 16, we discussed the idea that the formation of some batholiths was connected with the subduction process at the margin of colliding plates. It was hypothesized that reheating and melting of the descending plate could provide rising, hot fluids as raw materials for batholith formation along the margins of the overriding plates (see Fig. 19-13).

Very often, following the culmination of major folding and after erosion wears the mountains down, the belt is rejuvenated by later upwarping, and the old structures still remaining are exposed. Rejuvenated fold belts are exemplified by the Alps, the Urals, and the Appalachians.

All of these features are well developed in the Appalachian belt, which bounds the stable interior on the east in a zone running northeast from Alabama to Newfoundland. This classical region, which served as the model for Figure 20-49, was discussed in terms of plate tectonics in Chapter 19. In the block diagram of the Appalachians of Figure 20-31, the remains of the deformed eugeosynclinal belt are depicted as the "older Appalachians." The folded miogeosyncline now shows as the Ridge and Valley belt in the "newer Appalachians."

Bounding the central stable region of North America on the south is a belt of folds and thrust faults not unlike the inner zone of the Appalachians. Its surface expression can be seen in the Ouachita Mountains of Arkansas and eastern Oklahoma, and the Marathon Mountains of western Texas. These mountains seem to be a continuation of the Appalachian belt, which curves west through Alabama, Mississippi, and Arkansas and then southwest to the Big Bend region of Texas.

On the west, the central stable region is bounded by a complex of orogenic zones of several types (refer to Fig. 20-46). This is the region of the North American Cordillera, a mountain belt containing some of the highest peaks on the continent. Across its middle section between San Francisco and Denver, the Cordilleran system is about 1600 kilometers (1000 miles) wide and includes several contrasting physiographic provinces: Region 24 of Figure 20-45, the Coast Ranges along the Pacific Ocean; the Great Valley of California; Region 23, the lofty Sierra Nevada; Region 22, the Basin and Range province (a region of faulted and tilted blocks showing as numerous narrow mountain ranges and valleys extending from the California–Nevada border to western Utah); Region 21, the high table land of the Colorado Plateau; Region 16, the rugged Rocky Mountains, which end abruptly at the edge of the Great Plains on the stable interior (Region 13).

The Cordilleran system is topographically higher and more extensive than the Appalachians because its main orogeny was more recent, having occurred in the last half of Mesozoic and early Tertiary time. However, the form and height of the Cordillera we see today are not due to this major episode of folding, faulting, plutonism, and metamorphism. Rather, they are manifestations of more recent events that took place in Tertiary and Quaternary time and rejuvenated the mountains. At that time, for example, the Colorado Plateau and the Central and Southern Rockies attained much of their present height as a result of a broad regional uplift. Stream erosion was accelerated, the mountain topography sharpened, and the canyons deepened. Block faulting, which broke the crust into mountains and valleys in the Basin and Range province and tilted the Sierra Nevada block, occurred in Tertiary and Quaternary time. At that time, too, volcanism spread sheets of ignimbrite widely over the southern parts of the

| Miogeosynclinal seas – limy, sandy bottoms | Eugeosynclinal seas – muds and volcanic rocks |

Figure 20-50
Geography of North America in early Ordovician time, about 475 million years ago, reconstructed from the evidence of today's rocks. Off the coasts are the miogeosynclinal and eugeosynclinal seas. [After "The Origin of Continents" by M. Kay. Copyright © 1955 by Scientific American, Inc. All rights reserved.]

Basin and Range province and covered large parts of the Pacific Northwest with lava. This culminating stage of uplift, block faulting, and volcanism served as a model for Figure 20-1. The geologist knows how to read through the confusion of these recent events and reconstruct the orogenic history of the region. The entire story of the Cordillera is a complicated one, and we tell it here in highly simplified form. It is a story that begins with geosynclines.

From the nature and distribution of rocks, geologists can reconstruct the distribution of lands and seas of the past. A map of North America as it was in the Ordovician period, some 475 million years ago, is shown in Figure 20-50. The main belt of the Cordillera existed at this time as two undersea troughs, trending in a north–south direction and separated in places by islands. These geosynclines received voluminous deposits of Paleozoic and earlier Mesozoic

rocks—primarily a marine section of volcanics, graywackes, and cherts in the outermost western eugeosynclinal belt, and a limestone, sandstone, and shale accumulation in the inner eastern miogeosynclinal belt. A restored section of these Ordovician geosynclines, one with all the effects of subsequent geological events removed (so that it looks as it did in Ordovician time), is shown in Figure 20-51.

Deformation accompanied by metamorphism and plutonism took place at various times in the Paleozoic and Mesozoic along much of the length of the eugeosyncline, but the climactic episode of deformation that ended geosynclinal conditions and refashioned much of the region into a land area began early in the Jurassic and extended well into Cretaceous time (Fig. 20-52). Intense folding and thrusting, followed by batholithic intrusions, deformed and uplifted this outer belt. These batholiths, and the de-

Figure 20-51
Restored section of Ordovician rocks from central Nevada to central Colorado, with subsiding geosynclinal belts in the west and stable interior to the east. [After *Stratigraphy and Life History*, edited by M. Kay and E. H. Colbert. Copyright © 1965 John Wiley & Sons.]

Figure 20-52
Structural history of north-central Nevada, illustrated diagrammatically. (a) Deposition of eugeosynclinal and miogeosynclinal formations during early to middle Paleozoic time. (b) Eastward thrusting of eugeosynclinal over miogeosynclinal deposits during late Mississippian or early Pennsylvanian time. (c) Renewed miogeosynclinal deposition over thrust sheets during Pennsylvanian and Permian time. (d) Renewal of eastward thrusting during mid-Mesozoic time. [After *The Evolution of North America* by P. B. King. Copyright © 1977 by Princeton University Press. Redrawn with permission of Princeton University Press.]

formed and metamorphosed sediments they intruded, now form large parts of the Klamath Mountains of southwestern Oregon and northern California and the Sierra Nevada of eastern California.

As in the Appalachians, the orogeny reached its climax earlier in the outermost, seaward belt. Thus the deformation of the Cordillera progressed in a complex wave to the east. It culminated in late Cretaceous and early Tertiary time, as the miogeosyncline and the shelf deposits along the adjacent margin of the stable continental platform further to the east were deformed by an episode of intense faulting and thrusting. This phase of the orogeny deformed the geosynclinal deposits of the miogeosyncline from Central Nevada eastward to the edge of the continental platform area in Wyoming, central Colorado, and New Mexico, along what is now the eastern edge of the Rocky Mountains. Here, the deformation warped the relatively thin sediments of the continental platform into high, broad anticlines that have since been eroded to expose the basement granitic rocks. The Precambrian Pike's Peak granite of the Colorado Front Range is one of these. The deformations of the geosynclines and the intrusions of batholiths accompanying this great orogeny are preserved in the record of the rocks still remaining,

as in Figure 20-41, a section across the Cordillera near the Canadian border.

Well after the compression of the two great troughs, and mostly in late Tertiary time, the spectacular episode of **block faulting,** mentioned earlier, occurred in a region extending southeast from southern Oregon to Mexico and including Nevada, western Utah, and parts of eastern California, Arizona, New Mexico and western Texas. This latest structural imprinting, superposed on the earlier-deformed geosynclinal rocks, is responsible for the present-day features of the Basin and Range province. Thousands of high-angle faults sliced the crust into innumerable upheaved and downdropped blocks, forming hundreds of discontinuous, narrow mountain ranges and intervening, alluvium-filled basins separated by normal faults. Successive movements along the faults over millions of years resulted in the large vertical displacements evident today (Figs. 2-13 and 20-53,c). Some of the faults have remained active through the Cenozoic. Unlike folded mountains (Fig. 20-53,b), such as those of the Appalachians, which uplift primarily unmetamorphosed sedimentary geosynclinal deposits, the kinds of rocks and structures exposed in **fault-block mountains** vary greatly. Plutons, lavas and tuffs, metamorphic rocks, and folded geosynclinal deposits can be

Figure 20-53
Mountains vary in form and origin. (a) Mountains formed by volcanic action. (b) Mountains resulting from folded layers of rock. (c) Mountains formed from fault blocks. (d) Mountains originating in vertical uplift. [After U.S. Geological Survey.]

Figure 20-54
Fault-block mountains. The Sierra Nevada (skyline) viewed from the Panamint Mountains, California. Sierra fault scarp in distance. In the middle ground is the Argus range, a late-Quaternary upfaulting of Plio-Pleistocene basalts. A small fault valley, far side up, cuts the alluvium of Panamint Valley, below the center of the picture. [Photo by W. B. Hamilton, U.S. Geological Survey.]

found in the different ranges. The intervening lowlands, once formed, accumulate sediments eroded from the adjacent mountains of upthrown blocks.

The Sierra Nevada fault block consists of granitic batholiths and tightly folded and metamorphosed beds, structures formed during the Late Jurassic–Early Cretaceous orogeny of the western trough previously mentioned. The mountains of this earlier episode were worn down, leaving a deeply eroded remnant after the Mesozoic. About 10 million years ago, in Pliocene time, the block was pushed up on the east and tilted to the west. In 1872, the bounding fault on the east was the site of one of the greatest earthquakes in United States history. Mt. Whitney is one of many peaks of the Sierra Nevada standing more than 4000 meters above sea level.

Some other examples of fault-block mountains are the Wasatch Range of Utah, the Teton Range of Wyoming, and the tilted edges of the rift valleys of east Africa and the Dead Sea–Jordan Valley rift of Israel.

As mentioned earlier, the present mountainous topography of the Rocky Mountains is due to epeirogeny—a broad upwarping that took place in Cenozoic time, after the earlier episodes of folding and deep erosion. The region was raised 1500–2100 meters (5000–7000 feet) in the past 15 or 20 million years, pushing Precambrian basement rocks and their veneer of later-deformed sediments above the level of their surroundings (Fig. 20-53,d). Other examples of **upwarped mountains** are the Adirondacks, the Black Hills, the Labrador Highlands, and the mountains of Fennoscandia.

The Colorado Plateau, the classic showplace

of geology discussed in Chapter 2, seems to be an island of the central stable region, cut off from the interior by the Rocky Mountain orogenic belt. Since the late Precambrian, it has been a stable shelf area—with no thick geosynclinal deposits and no major orogeny, with movements mainly up and down, and with slight deformation in places into broad folds and basins. Volcanics and sedimentary debris from adjacent mountains filled the lowlands of the plateau in Cenozoic times.

The Coast Ranges of California lie between the Great Valley and the Pacific Ocean. These mountains contain rocks younger than those to the east. Great thicknesses of clastic rock, gray-wackes, shales, cherts, and pillow basalts accumulated in a geosyncline that formed seaward of the troughs discussed earlier, mainly after the climax of the orogenies to the east. These deposits show strong deformation in the form of a series of long fault slices trending generally northwestward, some of which were in existence as far back as mid-Tertiary and others of which, such as the famous San Andreas fault, are still active today.

Just how the spectacular Cordilleran orogenies just described can be fitted into the framework of plate tectonics is not entirely clear, and many geologists are now beginning to work on this important question. A plate-tectonics treatment of the development of the Sierra Nevada and the Basin and Range province, involving subduction and magma generation over the past 100 million years, is shown in Figure 20-55.

The Atlantic **coastal plain** and the **continental shelf,** its offshore extension (see Chapters 5 and 19), are features that began developing after the close of the Appalachian orogeny. The outer metamorphic zone of the Appalachians was block-faulted in Triassic time, and a series of long, narrow, down-dropped grabens developed along a belt running from South Carolina to Nova Scotia. These basins trapped a thick series of red, clastic deposits, which were later intruded by basaltic sills and dikes. The Connecticut River valley and the Bay of Fundy are examples (Fig. 20-56).

Following this, in early Cretaceous time, the deeply eroded and beveled coastal plain and continental shelf began to subside and to receive sediments from the continent. Cretaceous and Tertiary sediments up to 5 kilometers thick filled the slowly subsiding trough, and even more material was dumped into the deeper water of the continental rise (Fig. 19-16). This is the living geosyncline referred to in Chapter 19; it is possibly a forerunner of some future orogeny.

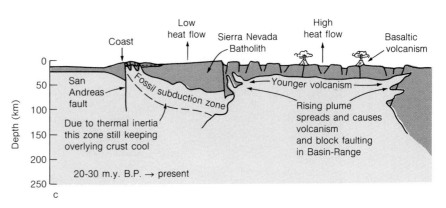

Figure 20-55
Evolution of the Sierra Nevada and Basin and Range province over the past 100 million years. Batholith is emplaced early in the subduction of the plates, about 80–100 million years before present (a). Secondary spreading due to rising plume under Great Basin accounts for volcanism, block faulting, and high heat flow there (c). [After T. L. Henyey and T. C. Lee, *Bull. Geol. Soc. America*, v. 87, pp. 1179–1187, 1976.]

Box 20-2 The Alps

The Alps, another great example of an orogenic belt, are a system of ranges extending for some 1000 kilometers (600 miles) in an arcuate course running from the French-Italian Mediterranean coast through Italy, Switzerland, and Austria. The highest peak is Mont Blanc in southeastern France, with an elevation of 4810 meters (15,781 feet). In the development of the Alps, a whole series of geosynclines separated by anticlinal ridges received Mesozoic deposits. The southern Triassic geosyncline was strongly disturbed by faulting and folding—but without a major magmatic phase—and developed into the Lombardy Alps (see Fig. 20-41). The central geosyncline, a Jurassic one, now the Pennine Alps (see figure), was subjected to extreme folding, with recumbent folds piled up one atop the other; it also experienced magmatic and strong metamorphic episodes. The northern geosyncline, which is now the Helvetides, is of Cretaceous age; it shows no magmatic phase, but strong folding with thrust sheets developing from asymmetric anticlines, the sheets seemingly piled upon one another. In a later stage of compression and uplift, huge masses of sediments were detached from the rising belt and glided down the flanks of ranges, pulled by gravity and intricately folded as they slid into neighboring troughs in which Tertiary sediments were accumulating. The Alps have been termed unique in the grandeur of their scale and the complexity of their folding and overthrusting.

By Pliocene time, these complex structures were eroded to a low terrain. The present grandiose topography of the region reflects rather recent epeirogeny, with most of the uplift and erosion having occurred prior to the Pleistocene glaciation.

Movement of the African block against Europe has been proposed as the source of the Alpine orogeny, which has been developing since early Mesozoic time.

Rugged topography of a young mountain belt. View over Bedretto Valley, Switzerland, to the front of the Pennine Alps on the left. The formations behind the front have glided a long distance from their original place of deposition to a position over the beds in the foreground. [Swissair.]

The Gulf coastal plain and shelf are continuous extensions of the Atlantic ones, though interrupted in a way by Florida. The Mississippi, Rio Grande, and other rivers draining the interior of the continents have delivered sediments to fill a trough some 10–15 kilometers (40,000–50,000 feet) deep running parallel to the coast (Fig. 20-57). The Gulf coastal plain and shelf are a rich reservoir of petroleum and natural gas. The Atlantic shelf is now being actively explored for these and other resources.

DEFORMATIONAL FORCES

Ever since deformation of the crust was first recognized, geologists have speculated about the origin of the forces that shape the Earth's surface features. At one time, orthodox thought had it that the Earth was supposed to be shrinking, and the crust was likened to a wrinkled skin, like that of a dried apple. For a short time, recently, a few proposed that the Earth was expanding, in order to account for the fragmentation of continents and the opening of ocean basins. Convection currents in the mantle have been invoked at various times in the past—to move continents, to erode mountain roots, to downbuckle the crust.

In Chapter 19, a hypothesis was described that was startling in its simplicity: that at least some geosynclinal-orogenic cycles were controlled by plate tectonics. It was proposed that the geosynclinal phase may be a tensional feature that forms when a continent fragments and the trailing edges of the separating plates subside because of the cooling and thermal contraction of the spreading lithosphere. The Triassic graben and the geosyncline now filling off the Atlantic Coast would then be consequences of the opening of the Atlantic Ocean, which began about 180 million years ago. To generalize, the continental shelves surrounding other young oceans, such as the Indian, Antarctic, and Arctic oceans, would be of the Atlantic type, formed with the breaking and separation of pre-existing larger continents in Mesozoic and Cenozoic times (see Figs. 19-18, 19-20). When a continental margin coincides with the leading edge of a plate in collision with another plate, the hypothesis predicts folding, faulting, earthquakes, magmatism, and volcanism. This can be seen in the circum-Pacific and Alpine–Himalayan belts, which are active today. It would follow that the orogenic belts discussed in the previous section were formed when blocks of continental crust

0   10 km

Granitic intrusives
Pre-Triassic

Deformed and
metamorphosed sediments
Pre-Triassic

Triassic sandstones
and shales with
interbedded basaltic
sills, surface flows,
dikes

Figure 20-56
Diagrammatic section of Triassic basins of Connecticut. Nonmarine sediments were trapped in basins formed by tilted fault blocks. Basaltic flows intruded and covered these deposits.

Figure 20-57
Schematic section across the Gulf of Mexico from Texas to Yucatan, showing inferred thicknesses of Mesozoic and Cenozoic sediments. Maximum thickness near the Texas coast may exceed 10 km. [After *The Evolution of North America* by P. B. King. Copyright © 1977 by Princeton University Press. Redrawn with permission of Princeton University Press.]

collided with other crustal plates and crumpled marginal geosynclines during episodes of closing of the ancient Atlantic and Pacific oceans. The asymmetric structure of an orogenic belt is accounted for by the basic asymmetry of an oceanic plate plunging under an overriding continental plate along the collision boundary (see Figs. 19-17, 19-18).

The force that drives plate tectonics must still be specified. As we mentioned in previous chapters, some form of mantle convection is usually invoked at this early stage in the development of the hypothesis. Upwarping, block faulting, and slow vertical movements of the stable interior are among the elements that have yet to be integrated with the plate-tectonics concept. This integration may have to await the next generation of geologists and geophysicists.

SUMMARY

1. When rocks are subjected to stresses, they deform. Laboratory studies show that rocks vary in strength. Some deform by plastic flow, and some fracture—depending on the kind of rock, the temperature, the surrounding pressure, the magnitude of the stress, and how fast it is applied.

2. Geologic structures in rock formations that result from deformation include folds, domes, basins, joints, and faults. The geologist begins to deduce the deformational history of a region by fixing the ages of the formations using radioactive isotopes or fossils. He then tries to bracket the age of the deformation by finding a younger undeformed formation lying unconformably on an older deformed bed. Sediments that accumulate as a result of deformational movements also provide clues.

3. Forces acting within the crust can deform large regions. In some cases, the regional movements are simple up-and-down displacements (epeirogeny) without much deformation of the rock formations. In other cases, horizontal forces can produce extensive and complex folding and faulting (orogeny).

4. A continent typically is divided into large regions that have had different deformational histories. North America, for example, contains a large central stable region that has been relatively undisturbed since Precambrian time, except for gentle vertical movements. Surrounding the stable interior are orogenic belts—the mountainous Cordillera and Appalachians, which were deformed by folding and faulting and were subjected to plutonism and metamorphism at various times in the Paleozoic, Mesozoic, and Cenozoic eras.

5. A typical orogenic episode is preceded by subsidence of marginal troughs in which sediments then accumulate. These geosynclines are subsequently deformed. Great folds and thrusts are generated, along with metamorphism and intrusion by batholiths. The resulting belt is then uplifted and eroded. A culminating stage of uplift or block faulting again raises the region, which accounts for many of the mountainous features we see today. An explanation of orogeny in plate-tectonic terms would have the deformation phase associated with plate collisions.

EXERCISES

1. Evidence of vertical crustal movements is frequently found in the geologic record. Give some examples of such evidence. Describe the geologic evolution of a region that leads to the formation of mesas, buttes, and tablelands bounded by high cliffs.

2. If the Greenland and Antarctic ice caps were to melt, how much would sea level rise? Assume that the ice caps average about 2 kilometers in thickness; the areas of the Greenland ice cap and the Antarctic ice cap are 2×10^6 square kilometers and 10^7 square kilometers, respectively.

3. Draw a geological cross section that tells the following story. A series of marine sediments were deformed into folds and thrust faults. This was followed by erosion. Volcanic activity ensued, and lava flows covered the eroded surface. A final stage of block faulting broke the crust in numerous places.

4. Anticlines are upfolds and synclines are downfolds. Nevertheless, one often finds synclinal ridges and anticlinal valleys. Explain.

5. Summarize the stages of a typical orogenic episode in a series of sketches. Provide legends for the sketches.

6. Summarize the main features of the major structural regions of a continent other than North America (orogenic belts, shields, platforms, coastal plains, shelves).

7. If a new mid-ocean ridge developed, with a spreading rate of 2 centimeters/year and a length of 10,000 square kilometers, how much would sea level rise? Assume that the cross section of the new ridge is the 2 centimeter/year profile shown in Box 20-1. Take the area of the world oceans as 350×10^6 square kilometers. If the spreading rate were faster, would the sea-level change be larger or smaller?

BIBLIOGRAPHY

Billings, M. P., *Structural Geology*. Englewood Cliffs, New Jersey: Prentice-Hall, Inc., 1973.

Dott, R. H., Jr., and R. L. Batten, *Evolution of the Earth*. New York: McGraw-Hill Book Co., 1976.

Hills, E. S., *Elements of Structural Geology*. New York: John Wiley & Sons, 1963.

King, P. B., *The Evolution of North America*. Princeton Univ. Press, 1959.

Wilson, J. Tuzo (compiler), *Continents Adrift—Readings from Scientific American*. San Francisco: W. H. Freeman and Company, 1970.

21

THE PLANETS:
A SUMMARY OF CURRENT KNOWLEDGE

The planets fall into two groups—the gaseous, giant, outer planets, which have retained their Sun-like composition, and the small, stony, Earth-like, inner planets. Space exploration has opened up Earth's neighbors—the Moon, Mars, and Venus—for geological study, and they show surprising diversity. The Moon was geologically active in its early history, but it has been dead for three billion years. Mars, like Earth, is geologically youthful, and shows evidence of recent volcanism, of tectonism, and surprisingly, of erosion by water and wind, despite the absence of liquid water and the presence of only a very thin atmosphere. Venus, Earth's twin in many respects, is blanketed by a thick, heavy atmosphere of CO_2, which causes oven-hot temperatures to occur at the surface. Only when we know why the planets followed different evolutionary paths will we understand Earth's workings and environment and why life could originate here.

Human interest in the planets dates back to prehistoric times, when the ancients noticed that a few of the brightest stars seemed to drift across the sky, not following the pattern of daily and annual motion of the fixed stars. It was the Greeks who called them *planetai,* or wanderers, and first mapped their paths, and it was the Romans who named them after their gods: Mercury, Venus, Mars, Jupiter, and Saturn.

The invention of the telescope—first used to explore the skies by Galileo in 1609—opened the possibility for describing distinctive planetary features. Viewed through the telescope, the planets appeared to be discs, rather than points of light like the stars. They had individual features—Saturn with its rings; Jupiter with its alternating bands of yellow, blue, and brown clouds and its coterie of moons; Mars with its seasonally changing ice caps and its supposed canals; and, of course, our cratered Moon with its highlands and "seas." The asteroid belt and the outermost planets Uranus, Neptune, and, finally, Pluto were discovered in later centuries by astronomers searching the skies with ever more powerful telescopes. As early as the nine-

teenth century, some geologists turned their attention to the Moon, seeking to explain its surface features in terms of Earth experience.

After World War II, new ideas of the origin of our solar system, and of the origin of the Moon in particular, started a revival of research in solar-system astronomy.

Space exploration since the first successful satellite in 1957 has quickened interest in the planets. Recent years have seen the birth of a new science, **planetology,** the comparative study of Earth and the other planets. Manned exploration of the Moon, automated and instrument-laden planetary satellites and probes, radar and radio telescopes exploring with radio waves rather than with light, optical telescopes fitted with electronic devices to sense faint infrared and other invisible radiation in addition to light—these are the powerful new methods of this infant science.

In this chapter, we will review some of the recent discoveries of planetology. Perhaps the most intriguing aspect of the study of other planets is that we may one day arrive at a general theory of planetology that will account for both the origin of our solar system and the evolution of the individual planets with their differing features. Only in this way will we really come to understand our own Earth, its workings, its environment, and the reasons why life could originate here.

The framework upon which planetary scientists currently hang their hypotheses of planetary formation assumes the existence of a primitive solar nebula that condensed into planetary materials, followed by accretion into planets. The planetary objects subsequently evolved under a variety of processes—bombardment by meteorites, igneous differentiation and formation of cores, crusts, and atmospheres, each planet following its unique course depending on its initial size, how fast it accreted (which determined its initial temperature), its composition, and distance from the Sun.

SOME VITAL STATISTICS OF PLANETS

Our solar system is made up of the Sun, 9 planets, 32 satellites, and countless asteroids and comets inhabiting a region some eight billion miles across, yet this is a minuscule domain by cosmic standards. To bring planetary sizes and distances into perspective, one might think of the Sun as a baseball. A grain of sand about 30 feet away, then, would represent Earth; Jupiter would be a pea 150 feet away; Pluto, the outermost planet, would be another sand grain about 1200 feet distant; and the nearest star would be another baseball 1500 miles away. The layout of the planets, held in elliptical, approximately regularly spaced orbits by the sun's gravitational attraction, is shown in Figure 1-3. Except for Pluto and Mercury, the planetary courses around the Sun lie approximately in the **ecliptic,** which is the name for Earth's orbital plane. Mercury's orbit is tilted 7°, and Pluto's is tilted an anomalous 17° from the ecliptic, as the figure shows. It has recently been discovered that Pluto's orbit comes quite close to Neptune at times, and that it actualy lies inside Neptune's orbit over a portion of its path. This new result suggests that Pluto may be an escaped satellite of Neptune. The asteroid belt fills a conspicuous gap between Mars and Jupiter; it contains perhaps 100,000 small bodies in orbit around the Sun, an estimate obtained by viewing this region through large telescopes.

Table 21-1 lists the vital statistics of each planet—its dimensions, its mass and density, the lengths of its day and year, the pull of its gravity, and so on. "Vital" is an appropriate word: in this age of space exploration, planetary masses, dimensions, and positions are essential elements in planning the navigation of spacecraft. Planetary diameters are measured using telescopic observations or radar. To determine a planet's mass, one must see how its gravitational attraction affects the motion of celestial bodies that pass nearby, such as other planets, satellites, comets, asteroids, and, nowadays, spacecraft. A planet's density, which is simply its mass divided by its volume, is a key factor in determining its composition, because the elements pres-

Table 21-1
Vital statistics of the planets.

Planet	Diameter (km)	Mass (Earth = 1)	Density (Water = 1)	Gravity (Earth = 1)	Number of satellites	Time for one rotation on axis (Earth hours or days)	Time for one revolution around Sun (Earth years)	Distance from Sun (10^6 km)	Distance from Sun (10^6 mi)	Composition of atmosphere
Terrestrial planets										
Mercury	4,835	0.055	5.69	0.38	0	59 days	0.241	57.7	36.8	none
Venus	12,194	0.815	5.16	0.89	0	243 days	0.616	107	66.9	CO_2
Earth	12,756	1.00	5.52	1.00	1	1.00 days	1.00	149	92.6	N_2, O_2
Mars	6,760	0.108	3.89	0.38	2	1.03 days	1.88	226	141	CO_2, N_2, Ar
Giant planets										
Jupiter	141,600	318.	1.25	2.64	12	9.83 hr	11.99	775	482	H_2, He
Saturn	120,800	95.1	0.62	1.17	10	10.23 hr	29.5	1421	883	H_2, He
Uranus	47,100	14.5	1.60	1.03	5	23.00 hr	84.0	2861	1777	H_2, He, CH_4
Neptune	44,600	17.0	2.21	1.50	2	22.00 hr	165.	4485	2787	H_2, He, CH_4
Pluto	14,000?	0.8?	4.2?	?	0	6.39 days	248.	5886	3658	?

ent, and the compounds they form, have characteristic densities, and the mean density of the planet depends on the details of the mix.

The planets—except for Pluto, about which little is known—can be separated into two distinct groups: the inner, small, high-density terrestrial planets and the outer, large, low-density giant planets, as Table 21-1 indicates. The terrestrial planets resemble the Earth in density, and it is reasonable to expect a similar composition—namely, a rocky ball mainly of magnesium silicates, admixed with varying amounts of iron. The giant planets are more like the Sun in density and, therefore, in composition; they are light because, like the Sun, they are largely composed of hydrogen and helium, the lightest elements. In this way, the giant planets seem to have preserved much of the composition of the original solar nebula. Saturn is actually less dense than water—which means that it would float, if an ocean big enough could be found.

The Earth-like planets somehow lost the lighter elements or never had them. Perhaps because of their smaller mass and weaker gravitational pull they couldn't hold on to these light gases. More likely, according to the chemical-condensation-sequence model described in Chapter 1, these elements did not condense from their gaseous state because of the high temperatures near the Sun, and were expelled from the inner reaches of the solar system before the terrestrial planets formed.

The Earth, "with its atmosphere and oceans, its complex biosphere, its crust of relatively oxidized, silica-rich, sedimentary, igneous, and metamorphic rocks overlying [a magnesium silicate mantle and a core] of metallic iron, with its ice caps, deserts, forests, tundra, jungles, grasslands, fresh-water lakes, coal beds, oil deposits, volcanoes, fumaroles, factories, automobiles, plants, animals, magnetic field, ionosphere, mid-ocean ridges, convecting mantle, . . . is a system of stunning complexity." This quotation, essentially a one-paragraph summary of much in this book, is from a popular article by geochemist John S. Lewis. It is given here in order to set the scene for the discussion of the other, vastly different planets. It is essential to remember Earth's history when we come to consider her neighbors in the solar system.

THE MOON

Earth's satellite is exceptional, in that it is so large compared to its parent planet. For this reason, it is often regarded as a planet—a part-

ner to the Earth—rather than a mere satellite. The Moon is the best-known planet next to Earth, thanks to its proximity and the programs of manned and unmanned lunar exploration that have been conducted by the United States and the Soviet Union.

Project Apollo. The signal to proceed with Project Apollo, the American program of manned lunar exploration, was given by President John F. Kennedy. It was basically a politically motivated decision made at a time when the superpowers were competing for world leadership. In those days, it was supposed that a demonstration of superior space technology was also a demonstration of a superior political-economic system. Regardless of their origin as a nonscientific enterprise, the Apollo missions have paid off handsomely in terms of scientific discoveries. One might even say that the explorations of the sea floor and the Moon shared in opening the renaissance of major discoveries and new theories in the Earth sciences.

Lunar exploration provided photography of unprecedented resolution; data from a network of emplaced observatories containing seismographs, magnetometers, and other geophysical tools; and, most important, Moon rocks. Although much (if not all) of this could have been achieved eventually with unmanned, automatic spacecraft, the value of having reasoning, trained human beings collecting samples and emplacing instruments should not be underestimated.

Lunar Provinces. The view of the Moon in Figure 21-1 shows the major provinces of the Moon, together with locations of the landing sites of the exploratory missions. This side always faces the Earth because, for some not fully understood reason, the Moon rotates only once on its axis for each revolution around the Earth. Although the far side of the Moon has been photographed from lunar-orbiting spacecraft (Fig. 21-2), current technology prevents us from landing there. The lighter-colored, highly cratered highlands stand out from the large, dark basins, first called maria (singular: mare), or seas, by Galileo because they resembled oceans in the blurred view through his rudimentary telescope.

Surface Processes on the Moon. The Moon's gravity is only one-sixth that of Earth. It lacks the gravitational pull to retain an atmosphere as Earth does, and it lacks water. For these reasons, and also because it is tectonically almost

The Apollo 17 mission included Dr. Harrison Schmitt, a petrologist trained at Caltech and Harvard. He was the first geologist to walk on the lunar surface. Earlier astronauts, who were flyers by profession, were nevertheless well versed in the rudiments of geology. Schmitt was elected to the U. S. Senate from New Mexico in 1976.

LUNAR LANDING SITES

Apollo 11: Sea of Tranquility   Apollo 12: Ocean of Storms   Apollo 14: Fra Mauro   Apollo 15: Hadley–Apennine   Apollo 16: Descartes   Apollo 17: Taurus–Littrow

Figure 21-1
View of the lunar surface, identifying major features and showing Apollo landing sites. [U.S. Air Force Aeronautical and Chart Information Center and National Aeronautics and Space Administration.]

Figure 21-2
Apollo 8 view of the Moon over east limb. Right half of photograph covers regions not visible from Earth. Bright rayed crater at top right is Bruno. For comparison with previous figure, irregular mare in left center is Fecunditatis. Mare Crisium is above it. [From National Aeronautics and Space Administration.]

Imagine the excitement among geologists when the first lunar rocks picked up by the Apollo astronauts proved to be 3.6 billion years old! This was no lucky find. All Moon rocks examined so far were formed or recrystallized 3.1–4.6 billion years ago. (These dates are derived from radiometric dating in Earth laboratories.) Consistent with these indications that the Moon has been geologically inactive for more than 3 billion years, the seismographs installed by the astronauts have indicated that the rate of seismic energy release by moonquakes is one million times less than that of earthquakes. This negligible amount of moonquake activity clinches the idea that the Moon is now tectonically almost dead. We might also have reached the same conclusion from photographs that show none of the trademarks of plate tectonics—no globe-circling volcanic ridge-rifts, no transform faults, no extensive trenches with adjacent mountains—in short, no moving plates. Not only is the Moon "dead," but when it was "alive" it had a different life style.

In the absence of erosion and orogeny as we know them on Earth, what does shape the lunar surface? What accounts for the principal morphological feature on the lunar surface—the nearly circular craters ranging in diameter from inches to hundreds of miles? The craters themselves, rimmed with rubble, often with rays (which are narrow, bright streaks of debris radiating outward), provide the clues (Figs. 21-2, 21-5). The Moon's surface, unprotected by a blanket of air, has been riddled by meteorite impacts for the past 4.6 billion years. Coming in with velocities of as much as 150,000 kilometers per hour (roughly 100,000 miles per hour), these celestial projectiles punch into the crust, vaporize, and explode when the energy of motion is almost instantaneously converted into heat. The blast excavates a crater, throwing out debris locally in the form of a surrounding rim, but also hurling ejecta to distant points. To give some idea of what an impact can do, a meteorite 3 meters (roughly 10 feet) in diameter and weighing 50 tons explodes with the energy of 10 kilotons of TNT and blasts out a crater 150 meters (roughly 500 feet) in diameter. A large meteorite weighing 10^6 tons explodes with as much energy as is released each year by earthquakes.

If the incoming body is big enough, a mare hundreds of miles in diameter can be excavated (see Figs. 21-1 and 21-2). In the smaller gravity field of the Moon, unimpeded by air, huge amounts of ejecta can be hurled for hundreds of

Figure 21-3
Schematic illustration of Alsep, the automatic observatory left behind on the surface of the Moon by the Apollo astronauts, showing several of the experiments deployed on the lunar surface. Data from seismographs, magnetometers, heat flow probes, gas detectors will be transmitted back to Earth for many years. In the active seismic experiment, a mortar fires an explosive charge on signal from Earth to generate seismic waves in the lunar crust, which are picked up by the geophones. [From National Aeronautics and Space Administration.]

dead, the surface features of the Moon are profoundly different from those of the Earth. As we have seen in earlier chapters, Earth's surface is molded by two opposing natural forces: air and water erode rocks and remove the debris to the oceans, whereas plate motions, along with associated mountain-making and volcanism, continually renew the surface. As a result of this ongoing process of creation and destruction, most of the Earth's surface features are fresh ones—younger than 200 million years, that is, formed in the last few percent of geological time. To be sure, many older relics, both rocks and structures, that date back 3–3.7 billion years can be found on continents, but these rocks cover only a small fraction of the Earth's surface.

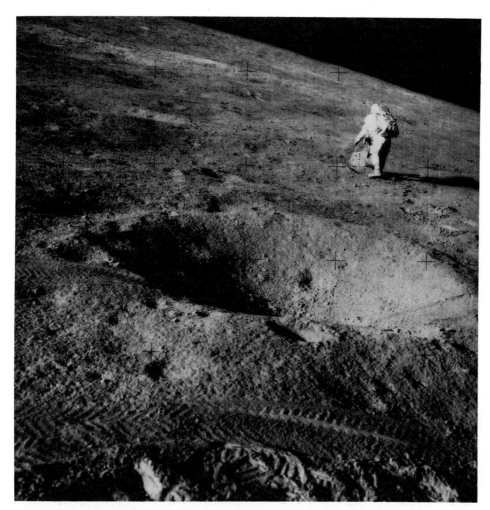

Figure 21-4
Apollo 15 photograph of cratered, undulating surface showing fine-grained lunar
"soil" or regolith with widely scattered pebbles and cobbles. Large block in front
of astronaut was ejected from a distant impact. Tire marks from lunar rover in
foreground. [From National Aeronautics and Space Administration.]

kilometers, scarring the surface and littering it with soil and blocks of rock. Some of the ejecta fall back to the surface with high enough speed to punch out secondary craters at some distance from the primary crater.

A giant collision can throw up immense piles of rock—enough to form mountains. The most famous example is the great collision site known as Mare Imbrium, the largest circular basin on the moon. The massive Apennine Mountains, which tower some 5 kilometers (3 miles) above the floor of the basin on its southeast margin, were formed in this cataclysmic event, as were piles of rubble and numerous grooves, ridges, and secondary craters radiating from the colli-sion area. This region was the landing site for the Apollo 15 mission (landing site 15 in Fig. 21-1). The astronauts drove to the front of the Apennines in their lunar rover, collecting rocks and photographing the terrain.

Craters from meteorite impacts are known on Earth. They are rare because the atmosphere slows all but the largest bodies and literally burns up (oxidizes) the smaller ones, almost all of them completely by the time they hit Earth. The bright light of shooting stars is produced by that burning. The evidence of impact of the larger objects that manage to get through is obliterated as a result of erosion by wind and water and burial by sediments. Craters and old

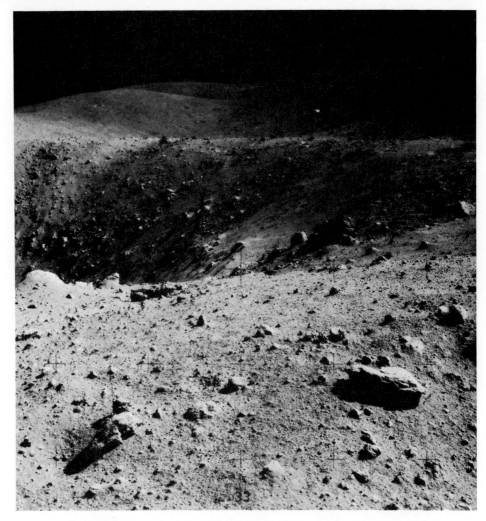

Figure 21-5
Apollo 16 mission to Descartes. The photograph was taken from the rim of a crater about 1 km in diameter and 230 m deep. The rim, 50 m high, is a flap of lunar formations blown out and overturned by the impact explosion. A meteorite about the size of a football field would have produced a crater this big. The rocks in the foreground are breccias. [From U.S. Geological Survey and National Aeronautics and Space Administration.]

buried structures believed to have been caused by impacts are called **astroblemes,** which means "star wounds" (Fig. 21-6). It has been estimated that one crater with a diameter greater than one kilometer is punched out by a meteorite every 50,000 years on Earth.

Craters on the Moon can be preserved for fantastically long times. The only processes working to erase them are a sort of sand blasting by small, high-velocity meteorite grains, called **micrometeorites,** blanketing by ejecta from other impacts, a direct hit by another meteorite,

or burial by a lava flow. The contrast between a young and old crater side by side in Figure 21-7 shows that the eroding effect of micrometeorites tends to round off the sharp edges and to fill the bottoms of craters. The pitted surface of a Moon rock exposed to micrometeorite bombardment can be seen in Figure 21-8. The process of wearing down is extremely slow—perhaps 10–20 feet of abrasion in the 4.6 billion years of the lifetime of the Moon. A crater is more likely to be obliterated by burial under ejecta from nearby craters than by micrometeorite

Figure 21-6
Meteor Crater near Flagstaff, Arizona, is about the same size as the lunar crater in Figure 21-5. It was caused by the impact of a large meteorite in prehistoric times. Thousands of fragments of the meteorite have been found nearby. [From U.S. Geological Survey.]

Figure 21-7
Lunar landscape, showing contrast between old and young craters. Old craters have rounded rims and filled bottoms as result of erosion by micrometeorite bombardment. Young craters have sharp edges and bright rays emanating from them. [U.S. Geological Survey and National Aeronautics and Space Administration.]

Figure 21-8
"Great Scott" rock, a vesicular mare basalt, collected during the Apollo 15 mission.
Note big, glass-lined "zap" pit caused by micrometeorite impact just left of center.
[From U.S. Geological Survey and National Aeronautics and Space Administration.]

erosion. The larger the crater, however, the better its chances of survival. Craters larger than a few hundred feet might survive for billions of years.

The Regolith. The Moon has a soil of sorts that is called the **regolith.** It is not a soil in the conventional sense of the word, as is the Earth's soil (see Chapter 4), which results from the breakdown of rocks mainly by the chemical and mechanical actions of water. The lunar regolith is simply the accumulated fragmental debris of billions of years of exposure to bombardment by meteorites, cosmic rays, and particles blown out from the Sun (the solar wind), as depicted in Figure 21-9. Its thickness generally ranges from a few meters to a few tens of meters. It accumulates at the remarkably slow rate of about one millimeter per million years. Contrast this with the sediments of the deep sea of the Earth, which are laid down 5000 times more rapidly. Geochemists have also found a way to determine that the rate of turnover or "gardening" of the

lunar soil due to the continuous bombardment is about 1 meter in 0.5 billion years. The lunar soil is particularly important because it is a mixture of materials thrown in from many different areas. One sample of soil, therefore, helps us to figure out what the rocks are like in other places on the Moon from which samples might not otherwise be collected. Figures 21-4 and 21-5 show what the surface of the regolith looks like. Close inspection shows that, in addition to rock fragments, glass spherules are an important component. Presumably, these are formed at the sites of impacts, where melting is induced by the shock and the liquid rock is ejected as a fine spray. The droplets form glassy spherules if they freeze in flight, or they splatter rocks with a glassy crust if they remain molten until they land.

Lunar Stratigraphy. Mapping geology from photographs is called photogeology. Lunar geologists have used photographs to get relative

Figure 21-9
The original crust of the moon, still present under the highlands, was broken up by large impacts, following which the basins were flooded by basaltic lava. Erosion of the surface, extremely slow compared to the rate of the process on Earth, removes only about a millimeter in a million years. Bombardment by micrometeorites is believed to be the main cause. Larger meteorite impacts occur rarely, but they create craters and scatter ejecta over large distances. The regolith, up to a few tens of meters thick, is the accumulated, fragmental debris of billions of years of exposure to meteorite bombardment, cosmic rays, and the solar wind. [After "The Carbon Chemistry of the Moon" by G. Eglinton, J. R. Maxwell, and C. T. Pillinger. Copyright © 1973 by Scientific American, Inc. All rights reserved.]

ages of different regions of the Moon by counting the density of craters. The oldest terrain should show the highest crater count simply because it has been bombarded for the longest time. The densely cratered highlands, for example, in the south-central portion of the Moon (Fig. 21-1), are the oldest regions. In many places, the highlands are covered by ejecta blankets thrown out from the circular maria. This cover is punctured by more craters than the lava surface of the maria. Hence the impact that produced the ejecta blanket must be older than the volcanism that filled the maria with lava. The reader may wish to establish relative ages of the different features in Figure 21-2 by using this simple method of crater counting, as well as by looking for other evidence of "freshness," such as craters with sharp-edged features, or bright rays that have not yet disappeared due to erosion or other aging effects.

Stratigraphic mapping on the Moon—that is, working out the chronological relations of the many lunar surface features—is quite different from similar procedures on the Earth. There are no fossils, and the events that define periods are quite different in nature and time scale from those on the Earth. Just as on Earth, however, the law of superposition—which places the youngest materials at the top of a stack of layers—is used in establishing relative ages of the principal formations: the original crust, lava flows and ejecta blankets of varying ages, and the regolith. Figure 21-10 shows one proposal for defining time periods on the Moon on the basis of crater counting, the law of superposition, and radiometric dating of returned lunar samples.

To be sure, the law of superposition holds on the Moon, but sometimes it must be inverted. Consider the case of material ejected from a

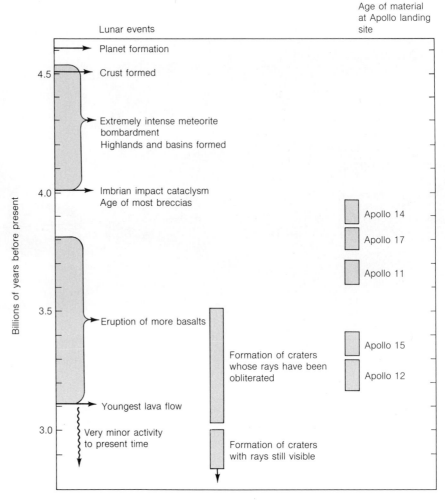

Figure 21-10
Lunar chronology and ages of material at Apollo landing sites.

crater, as in Figure 21-5. The deepest rocks encountered by the projectile become concentrated at the top of the ejecta that forms the rim. The stratigraphy is inverted, as if the formation were a flap laid over on itself. The shallowest ejecta are found on the surface, but farther out on the ejecta blanket. These features have been discovered on Earth in connection with underground nuclear explosions that were shallow enough to "blow out."

An unexpected and major discovery of lunar stratigraphy is the extreme intensity of the meteorite bombardment of the Moon and presum-ably the terrestrial planets in the first 600 million years following their formation. After about 4 billion years ago, the bombardment flux decreased rapidly. It may be that violent collisional events constituted the major process for shaping the surfaces of the young planets, obliterating most of their early history.

The Maria. Controversy raged for years prior to the Apollo program, about the nature of the material in the maria. The lunar basins are not filled with sediments deposited in ancient seas, nor are they filled with dust abraded from the

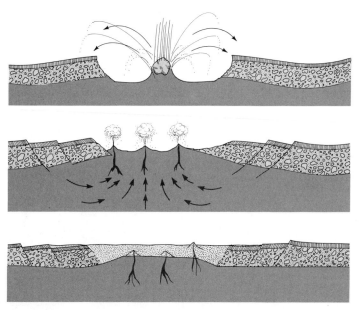

Figure 21-11
Model for the origin of the lunar maria. (a) The impact of a large meteorite excavates a basin, ejecting material to great distances. (b) The high temperatures generated by the impact cause volcanic activity. Alternatively, volcanism may be caused
by fractures that reach partially molten rock beneath the lunar crust. (c) The basin
fills with lava from the interior. [After National Aeronautics and Space Administration.]

highlands, as some had supposed. Analysis of
the returned samples from three maria (Tran-
quilitatis, Fecunditatis, and Procellarum) leaves
no doubt about the answer. They are flooded by
layer upon layer of basaltic lava, not unlike the
basaltic flows of Iceland or the Columbia River
Plateau discussed in Chapter 15. Apparently
when the maria basins were plowed out by the
impact of large meteorites early in the Moon's
history, the partially molten interior was exposed and lava subsequently flowed out to fill
the depressions (Fig. 21-11). Mare Crisium and
Mare Fecunditatis, both good examples of this,
can be seen in the northwestern and western
portions, respectively, of Figure 21-2. The
Apollo 15 astronauts visited Hadley Rille, a
long, narrow channel incised in Mare Imbrium,
running parallel with the Apennine front. The
astronauts could see and photograph ledges in
the canyon wall that were some 60 meters thick.
These are individual lava flows, layers that
flowed one on top of the other in the process of
filling the basin. Hadley Rille is thought by
some to be the result of the collapse of an underground lava tunnel whose roof caved in after
the lava ceased flowing.

**Lunar Rocks—What They Are and What
They Reveal.** Many hundreds of pounds of
rocks have been returned to the Earth from the
Moon. This precious cargo has been disseminated to hundreds of specialists all over the
world. The United States and the Soviet Union
have recently agreed to exchange lunar material
and to cooperate in other ways in lunar exploration. Many investigators were given new laboratories by NASA, with funds to develop analytical equipment of unprecedented precision, to
ensure that all possible information be gleaned
from the lunar samples. In this way, lunar exploration has inspired international cooperation
and spurred innovations that might otherwise
have been delayed.

The Moon's crust turns out to be a relatively
simple assemblage of rocks compared to that of
Earth. The highlands are formed of anorthosite,
an igneous rock consisting predominantly of
calcium-rich plagioclase feldspar. This material
may represent the first melting episode on the
Moon, perhaps dating back 4.6 billion years,
nearly to the beginning of the solar system.
Because anorthosite is rich in aluminum, a light
element, and poor in iron, one of the heaviest

Figure 21-12
Vesicular basalt collected by Apollo 15 astronauts. The holes, or vesicles, were gas bubbles "frozen" into the lava when it solidified. [From National Aeronautics and Space Administration.]

elements, it is relatively light; its crystals remained on top to form a primitive crust. This crust was later broken up by large impacts, following which the basins were flooded by iron-rich basalt.

The lunar basalt began to flow out perhaps 4.1 billion years ago, but the most extensive mare flooding occurred between 3.8 and 3.1 billion years ago. It is startling that the Hawaiian volcano Kilauea is still erupting on Earth today, yet the youngest lava on the Moon in 3 billion years old! For some as yet unexplained reason, internal activity on the Moon mostly ceased at this point, as if the internal heat engine were shut off. The Moon simply stopped evolving (in the sense that its surface features have since changed relatively little) somewhat more than 3 billion years ago, leaving a "half-baked" planet with its ancient record still preserved. Four billion years ago, Earth's crust may have had a similar composition; but Earth continued on its evolutionary path to this very day, producing a complex and rich variety of rocks, an ocean, and an atmosphere, and initiating organic evolution.

(Not a shred of evidence of biological life has been found on the lunar surface.)

In general terms, the Moon's basalt is similar to the commonest volcanic rock on Earth, yet lunar rocks differ in several essential features from their Earth counterparts. Materials that vaporize at relatively low temperatures—such as water, carbon, nitrogen, sulfur, chlorine, mercury, zinc, and lead—are depleted in Moon rocks. On the other hand, Moon rocks are enriched in certain refractory elements—that is, elements that are not easily melted, such as aluminum, titanium, and zirconium. The extreme dryness of the Moon rocks is striking. Even the driest Earth rocks show the presence of some water bound in various physical and chemical ways, but water is absent from Moon rock. Astronauts can forget about trying to find water on the Moon to sustain supposed future settlements.

The big question is, at what stage did the Moon undergo this gain and loss of materials? Some specialists believe that these depletions and enrichments existed in the original matter

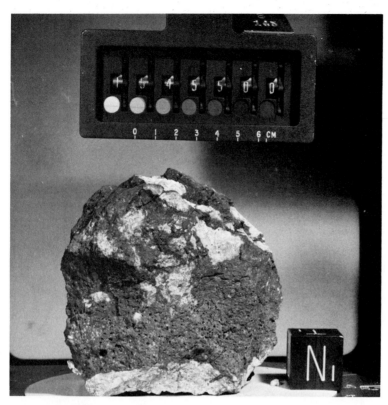

Figure 21-13
Lunar sample collected by the Apollo 15 astronauts near the Apennine Mountain front. The rock is a blocky, angular breccia. [From National Aeronautics and Space Administration.]

that formed the Moon and that the Moon started off as chemically different from the Earth. The Moon may have formed in another part of the solar system in a high-temperature environment, which resulted in the loss of the volatile elements; subsequently, it was "captured" by the Earth. Alternatively, the Moon may have formed near the Earth, but, because of its smaller size, may simply have captured different chemical elements than the Earth did. Other hypotheses exist—for example, that the Moon formed by spinning off from the outer layers of Earth soon after it was differentiated. The debate about the Moon's origin will continue for some time.

A photograph of the Moon taken a few hundred million years ago would show essentially the same features as a modern picture—Figure 21-2, for example. Astronaut David Scott demonstrated this dramatically on the Apollo 15 mission when he picked up a rock at the foot of the Apennines that, as it turned out, had been lying there unmoved for 400 million years! A picture of the Earth taken 200 million years ago

would show a surface completely different from the one the Earth shows today. The Atlantic would not yet have been formed and the map would be dominated by the supercontinent Pangaea. Incidentally, the youth of the Earth's surface features dispels the old speculation that the Moon was torn out of the Earth, leaving the Pacific Ocean as a scar. The Pacific is a recent feature of this rapidly changing planet, and it couldn't have existed in its present shape or form 4.6 billion years ago.

One additional rock type should be mentioned because, although it has the same name as an Earth rock of similar appearance, it is peculiar to the Moon and extremely abundant there: the **lunar breccia**. Rocks of this type are cohesive agglomerates or clusters of rock fragments and fine regolith, apparently stuck together by the heat and pressure generated at the sites of meteorite impacts (Fig. 21-13). The rocks in the lunar highlands, the oldest regions of the Moon, are predominantly breccias, testifying to the cataclysmic meteorite bombardment early in lunar history.

Magnetized Rocks and Mascons. Two additional discoveries, seemingly contradictory, should be mentioned in our discussion of the Moon. Lunar rocks were found to be magnetized. This remanent magnetization in the returned samples cannot be isolated examples because a magnetometer aboard a satellite launched into lunar orbit by the Apollo 15 astronauts shows that the whole lunar crust has a small residual magnetism. The simplest explanation is that the Moon once had its own planetary magnetic field. If so, it existed at the times of formation of the magnetized rocks—that is, from the earliest moments in lunar history, when the primitive crust formed, to about 3.1 billion years ago, when the youngest mare basalts poured out. From our experience on Earth (Chapter 18), we surmise that planetary magnetic fields are caused by fluid convection in a molten-iron core, and many scientists have concluded that the Moon was hot enough to produce a small, molten-iron core in its early history. Some time after 3.1 billion years ago, the Moon supposedly cooled down enough for the iron to freeze into a solid, and the magnetic field was suppressed. Thus, the magnetism of its rocks may imply that the Moon had a hot interior, at least until about 3 billion years ago.

The word **mascons** is a contraction for mass concentrations. Scientists at the Jet Propulsion Laboratory discovered that spacecraft orbiting the Moon were mysteriously pulled toward the surface when they passed over certain locations. These places with higher gravitational attraction turned out to be the circular maria (Fig. 21-14). Apparently, massive bodies, or mascons, lie in or

Figure 21-14
Gravity-anomaly contours on the moon. Note how the higher gravity values, shown by the concentration of circular contours, are centered on the circular maria—evidence that massive bodies, or mascons, lie in or under these basins. [From National Aeronautics and Space Administration.]

under the circular basins, and they tug gravitationally on a satellite each time it flies over. Aside from the question of what the mascons might be, the most fascinating question is how these heavy objects could survive near the lunar surface without sinking into the interior in the 3-4 billion year period since the basins were formed. Recall that, on Earth, a surface load such as a continental glacier depresses the crust in only a few thousand years, effectively sinking it until it is supported buoyantly (Chapter 18). The large positive gravity anomalies of the mascons show that this has not yet occurred on the Moon, although 3-4 billion years have elapsed. This means that an outer layer of the Moon, perhaps 1000 kilometers thick (see Fig. 21-15), has been strong, rigid, and, therefore, cold for 3-4 billion years, not warm, plastic, and weak, as we might suppose from the evidence of lunar volcanism and magnetized Moon rocks. As to the nature of mascons, some scientists speculate that they are the buried remains of the massive meteorites whose impacts created the basins. Most believe that when the primitive crust was punctured, matter from the interior spurted out—more than enough to fill the excavation—and cooled to form a dense plug of mantle material where light crust had formerly been.

Moonquakes and the Lunar Interior. As we have mentioned, the Moon exhibits less seismic activity than the Earth by a factor of about a trillion, another indication of a geologically "dead" planet. Seismologists were surprised to discover, however, that the tiny and infrequent moonquakes are concentrated around the time when the Moon is closest to the Earth—that is, when the tides of the Moon, pulled by Earth's gravity, are at a maximum. An old theory that tidal stresses can trigger quakes has been difficult to prove on Earth, but apparently works on the Moon. The moonquakes occur at the unusually great depths of 800-1100 kilometers, about halfway to the lunar center, near the boundary between a thick, strong lunar lithosphere and an underlying "soft," partially molten core (Fig. 21-15). Seismologists also tell us that the lunar crust is highly fractured in its outer portions, presumably because of the intense bombardment by meteorites.

What Does It All Mean? It is a difficult task for the authors of a textbook to pull together this wealth of new and often contradictory material on the Moon when the experts themselves have

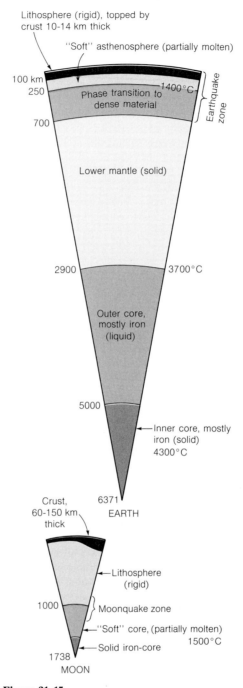

Figure 21-15
Comparison of internal structure of Earth and Moon. Note thick, strong, unbroken lithosphere on Moon in contrast to thin lithosphere on Earth, which breaks into plates moving over the asthenosphere. Moonquakes are tiny and infrequent and occur halfway toward lunar center; earthquakes are a feature of Earth's outer layers, where plate tectonics takes place.

not yet done so to everyone's satisfaction. Perhaps, in time, a concept with the simple elegance and synthesizing power of the concept of plate tectonics on Earth will emerge to unify the lunar data.

Whatever concept does emerge must begin with a Moon that formed 4.6 billion years ago from starting materials that were probably different chemically from those that formed the Earth. The Moon heated up rapidly, perhaps because of fast accretion, and extensive melting occurred very early in lunar history. A primitive crust of anorthosite floated to the surface, and iron probably went down to form a small molten core and start a magnetic field. The first 600 million years was a time of intense bombardment by meteorites; the ancient crust was heavily cratered, as evidenced by the brecciated relics in the highlands. Great impacts excavated mare basins, which were later filled with basalts from the lunar interior, perhaps due to a second episode of partial melting of the outer portions of the Moon. The core solidified and the outer layers cooled rapidly about 3 billion years ago, forming a strong lithosphere about ten times thicker than Earth's lithosphere. What the scientists must come up with is a thermal mechanism whereby the Moon was initially hot enough to undergo igneous differentiation, form crust and core, and then undergo a later stage of large-scale volcanism and fill the mare basins with basalt. They must explain how the Moon could cool fast enough to shut off volcanism abruptly and form a thick, strong lithosphere to support the mascons. The Moon has been essentially dead for 3 billion years. Its surface has been modified somewhat by a reduced amount of meteorite bombardment, but the large-scale ancient features have remained unchanged.

Moon geologists do not have all the answers at this time, but they are working on materials that date back to the early days of the solar system—in a sense, Rosetta stones waiting to be deciphered.

MERCURY

Before the 1974 Mariner 10 flight, Mercury appeared as a fuzzy globe to Earth-based astronomers. The dramatic photographs and data radioed back by the space craft were startling in their indication that the planet has a Moon-like surface and an Earth-like interior (Figure 21-16).

Mercury is the most dense of all the planets, indicating the presence of a large iron core (like that of Earth, only more so) extending outward perhaps three-fourths of its radius. It has a lightweight silicate crust with heavily cratered regions like the lunar highlands and vast smooth areas like the maria. There is a trace of an atmosphere, one-hundred billionth as dense as Earth's and mostly helium. Unexpectedly, it has a weak but definite magnetic field, perhaps a remanent field of an ancient core dynamo that has stopped working.

Since it is the planet closest to the Sun, one would expect its bulk constitution to be the richest in refractory elements, accounting for its large iron core. Like the Moon and presumably the other terrestrial planets, it underwent early chemical differentiation, with formation of crust and core, and received the same intense meteorite bombardment in the first half-billion years of its existence. The fact that the record of this ancient cataclysm is mostly preserved in the present surface implies that Mercury, like the Moon but unlike Earth, has been tectonically quiet for the past 3–4 billion years.

Mercury's surface receives the most intense solar radiation of all planets in our solar system, with temperatures as high as $425°C$ ($800°F$) during the day. A night on Mercury lasts 88 Earth days, giving the surface time to cool down to $-175°C$ ($-280°F$). This temperature range of $600°C$ is the widest in the solar system.

VENUS

Venus is the nearest thing to being Earth's twin—in mass, diameter, density, gravity, and distance from the Sun (see Table 21-1). But here the similarity ends, according to the latest results using radar and automated space probes. From radar observations comes the information that Venus rotates at the extremely slow rate of once in 243 Earth days and the peculiar discovery that its rotation, though opposite to that of Earth, is synchronized with the movements of the Earth in that it presents the same face to us every time it swings by in its orbit.

Venus is completely covered by clouds that mask its surface from the view of Earth-based astronomers, but radar waves bounced off the planet reveal linear mountain chains, structures that appear like large volcanoes and impact craters, and a channel 1500 kilometers long that resembles a rift valley.

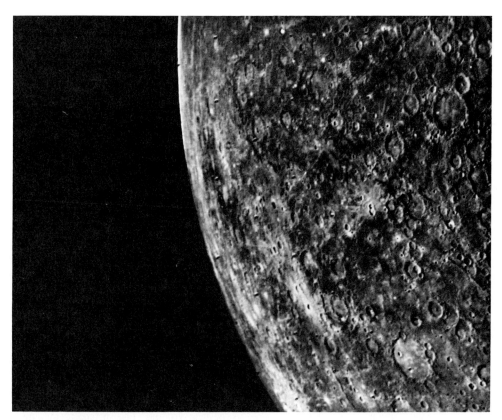

Figure 21-16
Mariner 10 photograph of the southwestern quadrant of Mercury taken from a distance of 200,000 km (120,000 mi) reveals features 5000 times smaller than could be seen by the best Earth-based telescopes. Largest craters seen in this picture are about 100 km (60 mi) in diameter. [From National Aeronautics and Space Administration.]

In 1975 two Soviet spacecraft, Venera 9 and 10, landed on the surface, about 2200 km apart. This was an amazing technological feat in view of the crushing atmospheric pressure (100 times greater than on Earth, nearly 1 ton per square inch) and searing temperature of 475°C (890°F) at the surface. This is hot enough to melt such metals as lead and tin. The spacecraft survived for only an hour but managed to radio back the first photographs of the Venusian landscape. Venera 9 showed a field of angular rocks with sharp edges and flat sides lying on a firm surface. Since the winds in the dense atmosphere and the high temperatures would be efficient erosional agents, the angular rocks were probably formed recently. Venera 10 showed a different scene, more in keeping with the expectation of severe erosion: large, smooth, rounded rocks that appeared like a weathered outcrop of broken granite, lying partially buried in a fine, dark material. X-ray activity measured on the surface also indicates the presence of granitic rock. The radar and photographic data, limited as they are, seem to indicate that, unlike the Moon and Mercury, Venus is a geologically active planet, more like Earth. The Soviet scientists go so far as to state that the presence of newer rocks "testifies to recent catastrophic processes like volcanic eruptions or earthquakes."

Venus differs profoundly from Earth in the nature of its atmosphere. It is covered by a thick blanket of carbon dioxide. More than 95 percent of the Venusian atmosphere is made up of this gas; the Earth's atmosphere, by comparison, is only 0.03 percent carbon dioxide. Water vapor and other gases are present, but in extremely small amounts compared to the great quantitites in the Earth's biosphere. The heavy, poisonous atmosphere, incredibly high temperatures, and clouds of corrosive sulfuric acid droplets would fit a description of hell. Certainly no organic life could exist on the surface.

What makes Venus hot is its insulating blanket of carbon dioxide. Solar energy is trapped by the atmosphere, which warms up as a result. This is entirely analogous to the much milder greenhouse effect on Earth (Chapters 1 and 12).

Venus has no magnetic field—perhaps because it has lacked a fluid core, or perhaps the rotation of a planet is also important in generating a magnetic field and Venus rotates too slowly, or maybe like the Moon, it once had one but lost it.

These profound differences between Venus and Earth pose difficult questions: How could two planets, so similar in many respects, evolve so differently? Could it be that Venus, though Earth's neighbor, was just enough closer to the Sun so that it was too hot for water vapor to condense into oceans and carbon dioxide to be locked up in surface rocks? The absence of life prevented oxygen from becoming an important constituent of the atmosphere. It has been estimated that if Earth were only 10 million kilometers (6 million miles) closer to the Sun, its climate would be similar to that of Venus.

MARS

Mars has been a planet favored by scientific speculators and science-fiction writers. Some have thought that Mars is like Earth, and that it has canals, a seasonally varying cover of vegetation, and even intelligent life. Others have thought it to be a tectonically dead planet like the Moon. These and other speculations have been laid to rest as a result of data radioed to Earth by the Mariner 9 spacecraft, which orbited Mars for 11 months in 1971 and 1972, and the Viking project, which put two spacecraft into Martian orbits and landed two scientific packages on the surface in 1976. Thousands of color photographs were taken from orbit with unprecedented resolution: features a few tens of meters across were clearly visible, in contrast with the 80-kilometer resolving ability of Earth-based telescopes, upon which so many of the early speculations depended. The landers were primarily designed to search for life, but contained high-resolution cameras, seismographs, analytical chemistry equipment, and instruments for meteorological and other experiments.

Mars, the outermost of the terrestrial planets, travels in the next orbit to Earth's, going out from the Sun. Its diameter is a little over half that of the Earth, its mass about one-eighth, and its gravity is about two-fifths as strong. Mars has a density somewhat less than Earth's, but, when allowance is made for its smaller size and reduced internal pressures, its "uncompressed density" turns out to be the same as the Earth would have. This means that its overall composition is probably not much different from Earth's.

By coincidence, the Martian day and the Earth day are of nearly the same length, and the angle that the axis of rotation forms with the orbital plane is nearly the same for both planets. The Martian year is 687 Earth days. Mars has no large-scale magnetic field comparable to that of Earth today, but a small field cannot yet be ruled out.

The Viking data confirm that Mars has an atmosphere about 150 times thinner than Earth's. It is composed mostly of carbon dioxide (95 percent), nitrogen (2–3 percent), argon (1–2 percent), oxygen (0.1–0.4 percent), and water (0.01–0.1 percent). Water cannot now exist freely on the surface; it would evaporate quickly in the near vacuum. The surface temperatures are more extreme than those on Earth, ranging from about 25°C (roughly 80°F) at the equator to about −125°C (roughly −190°F) at the poles. At the Viking I landing site the daily temperature varied from −90°C to −10°C. Wind velocities of 270 kilometers per hour (roughly 170 miles per hour) can blow up in gigantic storms that cover the planet with dust for weeks at a time. One such dust storm blurred the view of the Mariner 9 television cameras for many weeks and delayed the schedule of receiving pictures.

The portrait of Mars that has emerged from thousands of Mariner 9 and Viking photographs is one of a planet that has been shaped by a variety of processes. Among these are bombardment of the surface by meteorites, volcanism, tectonic activity, erosion by running water, action by wind, and sapping or undermining of ground layers by melting subsurface ice. Thus Mars is the product of processes that occur on the Moon and on Earth, but with a unique mix that has led to a distinctive history and character. The major geologic features of the Martian surface are summarized in a planetary map in Figure 21-17.

Preliminary Viking data indicate that most of the Martian surface is old. The crater density, an

Figure 21-17

Geologic features of Mars shown on a physiographic map. [From "Mars" by James B. Pollack. Copyright © 1975 by Scientific American, Inc. All rights reserved.]

Permanent ice cap

Layered terrain

Etched plains

Volcanic constructs

Volcanic plains

Moderately cratered plains

Cratered plains

Chaotic hummocky terrain

Fretted hummocky terrain

Knobby hummocky terrain

Channel deposit

Undivided plains

Grooved terrain

Undivided cratered terrain

Mountainous terrain

Alba Patera

Olympus Mons

Mangala Vallis

Tharsis Ridge

Labyrinthus Noctis

Valles Tithonius Chasma

Mariners

Nirgal Vallis

Argyre

Elysium

Isidis

Hellas

Noachis

Figure 21-18
Viking 1 photograph of the great Martian volcano, Olympus Mons. The 24-km-high (15 mi) mountain is about 600 km (375 mi) across at the base and would extend from San Francisco to Los Angeles or Boston to Baltimore. Note the complex, multiple vent, main crater and the steep cliffs that drop off from the mountain's flanks to the surrounding plain. [From U.S. Geological Survey and National Aeronautics and Space Administration.]

approximate age indicator, ranges from about one-tenth to the same as that of the 4-billion-year-old lunar highlands. Most of the volcanic and tectonic activity ended about 2.5 billion years ago.

The contrast between the northern and southern hemispheres is striking. The southern hemisphere is predominantly ancient cratered terrain, probably similar in age to the lunar highlands. The two large impact basins of the southern hemisphere, Hellas and Argyre, are ringed by mountains formed from basin ejecta.

They appear quite similar to Imbrium and other lunar mare basins, but are more eroded. Great sand dune fields are found in this area.

The northern hemisphere is the site of most of the Martian volcanism. Volcanic structures on Mars consist of enormous shield volcanoes, domes, cones, and large volcanic plains. The shield volcano Olympus Mons—600 kilometers wide at the base, 24 kilometers high, and with a summit caldera 80 kilometers wide (Fig. 21-18)—may be the largest volcano in the solar system. The lava plains show flow features sim-

Figure 21-19
Some erosional features on Mars near the Viking 1 lander site photographed from a height of
1600 km (992 mi). The knobs and hummocks to the lower right are the erosional remnants of
an old crater rim. The flow of water was from lower left to upper right. The teardrop-shaped
islands formed when the water flowed around obstacles presented by an existing crater.
Layering can be seen on the sides of the island. The crater density indicates that the floodplain surface is old and that the flooding occurred a long time ago. [From National Aeronautics and Space Administration.]

ilar to those on the lunar lava plains—wrinkle
ridges and lobed escarpments at the fronts of
individual lava flows. The cratered plains are
thought to be older volcanic features.

The permanent ice caps, composed of water
ice, expand seasonally by the precipitation of
carbon dioxide ice. The polar regions are ringed
by extensive areas of layered deposits, sand
dunes, and ice-free zones, suggesting a complicated climatic history.

The chaotic terrains (Fig. 21-17) are thought
to have formed by sapping or melting of subsurface ice, resulting in the collapse of overlying
layers, leaving an incoherent array of broken
slabs of rock. Fretted terrain, which may have a
similar origin, shows as a lowland dotted with
numerous isolated mesas and bounded by cliffs
with an intricate geometry. It appears as if the

cliffs retreat as a result of the melting of subsurface ice and the seeping of water from their
bases. The cliffs are undermined, and landslides
result.

The evidence for large-scale water erosion on
Mars is overwhelming. Large areas exhibit evidence of ancient catastrophic flooding without
indications of ancient seas or accumulations of
sediments. Among the features observed are
sinuous channels with tributary systems and
large, braided channels with bars and tear-drop
shaped islands (Fig. 21-19). Gullies can be seen,
similar to drainage channels on Earth's desert
hillsides.

But where is the water? The present CO_2
atmosphere has too low a pressure for liquid
water to survive (it would vaporize), and the
vapor content of the atmosphere is too small.

The required water must occur as ice under present conditions. Moreover, about 5 to 20 times more CO_2 had to be present in the past for atmospheric pressures to be large enough to force water into the liquid state. Somewhere on Mars there is probably a large hidden inventory of ice, both the H_2O and the CO_2 varieties.

The polar ice caps contain some of the needed water. If the ice were some hundreds of meters in thickness, as some believe, and if all the ice melted at once, there would be enough water to cover the planet to a depth of 0.5 meter. Water and CO_2 could also be stored as ice in the Martian regolith, which could be as much as 1 kilometer thick. During warm periods, perhaps triggered by volcanism or climatic fluctuations due to slow periodic changes in the geometry of the Martian orbit, the frozen water and CO_2 could be released. The terrains that exhibit collapse features, with channels that seem to drain them, support this idea.

Among the most spectacular features are the deep canyons and great crack-like rifts. One immense system of canyons, Valles Marineris, just south of the equator, makes the Grand Canyon of the Colorado look puny; in round figures it is about 2700 kilometers long, and in places 500 kilometers wide and 6 kilometers deep. These structures are tectonic in origin, indicative of large-scale tensile (stretching) forces, perhaps connected with uplift and volcanism elsewhere. Fluvial erosion and sapping have also contributed to the morphology of the canyons (Fig. 21-20).

Unlike Earth, Mars shows no evidence of plate tectonics. Mountain systems forming under compression at convergent plate boundaries, linear ridge-rifts indicative of spreading boundaries, transform faults with large differentiated horizontal displacements—these are all lacking. The Viking seismograph has not detected any Mars quakes in the first few months of operation. Perhaps the lithosphere is too thick to break into plates, as on the Moon, or else convection in the interior is not as active as on Earth.

Hundreds of photographs have been taken in color at each of the Viking landing sites by the surface camera. The surface of Mars is a bright red color (as any amateur astronomer would have predicted). Both sites show a field of fine-grained, sand-like material littered with boulders. The Viking 1 landing site (22.4°N,

47.5°W) shows a dune field of fine-grained sand. Bedrock outcrops can be seen, and large numbers of rocks are strewn over the surface; both vesicular and fine-grained rocks are in evidence, with indications of chemical weathering and wind-faceting (Fig. 21-21).

The Viking 2 landing site (47.9°N, 225.9°W) was chosen for its northerly location in the hopes that more water would be present and the chance of finding life increased. The spacecraft came down in a boulder-strewn, flat, reddish desert cut by troughs that seem to form a polygonal network. Unlike the view from the first lander, no outcrops or dunes are seen. The blocks are highly vesicular and appear to be volcanic in origin, but transported as ejecta from a distant impact.

No signs of large organisms are apparent in the photographs at either landing site. Nevertheless, the environment is more hospitable to life than had been expected (traces of nitrogen, oxygen, water vapor). Several experiments were designed to search for microscopic life. They were sensitive enough to detect signs of life in soils from Antarctica and from barren Earth deserts. The tests made on Mars revealed a surprisingly active surface, subject to diverse interpretation. The consensus is that the activity is chemical in nature, caused by the presence of a strong oxidizer rather than living things.

JUPITER

The largest of the giant gas planets, Jupiter, with a volume 1300 times greater than the Earth's, contains more than twice the mass of all the other planets combined. It is now thought to be a gaseous and fluid planet without solid surfaces. Had it been somewhat more massive, Jupiter might have attained internal temperatures as high as the ignition point for nuclear reactions, and it would have flamed as a star in its own right. As mentioned earlier, Jupiter and the other giant planets are of a low-density type quite distinct from the terrestrial planets: they are composed predominantly of such substances as hydrogen, helium, ammonia, and methane. Much of Jupiter's interior may be in the form of liquid, metallic hydrogen. Normally, hydrogen is a gas, but under pressures of millions of kilograms per square centimeter, which exist in

Figure 21-20
Viking 1 photomosaic of the enormous canyon Valles Marineris from a height of 4200 km (2600 mi); north is to the top. The principal canyon crosses the bottom half of the picture in an east-west direction. The northern wall of the main canyon shows several large landslides. A series of branching channels cut into the plateau on the bottom from the south wall. These may have been formed by slow erosion as a result of the release of groundwater. Other branches of the canyon are visible at top. [From National Aeronautics and Space Administration.]

the deep interior of Jupiter, the hydrogen atoms may lock together to form a liquid with the properties of a metal. Some scientists believe that the innermost core of Jupiter may be rocky, or metallic like the core of the Earth.

Jupiter rotates very fast, once every 9.8 hours. As a result, its clouds, which are composed largely of frozen and liquid ammonia compounds, have been whipped into alternating dark and bright bands that circle the planet at different speeds in different latitudes (Fig. 21-22). The puzzling Great Red Spot changes size as it hovers in the southern hemisphere. It may be a gigantic hurricane, which because of its large size (the Earth could easily fit inside it), lasts for hundreds of years.

Jupiter gives off twice as much heat as it receives from the Sun. Perhaps this is primeval heat or heat generated by the continued gravitational contraction of the planet. Another star-like characteristic of Jupiter is its twelve satel-lites, which, like a miniature model of the solar system, decrease in density with distance—from rocky moons close to Jupiter to icy moons farther away. If Jupiter were about 70 times more massive, it would have become a star. Jupiter is the best-preserved sample of the early solar nebula, and, with its satellites, may contain the most important clues about the origin of the solar system.

Radio telescopes pointed at Jupiter pick up intense bursts of radio energy, apparently originating in a radiation belt quite similar to the Van Allen radiation belt, which surrounds the Earth. This means that Jupiter must have a powerful magnetic field (probably originating in the liquid, metallic interior) that traps charged particles from the Sun, sending out radio waves in the process. Fascinating, and as yet unexplained, is the observation that the radio emanations are definitely influenced by the position of Io, the second closest of Jupiter's moons.

Figure 21-21
This spectacular picture of the Martian landscape by the Viking 1 Lander shows a dune field littered with boulders, a view remarkably similar to many seen in the deserts of Earth. The picture covers an angle of 100°, looking northeast at left and southeast at right. The sharp dune crests indicate the most recent wind storms capable of moving sand over the dunes blew in the general direction from upper left to lower right. Small deposits downwind of rocks also indicate this wind direction. Large boulder at left is about 8 m (25 ft) from the spacecraft and measures about 1 by 3 m (3 by 10 ft). The meteorology boom, which supports Viking's miniature weather station, cuts through the picture's center. The sun rose two hours before the picture was taken, and is about 30° above the horizon near the center of the picture. [From National Aeronautics and Space Administration.]

Figure 21-22
Jupiter, as photographed by the Pioneer 11 space craft at a distance of 1,100,000 km (600,000 mi). The great red spot, possibly a gigantic storm, and the alternating bands of dark and light clouds are visible. [From National Aeronautics and Space Administration.]

Figure 21-23
Saturn and its ring system, photographed by the 100-inch telescope. [From Hale Observatories.]

Figure 21-24
Photograph of a piece of the Allende meteorite, thought to have formed early in the history of the solar system. Black crust on top is due to melting from frictional heating in flight through the atmosphere. [Smithsonian Astrophysical Observatory.]

SATURN

The second largest planet, Saturn, is also the lightest planet. It is much like Jupiter—it rotates rapidly, shows colored bands of clouds across its face, and has a large family of ten satellites. Saturn, however, has one feature not shared by any other planet—its four rings (Fig. 21-23). The rings are thought to be countless ice particles, or ice-covered dust and rock, whirling in orbit around the planet in a belt anywhere from a few inches to a few miles thick. The rings are thought to be the fragments of a satellite that broke up, because of tidal forces, when it spiralled too close to Saturn—or, alternatively, material that never accreted to form a satellite, because a single body of any size could not exist so close to the planet.

URANUS, NEPTUNE, AND PLUTO

Not much is known about Uranus and Neptune, the outermost of the giant planets, nor of Pluto, the ninth and most distant planet, beyond the data given in Table 21-1. Following the discovery of Uranus by telescope in 1781, the existence of Neptune and Pluto was predicted mathematically, because Uranus seemed to deviate from its predicted orbit, indicating that it might be influenced by the gravitational attraction of unknown planets. With the aid of these mathematical hints, Neptune was found in 1846 and Pluto in 1930.

METEORITES

The prevailing view is that meteorites are broken fragments formed by collisions between asteroids orbiting the Sun in the belt between Mars and Jupiter. They are deflected into orbits that cross the path of Earth, which sweeps them up.

Some of the asteroids may have been differentiated prior to breakup, with formation of an iron core, a stony mantle, and a crust. Other asteroids may have maintained their primitive mix of the original accretion products without undergoing chemical zonation.

It may be that the fragmentation of the outer layers of the asteroids gave rise to the stony meteorites, the most abundant ones, made up of silicate minerals, mostly olivine and pyroxene.

Deeper fragmentation, involving breakup of the core, could account for the stony-iron and the iron meteorites. Some meteorites appear to be unheated, unmelted, undifferentiated primordial materials—perhaps actual samples of the condensates from the early solar nebula, perhaps containing grains that existed even before the Sun was formed. These are receiving much attention now because of the unique information they contain.

Meteorites usually show formation ages of about 4.5 billion years, although breakup of their parent bodies may be as recent as 10 million years. The age of formation, determined by radiometric dating, was used to fix the time of formation of the solar system.

Meteorites range in size from fine dust particles to bodies many miles in diameter, which gouge out large craters or astroblemes when they impact the Moon, Mars, or Earth. Meteoritic dust falls almost continually on Earth. However, the larger, more spectacular meteorites that survived the fiery flight through the atmosphere were the only source of information about extraterrestrial materials before the lunar samples were collected. Their nature and origin are highly controversial, and hundreds of books and articles have been written about them.

SUMMARY

1. The planets of the solar system fall in two distinct groups: the small, stony, inner, Earth-like planets, which have been opened up for geological examination as a result of space exploration, and the gaseous, giant, outer planets, which are more Sun-like in their compositions.

2. The Moon was geologically active in its early history. Lunar rocks show the planet to have been differentiated and subjected to volcanism, but, for reasons not fully understood, the Moon became essentially inactive about 3 billion years ago. The absence of young rocks, the small number of moonquakes, and the great age of surface features confirm this conclusion. Without water or an atmosphere to foster erosion, and without the renewing forces of internal activity, the lunar surface has remained essentially unchanged for billions of years. Its features were mostly shaped during its earlier active phase, with meteorite impacts playing a major role. The major formations on the Moon are its original anorthositic crust, now found primarily in the highlands, basaltic lava flows primarily filling the maria, ejecta blankets of varying ages, and the lunar regolith. The lunar lithosphere is much thicker and stronger than Earth's and is able to support mascons.

3. Mercury is the smallest and densest planet. It has a large iron core and a silicate crust. Perhaps closeness to the Sun accounts for its lack of an atmosphere and the absence of the lighter, more volatile elements. Like the Moon, it has a heavily cratered surface, shows evidence of early differentiation, and has been geologically inactive for a long time.

4. Venus is similar to Earth in mass, size, density, and distance from the Sun, but there the resemblance ends. The surface is hidden by a thick and heavy blanket of carbon dioxide, which traps solar energy so that the surface temperature reaches 475°C. Radar data and photographs of the surface by the Venera spacecraft provide evidence of current geological activity.

5. The Mariner 9 and Viking flights have revealed that Mars has been shaped by a variety of processes, including bombardment by meteorites, volcanism, tectonic activity, erosion by running water, action by wind, sapping of surface layers by melting subsurface ice. Most of the Martian surface is very old. The atmosphere is very thin and mostly carbon dioxide. The water, inferred from erosional features, may be stored as ice in the polar ice caps or in the regolith. There is no evidence of plate tectonics. It appears that life is not present.

EXERCISES

1. The surface features of the Moon are profoundly different from those of Earth. Describe these differences and explain why they occur.

2. The Earth and Moon are of comparable age, yet Earth's surface is youthful compared to the old surface features of the Moon. Most rocks on the surface of the Moon are about 3 billion years old or older, whereas most rocks on Earth's surface are younger than about 200 million years. Why?

3. What is the implication of the fact that mascons are found on the Moon and not on Earth?

4. Moon rocks and soil differ from Earth rocks. How? Why?

5. Contrast the geology of Mars and Earth, indicating similarities and differences.

6. If humans were forced to leave Earth because of some kind of catastrophe, where could they migrate to with the best chance of surviving?

7. In size, mass, and distance from the Sun, Venus is nearly Earth's twin. Yet the two planets are radically different. Describe these differences, and hazard a guess as to why they exist.

8. Mars has been explored with unmanned spacecraft, which landed on the surface. The primary mission was to search for life. If you were the chief scientist, to which of the geological provinces of Mars would you send your spacecraft to maximize the chance of finding living forms? Why?

BIBLIOGRAPHY

Bergamini, David, *The Universe*. New York: Time-Life Books, 1969.

Brandt, J. C., and S. P. Maran, *New Horizons in Astronomy*. San Francisco: W. H. Freeman and Company, 1972.

Lewis, J. S., "The Chemistry of the Solar System," *Scientific American*, March 1974.

"Mars" Issue, *Science*, v. 194, no. 4260, October 1, 1976. (The "Reports" section contains many articles about Viking experiments.)

Simmons, Gene, *On the Moon with Apollo 17*. Washington, D.C.: U.S. Government Printing Office (Stock Number 3300-00470), 1972.

Scientific American, *The Solar System*. San Francisco: W. H. Freeman and Company, 1975. (Many articles on the planets and smaller bodies of the solar system.)

22

MATTER AND ENERGY FROM THE EARTH

In the course of the evolution of civilization, humans have steadily broadened their use of the mineral and energy resources of the Earth. Since the eighteenth century, the abundance of fossil fuels has provided the industrial nations of the world with cheap power, but they are faced today with a declining supply of these conventional sources of energy. In the next few decades, the geological hunt for new supplies of oil, gas, and coal will be coupled with exploration for new uranium ore reserves and a search for alternative energy supplies. High-grade sources of many vital metal ores and other useful minerals are becoming harder to find, and the many lower-grade deposits can be exploited only if abundant energy is available.

Unlike other living things, humans have learned to use the materials of the Earth to modify their environment extensively. We mine metal ores, coal, and salt. We drill for oil and gas. We strip away surface deposits on land and evaporate sea water to get dissolved metals. In our increasingly systematic search of the globe for new sources of the materials we depend upon, we use our geological knowledge of the ways in which already discovered natural segregations are distributed in order to find more of them. At the same time, we rely on a plentiful supply of energy for concentrating, smelting, and refining the materials from their natural, impure forms to the final products that are machined or molded into various components of our technology. The source of the energy is itself in the Earth as oil, gas, coal, or uranium ore.

The metals that we use for machinery, the phosphate rock prepared for fertilizer, and the salt used in food never disappear. Some we return to Earth as refuse—one of several forms of man-made deposits. Some dissolve in sanitary drainage waters that find their way into groundwaters and into rivers and eventually into the ocean, just like the dissolved materials from weathering. In this sense, humans are hyperac-

tive agents of erosion. Even though the used material is not really destroyed, much of it is so widely dispersed that it is recoverable only with a huge expenditure of energy. For this reason, inordinate amounts of energy may be required to gather together and refine used materials for recycling. Energy, in contrast to the matter that we consume, is not returnable. It is permanently lost to Earth. Regardless of which process we use, electrical, kinetic, or chemical, energy is converted to heat and irretrievably radiated to space.

Because the prospect of maintaining or increasing our supply of energy underlies all resource problems, we will first review the existing and potential sources.

ENERGY FROM FOSSIL FUELS

A wood fire, the extremely rapid oxidation of organic matter, is, in a superficial sense, deferred respiration. Throughout its lifetime, a tree respires, essentially as animals do, by slow controlled oxidation of organic substances in cells. The decay of a tree following its death is another slow oxidation process, depending, like

Energy permanently lost to
space by infrared radiation

Figure 22-1
The cycle of mining, preparation, use, and discard
of useful Earth materials is one in which a naturally
segregated resource, such as an iron ore body, is
mined, processed, and fabricated and then returned
to Earth in a dispersed, heterogeneous mixture.

Use

Manufacture and
fabrication

Discard

Energy
consumed

Recycling

Purification or
preparation for use

Deterioration
and decay

Energy
consumed

Earth materials
mined

Dispersal to
junkyard, dump

Energy
consumed

Earth

Naturally
segregated
resource

Heterogeneous mixture
deposited or buried
on land or on sea floor

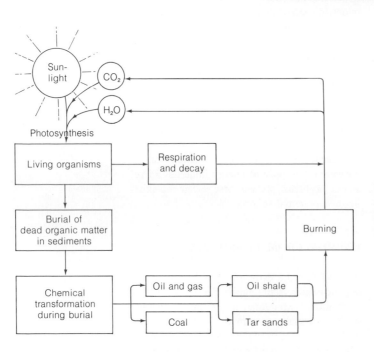

Figure 22-2
Photosynthesis produces organic matter that is buried, transformed, and so becomes a "fossilized"
product of photosynthesis—a fossil fuel.

respiration, on the organic matter produced by photosynthesis. Thus we can look upon a piece of wood or any piece of plant matter as a photosynthetic product that can be returned, by respiration during life, by slow decay, or by burning, to the carbon dioxide and water from which it was made. If the wood was buried and transformed into coal (see Chapter 11) 250 million years ago and we burn it today, we are utilizing the energy stored by photosynthesis from late Paleozoic sunlight. We are burning a "fossil," and we can refer in the same way to all natural organic materials, ranging from coal to oil and gas, including oil shales, tar sands, and other geologic formations, as **fossil fuels.**

The industrial revolution of the nineteenth century was powered by the energy from coal—in Britain, from the coal fields of England and Wales; in continental Europe, from the coal basins of western Germany and bordering countries; and in North America, from the Appalachian coal fields of Pennsylvania and West Virginia. As industrialization expanded, so did our hunger for coal, and geological exploration for this fuel spread over much of the world, from the Arctic deposits of Spitzbergen to Australia. Coal production climbed at an ever-accelerating pace.

Half a century after the first oil well in America was drilled in 1859, oil and gas were beginning to displace coal as the fuel of choice. Not only were they found to burn more cleanly, producing no ash, but they could be transported by pipeline as well as by rail or ship. When oil exploration entered its heyday, the application of geology and geophysics to the search for prospects was combined with a rapidly developing innovative technology for drilling ever more deeply and rapidly. The independent "wildcatter" who drilled in new territory was typically a self-trained geologist who learned how to recognize the permeable rocks and geologic structures in which oil might be found. Understanding of the geologic conditions under which oil and gas are formed came quickly from the data of oil exploration and inferences from the chemical composition of petroleum and natural gas.

PETROLEUM AND NATURAL GAS

Crude oil is made up of a great variety of **hydrocarbons**—compounds whose molecules are chains of carbon atoms with hydrogen atoms attached. Crude oil also contains some impurities, notably sulfur. The **paraffins,** a major subdivision of the hydrocarbons, are saturated compounds—that is, each carbon in the chain has attached to it all the hydrogens it can hold. The number of hydrogens in relation to the number of carbons is given by the general formula C_nH_{2n+2}. Methane (CH_4), or marsh gas, is the smallest and lightest member of the paraffin series. Methane and the other short-chain compounds are gases at room temperature and atmospheric pressure; examples are ethane (C_2H_6) and butane (C_4H_{10}). Natural gas is a mixture of methane and other light paraffins. The mixture heptane, octane, and nonane (C_7H_{16} to C_9H_{20}) is what we know as gasoline. Lubricating oils are mixtures of still longer-chain paraffins.

How Oil and Gas Form. Small amounts of hydrocarbons and related compounds occur in organisms of all kinds, from algae to elephants. Other biological compounds can be transformed into hydrocarbons by organic chemical reactions in sediments. Nowhere else on Earth, neither in igneous nor in metamorphic rocks, are hydrocarbons of similar nature formed. Petroleum, like coal, is a biological product—the organic debris of former life, buried, transformed, and preserved in sediments.

The conditions of preservation are a favorable balance between the production of organic matter and its destruction by the scavenging of other organisms or by inorganic oxidation. These conditions are met where productivity of organic matter is high, such as in the coastal waters of the sea, where large numbers of organisms thrive and where the supply of oxygen in bottom sediment layers is not enough to oxidize all organic matter. Many offshore sedimentary basins on continental shelves—and perhaps also sedimentary accumulations on continental rises—satisfy these conditions; in such enironments, and to a lesser degree in many others, small amounts of organic matter are buried and protected from oxidation. During the millions of years of burial, chemical reactions slowly transform a fraction of this material into liquid and gaseous hydrocarbons. These fluids tend to be squeezed out of compacting muddy sediments into adjacent permeable beds, such as sandstones or porous limestones. The low density of oil and gas causes them to migrate to the highest place they can reach, where they float on top of the water in the pores of the formations.

The geologic environment that favors the large-scale accumulation of oil is a combination

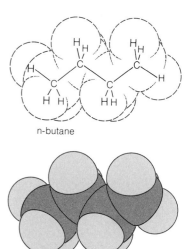

n-butane

Figure 22-3
The structure of butane, a paraffin compound containing four carbon atoms and ten hydrogen atoms. [From *College Chemistry* (3rd ed.) by Linus Pauling. W. H. Freeman and Company. Copyright © 1964.]

556

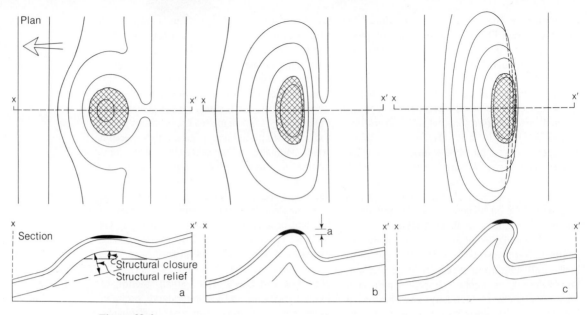

Figure 22-4
Idealized structural maps and sections of typical anticlinal dome folds; such folds are characteristic of many traps containing oil and gas pools (oil, shaded and black). Arrow shows direction of dip; contour lines show elevation of top bed with respect to sea level. [From *Geology of Petroleum* (2nd ed.) by A. I. Levorsen. W. H. Freeman and Company. Copyright © 1967.]

of structure and rock types that create an impermeable barrier to upward migration—an **oil trap.** In order for the accumulation to qualify as an **oil field,** the oil-bearing formation must be permeable enough to allow the crude oil to be pumped out. The typical trap-forming structure is an anticline in which a permeable sandstone is overlain by an impermeable shale. The oil and gas accumulate at the highest part of the fold, the gas highest, the oil next, both floating on the water that saturates all permeable formations. Other structures may trap oil in similar ways. For example, displacement at a fault may place a dipping permeable limestone bed opposite an impermeable shale, creating a trap for oil. A dipping sandstone bed may thin out against a shale and form a stratigraphic trap—one that is primarily the result of the original sedimentation pattern rather than of later structural deformation.

Geologists have mapped thousands of structural or stratigraphic traps, all conceivably favorable to oil accumulation, but only a fraction of them have proved to contain any oil or gas. The structures alone are not enough: the oil has to be available to migrate into them. There is a sequence of necessary geologic events that lead to oil accumulation, no one of which can be omitted, though the precise order of steps may vary.

1. Organic matter must be produced in some quantity in the environment.
2. Organic matter must be buried in the sediment before being destroyed by oxidation.
3. Some part of the organic matter must be transformed by slow chemical reactions to oil and gas.
4. The now-fluid organic matter in the sediment must migrate into nearby permeable beds.
5. The permeable beds must be deformed either by folding or faulting to form structural traps, or stratigraphic traps must be produced by conditions of sedimentation.
6. The oil-containing sediment must not be transformed into slate or higher-grade metamorphic rocks or the organic matter will be transformed by heat into a non-hydrocarbon black carbonaceous material of no value.
7. Structural deformation in general must not be extremely severe. Intensely fractured rocks may render traps ineffective by causing leakage.

8. The beds must remain buried. If exposed to erosion, the oil may be dissipated.

9. The pore spaces of the permeable formations must not be so filled with swelling clays or mineral cements deposited by groundwaters that the permeability will be reduced to the point that the oil cannot be pumped out of the formation.

With such a long list of requisites, one might wonder that there is as much oil as there is. Yet the probability of all those events happening in the right order is fairly high. A great quantity of organic matter *is* produced and buried in the sediments on and around continents, and the normal pattern *is* for that organic matter to be transformed slowly to oil. Stratigraphic and structural traps abound in most sedimentary basins. Although sediments are intensely deformed in mountain chains, the greater part of any continent consists of sediments of all ages that are only gently deformed and are subjected at most to mild warming by deep burial. Thus oil is not an unusual geologic product. Rather, we expect to find it where conditions are right, and the successful results of exploration during the past century have borne out those expectations.

The World Distribution of Oil and Gas. If you were to visit the exploration and research offices of any large oil company, you would be able to find maps and reports of all of the sedimentary rock terranes in which the company has operated, for where there is sediment, there may be oil. For example, thirty-one states of the fifty United States produce commercially marketable oil, and some small occurrences are known in most of the others. Canada produces oil from many of its provinces. Most of the countries of South America and Europe produce oil. Once considered oil-poor, Africa now produces a respectable quantity. Indonesia has many oil fields, and exploration of parts of Southeast Asia looks promising. This is not to say, however, that the world distribution is uniform; rather, it is most uneven. The two richest and most important oil-producing regions are the Middle East and the area between the Gulf of Mexico and the Caribbean. The Middle East includes about two-thirds of the known reserves of the world in the oil fields of Iran, Kuwait, Saudi Arabia, Iraq, and the Baku Region of the U.S.S.R. The highly productive Gulf Coast-Caribbean area includes the Louisiana-Texas

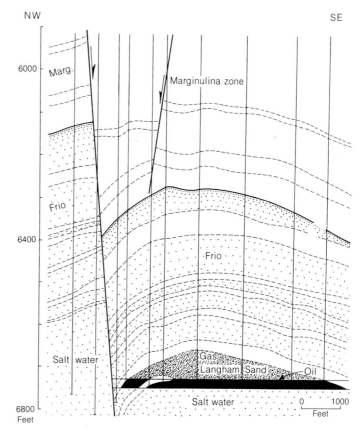

Figure 22-5
Section through the Amelia field, Texas, showing the relations between a fold and a fault and how gas and oil are trapped above a groundwater line. The dip into the down side of the fault is contrary to most faulting, except in the system of faults parallel to the Gulf Coast in Louisiana and Texas, of which this is an example. [From Hamner, *Bull. Amer. Assoc. Petrol. Geol.* v. 23, p. 1647.]

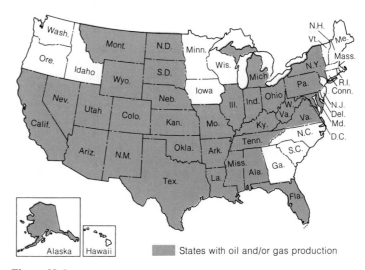

Figure 22-6
The oil producing industry in the United States, 1972. [From *The Oil Producing Industry in Your State,* Independent Petroleum Association of America, 1972.]

It is tempting to speculate that the lack of oil in Triassic sediments is related to a time of early rifting of Pangaea, when there was much less continental shelf and rise available in a single large continent.

One analysis of the chances of oil spills on the East Coast of North America predicts that less oil would be spilled from drilling platforms and off-shore pipelines than from fleets of oil tankers required to supply coastal states. This assumes no major events such as that of Santa Barbara.

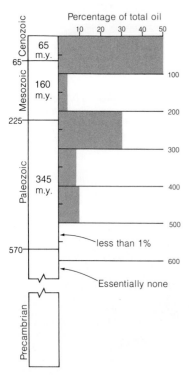

Figure 22-7
Percentage of the world's total past production and proven reserves of oil by age distribution in 100-million-year intervals. More than 80 percent of the world's known oil is found in rocks formed in the last 6 percent of geologic time.

province, Mexico, Colombia, Venezuela, and Trinidad.

Why this uneven distribution? A political scientist once jokingly asked one of us, "Why is it that oil is always found in underdeveloped countries?" The distribution of oil, of course, is determined not by political boundaries but by geologic history. The age range of sediments from which oil is produced gives some idea of the reasons for the distribution. There is practically no oil in Precambrian rocks and very little in Cambrian rocks. Rocks of the Triassic Period also contain very little. Oil produced from rocks of these periods amounts to less than one percent of the world's total production. For all practical purposes, we can say that no oil is produced from Pleistocene rocks. But Cenozoic sediments, those deposited only in the last 70 million years of the Earth's 4.7 billion year history, account for about 60 percent of the total. Another large fraction, about 25 percent, comes from rocks of Mesozoic age, the next older era. Only about 15 percent comes from Paleozoic rocks.

The correlation of geologic age and oil production is made understandable in terms of the processes that destroy oil or allow it to disperse at the surface. The older the rock formation is, the more likely it will be eroded or involved in metamorphism and deformation that would eliminate the oil. The Cenozoic thus may represent the normal abundance of oil. Older oil-producing formations are those that have escaped the ravages of time—exposure to destructive geologic events. If we were living in the Triassic period, we would probably find oil most abundant in late Paleozoic rocks.

Oil in the Middle East is concentrated largely in thick Cenozoic and Mesozoic sediments deposited in and adjacent to a major geosyncline situated along the southern margin of the Asian continent. Sedimentation has been accompanied by a variety of deformation structures and stratigraphic traps. There is no evidence of metamorphism, and relatively few of the sediments have been destroyed by erosion.

Continental Shelf Oil. Continental shelves are good places to explore for oil, as has been known since the general nature of their structure was worked out in the 1940's and 1950's. They easily meet the requisites for accumulation: the sediments are young, unmetamorphosed, mildly deformed, and little eroded. The shelves of the world have been geophysically combed for favorable structures by the major oil companies in anticipation of the large amounts of oil expected to be found there. Drilling on continental shelves, however, is not without its problems. A major one is the difficulty and expense of drilling in deep water. At this time, wells in offshore areas of Louisiana, Texas, and California easily can be drilled in water as much as 100 meters deep. That depth can be increased at least two to four times without much additional difficulty. In order to drill in much deeper water—on continental slopes and rises—new kinds of drilling technology are being developed. The Glomar Challenger's equipment, which has been used to drill the holes for the deep-sea drilling program, has served as a prototype for this technology.

Another major problem of offshore drilling is the prevention of oil pollution. The name "Santa Barbara" calls to mind the environmental damage that resulted from the accidental release of oil from an offshore drilling platform there in 1969, but many other accidents of that kind have not made the headlines. Though it is difficult if not impossible to guarantee a "100 percent safe" drilling well, it *is* within the realm of possibility to devise technological systems and controls that would greatly reduce the chances of a serious accident. If there is adequate development and enforcement of safety procedures, offshore drilling need not pose an important threat to the oceans or nearby beaches. Flushing of oil tanks by ships at sea probably poses a more serious current danger. The important point is that there are large reserves of oil and gas under the sea bed that will eventually have to be drilled to satisfy the world's needs. We *can* tap those supplies without severe cost to the environment if precautions are taken. There is no doubt that we will be pushed to explore every conceivable oil resource as our present reserves are depleted, whether our increasing demands are slowed or not.

Oil: The Exhaustible Supply. Inconceivable as it may seem to the landowner who sees a "gusher" spurting oil from the derrick on his property, that oil well will eventually run dry. What the world wants to know is when all the wells will run dry. What is behind this loaded question are the facts of oil occurrence on Earth. Thirty years ago, many oil producers were optimistic; supplies seemed so immense, and so many scientific and engineering innovations held promise of tapping new sources, that no one needed to worry about the future. Since then, the rapidly accelerating world demand and a more sober analysis of the total quantity of oil

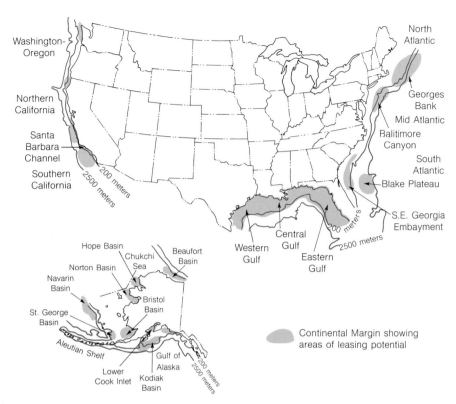

Figure 22-8
Areas of the Outer Continental Shelf that have been leased or are planned for leasing for oil and gas exploration. The Central and Western Gulf, and the Southern California area are active in exploration and production now. Two exploratory holes have been drilled off the Northeast Coast, one in the Baltimore Canyon area, the other on Georges Bank. [From U.S. Geological Survey.]

remaining on Earth has changed the picture.

The efforts of one man played an important role in changing attitudes about energy reserves. M. King Hubbert, a geologist-geophysicist working for the Shell Oil Company, started his analysis of the world oil situation about thirty years ago by estimating the total oil reserves. He argued that essentially all the oil in the Earth had formed during the 600 million years since the beginning of the Cambrian period and that new oil is being made at about the same rate. This means that it will take another million years for the natural formation of 1/600 of the oil that has so far been found. Thus it is clear that we cannot rely on natural processes to replenish the oil we pump out of the ground at so rapid a rate. We are dealing with a fixed supply that steadily dwindles as we use it. Three significant questions that need to be answered are: how great is the total supply, how much of it

have we already used, and at what rate do we expect to continue depleting the supply?

How does a petroleum geologist go about estimating the total amount of recoverable oil in the Earth? The individual oil well that discovers a new oil field gives only a hint of the ultimate size of the field. But from it the geologist learns how thick the oil-saturated porous beds are and how permeable they are, the permeability being a good guide to the ease of pumping the oil. As more wells are drilled, the productive areas are outlined and the volume of oil in the oil field becomes better known. Experience with older wells in the same geologic province gives some idea of how much oil might eventually be produced, for not all of the oil in the ground can be recovered, though improvements in recovery engineering are constantly being made. The general abundance and distribution of already drilled oil fields in the various kinds of sedi-

Oil companies are constantly searching for new engineering technologies to enhance the recovery of oil from existing oil fields. Water may be pumped into the periphery of an area to force more oil out of a central well. In order to loosen up very viscous oils and allow them to flow more easily, steam may be injected under pressure and then allowed to escape with the newly fluidized oil. All these methods have increased the proportion of oil that can be recovered, but we are still far from being able to get all of it.

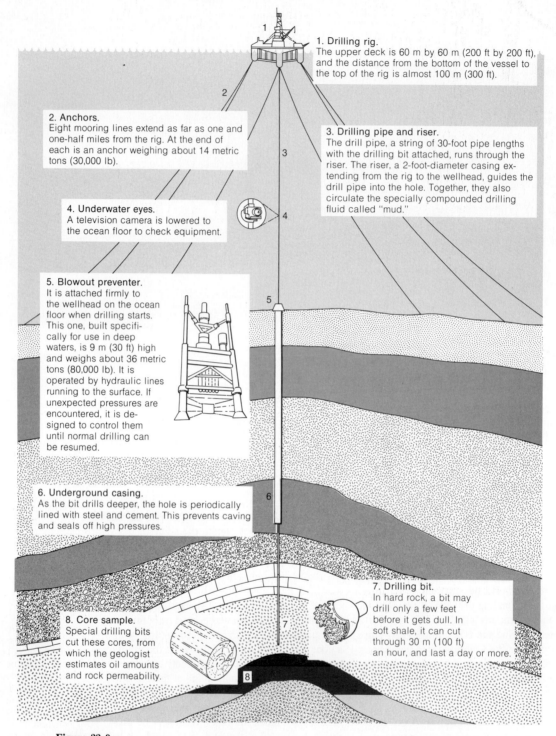

1. Drilling rig.
The upper deck is 60 m by 60 m (200 ft by 200 ft), and the distance from the bottom of the vessel to the top of the rig is almost 100 m (300 ft).

2. Anchors.
Eight mooring lines extend as far as one and one-half miles from the rig. At the end of each is an anchor weighing about 14 metric tons (30,000 lb).

3. Drilling pipe and riser.
The drill pipe, a string of 30-foot pipe lengths with the drilling bit attached, runs through the riser. The riser, a 2-foot-diameter casing extending from the rig to the wellhead, guides the drill pipe into the hole. Together, they also circulate the specially compounded drilling fluid called "mud."

4. Underwater eyes.
A television camera is lowered to the ocean floor to check equipment.

5. Blowout preventer.
It is attached firmly to the wellhead on the ocean floor when drilling starts. This one, built specifically for use in deep waters, is 9 m (30 ft) high and weighs about 36 metric tons (80,000 lb). It is operated by hydraulic lines running to the surface. If unexpected pressures are encountered, it is designed to control them until normal drilling can be resumed.

6. Underground casing.
As the bit drills deeper, the hole is periodically lined with steel and cement. This prevents caving and seals off high pressures.

7. Drilling bit.
In hard rock, a bit may drill only a few feet before it gets dull. In soft shale, it can cut through 30 m (100 ft) an hour, and last a day or more.

8. Core sample.
Special drilling bits cut these cores, from which the geologist estimates oil amounts and rock permeability.

Figure 22-9
Diagrammatic view of an offshore drilling rig. With the exception of the special equipment in the water, the drill hole is drilled in much the same way as in land-based drilling. [Courtesy Exxon Corporation.]

mentary basins are guides to estimating future reserves. For example, exploration has been so thorough in the older oil provinces, such as those of Pennsylvania, Illinois, Oklahoma, and Texas, that there is little doubt that more than 90 percent of the oil there has already been discovered (though not all of it has been pumped). These **proven reserves** are those that have been geologically outlined and at least partially drilled. Estimates of proven reserves are constantly being updated as the balance changes between the increase from new discoveries and the decrease by production at pumping wells.

The next step is the geological estimate of the future exploration of as-yet-untapped oil fields. With more than a hundred years worth of experience in drilling oil and the increase in the geological knowledge of the world, geologists can make a good guess about how much oil is left to find. Geological mapping of the land areas of the world is essentially complete, at least on a general scale, and we know where all of the sedimentary basins are. The large discoveries of the past four years in Alaska were welcome but not exactly a great surprise, for geologists had known for years that the area was favorable for oil exploration. We now have a good idea of the sedimentary basins under the permanent glacial ice of Antarctica, and sooner or later exploration and production methods may be developed that will allow oil drillers to go there too.

The companion to geological mapping of exposed formations on land is geophysical exploration. Since the early 1920's the major practical use of seismology has been in oil-field exploration (see Box 17-1). Reflected seismic waves reveal deeper subsurface structures and formation changes that are not apparent from surface mapping. This ability to "see" beneath the surface was utilized fully in the exploration of the continental shelves for structures favorable to oil accumulation. Newer, more sensitive seismic profiles sometimes show the presence of gas in buried formations. The combination of geology and geophysics has made possible reliable estimates of all the oil that may eventually be discovered and produced on land, in the ocean, and under glacial ice—what we call **petroleum resources.** In spite of all of the major new discoveries in Alaska and elsewhere, the known petroleum resources of the world have not changed much in the past decade, increasing confidence in the estimates. Of course, we can-

Figure 22-10
Proven reserves of crude oil in the United States, exclusive of Alaska. Dotted line estimated. [Modified from *Resources and Man,* National Academy of Sciences—National Research Council. W. H. Freeman and Company. Copyright © 1969.]

not completely rule out discoveries of a totally unpredictable kind. But we would be unwise to count on them.

How Much Oil Is Left? A recent estimate of world oil resources is shown in Figure 22-11. Huge as the total, about 2100 billion barrels, may seem, projections for the future must be based on how much of that total we have already used, the rate we are now using it, and the anticipated rate in the future. Since oil was first discovered in Pennsylvania in 1859, the total production up to 1969 was 277 billion barrels, about 10 percent of the total resource. From past production figures we can also see how the rate of use has jumped with steadily expanding industrialization. It took a little more than the first 100 years of oil production to pump the first half of all oil produced since the beginning, but only another ten years to pump the remaining half.

Though 90 percent of the world's oil is still in the ground, the proportion left in the ground in the United States (exclusive of Alaska), is much less than that, for the United States was one of the first countries to explore and produce oil systematically and efficiently. Of the approximately 204 billion barrels of ultimate produc-

The standard measure for oil production is the U.S. barrel, equal to 42 gallons or 159 liters. Because the density of oils from different fields varies appreciably, one can only state an average weight per barrel, about 140 kg or 310 lbs.

Figure 22-11
Petroleum resources of the world are depicted in an arrangement that can be read horizontally for original total resources and vertically for percentage. Thus the block on the left shows that the western hemisphere originally contained a little more than 500 billion barrels, of which the United States held about 19 percent. The figures for petroleum are derived from estimates made in 1967 by W. P. Ryman of the Standard Oil Company of New Jersey. They represent ultimate crude-oil production, including oil from offshore areas, and consist of oil already produced, proven and probable reserves, and future discoveries. Estimates as low as 1350×10^9 barrels have also been made. [From "The Energy Resources of the Earth" by M. K. Hubbert. Copyright © 1971 by Scientific American, Inc. All rights reserved.]

tion estimated for the United States by Hubbert in 1972, about 110 billion barrels has already been produced and burned up. Of the 204 billion barrels of petroleum resources, more than 145 billion barrels has already been discovered (as of January 1, 1972) and thus constitute our proven reserves. Other estimates indicate that we have slightly more or slightly less, but even allowing for some error, the picture is clear: we have already discovered at least 75 percent of all that we may ultimately find. Much of the as-yet-undiscovered resource lies beneath the continental shelves. The discovery of Alaskan oil adds about another 35 billion barrels to the total resource (proven reserves of about 10 billion barrels at the Prudhoe Bay oil field), but really doesn't change the picture greatly. One must remember that 30 billion barrels is less than a 10-year supply for the United States at current rates of use. The story is summarized in Figure 22-12, which indicates that we are well past the halfway mark in our rapid burning up of our oil resources.

The picture for natural gas is much the same as that for oil. Though it has been exploited a little less rapidly than oil, natural-gas production in this country will probably peak in the 1970's and then decline. The world political and economic consequences of these facts of oil supply will continue to be a major factor in the next decades. Every student of international politics should study Figure 22-12 and ponder its implications. Yet oil and gas do not tell all the story, even though we depend on them heavily today. There are enormous supplies of energy from the other fossil fuels: coal, oil shale, and tar sands.

COAL

Coal has been used as a fuel for millenia, perhaps since early inhabitants of Wales used it for funeral pyres about 3000 or 4000 years ago. By the eighteenth century it was well established as a fuel for heating houses and then became the mainstay of the industrial revolution in the nineteenth and early part of the twentieth centuries. Coal was discovered in North America by several early explorers; the first were Louis Joliet and Jacques Marquette, who found it in Illinois in 1673. Major production began in the 1800's, and increased steadily with demands brought on by the emerging steel industry, the development of the railroad steam engine, increased use for general heating, and then the

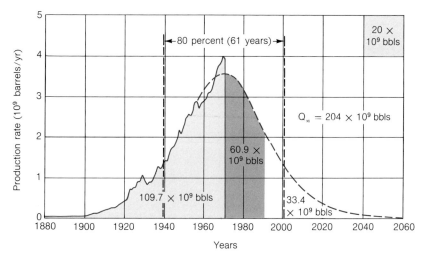

Figure 22-12
Complete cycle of crude-oil production in the United States and adjacent continental shelves, exclusive of Alaska, assuming a total ultimate production of 204×10^9 barrels. [From M. K. Hubbert, *U.S. Energy Resources: A review as of 1972*. Senate Comm. on Interior and Insular Affairs.]

growth of electrical power. As of 1970, about 133 billion metric tons of all kinds of coal had been mined. The increase in the rate of use slackened in the twentieth century, largely because oil and gas supplanted coal for so many uses. There is now a resurgence in coal production prompted by the oil reserve and price picture.

It is far easier to estimate coal reserves than oil and gas reserves. Like other sedimentary layers, coal beds extend over large areas, hence they can easily be mapped from surface exposures and their subsurface extent inferred. There has been much mining and exploration drilling for coal; in addition, many wells drilled for oil have penetrated coal-bearing formations. Because the coal-exploration geologist has a good idea of what kinds of sedimentary rock sections include coal and where to look for them (see Chapter 11), he is likely to be more concerned with thickness and quality of coal than with its presence or absence. For all of these geological reasons, accurate estimates of the world's coal reserves are easier to make. At the same time, they are more complicated. Reserves are estimated with respect to ease of recovery and to the heat value of the coal (Fig. 22-16, Table 22-1). Commonly, detailed evaluations are made by thickness categories of the coal that might be mined, the depth of rock overburden

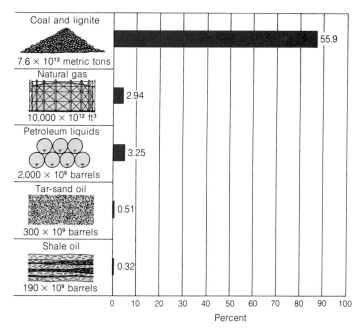

Figure 22-13
Energy content of the world's initial supply of recoverable fossil fuels is given in units of 10^{15} thermal kilowatt-hours. Coal and lignite, for example, contain 55.9×10^{15} thermal kilowatt-hours of energy and represent 88.8 percent of the recoverable energy. [From "The Energy Resources of the Earth" by M. K. Hubbert. Copyright © 1971 by Scientific American, Inc. All rights reserved.]

Figure 22-14
Energy contribution of coal and coal plus oil is portrayed in terms of their heat of combustion. Before 1900 the energy contribution from oil was barely significant. Since then the contribution from oil has risen much more rapidly than that from coal. By 1968 oil represented about 60 percent of the total. If the energy from natural gas were included, petroleum would account for about 70 percent of the total. Since 1968, despite all talk of substitution of coal for oil, there has been no great change in the relative proportions. [From "The Energy Resources of the Earth" by M. K. Hubbert. Copyright © 1971 by Scientific American, Inc. All rights reserved.]

in the case of strip mine reserves, and the quality of the coal. The last factor is usually displayed in terms of the rank, or metamorphic grade, of the coal. This ranges from lignite, the lowest stage, through the bituminous coals to the high-rank anthracites (see Chapter 11, p. 294). The largest category, that of the bituminous coals, has been subdivided into grades of high, medium, and low volatile content. These gradings indicate the relative proportion of volatile gases released from the coal when it is heated; the less the volatile content, the higher the heat value of the coal in general and, therefore, the higher the grade. Volatile content is also related to the suitability of a coal for manufacturing coke, a product important for iron ore smelting.

According to the best estimates made by the U.S. Geological Survey, about 7.64 trillion metric tons of coal remains unexploited. Thus we have so far used up only 1.7 percent. These figures include only coal deposits minable by present technology. Trillions of tons of additional coal exists, but the deposits are either so deep or in such thin beds that we cannot easily mine them by current methods. There are many new technologies that may possibly allow the recovery of such coal. Some experiments have

Table 22-1
Estimated remaining coal resources of the United States. (Figures are for resources remaining in the ground.)

Category	Billions (10^9) of short tons
Identified resources	
Reserve base	424
Additional	1307
	1731
Hypothetical resources	
0–3000 ft overburden	1849
3000–6000 ft overburden	388
	2237
Total	3968

Source: From P. Averitt, *Coal Resources of the United States, January 1, 1974,* U.S. Geological Survey, 1974.

already succeeded in chemically transforming the coal into gas while it is underground, without using mines or miners. Other ideas include underground combustion and conversion to steam or electrical energy. In any event, there is enough coal to last for a long time.

The problems involved in the recovery and use of coal—problems that make it less desirable

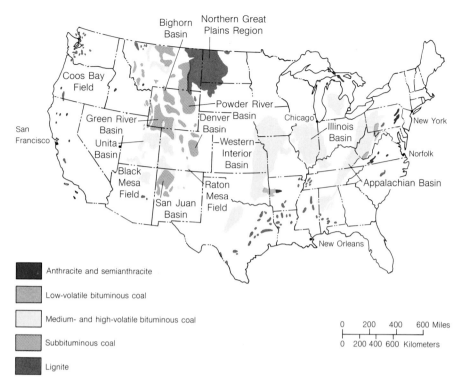

Figure 22-15
Coal fields of the conterminous United States. [After U.S. Geological Survey.]

	Identified resources	Undiscovered resources	
		0–3000-ft overburden	3000–6000-ft overburden
Recoverable	200*	1300	0
	190†		
Submarginal	1200		340

*In beds 42 in. or more thick for bituminous coal and anthracite, and beds 10 ft or more thick for subbituminous coal and lignite.

†In beds 28–42 in thick for bituminous coal and anthracite, and beds 3–5 ft thick for subbituminous and lignite.

Figure 22-16
Scaled diagram of coal resources in the United States (billions of short tons). The reliability of estimates decreases downward and to the right. [Compiled by P. Averitt, February 1972. U.S. Geological Survey.]

	Identified resources	Undiscovered resources	
		Extension of known resources	Undiscovered and unappraised
Recoverable	0	0	0
Paramarginal	160–600	850	500
Submarginal	1600	2500	20,000

Figure 22-17
Scaled diagram of oil-shale resources in the United States (billions of barrels). The reliability of estimates decreases downward and to the right. [Compiled by D. S. Duncan, February 1972. U.S. Geological Survey.]

than oil or gas—still remain. Much coal contains appreciable amounts of sulfur combined in the mineral pyrite (ferrous sulfide, FeS_2), which vaporizes during combustion to liberate noxious sulfur gas to the atmosphere. Coal ash amounts to several percent of the weight of the unburned coal, and poses a significant disposal problem. Though coal can be converted into oil in chemical engineering plants, the process is expensive. The smoke from coal combustion is a serious air pollution nuisance and must be controlled at the smokestack. Coal mining, particularly strip mining, can ravage the countryside. Underground mining accidents cost the lives of some miners each year, and many suffer from "black lung" and other pulmonary diseases. These human costs are as important to consider as possible dangers of other energy sources, such as nuclear reactors. None of these drawbacks, however, is likely to prevent the increased use of this important fuel, for it is one of the largest resources we have.

OIL SHALE AND TAR SANDS

Known for many years but practically untouched are large reserves of oil that can be extracted from oil shale and tar sands. Oil shales are fine-grained sedimentary rocks containing a high proportion of solid organic matter mixed with the various minerals; some contain small amounts of liquid oil. This organic matter, called **kerogen,** has the same general origin as the other common organic materials, all ultimately derived from plants and animal matter. This complex and poorly understood solid mixture of carbon compounds has an extremely important property that is of practical value. If it is heated and the vapors are distilled, oil can be recovered from the shale. Some oil shales can produce up to 150 gallons of oil per ton, but most yield about 25 to 50 gallons per ton.

Reserves of oil shales are known moderately well. Like coal, they occur as beds whose extent can be fairly reliably predicted. They are less abundant than coal, however, and have not been well explored in many parts of the world. Because many oil shales are too low in amount of recoverable oil to make mining economical, the total practical resource is far less than the total amount of oil shale. Geologists of the U.S. Geological Survey have estimated a total world resource of about 3100 billion barrels of oil contained in oil shales that would yield more than 10 gallons of oil per ton. That figure is half again as much as all liquid petroleum in the world, but it is deceptively high, for it must be reduced to only 190 billion barrels that are recoverable under mining technology known

Figure 22-18
Typical cliffs in the principal oil-shale group of the Green River Formation. Garfield County, Colorado. [Photo by D. E. Winchester, U.S. Geological Survey.]

today. But this is still a respectable figure and clearly a significant future resource.

A little less than half of the world's supply of oil shale, about 80 billion barrels, is in the Green River Shale of Eocene age in Wyoming, Utah, and Colorado. Though pilot plants have been in operation for years, little serious attempt has yet been made to exploit these rich reserves commercially, partly because up to now it has not been competitive in price with oil. In addition, disposal of immense tonnages of waste shale from the extraction process presents a serious problem, particularly in areas that do not have much water. The combination of difficulty, expense of extraction, and adverse effect on environment makes it unlikely that shale oil will be a major useable supply in the foreseeable future.

A more unusual occurrence of organic matter useable as fuel is an asphalt or **tar sand.** Oil of a type similar to liquid petroleum can be recovered from these sands, and geologic evidence points to the tar as being a transformed product of a once-liquid petroleum. Some deposits of tar sands are oil pools that have "dried up" and become tarry by loss of the volatile hydrocarbon

fractions; some are exposed at the surface by erosion. Others show signs of having been deposited as a combination of sand and oil, the oil having seeped from older formations. Some of the largest deposits, the Athabaska tar sands of Cretaceous age in Alberta, Canada, may be of this origin. The Athabaska deposit is a great resource that is now beginning to be exploited. Estimates are that 300 billion barrels of oil are recoverable from this one region. Tar sands are poorly known, and there are no reliable figures on world reserves. They are expensive to recover, the separation of the tar from the sand is difficult. As with oil shale, recovery technology will have most to do with its future as an energy resources.

THE FUTURE OF FOSSIL FUELS

One of the currently popular occupations of geologists, economists, and others concerned with energy sources is to estimate our future dependence on fossil fuels. M. King Hubbert, the dean of such predictors, has concluded that if oil and gas continue to be used mainly for

**The Body of the Earth:
Internal Processes**

a

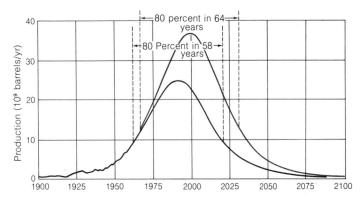

Figure 22-19
(a) Cycle of world coal production is plotted on the basis of estimated supplies and rates of production. The top curve reflects Averitt's estimate of 7.6×10^{12} metric tons as the initial supply of minable coal; the bottom curve reflects an estimate of 4.3×10^{12} metric tons. The curve that rises to the top of the graph shows the trend if production were to continue rising at the present rate of 3.56 percent per year. The amount of coal mined and burned in the century beginning in 1870 is shown by the black area at left. (b) Cycle of world oil production is plotted on the basis of two estimates of the amount of oil that will ultimately be produced. The colored curve reflects Ryman's estimate of 2100×10^9 barrels, and the black curve represents an estimate of 1350×10^9 barrels. [From "The Energy Resources of the Earth" by M. K. Hubbert. Copyright © 1971 by Scientific American, Inc. All rights reserved.]

their energy, and as the major resource for satisfying the world's continually climbing energy appetite, the great bulk of the world's supply will be exhausted in a century. Under these conditions the world's coal supply will last 300 to 400 years, but not that long if it is the main energy source. Oil shale and tar sands will add some years, but will not alter the picture greatly.

For the United States the energy problem is acute, for we will have used up the vast bulk of our oil and gas supplies sometime between 1990 and 2000. Already partially dependent on imports, we will then be wholly dependent on foreign supplies, on coal and oil shale, or sources of energy alternative to fossil fuels.

ALTERNATIVE ENERGY SOURCES

Some alternative energy sources are rather familiar, such as hydroelectric power from turbines driven by falling water. Hydroelectric power is clean and cheap. If all the available sites in the world were utilized for hydroelectric plants, the world's energy needs at present levels, now largely supplied by fossil fuels, could be barely satisfied. But think of the cost. Much of our beautiful scenery—mountain canyons, gorges, and waterfalls—would be drowned in reservoirs behind dams containing power plants. Great areas would be flooded by reservoirs, which would have only a limited "lifetime"; within a few decades, or a century at most, they would become so silted up with sediment brought in by streams that the dams would become useless. It is doubtful that we can or would want to solve the world's energy problems by converting entirely to water power.

The movement of powerful tides can be used in some places to generate hydroelectric power. The French hydroelectric plant at La Rance uses strong tides surging back and forth across an estuary. The Passamaquoddy tidal power project in Maine and New Brunswick has been proposed to the U.S. Congress for years to do the same. Yet if all the available tidal power sites in the world were utilized, it would add only 1 percent to the total possible water power of the Earth.

Solar energy is another source of power that scientists have been investigating. In a very specialized way, it has shown its usefulness in powering artificial satellites and scientific experiments on the Moon. Since all of our major natural energy sources come from the Sun anyway, why not convert its rays to power? The power of the Sun's rays, if all were converted, would amount to about a hundred-thousand times the present electric-power capacity of the world, more than enough if it could be done. It is nondepletable; the Sun will continue to shine at least for the next several billion years. The major problem is that we must harvest the Sun's rays over a great area if we are to produce much power for a central electricity generator. The average solar power available is only about 0.024 of a watt for each square centimeter of ground surface illuminated. It has been calculated that to generate 1000 megawatts, a power plant would need at least ten times that much solar energy, and that would require a large collecting area, about 42 square kilometers. To power a significant part of the North American continent completely in this way would require many thousands of square kilometers. One proposal envisions using a great area of desert in the southwestern United States for a solar power plant. Space requirements probably limit the future for solar energy as a source of centrally generated electricity for much of the world, but there is a future for solar energy in other ways. Solar energy may assume an important role in heating buildings and making hot water in regions where sunny days are frequent enough, as in most of the United States. Many experimental homes and larger buildings are being built to use solar energy in part.

Geothermal power. Because of the strong association of heat and steam with energy and power, it was natural for power engineers to turn their attention to using the Earth's heat to drive electrical generators, especially in regions of active hot springs and geysers. In 1904, Italian engineers first put the natural steam vents at Larderello to work to make power. That plant can now produce 370 megawatts (million watts) of electricity. In the past few decades, generating plants have been built in the United States, Japan, the Soviet Union, New Zealand, and other countries, all taking advantage of abnormally high heat flow produced by volcanic activity. The United States plant, at the Geysers, 75 miles north of San Francisco, is in its second decade of production and is now producing more than 400 megawatts from almost 100 steam wells. In a few years that plant plans to expand to a capacity of 847 megawatts, enough to supply all the electricity needs of San Francisco. Interest is now great in the development of geothermal power in the Imperial Valley in

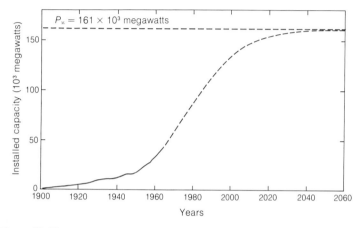

Figure 22-20
United States installed and potential waterpower capacity. The ultimate maximum power capacity, P_x, has been estimated by the Federal Power Commission to be about 161,000 megawatts. [From *Resources and Man*, National Academy of Sciences–National Research Council. W. H. Freeman and Company. Copyright © 1969.]

Figure 22-21
In a recently proposed solar power plant, sunlight falls on specially coated collectors and raises the temperature of a liquid metal to 1000°F. A heat exchanger transfers the heat so collected to steam, which then turns a turbogenerator as in a conventional power plant. A salt reservoir holds enough heat to keep generating steam during the night and when the sun is hidden by clouds. [From "The Conversion of Energy" by C. M. Summers. Copyright © 1971 by Scientific American, Inc. All rights reserved.]

southern California. At the beginning of 1974 the world energy production from all geothermal sources was 1100 megawatts. Most of this comes from Italy, New Zealand, and the United States.

The United States now produces about 350,000 megawatts from all power sources. It is estimated, according to a National Science Foundation report, that by 1985 the Geysers and all other geothermal energy sources in the United States, if fully utilized at highest efficiency, will have the potential of supplying a little less than half the power needed now. That is not quite as good as it sounds, though, because energy demands in the United States are *doubling* every eight years. It is also a very optimistic estimate. A more realistic appraisal is given by Donald E. White of the U.S. Geological Survey. He has calculated that if all the world's useable geothermal power were fully utilized, about 60,000 meagawatts would be available each year for 50 years until total depletion, which is of the same general amounts as would

be available from tidal power if it were fully exploited. Geothermal power thus will not satisfy the world's demands by any means. In those regions of recent or active volcanism, where geothermal power can be produced, there are some serious disadvantages that temper its attractiveness. Tapping heat sources in the ground requires drilling wells and pumping steam or hot water from volcanically heated underground water reservoirs. That is why geothermal power is a depletable resource, for it is like the continued pumping of ordinary ground-water aquifers, which may result in using up the water (see Chapter 6). These hot waters cannot be recharged *and* heated rapidly enough to maintain the supply indefinitely. Experience at Lardarello, Italy, the oldest geothermal field, shows that wells maintain their heat and water output for only about 10 years. More and more wells have had to be drilled to maintain high power production, and it is apparent that the whole field is being depleted. Superheated water used in some plants dissolves much material from

Table 22-2
Estimated heat content of geothermal resource base of the United States (heat in the ground, without regard to recoverability).

Type of system	Identified systems		Identified + estimate for undiscovered
	Number	Heat content (10^{18} cal)*	Heat content (10^{18} cal)*
Hydrothermal convection systems (to 3 km depth, ~10,000 ft, near the maximum depth drilled in geothermal areas).			
Vapor-dominated (steam) systems	3	26	~50
High-temperature hot-water systems (over 150°C)	63	370	~1,600
Intermediate-temperature hot-water systems (90° to 150°C)	224	345	~1,400
Total	290	~741	~3,050
Hot igneous systems (0 to 10 km) Molten parts of 48 best known, including Alaska and Hawaii		~13,000	
Crystallized parts and hot margins of same 48		~12,000	
Total		~25,000	~100,000
Regional conductive environments (0 to 10 km; all 50 states subdivided into 19 heat-flow provinces of 3 basic types, Eastern, Basin-and-Range, and Sierra Nevada).			
Total, all states		~8,000,000	~8,000,000
Overall total		8,025,741	8,103,050

Source: From D. F. White and D. L. Williams, Assessment of Geothermal Resources of the United States—1975, U.S. Geological Survey, 1975.
* 10^{18} calories is equivalent to the heat of combustion of ~690 million barrels of petroleum or ~154 million short tons of coal.

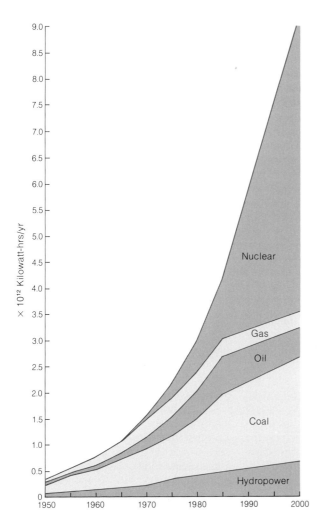

Figure 22-22
Net United States production of electricity by primary source, 1950-2000. This prediction assumes a steadily increasing role for nuclear power in the next decades. (From *Energy and the Environment.* U.S. Council on Environmental Quality, 1973.]

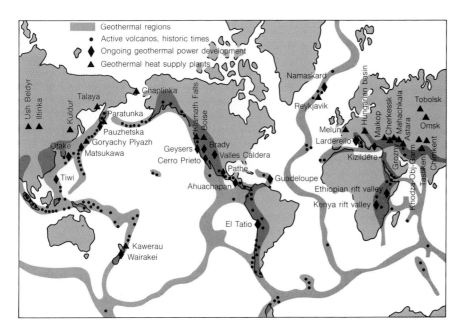

Figure 22-23
The geothermal regions of the world are in general the zones of active volcanism. [From *Oil and Gas Journal,* May 13, 1974, p. 103.]

rock and pipes and thereby produces a significant pollution problem when discharged into streams. Thus, in spite of some attractive features, the pollution side-effects, the limited amount of power obtainable, and the costs of obtaining it may not make geothermal power the best answer for all geothermal regions. And it certainly does not answer the needs of the many millions of people living in the interior or along the eastern edge of North America, where volcanic heat sources have geologically long ago cooled off. For that population, the need for great power supplies is likely to be met ultimately by nuclear reactors.

NUCLEAR POWER

Nuclear physicists foresaw the possibility of peaceful uses of the gigantic amounts of energy stored in the atomic nucleus even before they were able first to liberate it in the form of an atomic bomb in 1944. Their predictions have started to come true as countries all over the world are building new atomic reactors at an increasing rate. In its full potential, nuclear energy can supply virtually unlimited power to the world. In this book we cannot go into the complex of matters relating to the best engineering designs, reactor safety, radioactive leakage to the environment, or thermal pollution. Those are technological problems that will need to be solved before we can light up the world with all the power it wants, whether for the United States' highly advanced needs or for the growing demands of the newly developing countries. But one aspect of nuclear energy is most definitely in the geologic province: the question of reserves of nuclear fuel—in particular, uranium.

The older and still most widely used nuclear energy plants use the fission of Uranium-235 (U^{235}), the radioactive isotope whose nucleus spontaneously splits. When enough of this element is brought together in a carefully engineered assembly, called a pile, the controlled fission reaction proceeds steadily to produce a great quantity of energy, released as heat. Fission of one gram of U^{235} liberates energy equivalent to about 2.7 metric tons of coal or 13.7 barrels of crude oil. The uranium is "used up" by this process, appearing as various fission products, other elements that cannot be used for energy production. An average nuclear power plant of this type, producing 1000 megawatts of electricity, will use up about 3 kilograms (6.6 pounds) of U^{235} each day. Uranium-235 constitutes only one atom out of every 141 of the average mixture of uranium isotopes mined (usually referred to as U_3O_8), so the amount of U_3O_8 production needed to support a large number of reactors is large. The U.S. Atomic Energy Commission calculates that at projected rates of nuclear power plant production, the United States will need a reserve of 650,000 tons of U_3O_8 by 1980.

The estimated reserves of U_3O_8 ore available in the United States that are of high enough quality to be mined under present economic conditions amount to just a little over that, about

Figure 22-24
In a nuclear power plant (a) the fission of uranium-235 releases the energy to make steam, which then goes through the same cycle as in a fossil-fuel power plant. Under development are nuclear breeder reactors (b), in which surplus neutrons are captured by a blanket of nonfissile atoms of uranium-238 or thorium-232, which are transformed into fissile plutonium-239 or uranium-233. The heat of the reactor is removed by liquid sodium. [From "The Conversion of Energy" by C. M. Summers. Copyright © 1971 by Scientific American, Inc. All rights reserved.]

	Identified resources	Undiscovered resources	
		In known districts	In unknown districts
Recoverable	250	500	250
Submarginal	200	400	

Figure 22-25
Scaled diagram of uranium resources of conventional deposits in the United States (thousands of short tons of U_3O_8). The reliability of estimates decreases downward and to the right. [Compiled by A. P. Butler, Jr., and W. I. Finch, February 1972. U.S. Geological Survey.]

660,000 tons. The world reserve picture is somewhat brighter, there being about twice as many tons in reserve as needed for projected increases, which are about double the needs of the United States. As with the fossil fuel reserve situation, there are still new discoveries of uranium being made. Nevertheless, geological estimates of uranium ore indicate that there will not be much more than a 25-year supply of high-grade ore before the supply runs out, and we will have to mine poorer ores.

Uranium is present in very small amounts in the Earth's crust, constituting only 0.00016 percent of the average crustal rock. It is typically present as small quantities of the mineral uraninite (UO_2), frequently called by its common name, pitchblende, in granites and other silicic rocks and associated hydrothermal veins. Under near-surface groundwater conditions this uranium may become oxidized and dissolved, transported in the groundwater, and later reprecipitated as uraninite if it becomes reduced by organic matter, which it may encounter in sedimentary rocks. The richest ores in the United States occur in the Triassic and Jurassic sedimentary rocks of the Colorado Plateau in western Colorado and adjacent parts of Utah, Arizona, Wyoming, and New Mexico. Rich Canadian deposits are found both in hydrothermal veins in the Great Bear Lake region of the Northwest Territories and Precambrian conglomerate sediments north of Lake Huron in Ontario. It is these rich deposits that are esti-

mated as reserves, and because of the great effort in uranium exploration after World War II, we know where most of them are.

The story does not end here, however, for there are much larger reserves of lower quality ore, many of which are in the Colorado Plateau region. In addition, there are abundant low-grade deposits in the Devonian Chattanooga Shale, a black, organic-rich sediment underlying large parts of Tennessee, Kentucky, Ohio, Indiana, and Illinois in the flat-lying region of sediments on the western border of the Appalachian Mountains and interior regions. This formation contains uranium equivalent in energy to 5000 barrels of oil for each square meter of its surface. These huge reserves can be exploited when new technology, the breeder reactor, is developed to the point that they can be economically mined. By going to lower-grade ores, we can plan on the basis of thirty or more times the present resources, more than enough to satisfy our needs for far into the future.

The breeder reactor will make the picture brighter because it does not simply use up the U^{235}, as do the fission reactors. In the breeder, U^{235} fission is used to create new radioactive elements, such as plutonium-239 from uranium-238, and more nuclear fuel is produced than consumed. In addition, it increases the number of useable ores; the entire supply of natural uranium and thorium can be used instead of only U^{235}. Breeders are under active development in various countries, and some are already producing power. Technological problems remain, particularly in the important area of reactor safety, but there is reason to believe that the breeder can be made safe and efficient as a major supplier of power for the world.

Nevertheless, there remain some serious questions about the future of breeder reactors. The plutonium produced by the breeder is the same material that is used to manufacture nuclear bombs. A mere 25 kilograms (55 pounds) of plutonium is enough to make a big bomb, and each reactor might contain as much as 2.5 tons of this strategic material. Security of such a storehouse of plutonium in many widely scattered plants in many countries is not an easy problem to deal with. Finding ways to avoid widespread nuclear proliferation among many countries—and even among criminal groups—will be a central political issue in nuclear energy. The toxicity of plutonium is another matter for concern, and points to another issue that must be faced when we expand our nuclear power plant: how to dispose of radioactive waste (see Chapter 12, p. 322). As yet there is no generally agreed upon plan for storage of high-level wastes for the hundreds or thousands of years required before they cease to be dangerous. No one wants to leave to our next generations the combined legacy of depleted energy resources and an unmanageable environmental hazard.

Beyond the breeder, nuclear physicists are looking to the possibility of building a fusion reactor, utilizing the same nuclear processes that fuel the Sun, in which the heavy hydrogen isotope deuterium can be made to react to produce helium with an immense production of energy. Small laboratory models have been built that show promise. Because deuterium is abundant as a minor constituent of the water of the oceans, reserves are not a problem. The fusion reactor of this type awaits the application of science and engineering to make a workable reactor that will make energy so abundant and cheap that the world will not need to worry about an energy crisis. If it cannot be made to work, and there is no guarantee that it can, we will have to wrestle with energy conservation in a far more serious way. Sooner or later, we will have to make difficult choices about what we spend our energy resources on. Even now it is apparent that we must reduce our inordinate demands on energy resources to avoid being forced to rely on unsafe or environmentally degrading power sources. That reduction implies questions of our appetite for energy-hungry machines and our expanding population.

MINERALS AS ECONOMIC RESOURCES

Aside from agricultural products, just about everything we use in modern society comes from the ground, including all of the metals and their alloys and the thousands of products made from the chemicals refined from natural deposits. At various places in this book, we have mentioned the practical uses of different minerals and rocks. In this section, we will survey a broad range of useful materials and discuss them in an economic context, because, at the moment that commercial utility enters the picture, matters of cost and price become important.

Just as fossil-fuel reserves are not limitless, neither are the economically recoverable deposits of many useful minerals. Thus the study of mineral reserves is as important to our subject as the study of their geologic occurrence. The distribution of mineral resources, economic aspects of their recovery, and estimates of reserves are parts of the specialized field called **economic geology.** Inevitably, students of this subject must know modern economics in addition to geology. Moreover, because it takes energy to mine and purify mineral deposits, the economics and geology of energy are important components of decision making in the mineral industry. One of the major decisions an economic geologist must make is whether a mineral deposit has economic significance, and that assessment depends on a knowledge of how mineral resources are distributed geologically.

What Is a Mineral Deposit? The chemical elements of the Earth's crust—the portion of the globe that is readily available to us for mining and drilling—are widely distributed in many different kinds of minerals, and those minerals are found in a great variety of rocks. From the beginning of this book, we have discussed examples of how nature homogenizes materials at some times and places and segregates them at others. In most places, a particular element will be found in amounts that tend to be close to its average abundance in the crust—that is, it is homogenized with the other elements. Segregation occurs in a smaller number of geologic situations. The occurrences of elements in much higher abundance—those in which some geologic process has operated to segregate much higher quantities of the element than normal—are the ones that interest us, because the richer the deposit, the cheaper it is to recover the resource, both in terms of energy and in terms of money. Rich deposits of metals are **ores;** the minerals containing these metals are **ore minerals.** Ore minerals include sulfides (the dominant group), oxides, and silicates. In addition, some metals, such as gold, are found in their **native** state—that is, uncombined with other elements.

The average crustal abundance of a number of economically important elements, determined by evaluation of a great many chemical analyses of all rock types, is shown in Table 22-3.

Some of the elements such as aluminum, iron, and magnesium, are so abundant that any average crustal rock could conceivably be used as a raw material, though not necessarily economically. In contrast are the elements of low abundance, such as gold, platinum, and mercury, which are present in such small amounts in the average rock that enormous quantities of rock would have to be refined to recover even small amounts. *Mineral deposits of economic value are those in which an element occurs in much higher abundance than the average crustal rock, sufficiently high to make it economically worthwhile to mine.* Many of the most valuable mineral deposits are metal-ore deposits, and much of economic geology is concerned with them.

The **concentration factor**—that is, the ratio of the abundance of an element in a mineral deposit to its average abundance—is highly variable and depends on the particular element and its average crustal abundance (Table 22-4). Iron, one of the common elements of the crust, has an average abundance of 5.8%. A good iron ore contains 50% iron; thus its concentration factor is about 10. A less abundant metal, such as copper, which has a crustal abundance of 0.0058%, is concentrated by factors from 60 to 100 in its economic ores. Even more spectacular are the rarer elements, such as mercury or gold, which have concentration factors in the thousands. The crustal abundances of the elements are related to their atomic number and chemical affinities in a complex way, as has been described in Chapter 1. But the concentration factors, though generally increasing with decreasing crustal abundance, depend largely on the ways in which the metals are held in crystal structures, and their solubilities in various geologic solutions, such as groundwaters, hydrothermal solutions, or sea water.

Because the elements are so widely distributed in many common rocks, the issue of resources and reserves is dominated by costs of recovery. We could, theoretically, take almost any average rock and extract both abundant and

Table 22-3
Crustal abundance of economically important elements.

Name	Chemical symbol	Atomic number	Crustal abundance (% by weight)
Aluminum	Al	13	8.00
Iron	Fe	26	5.8
Magnesium	Mg	12	2.77
Potassium	K	19	1.68
Titanium	Ti	22	0.86
Hydrogen	H	1	0.14
Phosphorus	P	15	0.101
Manganese	Mn	25	0.100
Fluorine	F	9	0.0460
Sulfur	S	16	0.030
Chlorine	Cl	17	0.019
Vanadium	V	23	0.017
Chromium	Cr	24	0.0096
Zinc	Zn	30	0.0082
Nickel	Ni	28	0.0072
Copper	Cu	29	0.0058
Cobalt	Co	27	0.0028
Lead	Pb	82	0.00010
Boron	B	5	0.0007
Beryllium	Be	4	0.00020
Arsenic	As	33	0.00020
Tin	Sn	50	0.00015
Molybdenum	Mb	42	0.00012
Uranium	U	92	0.00016
Tungsten	W	74	0.00010
Silver	Ag	47	0.000008
Mercury	Hg	80	0.000002
Platinum	Pt	78	0.0000005
Gold	Au	79	0.0000002

Table 22-4
Concentration factors of some economically important elements needed for profitable mining.

Element	Crustal abundance (% by weight)	Concentration factor*
Aluminum	8.00	3–4
Iron	5.8	5–10
Copper	0.0058	80–100
Nickel	0.0072	150
Zinc	0.0082	300
Uranium	0.00016	1,200
Lead	0.00010	2,000
Gold	0.0000002	4,000
Mercury	0.000002	100,000

Sources: Data from B. J. Skinner, *Earth Resources*, Prentice-Hall, 1969; D. A. Brobst and W. P. Pratt, *Mineral Resources of the U.S.*, U.S. Geological Survey Prof. Paper 820, 1973.
* Concentration factor = abundance in deposit/crustal abundance.

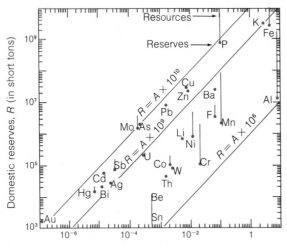

Figure 22-26
Domestic reserves of elements compared to their abundance in the Earth's crust. Tonnage of ore minable now is shown by a dot; tonnage of lower-grade ores whose exploitation depends upon future technological advances or higher prices is shown by a bar. [From McKelvey, 1973, "Mineral Resource Estimates and Public Policy," in *U.S. Mineral Resources,* U.S. Geological Survey.]

rare elements from it, given enough money and energy. So, from that point of view, it is clear that we will never "run out" of any vital elements. What is important is the exhaustion of high-grade mineral deposits that are relatively inexpensive to mine and purify. Because the distribution patterns of all elements are like those shown in Figure 22-25, once the deposits of the highest grade are mined out, we proceed to mine those of lower grades—that is, deposits whose concentration factors are lower. This is not always an orderly retreat to a deposit that is only a little lower in grade. We now mine some extraordinarily rich deposits of certain metals, such as mercury, and, when they are depleted, we will have to resort to deposits of ore that are much, much poorer. At some point in the history of mining a certain element, it may become economic to reuse (or "recycle") the element from worn-out manufactured materials that contain it. Gold and platinum, among other valuable metals, have been recycled for many years. Whether or not to recycle, of course, is

not just a matter of comparing the economics of recycling versus that of mining new deposits. An important consideration is the disposal of used items. The practice of recycling automobiles is now increasing, not so much because we need the scrap metal but because of the desirability of keeping the junked cars from littering the landscape and choking the side streets of our cities.

All such questions can be resolved in a reasonable way only if all costs are calculated—not only the costs of mining, smelting, and transportation, but those of waste disposal and pollution control, both by the producer and the consumer. Because energy costs are rapidly rising in response to the belated recognition that energy sources are not unlimited, and therefore out to be governed by the economics of scarcity rather than the economics of abundance, the cost pattern of mineral resources is bound to change drastically in the next decades. Smelting aluminum from its ore, for example, takes enormous quantities of electricity. It is estimated that the aluminum industry of the United States claimed 3 percent of the country's total power budget in 1965. For some materials, recovery from lower-grade ores will require such high expenditures of energy that it will be more economical to substitute other materials. In the future, we may well become familiar with costs of materials expressed in terms of units of energy, such as joules* per ton, as a measure on a par with dollars per ton.

The economic geologist, mindful of these costs, naturally seeks to minimize them, if he can, by finding new high-grade deposits rather than automatically resorting to the use of previously known lower-grade ones. The tools he uses for exploration are the subjects we have explored in this book. Understanding of Earth processes and Earth history, knowledge of how to use geophysics and geochemistry in exploration, and practical training in recognizing and mapping rocks and minerals in the field are brought together in the search. The prospector for mineral resources needs to be familiar with the geology of igneous, sedimentary, and meta-

---

*Energy is defined as the capacity for doing work. A **joule** is the work done when one **newton** of force is applied through a distance of one meter. A newton is the force required to accelerate one kilogram of mass one meter per second per second. A joule is equal to 0.2390 **calories,** the calorie being the amount of heat necessary to raise the temperature of one gram of water from **14°C.** to **15°C.** In electrical terms, the unit of power (the time rate at which work is done) is the **watt,** which is the production of energy at a rate of one joule per second. See appendix I.

morphic rocks, for mineral deposits are found in all three. But he becomes more specialized than most geologists, always looking for the special situation in which nature has segregated a purer product from the surrounding rock masses.

GEOLOGY OF MINERAL DEPOSITS

A mineral segregation is the product of so many different kinds of geologic processes that we would need to restate most of this book to catalogue them. To give some idea of the origins of mineral deposits, we will describe some of the main kinds of geological occurrence of some of the elements of major economic importance.

Hydrothermal Deposits. Many of the most useful ore deposits are found in hydrothermal veins—that is, in joints and fractures filled with minerals precipitated by heated waters, usually those emanating from an igneous intrusion (see Chapters 14 and 16). Some of the ores are found in the veins themselves; others are found in the rock adjacent to the veins that have been altered by heating and infiltration by the vein-forming solutions, a process similar, in some ways, to contact metamorphism.

Most hydrothermal deposits are thought to be magmatic in origin because most are associated with igneous intrusions; in some places, several deposits occur around a single intrusion, and the veins are more abundant nearer the rocks of the intrusive bodies. The minerals found in hydrothermal veins are often similar to those found in volcanic and contact-metamorphic rocks, especially the sulfides of various metals: iron (FeS_2, pyrite), lead (PbS, galena), zinc (ZnS, sphalerite), mercury (HgS, cinnabar), and copper (CuS, covellite; Cu_2S, chalcocite; and $CuFeS_2$, chalcopyrite). Only some magmas appear to be closely associated with ore deposits; some of these liquids appear to have been particularly enriched in one or a group of metallic elements and so have generated hydrothermal veins rich in the sulfides of those metals. Some hydrothermal deposits do not seem to be clearly associated with any intrusion, and many economic geologists believe that these are the result of groundwater circulating through areas of abnormal heating that are related to an episode of regional metamorphism.

Where hydrothermal solutions reach the surface, they become hot springs and geysers, many of which precipitate different kinds of miner-

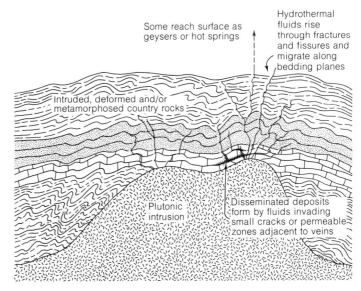

Figure 22-27
Many ore deposits are found in hydrothermal veins formed by hot solutions rising from magmas. As the solutions cool and react with surrounding rocks, they may precipitate ore minerals together with quartz, calcite, or other common vein-filling minerals.

als—including lead, zinc, and mercury ores—as they cool. At depth, such fluids deposit their metallic ores as they traverse the surrounding country rock and cool. Geochemists studying the ore-forming process have concluded that the ability of water to dissolve and later precipitate many of the metallic elements is dependent on the high temperatures and pressures found at depth in the crust and on chemical interactions with surrounding rocks. The ability of hot waters to carry significant quantities of metals in solution is partly the result of changes in the properties of the water itself and partly because, when the solutions become relatively concentrated in dissolved substances at high temperatures and pressures, interactions between those substances in solution promote greater solubility.

Much excitement was generated among economic geologists in 1962 when a deep well drilled near the Salton Sea in southern California penetrated rocks with concentrated hydrothermal solutions carrying very large amounts of

Deposits associated with spreading centers

Massive sulfides associated with submarine volcanics

Deposits associated with subduction at a continental border

Porphyry copper deposits

Deposits associated with subduction at island arcs

Volcano-sedimentary
copper sulfides

Sedimentary
sulfide type

Deposits associated with intracontinental hotspots

Tin, copper, lead, zinc, hydrothermal deposits

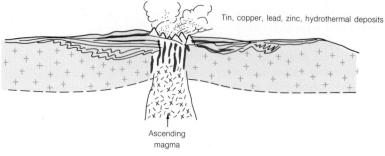

Ascending
magma

Figure 22-28
Metalliferous deposits associated with plate tectonic environments.

such metals as copper and silver. The hydrothermal solutions from the Salton Sea well apparently do not emanate from a deep magma, but are surface waters that have percolated downward into an area of high heat flow and have dissolved material from the rocks in their path. In this area—which may be an extension of the East Pacfic Rise under the continent—the rocks through which the solutions have passed are several kilometers in depth. The rocks there are apparently undergoing regional metamorphism, because the core samples brought up, which have been stratigraphically correlated with undeformed sedimentary rocks elsewhere, are low-grade metamorphic rocks.

In 1963, one year after the Salton Sea well was drilled, a most remarkable oceanographic find was made in the Red Sea: Several deep basins were discovered at the bottom that were filled with hot brines, dramatically hotter and much more concentrated in dissolved salts than the overlying normal Red Sea water. The bottom sediments of those basins are rich in precipitates of oxides and sulfides of copper, zinc, and other metals. Apparently, these hot brines are escaping from the sea floor after travelling upward through subsurface formations below the Red Sea—which lies in a rift-valley area, a young zone of sea-floor spreading. Since then, coring by the deep-sea drilling program has led to the discovery of other areas whose sediments are abnormally rich in such metal ores; one core brought up from sediments of the continental rise about 550 kilometers (350 miles) southeast of New York City contained a small vein of native copper.

These thus far unusual occurrences may provide a clue to a new interpretation of the worldwide distribution of ore deposits, a subject of continuing interest to economic geologists, who use such theories to guide them in their exploration efforts. The central idea of such theories has been the concentration of a major part of the world's ore deposits along major structural zones of the crust in rocks of a relatively few narrow age ranges distributed from the Precambrian to the present. New interpretations are now being proposed that link plate tectonics to major ore deposits by hypothesizing that plate divergences and convergences are the sites of much hydrothermal activity. One recent view is that of Peter Rona, an oceanographer who has been involved in the evolution of the theories of plate tectonics. Some of the following material in this section has been developed from his suggestions. We include it here as an example—not an example of established theory, but one hypothesis typical of the ferment in the field.

A great many of the major deposits of sulfide ores of hydrothermal origin or associated with volcanism or plutonism are found on modern or ancient plate-convergence boundaries, including those of the Coast Ranges, the Andes, the eastern Mediterranean to Pakistan, the Philippine Islands, and Japan. Many gold deposits, such as those of Alaska, Canada, and California, also seem to be associated with convergent plate boundaries of the present or past. The mechanism by which this gold was deposited may involve hydrothermal solutions associated with magmatic activity generated by a descending lithospheric plate in a subduction zone, the hydrothermal solutions having dissolved metals from the rocks they traversed in their circulation.

Divergent plate boundaries are the sites of the hot brines of the Red Sea and the Salton Sea, suggesting that hydrothermal fluids are generated by sea water or meteoric water invading fractured rocks in the high heat-flow zone along a spreading ridge, perhaps mixing with some magmatic water from upwelling basalt. Sulfide-ore deposits on the island of Cyprus in the Mediterranean are located along what may be a former mid-ocean ridge, a portion of which has since been uplifted. The stratigraphic sequence in this area extends downward from marine sediment, through extrusive volcanic rocks (including pillow lavas), to intrusive igneous rocks (mainly dikes), which overlie crystalline basement rocks. This sequence is typical of oceanic crustal sections. The hydrothermal ores of copper and iron are found in roughly elliptical basins—bodies comparable in size to the small hot-brine basins of the Red Sea—and the surrounding sedimentary rocks are chemically similar to metal-enriched sediments of active mid-ocean ridges. Other deposits may be associated with continental hot-spot volcanism; some tin deposits and hydrothermal copper ores may be of this type.

How well these ideas will serve the economic geologist in his explorations for new high-grade ores and mineral deposits remains to be seen. Though it does provide a new general framework, the mountain belts so far suggested for exploration are, for the most part, those that have already been singled out for exploration on the basis of earlier theories. How much undersea exploration may be stimulated is an open question—depending, in part, on the development of

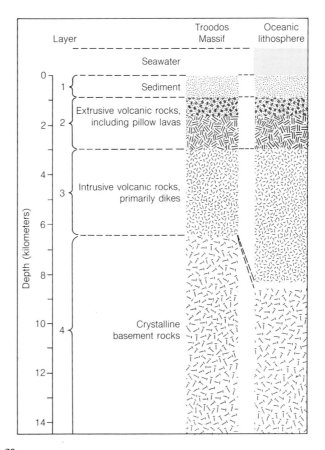

Figure 22-29 .
Close correspondence between the layered sequence of rocks in the Troodos Massif (left) and that of the oceanic lithosphere (right) is evident from this comparison. The geological structure of the Troodos Massif was determined directly from rock outcrops; the structure of the oceanic lithosphere was determined indirectly by seismic-refraction techniques. The sulfide ore bodies of the Troodos Massif are in the upper portion of layer made up of extrusive volcanic rocks. Pillow shapes form when volcanic lava cools on the sea floor. [From "Plate Tectonics and Mineral Resources" by P. A. Rona. Copyright © 1973 by Scientific American, Inc. All rights reserved.]

580

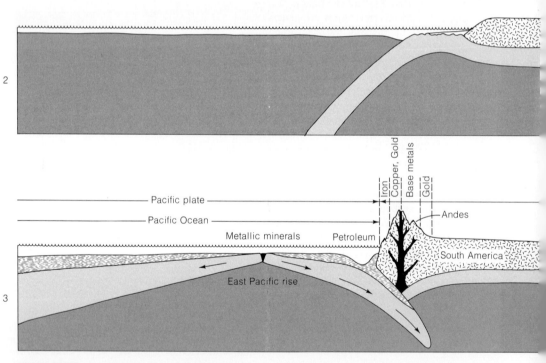

Figure 22-30

Role of plate boundaries in the accumulation of mineral deposits is exemplified in this sequence of cross-sectional views of the development of the South Atlantic Ocean, according to Peter A. Rona. In state 1 a single ancestral continent, called Pangaea, is rifted into two continents (South American and Africa) about a divergent plate boundary. In state 2 the oceanic crust created by the process of sea-floor spreading from the divergent plate boundary (a precursor of the mid-Atlantic ridge) rafts South America westward and is compensated for by the consumption of oceanic crust at a trench (a convergent plate boundary) that develops to the west of South America. Thick layers of rock salt, organic matter and metallic minerals accumulate in the Atlantic Sea during this early stage of continental drift. In state 3 continued sea-floor spreading from the mid-Atlantic ridge widens the Atlantic into an ocean, rafts South America westward over the trench,

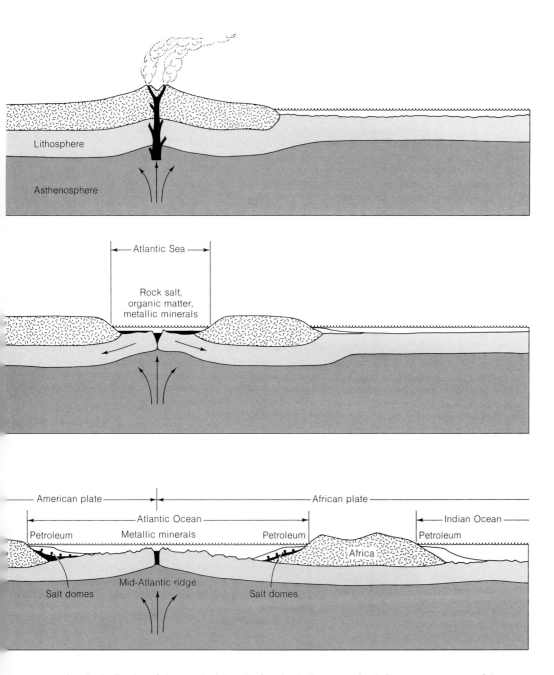

Lithosphere

Asthenosphere

Atlantic Sea

Rock salt,
organic matter,
metallic minerals

American plate

African plate

Atlantic Ocean

Indian Ocean

Petroleum

Metallic minerals

Petroleum

Petroleum

Africa

Salt domes

Mid-Atlantic ridge

Salt domes

reversing the inclination of the trench and producing the Andes mountain chain as a consequence of the deformation that develops at the convergent plate boundary along the western margin of South America. Metallic minerals that are melted from the Pacific plate as it plunges under South America ascend through the overlying crustal layers and are deposited in them to form the metal-bearing provinces of the Andes. Meanwhile, in the Atlantic Ocean, metallic minerals continue to accumulate about the mid-Atlantic ridge. Salt originating in the thick layers of rock salt that have been buried under the sediments of the continental margins rises in large, dome-shaped masses that act to trap the oil and gas that are generated from the organic matter that was preserved in the former Atlantic Sea. [From "Plate Tectonics and Mineral Resources" by P. A. Rona, Copyright © 1973 by Scientific American, Inc. All rights reserved.]

an efficient marine technology for deep-sea mining. In any case, the most difficult part of mineral prospecting is pinpointing the generally small ore bodies, most of which seem to be distributed sparsely in an irregular pattern along structurally favorable zones. Zeroing in on them is still mostly a matter of geological common sense and good luck, but newer methods of geophysical and geochemical prospecting show promise of being very helpful in this respect.

Once a hydrothermal deposit is found—perhaps from an outcrop, perhaps from a drill hole—the geologist and mining engineer must attempt to predict the extent of the deposit, both as a guide to future mining and as the basis for estimating reserves. Such predictions are based on the characteristic shapes of ore bodies. **Veins** are bodies of rock that have been deposited along joints, cracks, faults, dikes, bedding planes, or other zones of structural weakness that offered entry for the infiltrating hot waters. Like most igneous dikes, most veins are tabular—that is, thin in comparison to their length and width; others, sometimes called **lodes,** may be very thick, and some may even be pencil-like in shape. Some are uniform in thickness; others pinch and swell in an irregular manner. Many veins are easily distinguished from the surrounding rock because of their distinctly different mineral composition and texture; others may tend to merge imperceptibly with the surrounding rock in an extensive transition zone of rock alteration, and so may not be clearly distinguishable as veins in the field. Some veins contain cavities lined with crystals and crusts, remnants of gas pockets trapped in the fractures through which the hydrothermal solutions percolated.

Important hydrothermal deposits that are dispersed through much larger volumes of rock than vein deposits are called **disseminated deposits.** In igneous and sedimentary rocks alike, the dissemination takes place along abundant cracks and fractures; in sedimentary rocks, it may also take place along zones of higher permeability produced by variations in the lithology of the rocks. One important type of disseminated deposit is exemplified by the **copper porphyry** deposits of the southwestern United States and Chile. These deposits occur in a great number of tiny fractures in porphyritic felsic intrusives (granitic rocks with large feldspar or quartz crystals in a finer-grained matrix) and country rocks surrounding the higher parts of the plutons. Some unknown process associated with the intrusion or its af-

termath broke the rocks into millions of pieces, and hydrothermal solutions penetrated and recemented the rocks with tiny veins and pore fillings. Such widespread dispersal of the ore deposit produces a low-grade but very large resource of many millions of tons of ore, which may be mined economically by large-scale mining methods (see photograph of an open pit mine in one of these deposits in Fig. 3-1). The most common copper mineral in the porphyry is chalcopyrite ($CuFeS_2$).

Sedimentary rocks are the hosts of disseminated hydrothermal deposits in the lead-zinc province of the upper Mississippi Valley, which extends from southwestern Wisconsin to Kansas and Oklahoma. These ores are not associated with any known intrusion, and the evidence from the chemical and isotopic compositions of remnants of ore-depositing fluid encased in tiny cavities in quartz crystals, called **fluid inclusions,** is that the solutions were relatively low in temperature, no more than 150°C. The origin of such solutions is not known, but speculation centers on possible localized heat sources in the lower part of the lithospheric plate. The major minerals of these deposits are lead sulfide (galena, PbS) and zinc sulfide (sphalerite, ZnS). They have been deposited as **replacements** of calcite and dolomite in the surrounding limestones—that is, the solutions have dissolved some carbonate and replaced it with an equal volume of new crystals of sulfide.

Igneous and Contact-metamorphic Deposits. The most important igneous deposits are found as segregations of ore minerals near the bases of layered intrusives, which are formed as minerals crystallizing from a melt settle to the floor of a magma chamber to form distinct layers (see Chapters 14 and 16). One of the largest ore bodies of this type ever found is at Sudbury, Ontario. It is a large mafic intrusive lopolith containing great quantities of layered nickel, copper, and iron sulfides near its base. These sulfide deposits are believed to have formed from crystallization of a dense sulfide-rich liquid that separated from the rest of the cooling magma and sank to the bottom of the chamber before congealing. Important platinum and chromium deposits have been found in layered intrusives in South Africa and Montana. One of the most valuable minerals, diamond, occurs in ultramafic rocks called **kimberlites** that extend to the surface from deep in the crust and upper mantle, where the extremely high pressures needed for their formation are found. These rocks are in the form of narrow pipes, and the mechanism of their eruption to the surface is a matter of controversy.

In Chapter 16, contact metamorphism is described as the transformation of the mineral composition and texture of country rock along zones of contact with igneous intrusives. In this process, minerals of commercial value—such as garnet and emery (corundum), which are used for abrasives—may be formed. Some of the most important deposits of this type are iron ores, such as the small but high-grade deposit of magnetite (Fe_3O_4) near Cornwall, Pennsylvania, where a diabase has intruded and metamorphosed shale. In this, as in most contact-metamorphic deposits, the ore is the result of an interaction of the invaded rock with permeating material from the hot intrusion, not just an alteration produced only by heat and pressure without exchange of material.

Sedimentary Mineral Deposits. Chemical and mechanical segregations of many economically important minerals are the ordinary result of sedimentary processes. Limestones, separated out as chemical precipitates mainly by organisms, are used for agricultural lime, cement, and building stone. Pure sands, abraded and winnowed by waves and currents so that all materials other than quartz are removed, are the raw materials for glassmaking. Coarse sand and gravel, suitable for construction purposes, have been abundantly distributed in many areas of the northern United States and southern Canada by the Pleistocene glaciations; these materials are also widely distributed in channels and former channels of many rivers. Clays of high purity produced by prolonged weathering are used for pottery and ceramics, both for home and for industrial use. Evaporite deposits of gypsum, separated from sea water by fractional crystallization, are used for plaster, and sodium and potassium salts from evaporites have varied uses from table salt to fertilizer. Phosphate rocks—marine shales and limestones enriched in phosphate by the chemical action of deep-sea waters—are the major raw materials of the world's fertilizer industry.

Sedimentary ore deposits are some of the world's most important sources of copper, iron, and other metals. They are chemical precipitates formed in sedimentary environments to which large quantities of the metals were transported in solution. Some of the important sedimentary copper ores, such as those of the Permian Kupferschiefer (German for copper shale) beds of Germany, are possibly the products of interaction between metal-rich sulfides derived from hot brines of hydrothermal origin with bottom sediments.

The major iron ores of the Earth have been found in Precambrian sedimentary rocks. It is now thought that the low oxygen content of the Earth's atmosphere at that time (see Chapter 12, p. 312) allowed great quantities of iron to be transported in its soluble, reduced (ferrous) form into broad, shallow marine environments where it was oxidized to its insoluble (ferric) form and precipitated. In many of these basins, it was deposited in thin layers alternating with layers of chert. Such iron ores of alternating silica and hematite have been called **banded iron ores.** Post-Cambrian iron ores were formed in relatively small, restricted marine basins at times when abundant iron was being leached from the land surface by deep weathering. One of many hypotheses is that the iron was transported in reduced form from land to these basins by marine seepage of groundwaters that were sufficiently acid and poor in oxygen to dissolve large quantities of iron from soils and subsurface formations. In the marine environment, the iron combines with clays or oxidizes and precipitates.

Possibly the most widely publicized (and romanticized) type of mineral prospecting is "panning" for gold, in which the gold seeker shakes a flat pan of river sediment in hopes of turning up the glint of a nugget. Many rich deposits of gold, diamonds, and such heavy-metal ore minerals as magnetite and chromite (Fe_2CrO_4) are found in **placers,** deposits concentrated by the mechanical sorting action of currents. Ore minerals are some of the most common heavy minerals—those much denser than the abundant quartz and feldspar of most sand—that are concentrated by current action in some places in streams or along beaches. Because the heavy minerals settle more quickly out of the current than the lighter quartz and feldspar, they tend to concentrate in accumulations on river bottoms and bars, where the current is strong enough to keep the lighter minerals suspended and in transport. The same kind of concentration is induced by waves, which preferentially deposit heavy minerals on the beach or on shallow offshore bars. The gold panner does the same thing by shaking the water-filled pan and washing out the lighter minerals.

Some placers can be followed upstream to the location of the original mineral deposit from which they were eroded. Erosion of the Mother

Heavy minerals, including gold, settle quickly to bottom and stay in pan

Light minerals float off with spilled water

Figure 22-31
The gold pan, an old prospecting tool that remains useful.

Lode, an extensive gold-bearing vein system lying along the western flanks of the Sierra Nevada batholith, produced the placers that were discovered in 1848 and led to the California gold rush. The placers were discovered first, then their source. That was also the story of the Kimberley diamond mines of South Africa two decades later.

This brief summary of the geology of mineral deposits barely touches on the great diversity of geologic situations in which various minerals of value are found. Some minerals or ores are found mainly or only in one kind of deposit; others are found in many different situations. Table 22-5 shows the geologic occurrence of some of the principal kinds of mineral deposits.

Table 22-5
Principal types of economic mineral deposit.

Mineral deposit	Typical minerals	Geological occurrence	Uses	Major deposits Remarks
METALS PRESENT IN MAJOR AMOUNTS IN EARTH'S CRUST				
Iron	Hematite, Fe_2O_3 Magnetite, Fe_3O_4 Limonite, $FeO(OH)$	Sedimentary banded iron formation Contact metamorphic Magmatic segregation Sedimentary bog iron ore	Manufactured materials, construction, etc.	*Mesabi, Minn.; Cornwall, Pa.; Kiruna, Sweden* Resources immense; economics determines exploitation.
Aluminum	Gibbsite, $Al(OH)_3$ Diaspore, $AlO(OH)$	Bauxite: residual soils formed by deep chemical weathering	Lightweight manufactured materials	*Jamaica* Resources great, but expensive to smelt.
Magnesium	Dolomite, $CaMg(CO_3)_2$ Magnesite, $MgCO_3$	Dissolved in sea water Hydrothermal veins, limestones	Lightweight alloy metal, insulators, chemical raw material	Most extracted from sea water; unlimited supply.
Titanium	Ilmenite, $FeTiO_3$ Rutile, TiO_2	Magmatic segregations Placers	High-temperature alloys; paint pigment	*Allard Lake, Quebec; Kerala, India* Reserves large in relation to demand.
Chromium	Chromite, $(Mg, Fe(_2CrO_4$	Magmatic segregations of mafic and ultramafic rocks	Steel alloys	*Bushveldt, S. Africa* Extensive reserves in a number of large deposits.
Manganese	Pyrolusite, MnO_2	Chemical sedimentary deposits, residual weathering deposits, sea-floor nodules	Essential to steel making	*Ukraine, U.S.S.R.* World's land resources moderate, but seafloor deposits immerse.
METALS PRESENT IN MINOR AMOUNTS IN EARTH'S CRUST				
Copper	Covellite, CuS Chalcocite, Cu_2S Digenite, Cu_9S_5 Chalcopyrite, $CuFeS_2$ Bornite, Cu_5FeS_4	Porphyry copper deposits Hydrothermal veins Contact metamorphic Sedimentary deposits in shales (Kupferschiefer type)	Electrical wire and other products	*Bingham Canyon, Utah: Kuperschiefer: Germany; Poland*
Lead	Galena, PbS	Hydrothermal (replacement) Contact metamorphic Sedimentary deposits (Kupferschiefer type)	Storage batteries, gasoline additive (tetraethyl lead)	*Mississippi Valley: Broken Hill, Australia* Large resources, Many lower-grade deposits.

Mineral deposit	Typical minerals	Geological occurrence	Uses	Major deposits Remarks
Zinc	Sphalerite, ZnS	Same as lead	Alloy metal	Same as lead
Nickel	Pentlandite, $(Ni, Fe)_9S_8$ Garnierite, $Ni_3Si_2O_5(OH)_4$	Magmatic segregations Residual weathering deposits	Alloy metal	*Sudbury, Ontario* High grade ores limited; large resources of low-grade ores; also in sea-floor Mn nodules.
Silver	Argentite, Ag_2S In solid solution in copper, lead, and zinc sulfides	Hydrothermal veins with lead, zinc, and copper	Photographic chemicals; electrical equipment	Most produced as by-product of copper, lead, and zinc recovery.
Mercury	Cinnabar, HgS	Hydrothermal veins	Electrical equipment, pharmaceuticals	*Almadén, Spain* Few high-grade deposits with limited reserves.
Platinum	Native metal	Magmatic segregations (mafic rocks) Placers	Chemical industry; electrical; alloying metal	*Bushveldt, S. Africa* Large reserves in relation to demand.
Gold	Native metal	Hydrothermal veins Placers	Coinage; dentistry, jewelry	*Witwatersrand, S. Africa* Reserves concentrated in a few larger deposits.
NONMETALS				
Salt	Halite, NaCl	Evaporite deposits Salt domes	Food; chemicals	Resources unlimited; economics determines exploitation
Phosphate rock	Apatite, $Ca_5(PO_4)_3OH$	Marine phosphatic sedimentary rock Residual concentrations of nodules	Fertilizer	*Florida* High-grade deposits limited but extensive resources of low grade deposits.
Sulfur	Native sulfur Sulfide ore minerals	Caprock of salt domes (main source) Hydrothermal and sedimentary sulfides	Fertilizer manufacture; chemical industry	*Texas: Louisiana; Sicily.* Native sulfur reserves limited but immense resources of sulfides.
Potassium	Sylvite, KCl Carnallite, $KCl \cdot MgCl_2 \cdot 6H_2O$	Evaporite deposits	Fertilizer	*Carlsbad, New Mexico* Great resources of rich deposits.
Diamond	Diamond, C	Kimberlite pipes Placers	Industrial abrasives	*Kimberly, S. Africa* Synthetic diamond now commercially available.
Gypsum	Gypsum, $CaSO_4 \cdot 2H_2O$ Anhydrite, $CaSO_4$	Evaporite deposits	Plaster	Immense resources widely distributed.
Limestone	Calcite, $CaCO_3$ Dolomite, $CaMg(CO_3)_2$	Sedimentary carbonate rocks	Building stone; Agricultural lime; cement	Widely distributed; transportation a major cost.
Clay	Kaolinite $Al_2Si_2O_5(OH)_4$ Montmorillonite* Illite*	Residual weathering deposits; sedimentary clays and shales	Ceramics: china, electrical; structural tile	Many large pure deposits; immense reserves of all grades.
Asbestos	Chrysotile, $Mg_3Si_2O_5(OH)_4$	Ultramafic rocks altered and hydrated in near-surface crustal zones	Nonflammable fibers and products	*Southeastern Quebec* Limited high grade reserves but great low grade reserves

*Formula highly variable; a hydrous aluminum silicate with other cations, such as Na, K, Ca, Mg.

FINDING NEW MINERAL DEPOSITS

As the Earth's human population grows larger at an ever increasing rate, and people all over the world demand higher standards of living (usually stated in terms of more food, goods, and materials), the requirements for mineral resources shoot upward. The total dollar value of all mineral resources, including fuels, produced in the United States has grown from less than $5,000,000,000 in 1925 to more than $21,000,000,000 in 1965. This fourfold growth in forty years (which includes some inflationary increases because of the lowering of the value of the dollar in that time period) took place in a highly industrialized society that had already built a huge technological capability and whose population had grown by only 150 percent. The rate of increase in countries that are rapidly developing their industries is even faster, and all countries have aspirations to increase their rates further.

The rate at which mineral resources are being used is much greater than the rate of population growth in the United States. This is shown by the increase in per capita consumption of almost all metals and other rock and mineral products. Most startling is the jump in the per capita

consumption of aluminum, which has multiplied more than twofold in the last fifty years so that now more than 16 kilograms (about 35 pounds) per year is produced for each person in the United States. Though other mineral products show smaller gains, they are all increasing at a rapid pace. These trends show no signs of diminishing: all segments of society demand more and new kinds of manufactured products and a volume of agricultural commodities highly dependent on the fertilizer industry, and those with lower incomes seek a greater share in the material wealth of their society.

Unequal sharing in the exploitation of mineral resources is an important fact on an international scale. North America, with less than a tenth of the world's population, uses almost three-quarters of the world's production of aluminum, while Asia and Africa, with about two-thirds of the world's population, use a little over 5 percent of the production. Again, the same extreme imbalance is true of other materials as well. We are now seeing how international relations can be deeply affected by struggles over the control of resources, as some nations have nationalized, or demanded a greater share in the profits of, oil or mining companies owned by corporations based in North America or Europe. In late 1973, some nations of the Middle East began to restrict exports of oil as a political response to Arab-Israeli hostilities, and the ensuing oil embargo signaled the overwhelming importance of oil to our economy. Shortlived as it was, it led to shortages of gasoline that woke people up—at least temporarily—to the realities of our dependence on oil imports. The same could happen with other resources, though it might not affect us on the same scale as an oil embargo.

A hard fact of life is that an equal per capita sharing of the world's resources would not bring everyone to a "satisfactory" level of consumption—if that could ever be defined—certainly not to a level of consumption anywhere near those of the affluent countries of Europe or North America. How can all of the world's peoples enjoy the benefits of the Earth's resources, benefits that require a highly technological society to utilize them in support of a great population? One of the needs is a great increase in the discovery and exploitation of mineral and energy resources. In a sense, we are all dependent on the skill of the economic geologist.

The prospect for future discovery of major resources is neither rosy nor bleak. It is not rosy

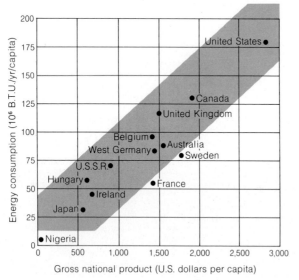

Figure 22-32
Commercial energy use and gross national product show a reasonably close correlation. The same general relationship also holds true for use of many metal ores. [From "Energy and Power" by C. Starr. Copyright © 1971 by Scientific American, Inc. All rights reserved.]

because most of the Earth's surface has been explored geologically to one extent or another, and it is not very probable that major ore bodies of the magnitude of the Sudbury nickel deposit will be discovered in outcrop. In addition, most known major mineral deposits are at least moderately well mapped, so there is little chance of finding appreciable new extensions of these deposits. Yet optimism remains a common quality among economic geologists. Though the major provinces in which abundant mineral deposits have been found are well known, the investigation of new regions may be stimulated by further exploration of the relation between plate boundaries and mineral deposits. In this search for new deposits, we will be searching below the surface more than ever, using a combination of methods: inference of subsurface geology from mapping of surface rocks, exploration drilling, and a battery of exploration techniques from geophysics and geochemistry.

The methods of experimental geophysics have been applied with great success to many resource-exploration campaigns. Most notable has been the use of shallow-explosion seismology in the hunt for geologic structures favorable for oil and gas accumulation, but other applications of seismology are also important in the search for distinctive structures or rock properties of ore bodies or other mineral deposits. Magnetic, electrical (mainly electrical-conductivity), and gravity mapping have likewise been used in the service of mineral exploration, both to reveal structures and to locate specific ore bodies. Airborne surveys of this type have been effective in locating good prospects, particularly in country difficult to cover on the ground, such as great areas of northern Canada and other polar terrain. Radioactivity is a property of great importance in prospecting for uranium ore. In the late 1940s and the 1950s, no prospector for uranium on the Colorado Plateau was well equipped without a radioactive-particle counter (usually a Geiger counter) to detect small quantities of radiation from uranium-235.

The application of geochemistry to mineral prospecting is a little less direct. The main object is to see if unusual concentrations of minor elements, which show up in some places in surface or subsurface waters, in soils, or in vegetation, are indicators of a buried mineral deposit. The amounts of an element present in a sample may be so small that only the most sensitive laboratory instruments can detect them, yet their variation may be sufficient to draw maps that can be interpreted to locate the

source of the elements in a mineral deposit. The elements may have been distributed to surface materials by small leakages from the original vein-depositing fluids of hydrothermal deposits, by weathering processes and soil formation of near-surface rock masses, or by circulating ground waters. The trace-element content (and possibly even the appearance) of vegetation may be a guide to small amounts of particular elements, diagnostic of a nearby ore body, that have been absorbed by the plants.

The effect of trace elements on soils and vegetation is now being explored in a new way by satellites. Launched in July, 1972, the Earth Resources Technology Satellite (ERTS) was designed to map the Earth's surface photographically in ways that may be applied to the discovery of mineral resources. The one-ton satellite is equipped with a television-camera system that photographs the Earth as it orbits, each frame covering an area of about 34,250 square kilometers (about 13,225 square miles). The camera takes pictures of the terrain by reflected red, blue-green, and infrared light—that is, it acts as if it used film sensitive only to those colors. By manipulating these images, various composite photographic images can be made that bring out fires, flooding, volcanic eruptions, different types of vegetation, and many different rock and soil types. The satellite photographs the same area every 18 days, so it can detect changes efficiently. In 1973, an Earth Resources Experiment Package, in some ways similar to ERTS, was included on Skylab, the first NASA space station. Landsat-1 and Landsat-2, the successors to ERTS, were launched in January 1975, and carry even more sophisticated equipment.

Through this type of surveying of the surface from a great distance, called **remote sensing,** geologists can detect the indirect effects on photographic imagery of small geochemical differences that might be related to mineral deposits. Of course, remote sensing does not need to be done exclusively by satellite. Black-and-white aerial photography from airplanes is the oldest form of remote sensing, and, by the time of World War II, such photography had been extended to color and infrared. But the capacity for photographic resolution and separation of the different parts of the electromagnetic spectrum has increased greatly in the past decades. Newer developments include mapping of terrain by a kind of radar, called side-scanning airborne radar, in which small-wavelength radio waves, beamed at topographic features, are reflected

Table 22-6
Concentrations of the elements in seawater and their values in elemental or combined form. (The elements are listed in order of abundance; those in italic type are in concentrations valued at $1 or more per million gallons of seawater.)

Element	Concentration $(lb/10^6 \ gal)^*$	as	Value ($/10^6 \ gal)
Chlorine	166,000	NaCl	924
Sodium	92,000	Na_2CO_3	378
Magnesium	11,800	Mg	4,130
Sulfur	7,750	S	101
Calcium	3,500	$CaCl_2$	150
Potassium	3,300	K_2O (equiv)	91
Bromine	570	Br_2	190
Carbon	250	Graphite	8×10^{-5}
Strontium	70	$SrCO_3$	2
Boron	40	H_3BO_3	3
Fluorine	11	CaF_2	0.35
Nitrogen	4	NH_4NO_3	1
Lithium	1.5	Li_2CO_3	36
Rubidium	1.0	Rb	125
Phosphorus	0.6	$CaHPO_4$	0.08
Iodine	0.5	I_2	1
Zinc	0.09	Zn	0.013
Iron	0.09	Fe_2O_3	0.001
Aluminum	0.09	Al	0.04
Molybdenum	0.09	Mo	0.004
Tin	0.03	Sn	0.05
Copper	0.03	Cu	0.01
Arsenic	0.03	As_2O_3	0.002
Uranium	0.03	U_3O_8	0.3
Nickel	0.02	Ni	0.02
Manganese	0.02	Mn	0.006
Titanium	0.009	TiO_2	0.003
Silver	0.003	Ag	0.02
Chromium	0.0004	Cr_2O_3	0.00001
Thorium	0.0004	ThO_2	0.0009
Lead	0.0003	Pb	0.00004
Mercury	0.0003	Hg	0.002
Gold	0.00004	Au	0.02
Radium	9×10^{-10}	Ra (in salts)	0.002

Source: From Resources and Man, National Academy of Sciences—National Research Council. W. H. Freeman and Company, 1969.
* One $lb/10^6 \ gal$ is approximately 0.000012 percent.

back to sensing equipment that produces a photographic type of image. The modern exploration geologist uses all of these methods to produce a better picture of the geology of a target region and to pick up patterns suggestive of mineral deposits that he can later check out on the ground. To put it figuratively, these methods have given the geologist bigger and better eyes for more effective surveillance of the Earth and seven-league boots with which to cover more territory.

Remote sensing has also been applied to the study of ocean resources, primarily the detection of changing patterns of life in the sea. Most of the minerals that we may recover from the ocean will come either from the water or from the sea floor, which has been studied by a variety of remote-sensing devices, such as echo-sounding instruments. The ocean is an immense storehouse of some easily extractable elements. For example, almost all magnesium is now recovered from evaporated sea water. It is the ease of recoverability from sea water that makes an element attractive rather than its abundance, because, as Tables 22-4 and 22-6 show, the concentration of almost every element is greater in crustal rocks than in sea water. Because silver is 900 times more concentrated in the average rock than in sea water, the cost of recovering it from the sea would have to be at least 900 times less than the cost of recovering it from rock in order for sea-water extraction to be economical. These figures suggest that, for most metals, it will be a long time before we "mine" sea water.

The element bromine, however, is a different story, as can be seen from Table 22-6: it is much more plentiful in sea water than in average crustal rocks. Bromine has been economically recovered from sea water for many years, and only recently has it been extracted more profitably from concentrated saline groundwaters, the so-called brines (see Chapter 6). These brines are a potential source for many other materials as well, for there are indications that some heavy trace metals may be concentrated in them.

Sodium chloride has been recovered from sea water probably since prehistoric times. In a great many coastal regions of the world, the separation of salt from sea water is an economic process. One of the best-known processing plants is in San Francisco Bay, where a series of evaporating basins is used to extract the pure salt.

The sea floor, which is being explored now for economic mineral deposits, has been hailed by many as the answer to many problems of

Figure 22-33
Landsat photograph of the Los Angeles area. This photograph has been computer-enhanced to improve definition of the original. The prominent line running from left to right across the middle of the photograph is the San Andreas fault. Running to the upper center diagonally from the San Andreas is the Garlock fault, separating the Tehachapi Mountains on the left from the Mojave Desert, the lighter area covering the upper right quarter of the picture. The dark triangle near the center left margin is the Wrightwood alluvial fan, coming from the San Gabriel Mountains. The Los Angeles Basin is at the lower right. [Courtesy A. F. H. Goetz, Jet Propulsion Laboratory.]

Figure 22-34
Manganese nodules dredged from the ocean floor helped to demonstrate the feasibility of mining the seabed for them. Deposits are estimated to be in the trillions of tons. [Photo by B. J. Nixon/Deepsea Ventures; Courtesy National Science Foundation.]

Manganese content in weight percent

| > 30 | 20–30 | 10–20 | 0–10 |

Figure 22-35
Distribution of manganese nodule deposits in the Northeast Pacific Ocean. [From Horn, Delach, and Horn, 1972, "Metal Content of Ferromanganese Deposits of the Oceans," Technical Report, Nat. Sci. Foundation Int'l. Decade of Ocean Exploration.]

apparent resource depletion. We discussed earlier how the idea of plate tectonics may be a stimulus to mineral exploration in the sea. But long before this, there were mining operations near shores that extended under the ocean floor from land. Because the continental borderlands have the same range of rocks as the nearby continental areas, they may contain the same range of mineral deposits as the land. The metal that seems likely to be the first candidate for deep-sea mining is manganese. In Chapter 11, we pointed out the widespread occurrence on the sea floor of manganese nodules, spheroidal aggregates of manganese, iron, and other metal oxides that range in size from tiny encrustations weighing less than a gram to large masses of several hundred kilograms. The majority of the nodules are a few centimeters in diameter. Interest in the possibility of economic recovery of the deposits has been strong in the past few years, both because of the gradual depletion of high-grade manganese ores on land and because the nodules are enriched in many other valuable metals, such as copper, nickel, and cobalt. The average nodule contains more than 20 percent manganese, 6 percent iron, and about 1 percent each of copper and nickel—a highly enriched ore by any standard.

The economic recovery of manganese nodules awaits the development of a technology of sea-floor surface mining that will be sufficiently cheap to match the current costs of recovery of known ores from land deposits. The location of rich fields of nodules on the sea floor, known earlier from coring, dredging, and bottom photography, is becoming better known by efficient scanning of the bottom by towed television cameras. The resolution of these cameras is good enough to read headlines in old newspapers that make up part of man's slowly accumulating garbage on the sea floor below shipping lanes. Though all of the oceans have not been mapped in detail, good reconnaissance maps of the major ocean basins have been prepared that show regions of high nodule abundance, some of which are areas potentially favorable for mining operations. Mining operations have been carried out on an experimental basis since 1970 by American and Japanese companies. The prospects for mining the sea floor are imminent—and make more urgent—an international agreement regarding economic exploitation of the sea. In the summer of 1973, a major convocation of nations began to work on the thorny international legal problems, all of which have political overtones. Meetings have continued since then, but a stable international agreement on the law of the sea seems to be some time off. Ultimately, some resolution of the question of ownership must be found before the resources of the sea can be used.

There are other resources under the sea that can be mined, including phosphate deposits, salt and sulfur from evaporite deposits and salt domes, and abundant sand and gravel for construction needs. Some of the regions that use the greatest amounts of sand and gravel are populous urban areas along coasts in northern latitudes, particularly in Europe and North America. In many of these regions, Pleistocene glaciation has left many sand and gravel deposits in kames, eskers, and outwash-plain deposits (see Chapter 9). Building has been so extensive in these areas for so many years that many high grade sources are now depleted. Offshore of these regions are continental-shelf deposits of much the same nature, originally deposited when continental glaciers overrode the offshore areas, like Cape Cod and Long Island, and also extensive glaciomarine deposits laid down by melting icebergs calved from the glaciers. Though glacial gravels are somewhat restricted to these areas, sand is much more widely distributed, covering much of the Atlantic continental shelf of North America, for example. About $100 million worth of these deposits is mined each year, and the expectations are that this figure will increase greatly in the future. The large bulk and low unit price of sand and gravel require efficient cheap recovery from the sea floor by dredging in relatively shallow water. Operations carried on so far have shown little or no ecological damage to the life of the sea in the area mined.

Rich as the ocean may be in some mineral resources, its major value as a resource for human needs may be something entirely different. It is now an important source of food for many maritime regions, and it is potentially a major source of food for the expanding population of the Earth. Pollution of the oceans presents a serious threat to the "farming" of the oceans for food, as well as offending our senses and interfering with the ocean as a prime recreation site. Up to now, we have used the oceans as a garbage dump. We have thrown into the sea everything from city sewage and garbage to toxic wastes from industrial processes and radioactive materials. All of this has not yet made a great impact on its composition, but there is no doubt that it will if we continue to accelerate such dumping. In comparison to the pollution

Figure 22-36
Distribution of the most favorable areas for some potential mineral resources off the Atlantic coast of the United States. The broken line denotes the position of the edge of the continental shelf, about 80 m deep in the south and about 140 m deep in the north. The area indicated for manganese nodules corresponds to the surface of the Balek Plateau. [After K. O. Emery, 1965, "Some Potential Mineral Resources of the Atlantic Continental Margin." U.S. Geol. Survey Prof. Paper 525-C.]

The Body of the Earth:
Internal Processes

In early 1977 a new law of the United States extended its territorial—and fishing—rights to 200 miles. Thus it joined a growing number of nations that seek to control their own marine resources by restricting access to coastal waters.

from existing sources, the threat to the ocean that will come from mining operations will be negligible. There may be local effects, and, to the extent to which they are unacceptable, mining companies will have to be responsible for limiting them. The matter of oil pollution has been discussed earlier, in connection with oil exploration on the continental shelves. As important as the matter of ownership is to future congresses of nations on the law of the sea, the matter of ocean pollution may yet overshadow it if world fisheries are threatened. But another question of conservation is now taking greater precedence: overfishing. Just as the bison was exterminated on the western plains in the nineteenth century, we are now exterminating the whale population of the sea. Many kinds of fish are slated for extinction, too, if some control is not exercised. We have to include in our definition of exhaustible resources the fish population of the seas. How well we use the sea will depend on how well we understand how it works and the extent to which the countries of the world will cooperate intelligently in its exploitation, regulation, and control.

In a larger sense, that is true of the whole Earth. We have only one. To live on it best, we must understand it better.

SUMMARY

1. Matter of the Earth is theoretically recyclable, but energy is permanently consumed when we use its resources.

2. Energy from fossil fuels—coal, oil, and gas—has been the mainstay of the world's industrialization.

3. Oil and gas form by the preservation and alteration of organic matter deposited in sediments that chemically transform part of it into liquid and gaseous hydrocarbons, compounds of carbon and hydrogen.

4. Oil and gas accumulate in structural and stratigraphic traps that confine the fluids with impermeable barriers.

5. Oil and gas are found in many of the buried sedimentary rocks of the Earth that have not been too compacted, deformed or metamorphosed to allow preservation of the hydrocarbons.

6. The geographic distribution of oil and gas is related to geologic age of sedimentary rocks accumulated in major geosynclines. Middle East oil is accumulated in thick Cenozoic and Mesozoic sediments in a major geosyncline.

7. We may expect that continental shelves, which are favorable areas for oil accumulation, will be explored more heavily in the future. In addition to dealing with the problems of drilling in deep water, those who drill for oil on the continental shelves must safeguard against oil spills that pollute the ocean and adjacent shorelines.

8. Oil is a depletable resource whose reserves will be steadily exhausted at present accelerating rates of use. The United States, exclusive of Alaska, has already produced about two-thirds of its total reserve. World reserves can be estimated, and the exhaustion of all oil and gas resources can be expected within the next century at projected rates of use.

9. Coal, derived from the compaction and chemical alteration of swamp vegetation, is present in great reserves in sedimentary rocks. We have used only 1.7 percent of the world's minable coal resources. Pollution caused by coal burning is a problem, but increased use of coal in the next decades seems certain.

10. Reserves of oil shale and tar sands are great, and may be extensively exploited in the next few decades as costs go up and technology improves.

11. Alternative energy sources are water power, solar energy, geothermal power, and tidal power, none of which has any immediate prospects of being a major answer to world energy needs.

12. The major alternative now envisioned is nuclear power from controlled fission reactors or, ultimately, in fusion plants. Known high-grade reserves of U-235 ore will not be adequate to support major use of conventional nuclear power plants for much more than a few decades, thus making urgent the development of fast breeder reactors and basic research leading toward fusion reactors.

13. Mineral deposits of economic value are those in which an element occurs in much higher abundance than the average crustal rock, sufficiently high to make it economically worthwhile to mine.

14. When high grade ores or other economic deposits are depleted, we can move to recover elements from less concentrated ores, though at greater cost, until in many cases it may become profitable to recycle.

15. Hydrothermal veins, which are some of the most important ore deposits, are formed by hot water emanating from igneous intrusions or by circulating groundwater in areas of high heat flow. Many of these may be related to boundaries of lithospheric plates. They may occur in vein or lode deposits or in such disseminated deposits as the copper-porphyry type.

16. Igneous and contact-metamorphic deposits occur as segregations of layered intrusives, such as the copper and nickel deposits of lopoliths, or in contact-metamorphic aureoles.

17. Sedimentary deposits include many of the chemical and mechanical segregations of such ordinary rocks as limestone, sand and gravel, and evaporite salt deposits. Sedimentary ores of copper and iron have formed in special sedimentary environments, the iron ores chiefly in Precambrian times. Placers are current-laid deposits that are rich in gold or other heavy minerals.

18. Finding new mineral deposits is vitally necessary to support an increasingly industrialized world civilization. Prospects for finding new resources, based on geological, geophysical, and geochemical prospecting, are good. The sea represents a largely untapped resource.

EXERCISES

1. What sedimentary environments favor the formation of sediments that contain much organic matter that would later be transformed to petroleum?

2. Do you think the mid-Atlantic ridge might be a good prospect for oil drilling, assuming that we can invent the technology to drill there? Why?

3. Given two permeable, anticlinal sandstones, one Ordovician, the other Miocene, which would you choose to drill first in the hope of finding large reserves of oil and gas?

4. Which of the following factors are most important in estimating the future supply of oil and gas: (1) rate of oil accumulation, (2) rate of natural seepage of oil, (3) rate of pumping of oil from known reserves, (4) rate of discovery of new reserves, (5) the total amount of oil now present in the Earth?

5. In terms of use and economic recovery, rank according to relative importance all of the different forms of fossil fuels today, and explain how their ranking might differ at the end of the next century.

6. How would you use knowledge of the distribution of plate boundaries to make a map showing the most likely areas of Earth to investigate for geothermal power?

7. In what important respects do uranium reserves differ from fossil fuel reserves?

8. What evidence might you marshal to show that a particular ore deposit was formed by hydrothermal solutions emanating from an igneous intrusion?

9. Why do you think that economic geologists might worry more about adequate future supplies of mercury ore than iron ore?

BIBLIOGRAPHY

Atwood, G., "The Strip-Mining of Western Coal," *Scientific American,* June 1974.

Committee on Resources and Man (National Academy of Sciences), *Resources and Man.* San Francisco: W. H. Freeman and Company, 1969.

Cook, E., *Man, Energy, Society.* San Francisco: W. H. Freeman and Company, 1976.

Hammond, A. L., W. D. Metz, and T. H. Maugh, II, *Energy and the Future.* Washington, D.C.: American Association for the Advancement of Science, 1973.

Levorsen, A. I., *Geology of Petroleum* (2nd ed.). San Francisco: W. H. Freeman and Company, 1967.

Mero, J. L., *The Mineral Resources of the Sea.* Amsterdam: Elsevier Publishing Company, 1965.

Park, C. F., Jr., and R. A. MacDiarmid, *Ore Deposits.* San Francisco: W. H. Freeman and Company, 1975.

Scientific American, *Energy and Power,* San Francisco: W. H. Freeman and Company, 1971.

Skinner, B. J., *Earth Resources* (2nd ed.). Englewood Cliffs, New Jersey: Prentice-Hall, Inc., 1976.

Skinner, B. J., and K.K. Turekian, *Man and the Ocean.* Englewood Cliffs, New Jersey: Prentice-Hall, Inc., 1973.

APPENDIXES

Conversion Factors: Metric-English

LENGTH

1 centimeter	0.3937 inch
1 inch	2.5400 centimeters
1 meter	3.2808 feet
1 foot	0.3048 meter
1 meter	1.0936 yards
1 yard	0.9144 meter
1 kilometer	0.6214 mile (statute)
1 kilometer	3281 feet
1 mile (statute)	1.6093 kilometers
1 mile (nautical)	1.8531 kilometers
1 fathom	6 feet
1 fathom	1.8288 meters
1 angstrom	10^{-8} centimeter
1 micrometer (formerly micron)	0.0001 centimeter

VELOCITY

1 kilometer/hour	27.78 centimeters/second
1 mile/hour	17.60 inches/second

AREA

1 square centimeter	0.1550 square inch
1 square inch	6.452 square centimeters
1 square meter	10.764 square feet
1 square meter	1.1960 square yards
1 square foot	0.0929 square meter
1 square kilometer	0.3861 square mile
1 square mile	2.590 square kilometers
1 acre (U.S.)	4840 square yards

VOLUME

1 cubic centimeter	0.0610 cubic inch
1 cubic inch	16.3872 cubic centimeters
1 cubic meter	35.314 cubic feet
1 cubic foot	0.02832 cubic meter
1 cubic meter	1.3079 cubic yards
1 cubic yard	0.7646 cubic meter
1 liter	1000 cubic centimeters
1 liter	1.0567 quarts (U.S. liquid)
1 liter	33.815 ounces (U.S. fluid)
1 gallon (U.S. liquid)	3.7853 liters

MASS

1 gram	0.03527 ounce (Avoirdupois)
1 ounce (Avoirdupois)	28.3495 grams
1 gram	0.03215 ounce (Troy)
1 kilogram	2.20462 pounds (Avoirdupois)
1 pound (Avoirdupois)	0.45359 kilogram

DENSITY

1 gram/cubic centimeter	62.4280 pounds/cubic foot

PRESSURE

1 kilogram/square centimeter	0.96784 atmosphere
1 kilogram/square centimeter	0.98067 bar
1 kilogram/square centimeter	14.2233 pounds/square inch
1 bar	0.98692 atmosphere
1 foot of water	0.03048 kilogram/square centimeter
1 kilometer of granite	265 kilograms/square centimeter (approx.)

ENERGY

1 erg	2.39006×10^{-8} calorie (gram)
1 erg	9.48451×10^{-11} BTU
1 erg	10^{-7} joule
Explosion equivalent to 1000 tons of TNT	4×10^{19} ergs

POWER

1 watt	10^{7} ergs/second
1 watt	0.001341 horsepower (U.S.)
1 watt	0.05688 BTU/minute
1 watt	0.73756 foot pound/second

Prefix Names of Multiples and Submultiples of Units

Prefix	Factor by which unit is multiplied
giga	10^{9}
mega	10^{6}
kilo	10^{3}
hecto	10^{2}
deka	10
deci	10^{-1}
centi	10^{-2}
milli	10^{-3}
micro	10^{-6}
nano	10^{-9}
pico	10^{-12}

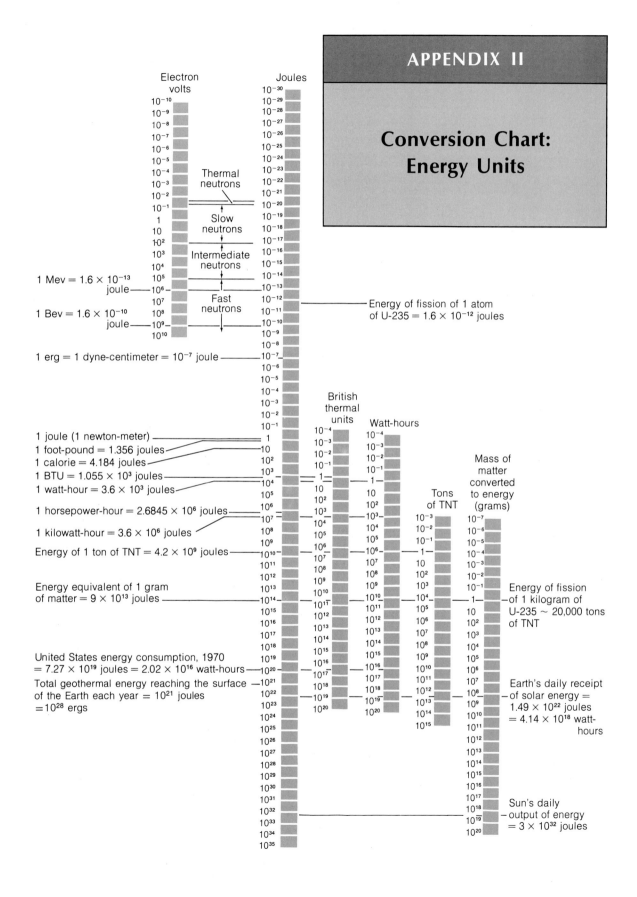

Conversion Chart: Energy Units

Electron volts

10^{-10}
10^{-9}
10^{-8}
10^{-7}
10^{-6}
10^{-5}
10^{-4}
10^{-3}
10^{-2}
10^{-1}
1
10
10^2
10^3
10^4
10^5
10^6
10^7
10^8
10^9
10^{10}

Thermal neutrons

Slow neutrons

Intermediate neutrons

Fast neutrons

1 Mev = 1.6×10^{-13} joule

1 Bev = 1.6×10^{-10} joule

1 erg = 1 dyne-centimeter = 10^{-7} joule

1 joule (1 newton-meter)
1 foot-pound = 1.356 joules
1 calorie = 4.184 joules
1 BTU = 1.055×10^3 joules
1 watt-hour = 3.6×10^3 joules
1 horsepower-hour = 2.6845×10^6 joules
1 kilowatt-hour = 3.6×10^6 joules
Energy of 1 ton of TNT = 4.2×10^9 joules

Energy equivalent of 1 gram of matter = 9×10^{13} joules

United States energy consumption, 1970 = 7.27×10^{19} joules = 2.02×10^{16} watt-hours

Total geothermal energy reaching the surface of the Earth each year = 10^{21} joules = 10^{28} ergs

Joules

10^{-30}
10^{-29}
10^{-28}
10^{-27}
10^{-26}
10^{-25}
10^{-24}
10^{-23}
10^{-22}
10^{-21}
10^{-20}
10^{-19}
10^{-18}
10^{-17}
10^{-16}
10^{-15}
10^{-14}
10^{-13}
10^{-12}
10^{-11}
10^{-10}
10^{-9}
10^{-8}
10^{-7}
10^{-6}
10^{-5}
10^{-4}
10^{-3}
10^{-2}
10^{-1}
1
10
10^2
10^3
10^4
10^5
10^6
10^7
10^8
10^9
10^{10}
10^{11}
10^{12}
10^{13}
10^{14}
10^{15}
10^{16}
10^{17}
10^{18}
10^{19}
10^{20}
10^{21}
10^{22}
10^{23}
10^{24}
10^{25}
10^{26}
10^{27}
10^{28}
10^{29}
10^{30}
10^{31}
10^{32}
10^{33}
10^{34}
10^{35}

Energy of fission of 1 atom of U-235 = 1.6×10^{-12} joules

British thermal units

10^{-4}
10^{-3}
10^{-2}
10^{-1}
1
10
10^2
10^3
10^4
10^5
10^6
10^7
10^8
10^9
10^{10}
10^{11}
10^{12}
10^{13}
10^{14}
10^{15}
10^{16}
10^{17}
10^{18}
10^{19}
10^{20}

Watt-hours

10^{-4}
10^{-3}
10^{-2}
10^{-1}
1
10
10^2
10^3
10^4
10^5
10^6
10^7
10^8
10^9
10^{10}
10^{11}
10^{12}
10^{13}
10^{14}
10^{15}
10^{16}
10^{17}
10^{18}
10^{19}
10^{20}

Tons of TNT

10^{-3}
10^{-2}
10^{-1}
1
10
10^2
10^3
10^4
10^5
10^6
10^7
10^8
10^9
10^{10}
10^{11}
10^{12}
10^{13}
10^{14}
10^{15}

Mass of matter converted to energy (grams)

10^{-7}
10^{-6}
10^{-5}
10^{-4}
10^{-3}
10^{-2}
10^{-1}
1
10
10^2
10^3
10^4
10^5
10^6
10^7
10^8
10^9
10^{10}
10^{11}
10^{12}
10^{13}
10^{14}
10^{15}
10^{16}
10^{17}
10^{18}
10^{19}
10^{20}

Energy of fission of 1 kilogram of U-235 ~ 20,000 tons of TNT

Earth's daily receipt of solar energy = 1.49×10^{22} joules = 4.14×10^{18} watt-hours

Sun's daily output of energy = 3×10^{32} joules

APPENDIX III

Numerical Data Pertaining to Earth

Equatorial radius:	6378 kilometers
Polar radius:	6357 kilometers
Radius of sphere with Earth's volume:	6371 kilometers
Volume:	1.083×10^{27} cubic centimeters
Surface area:	5.1×10^{18} square centimeters
Percent surface area of oceans:	71
Percent surface area of land:	29
Average elevation of lands:	623 meters
Average depth of oceans:	3.8 kilometers
Mass:	5.976×10^{27} grams
Density:	5.517 grams/cubic centimeter
Gravity at equator:	978.032 centimeters/second/second
Mass of atmosphere:	5.1×10^{21} grams
Mass of ice:	$25-30 \times 10^{21}$ grams
Mass of oceans:	1.4×10^{24} grams
Mass of crust:	2.5×10^{25} grams
Mass of mantle:	4.05×10^{27} grams
Mass of core:	1.90×10^{27} grams
Mean distance to Sun:	1.496×10^{8} kilometers
Rotational velocity:	7.292×10^{-5} radians/second (40,000 km/day linear velocity at equator)
Average velocity around Sun:	29.77 kilometers/second
Ratio—mass of Sun/mass of Earth:	3.329×10^{5}
Ratio—mass of Earth/mass of Moon:	81.303

APPENDIX IV

Properties of the Most Common Minerals of the Earth's Crust

	Mineral or group name	Varieties and chemical composition	Form, diagnostic characters	Cleavage, fracture	Color	Hardness
FRAMEWORK SILICATES	FELDSPAR	POTASSIUM FELDSPARS [KAlSi$_3$O$_8$] Sanidine Orthoclase Microcline	Cleavable coarsely crystalline or finely granular masses. Isolated crystals or grains in rocks, most commonly not showing crystal faces.	Two at right angles, one perfect and one good; pearly luster on perfect cleavage.	White to gray, frequently pink or yellowish; some green.	
		PLAGIOCLASE FELDSPARS [NaAlSi$_3$O$_8$] Albite [CaAl$_2$Si$_2$O$_8$] Anorthite		Two at nearly right angles; one perfect, one good. Fine parallel striations on perfect cleavage.	White to gray, less commonly greenish or yellowish.	6
	QUARTZ	SiO$_2$	Single crystals or masses of 6-sided prismatic crystals. Also formless crystals and grains or finely granular or massive.	Very poor or nondetectable; conchoidal fracture.	Colorless, usually transparent; also slightly colored smoky gray, pink, yellow.	7
SHEET SILICATES	MICA	MUSCOVITE [KAl$_3$Si$_3$O$_{10}$(OH)$_2$]	Thin, disc-shaped crystals, some with hexagonal outlines. Dispersed or aggregates.	One perfect; splittable into very thin, flexible, transparent sheets.	Colorless; slight gray or green to brown in thick pieces.	2–2$\frac{1}{2}$
		BIOTITE [K(Mg,Fe)$_3$AlSi$_3$O$_{10}$(OH)$_2$]	Irregular, foliated masses; scaly aggregates.	One perfect; splittable into thin, flexible sheets.	Black to dark brown. Translucent to opaque.	2$\frac{1}{2}$–3
		CHLORITE [(Mg,Fe)$_5$(Al,Fe)$_2$Si$_3$O$_{10}$(OH)$_8$]	Foliated masses or aggregates of small scales.	One perfect: thin sheets flexible but not elastic.	Various shades of green.	2–2$\frac{1}{2}$
DOUBLE CHAINS	AMPHIBOLE	TREMOLITE–ACTINOLITE [Ca$_2$(Mg,Fe)$_5$Si$_8$O$_{22}$(OH)$_2$]	Long, prismatic crystals, usually 6-sided. Commonly in fibrous masses or irregular aggregates.	Two good cleavage directions at 56° and 124° angles.	Pale to deep green. Pure tremolite white, vitreous luster.	5–6
		HORNBLENDE [Complex Ca,Na,Mg,Fe, Al silicate]			Dark green to black.	

LIGHT COLORED MINERALS, VERY ABUNDANT IN EARTH'S CRUST IN ALL MAJOR ROCK TYPES

DARK COLORED MINERALS ABUNDANT IN MANY KINDS OF IGNEOUS AND METAMORPHIC ROCKS

	Mineral	Composition	Crystal habit / occurrence	Cleavage / fracture	Color	Hardness
SINGLE CHAINS	PYROXENE — ENSTATITE–HYPERSTHENE [(Mg,Fe)₂Si₂O₆] DIOPSIDE [(Ca,Mg₂)Si₂O₆] AUGITE [Complex Ca,Na,Mg,Fe, Al silicate]		Prismatic crystals, either 4- or 8-sided. Granular masses and scattered grains.	Two good cleavage directions at about 90°.	Green and brown to grayish or greenish white. Light to dark green. Very dark green to black.	5–6
ISOLATED TETRAHEDRA	OLIVINE	[(Mg,Fe)₂SiO₄]	Granular masses and disseminated small grains.	Conchoidal fracture.	Olive to grayish green and brown.	$6\frac{1}{2}$–7
	GARNET	[(Ca,Mg,Fe,Al silicate)]	Isometric crystals, well-formed or rounded; high specific gravity, 3.5–4.3.	Conchoidal and irregular fracture.	Red and brown, less commonly pale colors.	$6\frac{1}{2}$–$7\frac{1}{2}$
CARBONATES	CALCITE	$CaCO_3$	Coarsely to finely crystalline in beds, veins, and other aggregates. Cleavage faces may show in coarser masses. Calcite effervesces rapidly, dolomite slowly, only in powders.	Three perfect cleavages, at oblique angles; splits to rhombohedral cleavage pieces.	Colorless, transparent to translucent; variously colored by impurities.	3
	DOLOMITE	$CaMg(CO_3)_2$				$3\frac{1}{2}$–4
HYDROUS ALUMINO-SILICATES	CLAY MINERALS — KAOLINITE [Al₂Si₂O₅(OH)₄] ILLITE [similar to Muscovite + Mg,Fe] MONTMORILLONITE [Complex Ca,Na,Mg,Fe Al silicate + H₂O]		Earthy masses in soils; bedded; in association with other clays, iron oxides, or carbonates. Plastic when wet; montmorillonite swells when wet.	Earthy, irregular.	White to light gray and buff; also gray to dark gray, greenish gray, and brownish depending on impurities and associated minerals.	$1\frac{1}{2}$–$2\frac{1}{2}$
SULFATES	GYPSUM	$CaSO_4 \cdot 2H_2O$	Granular, earthy, or finely crystalline masses. Tabular crystals.	One perfect, splitting to fairly thin slabs or sheets. Two other good cleavages.	Colorless to white. Transparent to translucent.	2
	ANHYDRITE	$CaSO_4$	Massive or crystalline aggregates in beds and veins.	One perfect, one nearly perfect, one good; at right angles.	Colorless, some tinged with blue.	3–$3\frac{1}{2}$
	HALITE	$NaCl$	Granular masses in beds. Some cubic crystals. Salty taste.	Three excellent cleavages at right angles.	Colorless, transparent to translucent.	$2\frac{1}{2}$
	OPAL–CHALCEDONY	SiO_2 [Opal is an amorphous variety; chalcedony is a formless microcrystalline quartz.]	Beds in siliceous sediments and chert; in veins or banded aggregates.	Conchoidal fracture.	Colorless or white when pure, but tinged with various colors by impurities in bands, especially in agates.	5–$6\frac{1}{2}$

LIGHT COLORED, TYPICALLY AS ABUNDANT CONSTITUENTS OF SEDIMENTS AND SEDIMENTARY ROCKS

Mineral or group name		Varieties and chemical composition	Form, diagnostic characters	Cleavage, fracture	Color	Hardness
MAGNETITE	IRON OXIDES	Fe_3O_4	Magnetic. Disseminated grains, granular masses; occasional octahedral isometric crystals. High specific gravity: 5.2.	Conchoidal or irregular fracture.	Black, metallic luster.	6
HEMATITE		Fe_2O_3	Earthy to dense masses, some with rounded forms, some granular or foliated. High specific gravity: 4.9–5.3.	None; uneven, sometimes splintery fracture.	Reddish-brown to black.	$5\frac{1}{2}$–$6\frac{1}{2}$
"LIMONITE"		$HFeO_2$ [*GOETHITE* is the major mineral of the mixture called "limonite," a field term.]	Earthy masses, massive bodies or encrustations, irregular layers. High specific gravity: 3.3–4.7.	One excellent in the rare crystals; usually an earthy fracture.	Yellowish-brown to dark brown and black.	5–$5\frac{1}{2}$
KYANITE	ALUMINOSILICATES	Al_2SiO_5	Long, bladed or tabular crystals or aggregates.	One perfect and one poor, parallel to length of crystals.	White to light-colored or pale blue.	5 parallel to crystal length 7 across crystals
SILLIMANITE		Al_2SiO_5	Long, slender crystals or fibrous, felted masses.	One perfect parallel to length, not usually seen.	Colorless, gray to white.	6–7
ANDALUSITE		Al_2SiO_5	Coarse, nearly square prismatic crystals, some with symmetrically arranged impurities.	One distinct; irregular fracture.	Red, reddish-brown, olive-green	$7\frac{1}{2}$
FELDSPATHOIDS	ALKALI SILICATES	*NEPHELINE* [(Na,K)AlSiO_4]	Compact masses or as embedded grains, rarely as small prismatic crystals.	One distinct. Irregular fracture.	Colorless, white, light gray. Gray-greenish in masses, with greasy luster.	$5\frac{1}{2}$–6
		LEUCITE [KAlSi_2O_6]	Trapezohedral crystals embedded in volcanic rocks.	One very imperfect.	White to gray.	$5\frac{1}{2}$–6
SERPENTINE	MAGNESIUM SILICATES	$Mg_6Si_4O_{10}(OH)_8$	Fibrous (asbestos) or platy masses.	Splintery fracture.	Green; some yellowish, brownish, or gray. Waxy or greasy luster in massive habit; silky luster in fibrous habit.	4–6
TALC		$Mg_3Si_4O_{10}(OH)_2$	Foliated or compact masses or aggregates.	One perfect, making thin flakes or scales. Soapy feel.	White to pale green. Pearly or greasy luster.	1

DARK MINERALS COMMON IN MANY ROCK TYPES

LIGHT COLORED MINERALS, MAINLY IN IGNEOUS AND METAMORPHIC ROCKS AS COMMON OR MINOR CONSTITUENTS

Group	Mineral	Class	Composition	Crystal form / occurrence	Cleavage / Fracture	Color	Hardness
DARK COLORED MINERALS COMMON IN METAMORPHIC ROCKS	CORUNDUM	OXIDE	Al_2O_3	Some rounded, barrel-shaped crystals; most often as disseminated grains or granular (emery) masses.	Irregular fracture.	Usually brown, pink, or blue. Emery black. Gem stone varieties: ruby, sapphire.	9
	EPIDOTE	SILICATES	$Ca_2(Al,Fe)Al_2Si_3O_{12}(OH)$	Aggregates of long prismatic crystals, granular or compact masses, embedded grains.	One good, one poor at greater than right angles. Conchoidal and irregular fracture.	Green, yellow-green, gray, some varieties dark brown to black.	6–7
	STAUROLITE		$Fe_2Al_9Si_4O_{22}(O,OH)_2$	Short prismatic crystals, some cross-shaped, usually coarser than matrix of rock.	One poor.	Brown, reddish, or dark brown to black.	7
METALLIC LUSTER, COMMON IN MANY ROCK TYPES, ABUNDANT IN VEINS	PYRITE	SULFIDES	FeS_2	Granular masses or well-formed cubic crystals in veins and beds or disseminated. Specific gravity high: 4.9–5.2.	Uneven fracture.	Pale brass-yellow.	6–6½
	GALENA		PbS	Granular masses in veins and disseminated. Some cubic crystals. Specific gravity very high: 7.3–7.6.	Three perfect cleavages at mutual right angles, giving cubic cleavage fragments.	Silver-gray.	2½
	SPHALERITE		ZnS	Granular masses or compact crystalline aggregates. Specific gravity high: 3.9–4.1.	Six perfect cleavages at 60° to one another.	White to green, brown, and black. Resinous to submetallic luster.	3½–4
	CHALCOPYRITE		$CuFeS_2$	Granular or compact masses; disseminated crystals. Specific gravity: 4.1–4.3.	Uneven fracture.	Brassy to golden-yellow.	3½–4
	CHALCOCITE		Cu_2S	Fine-grained masses. Specific gravity: 5.5–5.8.	Conchoidal fracture.	Lead-gray to black. May tarnish green or blue.	2½–3
MINERALS, FOUND IN MINOR AMOUNTS IN A VARIETY OF ROCK TYPES AND IN VEINS OR PLACERS	RUTILE	TITANIUM OXIDES	TiO_2	Slender to prismatic crystals; granular masses. Specific gravity: 4.25.	One distinct, one less distinct. Conchoidal fracture.	Reddish-brown, some yellowish, violet, or black.	6–6½
	ILMENITE		$FeTiO_3$	Compact masses, embedded grains, detrital grains in sand. Specific gravity: 4.79.	Conchoidal fracture	Iron-black metallic to submetallic luster.	5–6
	ZEOLITES	SILICATES	Complex hydrous silicates, many varieties of minerals, including analcime, natrolite, phillipsite, heulandite, and chabazite.	Well-formed radiating crystals in cavities in volcanics, in veins, and hot springs. Also as fine-grained and earthy bedded deposits.	One perfect for most.	Colorless, white, some pinkish.	4–5

APPENDIX V

Topographic and Geologic Maps

A map is a quantitative representation of the spatial distribution of some attribute or property of the Earth. It is a kind of graph in which the axes are lines of latitude and longitude and the positions of points on the surface (or beneath it) are plotted in relation to those axes or some other established reference. Geologists have frequent need of showing the configuration and nature of the geological materials at or near the surface in a meaningful way, so that they can construct a three-dimensional mental picture of the geology from this two-dimensional graph. Once the nature of maps becomes familiar, the map reader can become practiced at deducing much of the geologic structure and history of an area.

The use of topographic and geologic maps has spread widely throughout our culture. To the more traditional users of such maps—the geologists and surveyors—have been added city planners, industrial zoning commissions, and a large number of the public seeking recreational areas for hiking, camping, fishing, and other activities. In 1976 the U.S. Geological Survey distributed nearly 10 million copies of its 40,000 published topographic maps. Maps are a necessity for all kinds of geological and mineral resource studies, as well as for studies of groundwater, flood control, soil management, and such environmental concerns as land-use planning, which involves the location of highways, industrial areas, oil and gas pipelines, and recreational areas. Each may use maps with different emphasis for their specific needs, but all follow the same general conventions.

TOPOGRAPHIC MAPS

The beginning of a map is the choice of a suitable graphical framework to use for plotting the position of points on the globe onto a flat piece of paper. Since a curved surface cannot be made to lie flat without distortion, there will necessarily be some adjustments in order to approximate the true size and shape of an area, such as a lake, when it is mapped. Though there are a large number of ways of doing this, most topographic and geologic maps are made by means of **projections,** the term used for the method of transferring a three-dimensional surface onto a two-dimensional one, just as a camera transfers what it "sees" onto photographic film. The projections used for most maps strike a compromise between distortion of shape and maintaining true relative sizes of areas. The deviation from true size and shape is small for maps of relatively small areas of the globe, such as a county or a state, because the surface of a small area of this huge globe is for all practical purposes flat.

Because the size of the area covered, and thus the amount of detail that can be shown, is always important, we use the concept of **scale**— that is, the relation of a distance (or area) on the map to the true distance on the Earth. This is simply done by stating a ratio, such as 1:24,000, which indicates that a distance of one unit on the map represents a distance of 24,000 such units on the Earth. It does not matter what the units are: a map of scale 1:24,000 is the same whether we use metric or English systems. The scale can be thought of in any convenient units: 1 inch = 2000 feet, or 1 meter = 24 kilometers, or 10 centimeters = 2.4 kilometers. For convenience, maps have a graphic scale, usually at the bottom margin, in which distances such as one kilometer or one mile, usually with subdivisions, are shown as they would appear on the map. Common scales for detailed topographic and geologic maps are the 1 : 24,000, used by the U.S. Geological Survey for most modern maps, or a scale that is somewhat smaller (because the ratio is smaller) of 1 : 62,500, roughly an inch to a mile, which was used for many of the older maps. The scale used for regional maps covering much larger areas is 1 : 250,000. Scales of 1 : 1,000,000 are used for aeronautical charts. In 1976 the U.S. Geological Survey introduced the first of a new series of 1 : 100,000 all-metric topographic maps on which graphic scales show both kilometers and miles.

On most maps, natural and man-made features of the surface are represented by conventional symbols. Those used by the U.S. Geological Survey are typical. Rivers, lakes, and oceans are shown in blue. Topography is shown in brown. Man's structures are shown in black, with main highways and urban areas shown in red. Green shaded areas show wooded land. Some special symbols may be shown on the explanation, or **legend,** of the map, which is usually displayed along the bottom margin. Most complex to represent are the topographic elevations of the surface, usually shown on North American maps by contours (see Chapter 5 for discussion of various ways of showing topography.) Special maps are sometimes prepared to show environmental variables, such as the distribution of slopes of various steepness.

Topographic maps used to be made entirely by geologists or surveyors in the field. They first established a major network of points accurately located by surveying instruments with respect to latitude, longitude, and elevation. This major network, still used as a framework for most maps, was gradually extended from coast to coast across the continent. Within specific areas to be mapped, smaller networks of surveyed points were established and tied to the major network. Between points the locations were drawn in by sight by practiced topographers: surveyors, topographic engineers, or geologists. One can still see such surveyors operating at new highway or construction sites where high precision is needed. Since the advent of the airplane and the development of aerial photography in the 1930's and 1940's, most topo-

graphic maps are made by **photogrammetry,** the science of making measurements of position and elevation from aerial photographs. Because maps so prepared are checked on the ground and tied to the major surveyed network, they are the most accurate and precise maps available.

GEOLOGIC MAPS

Geologic maps are a representation of the distribution of rocks and other geologic materials or different lithologies and ages over the Earth's surface or below it. The geologist perceives the Earth not only in its surface expression of topography and patterns of land and water but in terms of its pattern of subsurface structures, stratigraphic sequences, igneous intrusions, unconformities, and other geometric relationships of rocks. Just as an anatomist can visualize the muscles and bones beneath the skin, so can a geologist visualize details of the Earth's subsurface. What the map looks like is very much a product of the geologic ideas—the concepts of origin or rocks and structure—that the geologist uses. An area mapped a hundred years ago might look somewhat different today as remapped. For example, some older maps of metamorphosed sedimentary rock terranes show relations of one rock type to another only in terms of lithology. The pattern is a complex and disorganized array of schists, gneisses, and other rock types. The same region, mapped later by a geologist who conceptualized the nature of the original sedimentary rocks by "looking through" the metamorphism, appears as a simpler, more organized pattern of a deformed sedimentary rock sequence with a superimposed pattern of different grades of metamorphism. So even though the rocks themselves have not changed, the way we look at them, and therefore the way we map them, has changed over the years.

Detailed geologic maps are normally constructed on a topographic map base. This serves the useful purpose of making it easy to locate geologic structures with respect to surface features of the Earth. It is also important because topography is so often related to the nature of the underlying rocks and their structures. Because it contains so much more information than a topographic map alone, a geologic map is the most valuable for many of the purposes for which maps are used.

Geologic maps are ordinarily made by a geologist who roams over the area and notes the kinds of rocks, sediments, and soils and their

1 ½ 0   1   2   3   4   5 miles

Contour interval 100 feet.

Topographic map (above) and geologic map with cross sections (facing page) of folded sedimentary rocks in the Valley and Ridge province of the Appalachian Mountains. Contours show the pronounced trends of valleys and ridges that reflect the parallel folds. The ridges have developed along the formations that are resistant to erosion, some at the crests of anticlines, such as Jack Mountain north of Crab Run, and others along the flanks of folds, such as Little Mountain. The valleys are in the easily eroded formations, some in synclines, such as Jackson River, some on anticlines, such as

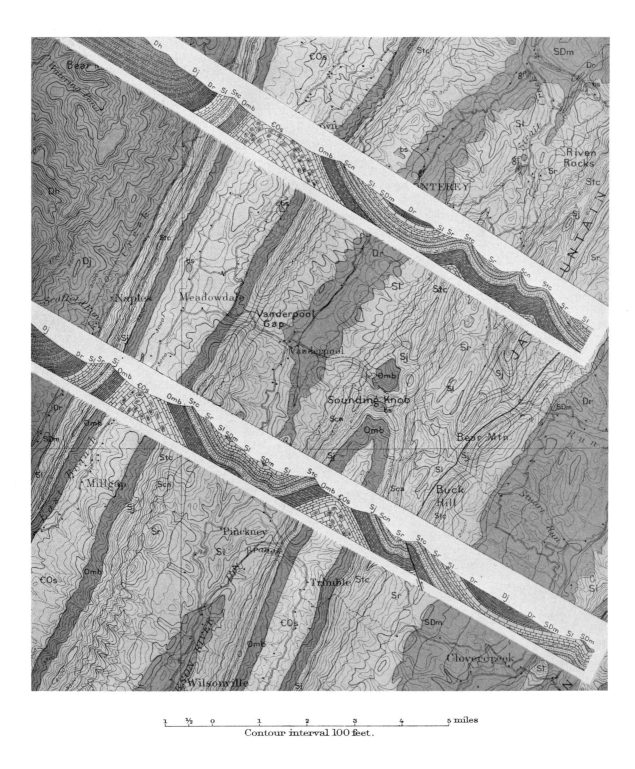

1	½	0	1	2	3	4	5 miles

Contour interval 100 feet.

East Branch, and some in the flanks of folds, such as Back Creek. On the geologic map the pattern of anticlines and synclines can be read from the positions of formations of different age, such as at East Branch, where the oldest rocks, Cambrian and Ordovician formations (COs), are at the surface bordered on both sides by younger formations of Ordovician and Silurian age (Omb, Stc, Sj, and others). The cross sections make these relationships clearer and add some detail. [From U.S. Geological Survey.]

structural and stratigraphic relationships. In modern times this is supplemented or even entirely supplanted by remote sensing by aerial photography or geophysical instruments. Remote, inaccessible regions, such as those in some polar or desert regions, may be mapped almost entirely by this method, with the geologist ground checking in scattered places. The mapping of the Moon is an extreme example of this approach. Mars is being mapped with no ground check at all except for the area immediately surrounding the landing site of Viking. The best and most accurate maps, however, are those made by traditional means, the geologist covering the ground on his own two legs to see most if not all of the outcrops; he is of course helped enormously by automobile, sometimes by helicopter, and, in some places, by horse or donkey.

The mapping proceeds by the following steps:

Principal Observations

Description of outcrop location, lithology, age, fossil content, and structural attitude as measured by dip and strike, direction of fault movement, fold axes, etc. (see Chapter 20). Plotting observations on work map.

First Integration

Conceptualizing the spatial relationship of one outcrop to another by stratigraphic correlation of rocks of the same age, facies, degree of metamorphism and deformation. Grouping of mappable rock units into formations. Drawing of lines on the primitive geologic map of inferred connections where formations are hidden. Compilation of the complete or composite stratigraphic sequence, ages of deformational or igneous intrusive events.

Synthesizing the Map

Visualizing the larger pattern of geologic relationships and constructing the map, together with geologic cross sections made both to help the geologist in his thinking and to illustrate more detail and inference from the map.

In the later stages, the geologist incorporates analyses of rock composition, radiometric determinations of absolute age, and such geophysical information as seismic, gravity, and magnetic data. He further draws on the geologic literature or his own experience of the geology of nearby and similar kinds of regions. The final result is the finished geologic map, a codified mass of information displayed in a form in which anyone familiar with geology can quickly read the nature of the Earth's crust in the area and a good deal of its geologic history.

Geologic maps are of many kinds. The most common shows the bedrock geology and gives a picture of what the land would look like if all soil were stripped away. Surficial geological maps, on the other hand, emphasize the nature of soils, unconsolidated river sediment, sand dunes, and whatever other materials, including outcrops, that appear at the surface. A special kind of surficial geological map is used for environmental hazards. One kind shows areas of high-angle or unsupported slopes that are likely to slump or slide (see Chapter 5). Tectonic maps show the disposition of large groups of rocks and their structural relationships to each other. Paleogeologic maps show a geologic map of a former land surface now buried beneath an unconformity. Whatever the geologic purpose, there is a map that can be made to show the relevant data. There is no question that the map is at one time both the best device for geological research into the origin of the distribution of important geologic characteristics over the Earth and the best way to illustrate the patterns discovered from such research.

GLOSSARY

Two-word entries are arranged according to common usage (for example, "Thrust fault" rather than "Fault, thrust"). Mineral names are defined in Appendix IV and therefore are generally omitted from the Glossary. Words that appear in *italic* type within a definition are defined elsewhere in the Glossary.

Aa: A blocky and fragmented form of lava occurring in flows with fissured and angular surfaces.

Ablation zone: The lower part of a glacier, where annual water loss exceeds snow accumulation.

Abyssal hill: A low, rounded submarine hill with a relief of 100 to 200 meters, common in deep ocean basins.

Abyssal plain: A flat, sediment-covered province of the sea floor that slopes at less than 1:1000.

Accumulation zone: The upper part of a glacier, where annual snowfall exceeds melting and evaporation.

Aeration: The amount of interstitial space in a soil that contains air and gases; the process of increasing this volume.

A-horizon: The uppermost layer of a soil, containing organic material and leached minerals.

Algal mat: A layered communal growth of algae observed in fossils and in present-day tidal zones associated with carbonate sedimentation.

Alkali metal: A strongly basic metal like potassium or sodium; a metal of group IA of the periodic table.

Alluvial fan: A low, cone-shaped deposit of terrestrial sediment formed where a stream undergoes an abrupt reduction in slope.

Alluvium: An unconsolidated terrestrial sediment composed of sorted or unsorted sand, gravel, and clay that had been deposited by water.

Alpha particle: A helium nucleus, emitted from a larger nucleus undergoing *radioactive decay.*

Amphibolite: A metamorphic rock containing mostly amphibole and plagioclase feldspar.

Amygdule: A vesicle or gas bubble in an igneous rock that has been filled with another mineral after the solidification of the lava.

Andesite: A volcanic rock type intermediate in composition between *rhyolite* and *basalt.*

Angle of repose: The steepest slope angle in which a particular sediment will lie without cascading down.

Angstrom: A length of 10^{-10} meter.

Angular momentum: The product of a body's angular velocity, or rotation rate, and its moment of inertia.

Angular unconformity: An unconformity in which the bedding planes of the rocks above and below are not parallel.

Anion: Any negatively charged ion; the opposite of a *cation.*

Anisotropic: Any material in which physical properties (for example, light transmission or seismic wave velocity) vary quantitatively with the direction in which they are measured.

Anorthosite: A plutonic rock composed primarily of calcium-rich plagioclase feldspar.

Anthracite: The most highly metamorphosed form of coal, containing 92 to 98 percent of fixed carbon. It is black, hard, and glassy.

Anticline: A fold, usually from 100 meters to 300 kilometers in width, that is convex upward with the oldest strata at the center.

Antiroot: An accumulation of higher-density material in the suboceanic crust that compensates for the low density of sea water.

Aphanitic texture: In igneous rocks, having a grain size that is so uniformly small that crystals are invisible to the naked eye.

Aquiclude: An impermeable stratum that acts as a barrier to the flow of groundwater.

Aquifer: A permeable formation that stores and transmits groundwater in sufficient quantity to supply wells.

Arkose: A variety of sandstone containing abundant feldspar and quartz, frequently in angular, poorly-sorted grains.

Arroyo: A steep-sided and flat-bottomed gully in an arid region that is occupied by a stream only intermittently, after rains.

Artesian well: A well that penetrates an *aquiclude* to reach an *aquifer* containing water under pressure. Thus water in the well rises above the surrounding water table.

Aseismic region: One that is relatively free of earthquakes. (Actually, all areas show some seismicity over a sufficiently long interval.)

Aseismic ridge: A submarine ridge which is actually a fragment of continental crust; distinguished from a *mid-oceanic ridge,* which is seismically active.

Ash: See *Volcanic ash.*

Asthenosphere: The worldwide layer below the *lithosphere* which is marked by low seismic wave velocities and high *seismic attenuation.* The asthenosphere is a soft layer, probably partially molten. It may be the site of convection.

Astrobleme: A circular erosional feature that has been ascribed to the impact of a meteorite or comet.

Asymmetrical fold: A fold that is inclined to one side. The dips of the two limbs are unequal.

Asymmetrical ripple: A ripple whose cross section is asymmetric, with a gentle slope on the upcurrent side and a steeper face on the downcurrent side.

Atmosphere (unit): A unit of pressure equal to 101,325 newtons per square meter, or about 14.7 pounds per square inch.

Atoll: A continuous or broken circle of coral reef and low coral islands surrounding a central lagoon.

Atomic number: The number of protons in the nucleus of an atom.

Atomic weight: The average weight of one atom of an element, relative to a standard weight of 12 for carbon.

Augen gneiss: A gneiss containing *phenocrysts* or *porphyroblasts* that have been deformed into eye-shaped grains or grain clusters.

Aureole: The area surrounding an intrusion that has been affected by contact metamorphism.

Axial plane: In folds, the plane that most nearly separates two symmetrical limbs. In a simple *anticline* it is vertical; in a complex folding it is perpendicular to the direction of compression.

Axis (fold): Within each stratum involved in a fold, there is an axis connecting all the points in the center of the fold, from which both limbs bend.

Axis of symmetry: An imaginary line about which an object (for example, a crystal) may be rotated $\frac{1}{2}$, $\frac{1}{3}$, $\frac{1}{4}$, $\frac{1}{6}$, or any other simple fraction of a turn without changing its appearance. The denominator corresponds to the order of the axis.

Backwash: The return flow of water down a beach after a wave has broken.

Banded iron ore: A sediment consisting of layers of chert alternating with bands of ferric iron oxides (hematite and limonite) in valuable concentrations.

Bankfull stage: The height of water in a stream that just corresponds to the level of the surrounding floodplain.

Bar: A unit of pressure equal to 10^6 dynes/square centimeter; approximately one atmosphere.

Bar (stream): An accumulation of sediment, usually sandy, which forms at the borders or in the channels of streams or offshore from a beach.

Barchan: A crescent-shaped sand dune moving across a clean surface with its convex face upwind and its concave *slip face* downwind.

Bar-finger sand: An elongated lens of sand deposited during the growth of a distributary in a delta. The bar at the distributary mouth is the growing segment of the bar finger.

Barrier island: A long, narrow island parallel to the shore, composed of sand, and built by wave action.

Basalt: A fine-grained, dark, mafic igneous rock composed largely of plagioclase feldspar and pyroxene.

Base level: The level below which a stream cannot erode: usually sea level, sometimes locally the level of a lake or resistant formation.

Basement: The oldest rocks recognized in a given area, a complex of metamorphic and igneous rocks that underlies all the sedimentary formations. Usually Precambrian or Paleozoic in age.

Basic rock: Any igneous rock containing mafic minerals rich in iron and magnesium, but containing no quartz and little sodium-rich plagioclase feldspar (see preferred term, *mafic rock*).

Basin: In *tectonics*, a circular, syncline-like depression of strata. In sedimentology, the site of accumulation of a large thickness of sediments.

Batholith: A great irregular mass of coarse-grained igneous rock with an exposed surface of more than 100 square kilometers, which has either intruded the country rock or been derived from it through metamorphism.

Bathymetry: The study and mapping of sea-floor topography.

Bauxite: A rock composed primarily of hydrous aluminum oxides and formed by weathering in tropical areas with good drainage; a major ore of aluminum.

Bedding: A characteristic of sedimentary rocks in which parallel planar surfaces separating different grain sizes or compositions indicate successive depositional surfaces that existed at the time of sedimentation.

Bed load: The sediment that a stream moves along the bottom of its channel by rolling and bouncing (see *Saltation*).

Beta particle: An electron emitted with high energy and velocity from a nucleus undergoing *radioactive decay*.

B-horizon: The intermediate layer in a soil, below the A-horizon, consisting of clays and oxide minerals. Also called the zone of accumulation.

Bicarbonate ion: The anion group HCO_3^- (having a charge of -1).

Biochemical precipitate: A sediment, especially of limestone or iron minerals, formed from elements extracted from sea water by living organisms.

Bioturbation: Reworking of existing sediments by organisms.

Bituminous coal: A soft coal formed by an intermediate degree of metamorphism and containing 15 to 20 percent *volatiles*. The most common grade of coal.

Block fault: A structure formed when the crust is divided into blocks of different elevation by a set of *normal faults*.

Blowout: A shallow circular or elliptical depression in sand or dry soil formed by wind erosion. (See also *Deflation*.)

Blueschist: A metamorphic rock formed under conditions of high pressure (in excess of 5 kb) and relatively low temperature, often containing the blue minerals glaucophane (an amphibole) and kyanite.

Bolson: In arid regions, a basin filled with *alluvium* and intermittent *playa* lakes and having no outlet.

Bottomset bed: A flat-lying bed of fine sediment deposited in front of a *delta* and then buried by continued delta growth.

Bouguer correction: The correction of a measured gravity value by an amount theoretically calculated to compensate for the mass of known topography around the station.

Bowen's Reaction Series: A simple schematic description of the order in which different minerals crystallize during the cooling and progressive crystallization of a *magma*.

Braided stream: A stream so choked with sediment that it divides and recombines numerous times, forming many small and meandering channels.

Breaker: An ocean wave that becomes unstably steep on encountering shallow water and collapses turbulently.

Breccia: A clastic rock composed principally of large angular fragments.

Breeder reactor: A planned nuclear reactor that would use the high-energy particles created in fission to create more fissionable fuel out of stable uranium or thorium isotopes.

Brine: Sea water whose salinity has been increased by evaporation; or groundwater with an unusual concentration of salts.

Brittle: Describes a material that breaks abruptly when its *elastic limit* is reached; the opposite of *ductile*.

Butte: A steep-sided and flat-topped hill formed by erosion of flat-lying strata where remnants of a resistant layer protect softer rocks underneath.

Calcium carbonate compensation depth: The depth in the oceans below which the solution rate of $CaCO_3$ becomes so great that no carbonate organisms or sediments are preserved on the sea floor.

Caldera: A large, circular depression in a volcanic terrane, typically originating in collapse, explosion, or erosion.

Canyon: A very large, deep valley with precipitous walls formed principally by stream downcutting.

Capacity (stream): A measure of the amount of sediment and detritus a stream can transport past any point in a given time.

Carbonate ion: The anion group CO_3^{-2} (having a charge of -2).

Carbonate platform: A submarine or intertidal shelf whose elevation is maintained by active shallow-water carbonate deposition.

Carbonate rock: A rock composed of carbonate minerals, especially *limestone* and *dolomite.*

Carbon-14 activity: The number of atoms of the isotope of carbon with atomic weight 14 that decay radioactively in a unit time.

Carbonic acid: The weak acid H_2CO_3, formed by the dissolution of CO_2 in water.

Cataclastic rock: A breccia or powdered rock formed by crushing and shearing during tectonic movements.

Cation: Any ion with a positive electric charge.

Central vent: The largest vent of a volcano, situated at the center of its cone.

Chemical differentiation: The formation of more than one igneous rock composition from a common magma as a result of crystals settling out as they form, thus removing certain elements from the remaining melt.

Chemical sediment: One that is formed at or near its place of deposition by chemical precipitation, usually from sea water.

Chemical weathering: The total set of all chemical reactions that act on rock exposed to water and atmosphere and so change its minerals to more stable forms.

Chert: A sedimentary form of amorphous or extremely fine-grained silica, partially hydrous, found in concretions and beds; commonly a chemical sediment.

C-horizon: The lowest layer of a soil, consisting of fragments of rock and their chemically weathered products.

Cinder cone: A steep, conical hill built up about a volcanic vent and composed of coarse pyroclasts expelled from the vent by escaping gases.

Cirque: The head of a glacial valley, usually with the form of one half of an inverted cone. The upper edges have the steepest slopes, approaching the vertical, and the base may be flat or hollowed out and occupied by a small lake or pond.

Clastic rock: A sedimentary rock formed from mineral particles (clasts) that were mechanically transported.

Clay: Any of a number of hydrous aluminosilicate minerals with sheet-like crystal structures, formed by weathering and hydration of other silicates; also, any mineral fragments smaller than $\frac{1}{256}$ mm.

Cleavage: (1) Of minerals: the tendency of a crystal to break along certain preferred planes in the crystal lattice; also, the geometric pattern of such breakage. (2) Of rocks: the tendency of a rock to break along certain planes; usually the result of *preferred orientation* of the minerals in the rock.

Coal: The metamorphic product of stratified plant remains. It contains more than 50 percent carbon compounds and burns readily.

Coastal plain: A low plain of little relief adjacent to the ocean and covered with gently dipping sediments.

Coefficient of thermal expansion: A measure of the increase in volume of a material relative to the original volume with increasing temperature.

Collision hypothesis: The theory that the material forming the planets was separated from the solar mass by an interstellar collision or near-miss.

Columnar jointing: The division of an igneous rock body into prismatic columns by cracks produced by thermal contraction on cooling.

Compaction: The decrease in volume and porosity of a sediment caused by burial.

Compensation (gravity): The mechanism by which segments of the crust rise or sink to equilibrium positions, depending upon the mass and density of the rocks above and below a certain depth, called the *compensation depth.*

Compensation depth: In relation to gravity, the critical depth in the above definition (see also *Calcium carbonate compensation depth*).

Competence (rock): The ability of a stratum to withstand deformation without fracturing or changing in thickness.

Competence (stream): A measure of the largest particle a stream is able to transport, not the total volume.

Composite cone: The volcanic cone of a *stratovolcano,* composed of both cinders and lava flows.

Concentration factor: The ratio of the abundance of an element in a mineral deposit to its average abundance in the crust.

Concordant contact: The planar contact of an intrusion that follows the bedding of the country rock.

Concordant stratification: Sedimentary layering in which successive bedding planes are parallel.

Conduction: See *Heat conduction.*

Confined water reservoir: A body of groundwater surrounded by impermeable strata.

Conformable succession: A sequence of sedimentary rocks that indicates continuous deposition with no erosion over a geologically long period.

Conglomerate: A sedimentary rock, a significant fraction of which is composed of rounded pebbles and boulders; the lithified equivalent of *gravel.*

Conservation of angular momentum: The physical law that the total angular momentum of a system of isolated bodies cannot change without outside interference.

Contact metamorphism: Mineralogical and textural changes and deformation of rock resulting from the heat and pressure of an igneous intrusion in the near vicinity.

Continental divide: An imaginary line connecting high points across a continent and dividing regions whose streams drain into one ocean from regions that drain into another.

Continental drift: The horizontal displacement or rotation of continents relative to one another.

Continental glacier: A continuous, thick glacier covering more than 50,000 square kilometers and moving independently of minor topographic features.

Continental rise: A broad and gently sloping ramp that rises from an abyssal plain to the *continental slope* at a rate of less than $1:40$.

Continental shelf: The gently sloping submerged edge of a continent, extending commonly to a depth of about 200 meters or the edge of the continental slope.

Continental shelf deposits: Sediments laid down in a tectonically quiet *syncline* at an intraplate continental margin.

Continental slope: The region of steep slopes between the continental shelf and continental rise.

Continuous reaction series: A reaction series in which the same mineral crystallizes throughout the range of temperatures in question, but in which there is a gradual change in the chemical composition of the mineral with changing temperature.

Contour map: A map that shows topography by means of contour lines. Each contour line connects points of equal elevation, and the elevation interval between lines is constant.

Convection: A mechanism of heat transfer through a liquid in which hot material from the bottom rises because of its lesser density, while cool surface material sinks.

Convection cell: A single closed flow circuit of rising warm material and sinking cold material.

Convergence zone: A band along which moving plates collide and area is lost either by shortening and crustal thickening or subduction and destruction of crust. The site of volcanism, earthquakes, trenches, and mountain-building.

Coordination number: In a mineral, the number of ions bonded to a given ion of opposite charge.

Coral: Colonial organisms with carbonate skeletons that live in sea water at sufficiently shallow depths to receive light from the surface.

Cordillera: If capitalized: the continuous mountain system extending from Alaska to extreme South America and ranging up to 1500 kilometers in width. If not: any similar chain of parallel mountain ranges.

Core: The central part of the Earth below a depth of 2900 kilometers. It is thought to be composed of iron and nickel and to be molten on the outside with a central solid inner core.

Coriolis effect: An apparent force that a moving object feels, tending to the right in the Northern hemisphere and to the left in the Southern. It is due to the Earth's rotation, which requires that objects near the equator have a greater eastward velocity than those nearer the poles.

Country rock: The rock into which an igneous rock intrudes or a mineral deposit is emplaced.

Covalent bond: A bond between atoms in which outer electrons are shared between them.

Crater: An abrupt circular depression formed by extrusion of volcanic material and its deposition in a surrounding rim or by explosive ejection of matter upon meteorite impact.

Craton: A portion of a continent that has not been subjected to major deformation for a prolonged time, typically since Precambrian or early Paleozoic time.

Crevasse: Any large vertical crack in the surface of a glacier or snowfield.

Cross-bedding: Inclined beds of depositional origin in a sedimentary rock. Formed by currents of wind or water in the direction toward which the bed slopes downward.

Cross-cutting: Having *discordant contacts* with the *country rock.*

Cross section: A drawing showing the features that would be exposed by a vertical cut through a structure.

Crust: The outermost layer of the *lithosphere,* consisting of relatively light, low-melting-point materials. The continental crust consists largely of *granite* and *granodiorite;* the oceanic crust is mostly *basalt.*

Crystal: A form of matter in which a *unit cell* of atoms, having a fixed chemical formula, is arranged regularly in all directions to form a repeating network.

Crystal face: A planar growth surface of a crystal.

Crystallinity: The proportion of crystals (as opposed to glass) in an igneous rock.

Cuesta: A ridge with one steep and one gentle face formed by the outcrop and slower erosion of a resistant, gently dipping bed.

Curie point: The temperature above which a given mineral cannot retain any permanent magnetization.

Datum plane: An artificially established, well-surveyed horizontal plane against which elevations, depths, tides, etc. are measured (for example, *mean sea level*).

Daughter element: Also "daughter product." An element that occurs in a rock as the end-product of the radioactive decay of another element.

Debris avalanche: A fast downhill *mass movement* of soil and rock.

Decay constant: A constant, different for each radioactive isotope, which indicates how rapidly that isotope breaks down spontaneously by *radioactive decay.* (See also *Half-life.*)

Declination: At any place on Earth, the angle between the magnetic and rotational poles.

Deflation: The removal of clay and dust from dry soil by strong winds.

Delta: A body of sediment deposited in an ocean or lake at the mouth of a stream.

Delta kame: A deposit having the form of a steep, flat-topped hill, left at the front of a retreating continental glacier.

Dendritic drainage: A stream system that branches irregularly and resembles a branching tree in plan.

Density: The mass per unit volume of a substance, commonly expressed in grams/cubic centimeter.

Density current: A subaqueous current that flows on the bottom of a sea or lake because entering water is more dense due to temperature or suspended sediments.

Deposition: A general term for the accumulation of sediments by either physical or chemical sedimentation.

Depositional remanent magnetization: A weak magnetization created in sedimentary rocks by the rotation of magnetic crystals into line with the ambient field during settling.

Depth recorder: See *Echo sounder.*

Desert pavement: A residual deposit produced by continued deflation, which removes the fine grains of a soil and leaves a surface covered with close-packed cobbles.

Detrital sediment: A sediment deposited by a physical process.

Diagenesis: The physical and chemical changes undergone by a sediment during *lithification* and *compaction,* excluding *erosion* and *metamorphism.*

Diatom: A one-celled plant that has a siliceous framework and grows in oceans and lakes.

Diatomite: A siliceous chert-like sediment formed from the hard parts of diatoms.

Diatom ooze: A fine muddy sediment consisting of the hard parts of diatoms.

Diatreme: A volcanic vent filled with breccia by the explosive escape of gases.

Differentiated planet: One that is chemically zoned because heavy materials have sunk to the center and light materials have accumulated in a crust.

Diffraction pattern: The pattern formed by the reflection of X-rays from the internal planes of atoms when a crystal is exposed to a beam of X-radiation.

Dike: A roughly planar body of intrusive igneous rock that has *discordant contacts* with the surrounding rock.

Dike swarm: A group of dikes emanating from a common magma chamber.

Diorite: A plutonic rock with composition intermediate between *granite* and *gabbro;* the intrusive equivalent of *andesite.*

Dip: The angle by which a stratum or other planar feature deviates from the horizontal. The angle is measured in a plane perpendicular to the strike.

Dip needle: A type of compass that measures the inclination of the Earth's magnetic field from the horizontal.

Dip-slip fault: A fault in which the relative displacement is along the direction of dip of the fault plane; either a normal or a reverse fault.

Discharge: The rate of water movement through a stream, measured in units of volume per unit time.

Disconformity: A special type of stratigraphic boundary, where bedding planes of sediments on either side of the boundary are parallel, but where there is evidence that a geologically significant timespan is not represented in the sedimentary record— that is, that sedimentation has not been continuous.

Discontinuity: See *Seismic discontinuity.*

Discontinuous reaction series: A *reaction series* in which the end members have different crystal structures (are distinct mineral phases).

Discordant contact: A contact that cuts across *bedding* or *foliation* planes, such as the contact between a *dike* and the *country rock.*

Disintegration constant: See *Decay constant.*

Disseminated deposit: A deposit of ore in which the metal is distributed in small amounts throughout the rock, and not concentrated in veins.

Distributary: A smaller branch of a large stream that receives water from the main channel; the opposite of a tributary.

Divergence zone: A belt along which plates move apart and new crust and lithosphere are created: the site of mid-ocean ridges, earthquakes, and volcanism.

Divide: A ridge of high ground separating two drainage basins emptied by different streams.

Dolomite: A carbonate mineral with the general formula $(Ca,Mg)CO_3$; also, a sedimentary rock composed primarily of this mineral.

Dome: In structural geology, a round or elliptical upwarp of strata resembling a short anticline.

Drainage basin: A region of land surrounded by divides and crossed by streams that eventually converge to one river or lake.

Drift (continental): See *Continental drift.*

Drift (geomorphology): A pileup of sand and sediment to the leeward (downcurrent) side of an obstacle.

Drift (glacial): A collective term for all the rock, sand, and clay that is deposited by a glacier either as *till* or as *outwash.*

Dripstone: See *Stalactite, Stalagmite.*

Drowned valley: A river valley flooded by the sea when sea level rises or the land subsides.

Drumlin: A smooth, streamlined hill composed of *till.*

Dry wash: An intermittent stream bed in an *arroyo* or canyon that carries water only briefly after a rain.

Ductile rock: A rock that can withstand 5 to 10 percent *strain* without fracturing after its *elastic limit* has been reached.

Dune: An elongated mound of sand formed by wind or water.

Dunite: An *ultramafic rock* composed almost entirely of the mineral olivine.

Duricrust: A hard surface crust made up of the products of chemical weathering in the desert; it can consist of silica, calcium carbonate, iron oxides, and other materials.

Earthflow: A detachment of soil and broken rock and its subsequent downslope movement at slow or moderate rates in a stream- or tongue-like form.

Earthquake: The violent oscillatory motion of the ground caused by the passage of seismic waves radiating from a fault along which sudden movement has taken place.

Ebb tide: The part of the tide cycle during which the water level is falling.

Echo-sounder: An oceanographic instrument that emits sound pulses into the water and measures its depth by the time elapsed before they return.

Ecliptic: The plane that contains the Earth's orbit around the Sun.

Eclogite: An extremely high-pressure metamorphic rock containing garnet and pyroxene.

Ecology: The science of the life cycles, populations, and interactions of various biological species as controlled by their physical environment, including also the effect of life forms upon the environment.

Economic geology: The study of and location of ores, fossil fuels, and other useful materials that occur in sufficient concentration to be marketable in a particular economy.

Elastic limit: The maximum stress that can be applied to a body without resulting in permanent *strain.*

Elastic rebound theory: A theory of fault movement and earthquake generation that holds that faults remain locked while strain energy accumulates in the rock, and then suddenly slip and release this energy.

Electron: A negatively charged particle with negligible mass orbiting around the nucleus of an atom. An electron has a mass of 9.1×10^{-28} gram and a negative charge of 1.6×10^{-19} coulomb.

Electron microprobe: An instrument that bombards a very minute sample with electrons to determine its chemical composition from the resulting X-radiation.

Elevation: The vertical height of one point on the Earth above a given *datum plane,* usually sea level.

Elliptical orbit: An orbit with the shape of a geometrical ellipse. All orbits are elliptical or hyperbolic, with the Sun occupying one focus.

Emission spectroscopy: The identification of elements by the characteristic wavelengths of light that they emit when heated. A prism separates the spectrum into characteristic bright lines.

Environment of deposition: A geographically limited area where sediments are preserved; characterized by its landforms, relative energy of currents, and chemical equilibria.

Eolian: Pertaining to or deposited by wind.

Eon: The largest division of geologic time, embracing several *eras,* (for example, the Phanerozoic, 600 m.y. ago to present); also any span of one billion years.

Epeirogeny: Large-scale, primarily vertical movement of the crust. It is characteristically so gradual that rocks are little folded and faulted.

Epicenter: The point on the Earth's surface directly above the focus or hypocenter of an earthquake.

Epoch: One subdivision of a geologic period, often chosen to correspond to a stratigraphic series. Also used for a division of time corresponding to a paleomagnetic interval.

Equilibrium: A stable state of a system. Once equilibrium has been reached, no further net change in the chemical or physical state of materials in the system, or in their proportions, will occur without some external interference (such as a change in temperature or pressure or addition of some component).

Era: A time period including several periods, but smaller than an eon. Commonly recognized eras are Precambrian, Paleozoic, Mesozoic, and Cenozoic.

Erosion: The set of all processes by which soil and rock are loosened and moved downhill or downwind.

Esker: A glacial deposit in the form of a continuous, winding ridge, formed from the deposits of a stream flowing beneath the ice.

Estuary: A body of water along a coastline, open to the ocean but diluted by fresh water.

Eugeosyncline: The seaward part of a *geosyncline;* characterized by clastic sediments and volcanism.

Eustatic change: Sea-level changes that affect the whole Earth.

Eutrophication: A superabundance of algal life in a body of water; caused by an unusual influx of nitrate, phosphate, or other nutrients.

Evaporite: A chemical sedimentary rock consisting of minerals precipitated by evaporating waters, especially salt and gypsum.

Exfoliation: A physical weathering process in which sheets of rock are fractured and detached from an *outcrop.*

Exobiology: The study of life outside the Earth.

Experimental petrology: Laboratory study of the response of rocks and minerals to different physical and chemical conditions, often using special apparatus to simulate the elevated pressures and temperatures found deep in the crust and upper mantle.

Extrusive rock: One formed from *lava* or from other volcanic material spewed out onto the surface of the Earth.

Facies: The set of all characteristics of a sedimentary rock that indicate its particular *environment of deposition* and which distinguish it from other facies in the same rock unit. Also, for a metamorphic rock, the particular range of pressure and temperature under which the rock recrystallized.

Fathometer: See *Echo sounder.*

Fault: A planar or gently curved fracture in the Earth's crust across which there has been relative displacement.

Fault-block mountain: A mountain or range formed as a horst when it was elevated (or as the surrounding region sank) between parallel normal faults.

Fault plane: The plane that best approximates the fracture surface of a fault.

Faunal succession: The evolutionary sequence of life forms, especially as recorded by the fossil remains in a stratigraphic sequence.

Feedback: Any system in which a process controls itself, either through negative feedback, which has the effect of damping out fluctuations in rate or process, or positive feedback, which has the effect of amplifying and preserving fluctuations.

Feldspar: General term for a group of aluminosilicate minerals containing sodium, calcium, or potassium and having a framework structure. Feldspars are the most common minerals in the Earth's crust.

Felsic: An adjective used to describe a light-colored igneous rock that is poor in iron and magnesium and contains abundant feldspars and quartz.

Ferromagnesian: Containing iron and/or magnesium as a major constituent.

Field relations: The pattern of contacts, faults, intrusions, and other boundaries where rock formations meet, from which the field geologist reconstructs the chronology and history of an area.

Fiord: A former glacial valley with steep walls and a U-shaped profile; now occupied by the sea.

Firn: Old, dense, compacted snow.

First motion: On a seismogram, the direction of ground motion at the beginning of the arrival of a *P*-wave. Upward ground motion indicates a compression; downward motion, a dilation.

Fissile: An adjective describing a rock that has a tendency to break into tabular fragments along parallel planes.

Flood basalt: A plateau basalt extending many kilometers in flat, layered flows originating in fissure eruptions.

Floodplain: A level plain of stratified alluvium on either side of a stream; submerged during floods and built up by silt and sand carried out of the main channel.

Flood tide: The part of the tide cycle during which the water is rising or leveling off at high water.

Flow cleavage: In a metamorphic rock, the parallel arrangement of all planar or linear crystals as a result of rock flowage during metamorphism.

Fluid inclusion: A small body of fluid that is entrapped in a crystal and has the same composition as the fluid from which the crystal formed.

Flume: A laboratory model of stream flow and sedimentation consisting of a rectangular channel filled with sediment and running water.

Focus (earthquake): The point at which the rupture occurs; synonymous with *hypocenter.*

Fold: A planar feature, such as a bedding plane, that has been strongly warped, presumably by deformation.

Fold axis: See *Axis.*

Fold belt: Synonym of *Orogenic belt.*

Foliation: Any planar set of minerals or banding of mineral concentrations, including cleavage, found in a metamorphic rock.

Foraminifer: A class of oceanic protozoa most of which have shells composed of calcite.

Foraminiferal ooze: A calcareous sediment composed of the shells of dead Foraminifera.

Foreset bed: One of the inclined beds found in *cross-bedding;* also an inclined bed deposited on the outer front of a *delta.*

Formation: The basic unit for the naming of rocks in stratigraphy: a set of rocks that are or once were horizontally continuous, that share some distinctive feature of lithology, and are large enough to be mapped.

Fossil: An impression, cast, outline, track, or body part of any animal or plant that is preserved in rock after the original organic material is transformed or removed.

Fossil fuel: A general term for combustible geologic deposits of carbon in reduced (organic) form and of biological origin, including coal, oil, natural gas, oil shales, and tar sands.

Fossil magnetism: See *Paleomagnetism.*

Fractional crystallization: The separation of a cooling magma into components by successive formation of and removal of crystals at progressively lower temperatures.

Fracture (mineralogy): The irregular breaking of a crystal along a surface not parallel to a crystal face. The nature of the surface texture is considered diagnostic.

Fracture cleavage: A set of closely spaced, parallel joints in a rock resulting from deformation and metamorphism.

Free-air correction: In gravity, the addition to a measured value of gravity of an amount theoretically calculated to correct for the effect of elevation only.

Free oscillation: The "ringing" or periodic deformation of the whole Earth at characteristic low frequencies after a major earthquake.

Friction breccia: A breccia formed in a fault zone or volcanic pipe by the relative motion of two rock bodies.

Fringing reef: A coral reef that is directly attached to a landmass not made of coral.

Fumarole: A small vent in the ground from which volcanic gases and heated groundwater emerge, but no lava.

Gabbro: A black, coarse-grained, intrusive igneous rock, composed of calcic feldspars and pyroxene. The intrusive equivalent of basalt.

Geochronology: The science of absolute dating and relative dating of geologic formations and events, primarily through the measurement of the abundances of radioactive *parent* and *daughter* elements in minerals and rocks.

Geologic cycle: The sequence through which rock material passes in going from its sedimentary form, through diagenesis and deformation of sedimentary rock, then through metamorphism and eventual melting and magma formation, then through volcanism and plutonism to igneous rock formation, and finally through erosion to form new sediments.

Geomorphic cycle: An idealized model of erosion wherein a plain is uplifted epeirogenically, then dissected by rapid streams (youth), then rounded by downslope movements into a landscape of steep hills (maturity), and finally reduced to a new *peneplain* at sea level (old age).

Geomorphology: The science of surface landforms and their interpretation on the basis of geology and climate.

Geosyncline: A major downwarp in the Earth's crust, usually more than 1000 kilometers in length, in which sediments accumulate to thicknesses of many kilometers. The sediments may eventually be deformed and metamorphosed during a mountain-building episode.

Geotherm: A curve on a temperature-pressure or temperature-depth graph that describes the way in which temperature in the Earth changes with depth. Different tectonic provinces are characterized by more or less rapid increase of temperature with depth. Alternatively, a curving surface within the Earth along which the temperature is constant (geoisotherm).

Geothermal power: Power generated by utilizing the heat energy of the crust, especially in volcanic regions.

Geyser: A hot spring that throws hot water and steam into the air. The heat is thought to result from the contact of groundwater with magma bodies.

Giant planet: One of the large planets outside the orbit of Mars, as opposed to the terrestrial planets.

Glacial rebound: Epeirogenic uplift of the crust that takes place after the retreat of a continental glacier, in response to earlier subsidence under the weight of the ice.

Glacial striations: Scratches left on bedrock and boulders by overriding ice, and showing the direction of motion.

Glacial valley: A valley occupied or formerly occupied by a glacier, typically with a U-shaped profile.

Glacier: A mass of ice and surficial snow that persists throughout the year and flows downhill under its own weight. The size range is from 100 meters to 10,000 kilometers.

Glacier surge: A period of unusually rapid movement of one glacier, sometimes lasting more than a year.

Glass: A rock formed when magma is too rapidly cooled (quenched) to allow crystal growth.

Glassiness: The content or extent of glass in an igneous rock.

Gneiss: A coarse-grained regional metamorphic rock that shows compositional banding and parallel alignment of minerals.

Gondwanaland: A hypothetical supercontinent comprising approximately the present continents of the southern hemisphere.

Graben: A downthrown block between two normal faults of parallel strike but converging dips; hence a tensional feature. (See also *Horst.*)

Graded bedding: A bed in which the coarsest particles are concentrated at the bottom and grade gradually upward into fine silt, the whole bed having been deposited by a waning current.

Graded stream: A stream whose smooth profile is unbroken by resistant ledges, lakes, or waterfalls, and which maintains exactly the velocity required to carry the sediment provided to it.

Granite: A coarse-grained, intrusive igneous rock composed of quartz, orthoclase feldspar, sodic plagioclase feldspar, and micas. Also sometimes a metamorphic product.

Granitization: The formation of metamorphic granite from other rocks by recrystallization with or without complete melting.

Granular snow: Snow that has been metamorphosed into small granules of ice.

Granulite: A regional-metamorphic rock with coarse interlocking grains, generally formed under conditions of relatively high pressure and temperature.

Gravel: The coarsest of alluvial sediments, containing mostly particles larger than 2 mm and including cobbles and boulders.

Gravimeter: An instrument for measuring the force of gravity at a given point on the Earth.

Gravity anomaly: The value of gravity left after subtracting from a gravity measurement the reference value based on latitude, and possibly the free-air and Bouguer corrections.

Gravity survey: The measurement of gravity at regularly spaced grid points with repetitions to control instrument drift.

Graywacke: A poorly sorted sandstone containing abundant feldspar and rock fragments, often in a clay-rich matrix.

Greenhouse effect: The heating of the atmosphere by the absorption of infrared energy re-emitted by the Earth as it receives light energy in the visible band from the Sun.

Greenschist: A metamorphic *schist* containing chlorite and epidote (which are green) and formed by low-temperature, low-pressure metamorphism.

Ground moraine: A glacial deposit of till with no marked relief, interpreted as having been transported at the base of the ice.

Groundwater: The mass of water in the ground below the *phreatic zone*, occupying the total pore space in the rock and moving slowly downhill where *permeability* allows.

Gully: A small steep-sided valley or erosional channel from 1 meter to about 10 meters across.

Guyot: A flat-topped submerged mountain or *seamount* found in the ocean.

Gyre: The circular rotation of the waters of each major sea, driven by prevailing winds and the *Coriolis effect.*

Half-life: The time required for half of a sample of a given radioactive isotope to decay. The half-life of an isotope is inversely related to its *decay constant.*

Hanging valley: A former glacial tributary valley that enters a larger glacial valley above its base, high up on the valley wall.

Hard coal: See *Anthracite.*

Hard water: Water that contains sufficient dissolved calcium and magnesium to cause a carbonate scale to form when the water is boiled or to prevent the sudsing of soap.

Heat conduction: The transfer of the rapid vibrational energy of atoms and molecules, which constitutes heat energy, through the mechanism of atomic or molecular impact.

Heat engine: A device that transfers heat from a place of high temperature to a place of lower temperature and does mechanical work in the process.

Heat flow: The rate at which heat escapes at the Earth's surface, related to the nature of the surface rocks and the rate at which heat is supplied to the crust from below.

Hill: A natural land elevation, usually less than 1000 feet above its surroundings, with a rounded outline. The distinction between hill and mountain depends on the locality.

Hogback: A formation similar to a *cuesta* in that it is a ridge formed by slower erosion of hard strata, but having two steep, equally inclined slopes.

Hooke's Law: The principle that the stress within a solid is proportional to the strain. It holds only for strains of a few percent or less.

Hornfels: A high-temperature, low-pressure metamorphic rock of uniform grain size showing no foliation. Usually formed by contact metamorphism.

Horst: An elongate, elevated block of crust forming a ridge or plateau, typically bounded by parallel, outward-dipping normal faults.

Hot spot: The surface expression of a mantle *plume.*

Hot spring: A spring whose waters are above both human body and soil temperature as a result of *plutonism* at depth.

Humus: The decayed part of the organic matter in a soil.

Hydration: A chemical reaction, usually in weathering, which adds water or OH^- to a mineral structure.

Hydrocarbon: An organic chemical compound made up of carbon and hydrogen atoms arranged in chains or rings.

Hydrologic cycle: The cyclical movement of water from the ocean to the atmosphere, through rain to the surface, through runoff and groundwater to streams, and back to the sea.

Hydrology: The science of that part of the *hydrologic cycle* between rain and return to the sea; the study of water on and within the land.

Hydrothermal activity: Any process involving high-temperature groundwater, especially the alteration and emplacement of minerals and the formation of *hot springs* and *geysers.*

Hydrothermal vein: A cluster of minerals precipitated by hydrothermal activity in a rock cavity.

Hypocenter: The point below the *epicenter* at which an earthquake actually begins; the focus.

Hypsometric diagram: A graph that shows in any way the relative amounts of the Earth's surface at different elevations with regard to sea level.

Igneous rock: A rock formed by congealing rapidly or slowly from a molten state.

Ignimbrite: An igneous rock formed by the *lithification* of *volcanic ash* and *volcanic breccia.*

Inclination: The angle between a line in the Earth's magnetic field and the horizontal plane; also a synonym for *dip.*

Index mineral: A mineral which forms or is stable over a restricted range of pressures and temperatures; useful in determining the conditions under which a rock has been metamorphosed.

Index of refraction: The ratio of the speed of light in a vacuum to the speed in a material; this ratio determines the amount that light is refracted as it passes into a crystal.

Infiltration: The movement of groundwater or hydrothermal water into rock or soil through joints and pores.

Interfacial angle: The angle between two faces of a crystal. The Law of Constancy of Interfacial Angles states that for any particular pair of crystal faces of a given mineral, this angle is constant, for it arises from the characteristic crystal symmetry of the mineral.

Interior drainage: A system of streams that converge in a closed basin and evaporate without reaching the sea.

Intermontane basin: A basin between mountain ranges, often formed over a graben.

Intrusion: An igneous rock body that has forced its way in a molten state into surrounding *country rock.*

Intrusive rock: Igneous rock that is interpreted as a former intrusion from its *cross-cutting* contacts, chilled margins, or other *field relations.*

Ion: An atom or group of atoms that has gained or lost electrons and so has a net electric charge.

Ionic bond: A bond formed between atoms by electrostatic attraction between oppositely charged ions.

Iron catastrophe: An event inferred to have taken place early in the history of the Earth, when the Earth had heated up sufficiently to cause iron to melt. The dense drops of molten iron would have coalesced and fallen in to the center of the Earth to form the *core;* this process would have converted a great deal of gravitational potential energy to more heat, and widespread melting in the Earth would have resulted.

Iron formation: A sedimentary rock containing much iron, usually more than 15 percent, as sulfide, oxide, hydroxide, or carbonate; a low-grade ore of iron.

Island arc: A linear or arcuate chain of volcanic islands formed at a convergent plate boundary. The island arc is formed in the overriding plate from rising melt derived from the subducted plate and from the asthenosphere above that plate.

Isochron: A line connecting points of equal age.

Isograd: A line or curved surface connecting rocks that have undergone an equivalent degree of metamorphism.

Isostasy: The mechanism whereby areas of the crust rise or subside until the mass of their topography is buoyantly supported or compensated by the thickness of crust below, which "floats" on the denser mantle. The theory is that continents and mountains are supported by low-density crustal "roots."

Isotope: One of several forms of one element, all having the same number of protons in the nucleus, but differing in their number of neutrons and thus atomic weight.

Isotope geology: The study of the relative abundances of isotopes in rocks to determine their ages (see *geochronology*) or conditions of formation.

Isotropic substance: One in which the magnitude of a physical property, such as transmission velocity of light, is independent of crystallographic direction.

Joint: A large and relatively planar fracture in a rock across which there is no relative displacement of the two sides.

Juvenile gas: Gases that come to the surface for the first time from the deep interior.

Kame: A ridge-like or hilly local glacial deposit of coarse alluvium formed as a delta at the glacier front by meltwater streams.

Karst topography: An irregular topography characterized by *sinkholes,* caverns, and lack of surface streams in humid regions because an underlying carbonate formation has been riddled with underground drainage channels that capture the surface streams.

Kerogen: A mixture of organic substances found in many fine-grained sedimentary rocks and a major constituent of oil shale.

Kettle: A small hollow or depression formed in glacial deposits when *outwash* was deposited around a residual block of ice that later melted.

Kilobar: A unit of pressure equal to 1000 *bars.*

Kimberlite: A *peridotite* containing garnet and olivine and found in volcanic pipes, through which it may come from the upper mantle.

Laccolith: A *sill*-like igneous intrusion that forces apart two strata and forms a round, lens-shaped body many times wider than it is thick.

Lahar: A mudflow of unconsolidated *volcanic ash, dust, breccia,* and *boulders* mixed with rain or the water of a lake displaced by a lava flow.

Laminar flow: A flow regime in which particle paths are straight or gently curved and parallel.

Landslide: The rapid downslope movement of soil and rock material, often lubricated by groundwater, over a basal shear zone; also the tongue of stationary material deposited by such an event.

Lapilli: Fragments of volcanic rock formed when magma is ejected into the air by expanding gases. The size of the fragments ranges from sand- to cobble-size.

Lateral moraine: A moraine formed along the side of a valley glacier and composed of rock scraped off or fallen from the valley sides.

Laterite: A distinctive kind of soil formed in tropical regions, where silica is rapidly weathered and leached from the soil. The resulting laterite soil is unusually rich in alumina and iron oxides.

Laurasia: Hypothetical supercontinent comprising approximately the present continents of the northern hemisphere.

Lava: Magma or molten rock that has reached the surface.

Lava tube: A sinuous, hollow tunnel formed when the outside of a lava flow cools and solidifies and the molten material passing through it is drained away.

Leaching: The removal of elements from a soil by dissolution in water moving downward in the ground.

Left-lateral fault: A *strike-slip fault* on which the displacement of the far block is to the left when viewed from either side.

Levee: A low ridge along a stream bank, formed by deposits left when floodwater decelerates on leaving the channel; also an artificial barrier to floods built in the same form.

Lignite: A very soft coal-like material formed by the burial of peat.

Limb (fold): The relatively planar part of a fold or of two adjacent folds (for example, the steeply dipping part of a stratum between an anticline and syncline).

Limestone: A sedimentary rock composed principally of calcium carbonate ($CaCO_3$), usually as the mineral calcite.

Lineation: Any linear arrangement of features found in a rock.

Lithic arenite: A sediment composed of sand-sized particles, many of which are rock fragments rather than mineral grains.

Lithification: The processes that convert a sediment into a sedimentary rock.

Lithology: The systematic description of rocks, in terms of mineral composition and texture.

Lithosphere: The outer, rigid shell of the Earth, situated above the *asthenosphere* and containing the *crust*, continents, and *plates*.

Lode: An unusually large vein or set of veins containing ore minerals.

Loess: An unstratified, wind-deposited, dusty sediment rich in clay minerals.

Longitudinal dune: A long dune parallel to the direction of the prevailing wind.

Longitudinal profile: A cross section of a stream from its mouth to its head, showing elevation versus distance to the mouth.

Longshore current: A current that moves parallel to a shore and is formed from the momentum of breaking waves that approach the shore obliquely.

Longshore drift: The movement of sediment along a beach by *swash* and *backwash* of waves that approach the shore obliquely.

Lopolith: A large *laccolith* that is bowl-shaped and depressed in the center, possibly by subsidence of an emptied magma chamber beneath the intrusion.

Lowland: Land of general low relief at the lower levels of regional elevation.

Low-velocity zone: A region in the Earth, especially a planar layer, that has lower seismic-wave velocities than the region immediately above it.

Lunar breccia: The lithified equivalent of the lunar *regolith*.

Luster: The general quality of the shine of a mineral surface, described by such subjective terms as dull, glassy, metallic.

M discontinuity: See *Mohorovičić discontinuity*.

Mafic mineral: A dark-colored mineral rich in iron and magnesium, especially a pyroxene, amphibole, or olivine.

Magma: Molten rock material that forms igneous rocks upon cooling. Magma that reaches the surface is referred to as lava.

Magma chamber: A magma-filled cavity within the lithosphere.

Magmatic water: Water that is dissolved in a magma or that is derived from such water.

Magnetic anomaly: The value of the local magnetic field remaining after the subtraction of the dipole portion of the Earth's field.

Magnetic coupling: The transfer of momentum between celestial bodies, especially dust and gas clouds, through magnetic forces.

Magnetic epoch: A geologically long period during which the Earth's magnetic field was of predominantly one polarity; the epochs immediately before and after a given epoch would by definition be characterized by a field of opposite polarity.

Magnetic events: Geologically short periods within magnetic epochs during which the field had a reversed polarity.

Magnetic north pole: (1) The point where the Earth's surface intersects the axis of the dipole that best approximates the Earth's field. (2) The point where the Earth's magnetic field dips vertically downward.

Magnetic reversal: A change of the Earth's magnetic field to the opposite polarity.

Magnetic stratigraphy: The study and correlation of polarity epochs and events in the history of the Earth's magnetic field as contained in magnetic rocks.

Magnetometer: An instrument for measuring either one orthogonal component or the entire intensity of the Earth's magnetic field at various points.

Magnitude: A measure of earthquake size, determined by taking the common logarithm (base 10) of the largest ground motion observed during the arrival of a *P*-wave or seismic surface wave and applying a standard correction for distance to the epicenter.

Manganese nodule: A small, rounded concretion found on the deep ocean floor that may contain as much as 20 percent manganese and smaller amounts of iron, copper, and nickel oxides and hydroxides.

Mantle: The main bulk of the Earth, between the crust and core, ranging from depths of about 40 to 2900 kilometers. It is composed of dense mafic silicates and divided into concentric layers by phase changes that are caused by the increase in pressure with depth.

Marble: The metamorphosed equivalent of *limestone* or other *carbonate rock*.

Mare: A dark, low-lying lunar plain, filled to an undetermined depth with mafic volcanic rocks. Plural: maria.

Mascon: A *concentration of mass* below the lunar surface; detected as a positive *gravity anomaly*, cause unknown.

Massive rock: A rock that is little or not at all broken by joints, cracks, foliation, or bedding, tending to present a homogeneous appearance.

Mass movement: A downhill movement of soil or fractured rock under the force of gravity.

Mass spectrometer: An instrument for separating ions of different mass but equal charge (mainly isotopes in geology) and measuring their relative quantities.

Matrix: Relatively fine-grained material in which coarser fragments or crystals are embedded; also called groundmass.

Maturity: A stage in the *geomorphic cycle* in which maximum relief and well-developed drainage are both present.

Meander: Broad, semicircular curves in a stream that develop as the stream erodes the outer bank of a curve and deposits sediment against the inner bank.

Mechanical weathering: The set of all physical processes by which an *outcrop* is broken up into small particles.

Medial moraine: A long strip of rock debris carried on or within a glacier resulting from the convergence of lateral moraines where two glaciers join.

Medical geology: The application of geological science to problems of health, especially those relating to mineral sources of toxic or nutritious elements and natural dispersal of toxic pollutants.

Mélange: A formation consisting of a heterogenous mixture of rock materials on a mappable scale. Fragments of diverse composition, size, and texture have been mixed and consolidated by tremendous deformational pressure.

Mesa: A flat-topped, steep-sided upland topped by a resistant formation; larger than a butte.

Mesosphere: The lower *mantle*.

Metamorphic grade: The relative intensity of metamorphism; that is, low-grade metamorphism implies low pressures and temperatures, and so on.

Metamorphic rock: A rock whose original mineralogy, texture, or composition has been changed due to the effects of pressure, temperature, or the gain or loss of chemical components.

Metamorphism: The changes of mineralogy and texture imposed on a rock by pressure and temperature in the Earth's interior.

Metastable: Describes a system that appears to be at *equilibrium*, in that no changes are observed to be taking place in it, but which we know is not in its most stable configuration for the given conditions. Metastable states may be preserved when the reactions required to bring the system into its stable state take place too slowly to be noticed on the time scale of our observations.

Metazoan: Multicellular life forms that first evolved in late Precambrian time.

Meteoric water: Rainwater, snow, hail, and sleet.

Meteorite: A stony or metallic object from interplanetary space that penetrates the atmosphere to impact on the surface.

Mica: General term for a group of hydrous aluminosilicate minerals with a sheet-like crystal structure, common in igneous and metamorphic rocks.

Micrometeorite: A meteorite less than 1 millimeter in diameter.

Microseism: A weak vibration of the ground that can be detected by seismographs and which is caused by waves, wind, or human activity, but not by an earthquake.

Mid-ocean ridge: A major elevated linear feature of the sea floor, consisting of many small, slightly offset segments, with a total length of 200 to 20,000 kilometers. Characteristic type of plate boundary occurring in a *divergence zone;* a site where two *plates* are being pulled apart and new oceanic *lithosphere* is being created.

Migmatite: A rock with both igneous and metamorphic characteristics that shows large crystals and laminar flow structures. Probably formed metamorphically in the presence of water and without melting.

Mineral: A naturally occurring, solid, inorganic element or compound, with a definite composition or range of compositions, usually possessing a regular internal crystalline structure.

Mineralogy: The study of mineral composition, structure, appearance, stability, occurrence, and associations.

Miogeosyncline: A *geosyncline* that is situated near a *craton* and receives chemical and well-sorted clastic sediments from the continent.

Moho: See *Mohorovičić discontinuity.*

Mohorovičić discontinuity: The boundary between *crust* and *mantle,* marked by a rapid increase in seismic wave velocity to more than 8 kilometers per second. Depth: 5 to 45 kilometers. Abbreviated "Moho" or "M-discontinuity."

Mohs scale of hardness: An empirical, ascending scale of mineral hardness with talc as 1, gypsum 2, calcite 3, fluorite 4, apatite 5, orthoclase 6, quartz 7, topaz 8, corundum 9, and diamond 10.

Monadnock: An isolated *hill* or *mountain* rising above a peneplain.

Monocline: The S-shaped fold connecting two horizontal parts of the same stratum at different elevations. Its central limb is usually not overturned.

Moraine: A glacial deposit of *till* left at the margin of an ice sheet. (See specifically by name, *Ground moraine, Longitudinal moraine, Medial moraine,* and *Terminal moraine.*

Mountain: A steep-sided topographic elevation larger than a *hill;* also, a single prominence forming part of a ridge or mountain range.

Mudflow: A mass movement of material finer than sand, lubricated with large amounts of water.

Mudstone: The lithified equivalent of mud, a fine-grained sedimentary rock similar to shale but more massive.

M.y.: Abbreviation for "million years."

Mylonite: A very fine lithified fault breccia commonly found in major thrust faults and produced by shearing and rolling during fault movement.

Native metal: A natural deposit of a metallic element in pure metallic form, not combined with other elements.

Neap tide: A tide cycle of unusually small amplitude, which occurs twice monthly when the lunar and solar tides are opposed—that is, when the gravitational pull of the Sun is at right angles to that of the Moon.

Nebula: An immense, diffuse body of interstellar gas and dust that has not condensed into a star.

Nebular hypothesis: A theory of the formation of the planets that states that a rotating nebula contracted and was then torn into fragments by centrifugal forces, with planets condensing from the fragments.

Neutron: An electrically neutral elementary particle in the atomic nucleus having the mass of one proton.

Neutron-activation analysis: A method of identifying isotopes of an element by bombarding them with neutrons and observing the characteristic radioactive decay products emitted.

Normal fault: A *dip-slip fault* in which the block above the fault has moved downward relative to the block below.

Nuclear geology: See *Isotope geology.*

Nuée ardente: A "glowing cloud" of hot volcanic ash, dust, and gas that moves rapidly downhill as a density current in the atmosphere.

Obduction: A process occurring during plate collision, whereby a piece of the subducted plate is broken off and pushed up onto the overriding plate; this mechanism probably explains why we find blocks of *ophiolite* on the continents.

Oblique-slip fault: A fault that combines some *strike-slip* motion with some *dip-slip* motion.

Obsidian: Dark volcanic glass of *felsic* composition.

Octahedral coordination: The packing of six ions around an ion of opposite charge to form an octahedron.

Oil field: An underground accumulation of oil and gas concentrated beneath an impermeable trap, preventing its escape upward.

Oil shale: A dark-colored shale containing organic material that can be crushed and heated to liberate gaseous hydrocarbons.

Oil trap: See *Trap.*

Old age: A stage in the *geomorphic cycle,* characterized by formation of a *peneplain* near sea level.

Oolite: A spherical *carbonate* particle precipitated from warm ocean water on a *carbonate platform;* also, a rock composed of such particles.

Ophiolite suite: An assemblage of *mafic* and *ultramafic* igneous rocks with deep-sea sediments supposedly associated with *divergence zones* and the sea-floor environment.

Optical mineralogy: The identification and study of minerals on the basis of their optical properties, as observed with a *petrographic microscope.*

Orbit: The elliptical or hyperbolic path traced by a planet or meteorite or satellite in the presence of a more massive body.

Ore: A natural deposit in which a valuable metallic element occurs in high enough concentration to make mining economically feasible.

Ore mineral: The mineral of an ore that contains the useful element.

Organic sediment: Carbon-rich deposits, such as coal, gas, and oil, formed by the decay of once-living material after burial.

Original Horizontality, Principle of: The proposition of Steno, that all sedimentary bedding is horizontal at the time of deposition.

Orogenic belt: A linear region, often a former *geosyncline,* that has been subjected to folding, and other deformation in a mountain-building episode.

Orogeny: The tectonic process in which large areas are folded, thrust-faulted, metamorphosed, and subjected to plutonism. The cycle ends with uplift and the formation of mountains.

Oscillation ripple: A ripple with a symmetrical cross section and a sharp peak formed by waves.

Outcrop: A segment of bedrock exposed to the atmosphere.

Outgassing: The release of *juvenile gases* to the atmosphere and oceans by volcanism.

Outwash: A glaciofluvial sediment that is deposited by melt-water streams emanating from a glacier.

Overturned fold: A fold in which a limb has tilted past vertical so that the older strata are uppermost.

Oxbow lake: A long, broad, crescent-shaped lake formed when a stream abandons a *meander* and takes a new course.

Oxidation: A chemical reaction in which electrons are lost from an atom and its charge becomes more positive.

Oxidized element: An element occurring in the more positively charged of two common ionic forms (for example, the Fe^{+3} form of iron, as opposed to Fe^{+2}).

Pahoehoe: A *basaltic* lava flow with a glassy, smooth, and undulating, or ropy, surface.

Paleoclimate: The average state or typical conditions of climate during some past geologic period.

Paleocurrent map: A map of depositional currents that have been inferred from *cross-bedding, ripples,* or other sedimentary structures.

Paleogeographic map: A map showing the surface landforms and coastline of an area at some time in the geologic past.

Paleomagnetism: The science of the reconstruction of the Earth's ancient magnetic field and the positions of the continents from the evidence of *remanent magnetization* in ancient rocks.

Paleontology: The science of fossils, of ancient life-forms, and their evolution.

Paleowind: A prevailing wind direction in an area, inferred from dune structure or the distribution of volcanic ash for one particular time in geologic history.

Pangaea: According to some theories, a great protocontinent from which all present continents have broken off by the mechanism of *sea-floor spreading* and *continental drift.*

Panthalassa: A hypothetical primaeval ocean covering two-thirds of the world except for the continent of Pangaea.

Paraffin: Hydrocarbons that contain chains of carbon and hydrogen atoms with the general formula C_nH_{2n+2}.

Parent element: An element that is transformed by *radioactive decay* to a different (daughter) element.

Peat: A marsh or swamp deposit of water-soaked plant remains containing more than 50 percent carbon.

Pedalfer: A common soil type in humid regions, characterized by an abundance of iron oxides and clay minerals deposited in the B-horizon by leaching.

Pediment: A planar, sloping rock surface forming a ramp up to the front of a mountain range in an arid region. It may be covered locally by thin *alluvium.*

Pedocal: A common soil type of arid regions, characterized by accumulation of calcium carbonate in the A-horizon.

Pegmatite: An igneous rock with extremely large grains, more than a centimeter in diameter. It may be of any composition but most frequently is granitic.

Pelagic sediment: Deep-sea sediments composed of fine-grained detritus that slowly settles from surface waters. Common constituents are clay, *radiolarian ooze,* and *foraminiferal ooze.*

Peléan eruption: A volcanic eruption accompanied by great explosions and emanations of hot gas and *nuées ardentes.* Named for Mont Pelée, Martinique.

Peneplain: A hypothetical extensive area of low elevation and relief reduced to near sea level by a long period of erosion and representing the end product of the ideal *geomorphic cycle.*

Perched groundwater: An isolated body of groundwater that is perched above and separated from the main water table by an aquiclude.

Peridotite: A coarse-grained mafic igneous rock composed of olivine with small amounts of pyroxene and amphibole.

Period (geologic): The most commonly used unit of geologic time, representing one subdivision of an *era.*

Period (wave): The time interval between the arrival of successive crests in a homogeneous wave train; the period is the inverse of the frequency of a cyclic event.

Permafrost: A permanently frozen aggregate of ice and soil occurring in very cold regions.

Permeability: The ability of a formation to transmit groundwater or other fluids through pores and cracks.

Petrographic microscope: An optical microscope designed for examining thin sections of rocks and minerals using polarized light.

Petrography: The study of rocks using the *petrographic microscope.*

Petroleum resources: The total quantity of natural oil in the Earth's crust that it may be possible to extract.

Petrology: The study of the composition, structure, and origin of rocks.

Phaneritic texture: A rock texture in which individual crystals are visible to the unaided eye.

Phase change: (1) The transformation of an element or compound from solid to liquid, gaseous to solid, etc. (2) The transformation of a solid mineral to a different solid form of different structure and density.

Phenocryst: A large crystal surrounded by a finer *matrix* in a *porphyry.*

Phosphate sediment: A sediment composed largely of calcium phosphate, usually as a variety of the mineral apatite and largely in the form of concretions and nodules.

Photogeology: The study of geologic features as exposed in aerial photographs of Earth or other planets.

Photolysis: The chemical breakdown of water into hydrogen and oxygen in the upper atmosphere by solar radiation.

Photosynthesis: The conversion of water, carbon dioxide, and the energy of sunlight into oxygen and organic compounds such as sugars by plants containing chlorophyll.

Phreatic eruption: A volcanic eruption of mud and debris caused by the expansion of steam formed when magma comes in contact with confined groundwater.

Phreatic zone: The zone of soil and rock in which pores are completely filled with groundwater. Also called the saturated zone.

Physical sedimentation: The deposition of *clastic* particles derived from erosion.

Pillow lava: A type of lava flow formed underwater, in which many small pillow-shaped tongues break through the chilled surface and quickly solidify, leading to a rock formation resembling a pile of sandbags.

Piracy (stream): The headward growth of one stream until it intersects the channel of another, whereupon all the water is diverted from the latter stream below that point.

Placer: A *detrital* sedimentary deposit of a valuable mineral or native metal in unusually high concentration, usually segregated because of its greater density.

Plain: An area of low relief, without major hills, valleys, or ridges; not necessarily at a low elevation.

Plane of symmetry: An imaginary plane passing through an object in such an orientation that each feature of the object on one side of the plane has a mirror image on the other side.

Planetary evolution: The process by which a differentiated planet is formed.

Planetesimal: A body of rock in space, smaller than a planet and attracted by gravity to other planetesimals in the formation of a planet.

Planetology: The science of the distribution, composition, and origin of matter in the planets of the solar system.

Plastic deformation: Deformation that proceeds to large strains at constant stress without fracturing.

Plate: One of the dozen or more segments of the *lithosphere* that are internally rigid and move independently over the interior, meeting in *convergence zones* and separating at *divergence zones.*

Plateau: An extensive upland region at high elevation with respect to its surroundings.

Plate tectonics: The theory and study of plate formation, movement, interaction, and destruction; the attempt to explain seismicity, volcanism, mountain-building, and paleomagnetic evidence in terms of plate motions.

Playa: The flat floor of a closed basin in an arid region. It may be occupied by an intermittent lake.

Plume: Hypothetical rising jet of hot, partially molten mantle material, supposed to be responsible for intraplate volcanism.

Plunging fold: A fold whose axis is not horizontal but dips. Thus progressively younger strata are found at the center of the fold as one travels along the direction of plunge, and the geologic map pattern is one of nested V-shaped outcrops of formations.

Pluton: A large igneous intrusion, formed at depth in the crust.

Plutonic: Pertaining to igneous activity at depth.

Plutonism: (1) The formation and worldwide distribution of plutons. (2) The eighteenth- and nineteenth-century theory that the Earth was at one time entirely molten.

Point bar: A deposit of sediment on the inner bank of a *meander* that forms because the stream velocity is lower against the inner bank.

Polarity epoch: See *Magnetic epoch.*

Polar wandering: An interpretation given to the observation that the position of the magnetic north pole, as inferred from the thermoremanent magnetization of rocks, varies with time as a result of plate movements.

Pole of spreading: An imaginary point on the Earth's surface that represents the emergence of an imaginary axis passing through the Earth's center and about which one plate moves relative to another; thus, for each pair of plates, there is a unique pole.

Polymorph: One of two or more alternative possible structures for a single chemical compound (for example, the minerals calcite and aragonite are polymorphs of calcium carbonate).

Pool: The deep part of an undulating stream bed.

Porosity: The percentage of the total volume of a rock that is pore space (not occupied by mineral grains).

Porphyroblast: A large crystal in a finer-grained *matrix* in a metamorphic rock; similar to a *phenocryst* in an igneous rock.

Porphyry: An igneous rock containing abundant *phenocrysts.*

Porphyry copper deposit: A *porphyry* that contains several percent of copper sulfides in veins and cracks in the rock and is of economic value as a source of copper.

Potable water: Water that is agreeable to the taste and not dangerous to the health.

Pothole: A hemispherical hole in the bedrock of a stream bed, formed by abrasion of small pebbles and cobbles in a strong current.

Ppm: Abbreviation for "parts per million."

Preferred orientation: Any deviation from randomness in the distribution of the crystallographic or grain shape axes of minerals in a rock; produced by flow in igneous rocks, directional stress during recrystallization of a metamorphic rock, or depositional currents during sedimentation.

Prograde metamorphism: Metamorphic reactions which occur as a result of increasing pressure and temperature.

Proton: An elementary particle found in the atomic nucleus with a positive charge of 1.602×10^{-19} coulomb and a mass of 1836 electrons; one H^+ ion.

Proto-sun: A large cloud of dust and gas gradually coalescing into a star under the force of gravity.

Protozoan: Simple, unicellular life forms that first evolved during the Precambrian.

Proven reserves: Deposits of fossil fuels whose location and extent are known, as opposed to potential but unproved ("discovered") deposits.

Pumice: A form of volcanic glass, usually of silicic composition, so filled with *vesicles* that it resembles a sponge and is very light.

P-wave: The primary or fastest wave traveling away from a seismic event through the solid rock, and consisting of a train of compressions and dilations of the material.

Pyroclastic rock: A rock formed by the accumulation of fragments of volcanic rock scattered by volcanic explosions.

Pyroclastic texture: The unsorted, angular texture of the fragments in a *pyroclastic rock.*

Pyroxene granulite: A coarse-grained regional-metamorphic rock containing pyroxene; formed at high temperatures and pressures deep in the crust.

Quartz arenite: A *sandstone* containing very little except pure quartz grains and cementing material.

Quartzite: (1) A very hard, clean, white metamorphic rock formed from a *quartz arenite* sandstone. (2) A quartz arenite containing so much cement that it resembles (1).

Quartzose sandstone: (1) A *quartz arenite.* (2) A clean quartz sandstone, less pure than a quartz arenite, that may contain a moderate amount of other *detrital* minerals and/or calcite cement.

Radial drainage: A system of streams running in a radial pattern away from the center of a circular elevation, such as a volcano or dome.

Radiative transfer: One mechanism for the movement of heat, in which it takes the form of long-wavelength infrared radiation.

Radioactive decay: The spontaneous breakdown of certain kinds of atomic nuclei into one or more nuclei of different elements, involving the release of energy and subatomic particles.

Radiolarian: A class of one-celled marine animals with siliceous skeletons that have existed in the ocean throughout the Phanerozoic Eon.

Radiolarian ooze: A siliceous deep-sea sediment composed largely of the skeletons of *radiolaria.*

Radiolarite: The lithified sedimentary rock formed from radiolarian ooze.

Radiometric dating: The method of obtaining ages of geological materials by measuring the relative abundances of radioactive parent and daughter isotopes in them.

Radius ratio: The ratio of the radius of an *anion* to the radius of a *cation,* which ratio determines the *coordination number.*

Ray: A linear landform of the lunar surface emanating from a large crater and extending as much as 100 kilometers outward, probably consisting of fine ejecta thrown out by the impact of a meteorite.

Reaction series: A series of chemical reactions occurring in a cooling magma by which a mineral formed at high temperature becomes unstable in the melt and reacts to form another mineral.

Recharge: In hydrology, the replenishment of groundwater by infiltration of *meteoric water* through the soil.

Recrystallization: The growth of new mineral grains in a rock at the expense of old grains, which supply the material.

Rectangular drainage: A system of streams in which each straight segment of each stream takes one of two characteristic perpendicular directions. The streams are usually following perpendicular sets of joints.

Recumbent fold: An *overturned* fold with both limbs nearly horizontal.

Reduced element: Of elements that have two different ions of different charge, the one with the less positive (more negative) charge is said to be reduced (for example, Fe^{+2} as opposed to Fe^{+3}).

Refraction (wave): The departure of a wave from its original direction of travel at the interface with a material of different index of refraction (light) or seismic wave velocity. (See also *Seismic refraction.*)

Regional metamorphism: Metamorphism occurring over a wide area and caused by deep burial or strong tectonic forces of the Earth.

Regolith: Any solid material lying on top of bedrock. Includes soil, alluvium, and rock fragments weathered from the bedrock.

Regression: A drop in sea level that causes an area of the Earth to be uncovered by sea water, ending marine deposition.

Relative humidity: The amount of water vapor in the air, expressed as a percentage of the total amount of water vapor that the air could hold at that temperature if saturated.

Relief: The maximum regional difference in elevation.

Remanent magnetization: See *Thermoremanent magnetization, Depositional remanent magnetization.*

Remote sensing: The study of surface conditions and materials of the Earth or other bodies by means of photography, spectroscopy, or radar observations from airplanes or satellites.

Replacement deposit: A deposit of ore minerals by hydrothermal solutions that have first dissolved the original mineral to form a small cavity.

Reserves: See *Proven reserves.*

Residence time: The amount of a given element or compound in a given body (especially the sea or atmosphere) divided by the average removal rate, assuming the system is in a *steady state.*

Respiration: The chemical process by which animals and plants convert their food into energy, through oxidation of carbohydrates; the process consumes oxygen and produces carbon dioxide.

Retrograde metamorphism: A situation in which a rock that has been metamorphosed to a fairly high grade is remetamorphosed by a later thermal event of somewhat lower intensity, so that lower-grade metamorphic mineralogy is superimposed on higher-grade mineral assemblages.

Reverse fault: A *dip-slip* fault in which the upper block, above the fault plane, moves up and over the lower block, so that older strata are placed over younger ones.

Reversible process: One that can proceed in either of two opposite directions, depending on the balance of the forces controlling it.

Rhyolite: The fine-grained volcanic or extrusive equivalent of granite, light brown to gray and compact.

Richter magnitude scale: See *Magnitude.*

Ridge: See *Mid-ocean ridge.*

Riffle: A shallow stretch of an undulating stream bed.

Rift valley: A fault trough formed in a *divergence zone* or other area of tension.

Right-lateral fault: A *strike-slip fault* on which the displacement of the far block is to the right when viewed from either side.

Ring dike: A dike in the form of a segment of a cone or cylinder, having an arcuate outcrop.

Rip current: A current that flows strongly away from the sea shore through gaps in the surf zone at intervals along the shoreline.

Ripple: A very small dune of sand or silt whose long dimension is formed at right angles to the current.

River order: See *Stream order.*

Rock: A solid, cohesive aggregate of grains of one or more *minerals.*

Rock cycle: The geologic cycle, with emphasis on the rocks produced; sedimentary rocks are metamorphosed to metamorphic rocks, or melted to create igneous rocks, and all rocks may be uplifted and eroded to make sediments, which lithify to sedimentary rocks.

Rock flour: A glacial sediment of extremely fine (silt- and clay-size) ground rock formed by abrasion of rocks at the base of the glacier.

Rock glacier: A glacier-like mass of rock fragments or *talus* with interstitial ice that moves downhill under the force of gravity.

Rockslide: A landslide involving mainly large blocks of detached bedrock with little or no soil or sand.

Rounding: The degree to which the edges and corners of a particle become worn and rounded as a result of abrasion during transportation. Expressed as angular, subrounded, well-rounded, etc.

Runoff: The amount of rain water directly leaving an area in surface drainage, as opposed to the amount that seeps out as groundwater.

Rupture strength: The greatest *stress* that a material can sustain without fracturing at one atmosphere confining pressure.

Sabkha: A characteristic boundary between a desert and an ocean, at which crusts of *evaporites* form above the high-water line.

Saltation: The movement of sand or fine sediment by short jumps above the ground or stream bed under the influence of a current too weak to keep it permanently suspended.

Sandblasting: A physical weathering process in which rock is eroded by the impact of sand grains carried by the wind, frequently leading to *ventifact* formation of pebbles and cobbles.

Sandstone: A *detrital* sedimentary rock composed of grains from $\frac{1}{16}$ to 2 millimeters in diameter, dominated in most sandstones by quartz, feldspar, and rock fragments, bound together by a cement of silica, carbonate, or other minerals or a *matrix* of clay minerals.

Saturated zone: See *Phreatic zone.*

Schist: A metamorphic rock characterized by strong *foliation* or *schistosity.*

Schistosity: The parallel arrangement of sheety or prismatic minerals like micas and amphiboles resulting from nonhydrostatic stress in metamorphism.

Scoria: Congealed lava, usually of mafic composition, with a large number of *vesicles* formed by gases coming out of solution.

Sea-floor spreading: The mechanism by which new sea floor crust is created at ridges in *divergence zones* and adjacent *plates* are moved apart to make room. This process may continue at 0.5 to 10 centimeters/year through many geologic periods.

Seamount: An isolated tall mountain on the sea floor that may extend more than 1 kilometer from base to peak. (See also *Guyot.*)

Secular variation: Slow changes in the orientation of the Earth's magnetic field that appear to be long lasting and internal in origin as opposed to rapid fluctuations, which are external in origin.

Sedimentary environment: See *Environment of deposition.*

Sedimentary rock: A rock formed by the accumulation and cementation of mineral grains transported by wind, water, or ice to the site of deposition or chemically precipitated at the depositional site.

Sedimentary structure: Any structure of a sedimentary or weakly metamorphosed rock that was formed at the time of deposition; includes bedding, cross-bedding, graded bedding, ripples, scour marks, mudcracks.

Sedimentation: The process of deposition of mineral grains or precipitates in beds or other accumulations.

Seif dune: A *longitudinal dune* that shows the sculpturing effect of cross-winds not parallel to its axis.

Seismic discontinuity: A surface within the Earth across which *P-wave* or *S-wave* velocities change rapidly, usually by more than ± 0.2 kilometer/second.

Seismicity: The world-wide or local distribution of earthquakes in space and time; a general term for the number of earthquakes in a unit of time.

Seismic profile: The data collected from a set of seismographs arranged in a straight line with an artificial seismic source, especially the times of *P-wave* arrivals.

Seismic reflection: A mode of seismic prospecting in which the *seismic profile* is examined for waves that have reflected from near-horizontal strata below the surface.

Seismic refraction: A mode of seismic prospecting in which the *seismic profile* is examined for waves that have been refracted upward from seismic discontinuities below the profile. Greater depths may be reached than through *seismic reflection*.

Seismic shadow zone: Region on the far side of the Earth's surface from an earthquake, not reached by *P-waves* from that earthquake because they have been deflected at the surface of the core.

Seismic surface wave: A seismic wave that follows the earth's surface only, with a speed less than that of *S-waves*. There are Rayleigh waves (forward and vertical vibrations) and Love waves (transverse vibrations).

Seismic transition zone: A seismic discontinuity, found in all parts of the Earth, at which the velocity increases rapidly with depth; especially the one at 400 to 700 kilometers.

Seismic travel time: See *Travel time curve*.

Seismograph: An instrument for magnifying and recording the motions of the Earth's surface that are caused by seismic waves.

Seismology: The study of earthquakes, seismic waves, and their propagation through the Earth.

Self-exciting dynamo: A system involving a rotating electrical conductor that creates and sustains its own magnetic field.

Series: A set of rocks formed in one area during a geologic *epoch*.

Settling velocity: The rate at which a sedimentary particle of a given size falls through water or air.

Shale: A very fine-grained *detrital* sedimentary rock composed of silt and clay which tends to part along *bedding* planes.

Shard (volcanic): An angular fragment of volcanic glass.

Sheeting: See *Exfoliation*.

Sheetwash: A flow of rainwater that covers the entire ground surface with a thin film and is not concentrated into streams.

Shield: A large region of stable, ancient basement rocks within a continent.

Shield volcano: A large, broad *volcanic cone* with very gentle slopes built up by nonviscous basalt lavas.

Shooting flow: A very fast form of water flow with a high velocity induced by steep slopes in the flow bed, typically developed in rapids.

Silicate: Any of a vast class of minerals containing silicon and oxygen and constructed from the tetrahedral group $(SiO_4)^{-4}$. The bulk of the crust is composed of silicate minerals.

Silicic rock: An igneous rock containing more than two-thirds silicon-oxygen tetrahedra by weight, usually as quartz and feldspar (for example, *granite*).

Sill: A horizontal tabular intrusion with *concordant* contacts.

Sill (topographic): A small submarine ridge that nearly separates or restricts water flow between two adjacent bodies of water.

Sinkhole: A small, steep depression caused in *Karst topography* by the dissolution and collapse of subterranean caverns in *carbonate* formations.

Sinking current: A downward movement of sea or lake water that has become denser through cooling or increased salinity or that sinks because of an onshore wind piling up water against the shore.

Sinuosity: The length of the channel of a stream divided by the straight-line distance between its ends.

Slate: The metamorphic equivalent of *shale;* a hard, gray, red, green, or black fine-grained rock with *slaty cleavage*.

Slaty cleavage: A *foliation* consisting of the parallel arrangement of sheety metamorphic minerals (see *Schistosity*) at an angle to bedding planes, and related to deformational structures, along which the rock tends to part.

Slickensides: Parallel grooves, ramps, and scratches on one or both of the inside faces of a fault, showing the direction of slip.

Slip (fault): The motion of one face of a fault relative to the other.

Slip face: The steep downwind face of a dune on which sand is deposited in cross-beds at the angle of repose.

Slope wash: The motion of water and sediment down a slope by the mechanism of *sheet wash*.

Slump: A collapse structure in unlithified sediments, caused by gravity sliding or collapse under the weight of later sediments.

Snowfield: An area of permanent snow that is not moving or whose movement is not visible.

Soft coal: See *Bituminous coal*.

Soft water: Water that is free of calcium and magnesium *carbonates* and other dissolved materials of *hard water*.

Soil: The surface accumulation of sand, clay, and humus that compose the *regolith*, but excluding the larger fragments of unweathered rock.

Soil creep: The imperceptible downhill flow of soil under the force of gravity. It is a shear flow with velocity decreasing downward, and occurs even on gentle slopes.

Solar wind: The flow of ionized gas (plasma) from the Sun toward the Earth, which interacts with the Earth's magnetic field.

Solid-solution series: A series of minerals of identical structure that can contain a mixture of two elements over a range of ratios (for example, plagioclase feldspars).

Solidus: A curve on a pressure versus temperature graph representing the beginning of melting of a rock or mineral.

Solifluction: The soil creep of material saturated with water and/or ice; most common in polar regions.

Solubility: The mass of a substance that can be dissolved in a certain amount of solvent, if chemical *equilibrium* is attained.

Solute: The substance dissolved in a *solvent*.

Solvent: A medium, usually liquid, in which other substances can be dissolved.

Sorting: A measure of the homogeneity of the sizes of particles in a sediment or sedimentary rock.

Spatter cone: A conical deposit of cooled *lava* congealed around a volcanic vent that disgorges mostly gas with occasional globs of molten rock.

Specific gravity: The ratio of the *density* of a given substance to the density of water.

Spheroidal weathering: The formation of spherical residual inner cores by the weathering of boulders.

Spit: A long ridge of sand deposited by longshore current and drift where the coast takes an abrupt inward turn. It is attached to land at the upstream end.

Splay deposit: A small *delta* deposited on a *floodplain* when the stream breaches a *levee* during a flood.

Spring tide: A tide cycle of unusually large amplitude that occurs twice monthly when the lunar and solar tides are in phase (compare *Neap tide*).

Stage (stream): The elevation of the water level of a stream measured against some constant reference.

Stalactite: An icicle- or tooth-like deposit of calcite or aragonite hanging from the roof of a cave and deposited by evaporation and precipitation from solutions seeping through limestone.

Stalagmite: An inverted icicle-shaped deposit that builds up on a cave floor beneath a stalactite, and formed by the same process as a stalactite.

Steady-state: An adjective that implies that a system is in a stable dynamic state in which inputs balance outputs.

Steepness (wave): The ratio of the height of a wave to its wavelength.

Stock (volcanic): An intrusion with the characteristics of a *batholith* but less than 100 square kilometers in area.

Stoping: The process by which an intruding igneous mass makes room for itself in the *country rock*—by breaking rock fragments off the walls and "absorbing" them when they sink.

Strain: A quantity describing the exact deformation of each point in a body. Roughly, the change in a dimension or volume divided by the original dimension or volume.

Strain seismograph: An instrument that measures changes of *strain* in surface rocks to detect seismic waves.

Stratification: A structure of sedimentary rocks, which have recognizable parallel beds of considerable lateral extent.

Stratigraphic sequence: A set of beds deposited that reflects the geologic history of a region.

Stratigraphic time scale: See *Time scale.*

Stratigraphy: The science of the description, correlation, and classification of strata in sedimentary rocks, including the interpretation of the depositional environments of those strata.

Stratovolcano: A volcanic *cone* consisting of both *lava* and *pyroclastic* rocks.

Stratum: A single sedimentary rock unit with a distinct set of physical or mineralogical characteristics or fossils such that it may readily be distinguished from beds above and below. Plural: strata.

Streak: The fine deposit of mineral dust left on an abrasive surface when a mineral is scraped across it; especially the characteristic color of the dust.

Streak plate: A ceramic abrasive surface for streak tests.

Streaming flow: A tranquil flow slower than *shooting flow.*

Streamline: A curved line representing the successive positions of a particle in a flow as time passes.

Stream order: The hierarchical number of a stream segment in *dendritic drainage:* the smallest tributary streams have order one and at each junction of streams of equal order the order of the subsequent segment is one higher.

Stress: A quantity describing the forces acting on each part of a body in units of force per unit area.

Striation: See *Glacial striation.*

Strike: The angle between true North and the horizontal line contained in any planar feature (inclined bed, dike, fault plane, etc.); also the geographic direction of this horizontal line.

Strike-slip fault: A fault whose relative displacement is purely horizontal (see also *Right-* and *left-lateral fault*).

Stromatolite: A fossil form representing the growth habit of an algal mat: concentric spherules, stacked hemispheres, or flat sheets of calcium carbonate and trapped silt encountered in limestones.

Subduction zone: A dipping planar zone descending away from a *trench* and defined by high *seismicity*, interpreted as the shear zone between a sinking oceanic plate and an overriding plate (see also *Convergence zone*).

Sublimation: A phase change from the solid to the gaseous state, without passing through the liquid state.

Submarine canyon: An underwater canyon in the continental shelf.

Subsidence: A gentle epeirogenic movement where a broad area of the crust sinks without appreciable deformation.

Superposed stream: A stream that flows through resistant formations because its course was established at a higher level on uniform rocks before down-cutting began.

Superposition, Law of: The principle stated by Steno that, except in extremely deformed strata, a bed that overlies another bed is always the younger.

Supersaturation: The unstable state of a solution that contains more solute than its solubility allows.

Surf: The breaking or tumbling forward of water waves as they approach the shore.

Surface wave: See *Seismic surface wave.*

Surf zone: An offshore belt along which the waves collapse into breakers as they approach the shore.

Surge: See *Glacier surge.*

Suspended load: The fine sediment kept suspended in a stream because the *settling velocity* is lower than the upward velocity of eddies.

Swash: The landward rush of water from a breaking wave up the slope of the beach.

S-wave: The secondary seismic wave, traveling slower than the *P-wave*, and consisting of elastic vibrations transverse to the direction of travel. It cannot penetrate a liquid.

Swell: An oceanic water wave with a wavelength on the order of 30 meters or more and a height of perhaps 2 meters or less that may travel great distances from its source.

Symbiosis: The interaction of two mutually supporting species who do not compete with or prey upon each other.

Symmetrical fold: One whose limbs *dip* at the same angle.

Syncline: A large fold whose limbs are higher than its center; a fold with the youngest strata in the center (compare *Anticline*).

System (stratigraphy): A stratigraphic unit larger than a *series*, consisting of all the rocks deposited in one *period* of an era.

Table land: A large elevated region with a surface of relatively low relief. (See also *Plateau.*)

Talus: A deposit of large angular fragments of physically weathered bedrock, usually at the base of a cliff or steep slope.

Tar sand: A *sandstone* containing the densest asphaltic components of petroleum—the end product of evaporation of *volatile* components or of some thickening process.

Tectonics: The study of the movements and deformation of the crust on a large scale, including *epeirogeny, metamorphism,* folding, faulting, and *plate tectonics.*

Terminal moraine: A sinuous ridge of unsorted glacial *till* deposited by a glacier at the line of its farthest advance.

Terrestrial planet: A planet similar in size and composition to the Earth; especially Mars, Earth, Venus, and Mercury.

Terrestrial sediment: A deposit of sediment that accumulated above sea level in lakes, *alluvial fans, floodplains, moraines,* etc., regardless of its present elevation.

Tetrahedron: A geometric form of four equal triangular sides, or an arrangement of four atoms around a fifth at the corners of such a form, as in $(SiO_4)^{-4}$.

Tetrapod: A vertebrate animal with four legs.

Texture (rock): The rock characteristics of grain or crystal size, size variability, rounding or angularity, and preferred orientation.

Thalweg: A sinuous imaginary line following the deepest part of a stream.

Thermal conductivity: A measure of a rock's capacity for heat conduction.

Thermal expansion: The property of increasing in volume as a result of an increase in internal temperature.

Thermonuclear reaction: A reaction in which atomic nuclei fuse into new elements with a large release of heat; especially a reaction that is self-sustaining. Occasionally used to include fission reactions as well.

Thermoremanent magnetization: A permanent magnetization acquired by igneous rocks in the presence of the Earth's magnetic field as they cool through the *Curie point.*

Thrust fault: A *reverse fault* in which the *dip* of the fault plane is relatively shallow.

Tidal current: A horizontal displacement of ocean water under the gravitational influence of Sun and Moon, causing the water to pile up against the coast at high tide and move outward at low tide.

Tidal flat: A broad, flat region of muddy or sandy sediment, covered and uncovered in each tidal cycle.

Till: An unconsolidated sediment containing all sizes of fragments from clay to boulders deposited by glacial action, usually unbedded.

Tillite: The lithified equivalent of *till.*

Time scale: The division of geologic history into *eras, periods,* and *epochs* accomplished through *stratigraphy* and *paleontology.*

Topographic map: See *Contour map;* also a schematic drawing of prominent landforms indicated by conventionalized symbols, such as hachures or contours.

Topography: The shape of the Earth's surface, above and below sea level; the set of landforms in a region; the distribution of elevations.

Topset bed: A horizontal sedimentary bed formed at the top of a *delta* and overlying the *foreset beds.*

Trace element: An element that appears in minerals in a concentration of less than 1 percent (often less than 0.001 percent).

Tranquil flow: See *Streaming flow.*

Transform fault: A *strike-slip fault* connecting the ends of an offset in a *mid-ocean ridge.* Some pairs of plates slide past each other along transform faults.

Transgression: A rise in sea level relative to the land which causes areas to be submerged and marine deposition to begin in that region.

Transition elements: Elements of atomic number 21 to 30, 39 to 48, and 72 to 80, and actinide series elements.

Transition zone: See *Seismic transition zone.*

Transpiration: The removal of water from the ground into plants, ultimately to be evaporated into the atmosphere by them.

Transverse dune: A dune that has its axis transverse to the prevailing winds or to a current. The upwind or upcurrent side has a gentle slope, and the downwind side lies at the *angle of repose.*

Trap (oil): A sedimentary or tectonic structure that impedes the upward movement of oil and gas and allows it to collect beneath the barrier.

Travel-time curve: A curve on a graph of travel time versus distance for the arrival of seismic waves from distant events. Each type of seismic wave has its own curve.

Travertine: A terrestrial deposit of limestone formed in caves and around hot springs where cooling, carbonate-saturated groundwater is exposed to the air.

Trellis drainage: A system of streams in which tributaries tend to lie in parallel valleys formed in steeply dipping beds in folded belts.

Trench: A long and narrow deep trough in the sea floor; interpreted as marking the line along which a plate bends down into a *subduction zone.*

Triple junction: A point that is common to three plates and which must also be the meeting place of three boundary features, such as *divergence zones, convergence zones,* or *transform faults.*

Tsunami: A large destructive wave caused by sea-floor movements in an earthquake.

Tufa: See *Travertine.* Not related to *Tuff.*

Tuff: A consolidated rock composed of *pyroclastic* fragments and fine *ash.* If particles are melted slightly together from their own heat, it is a "welded tuff."

Turbidite: The sedimentary deposit of a *turbidity current,* typically showing *graded bedding* and sedimentary structures on the undersides of the sandstones.

Turbidity current: A mass of mixed water and sediment that flows downhill along the bottom of an ocean or lake because it is denser than the surrounding water. It may reach high speeds and erode rapidly (see also *Density current*).

Turbulent flow: A high-velocity flow in which streamlines are neither parallel nor straight but curled into small tight eddies (compare *Laminar flow*).

Ultramafic rock: An igneous rock consisting dominantly of *mafic* minerals, containing less than 10 percent feldspar. Includes *dunite, peridotite, amphibolite,* and pyroxenite.

Unconformity: A surface that separates two strata. It represents an interval of time in which deposition stopped, erosion removed some sediments and rock, and then deposition resumed. (See also *Angular unconformity.*)

Unconsolidated material: Nonlithified sediment that has no mineral cement or *matrix* binding its grains.

Uniformitarianism, Principle of: The concept that the processes that have shaped the Earth through geologic time are the same as those observable today.

Unit cell: The smallest contiguous group of atomic structural units in a mineral that can be repeated in three directions to form a crystal.

Unsaturated zone: See *Vadose zone.*

Uplift: A broad and gentle epeirogenic increase in the elevation of a region without a *eustatic change* in sea level.

Upwarped mountains: Mountains elevated by *uplift* of broad regions, without faulting.

Upwelling current: The upward movement of cold bottom water in the sea, which occurs when wind or currents displace the lighter surface water.

U-shaped valley: A deep valley with steep upper walls that grade into a flat floor, usually eroded by a glacier.

Vadose zone: The region in the ground between the surface and the *water table* in which pores are not filled with water. Also called the unsaturated zone.

Valence electron: An electron of the outermost shell of an atom; one of those most active in bonding.

Valley glacier: A glacier that is smaller than a *continental glacier* or an icecap, and which flows mainly along well-defined valleys, many with tributaries.

Van der Waals bond: A bond much weaker than the *ionic* or *covalent,* which bonds atoms by small electrostatic attraction.

Varve: A thin layer of sediment grading upward from coarse to fine and light to dark, found in a lake bed and representing one year's deposition of glacial *outwash.*

Vector: A mathematical element that has a direction and magnitude, but no fixed position. Examples are force and gravity.

Vein: A deposit of foreign minerals within a rock fracture or *joint.*

Ventifact: A rock that exhibits the effects of *sandblasting* or "snowblasting" on its surfaces, which become flat with sharp edges in between.

Vertical exaggeration: The ratio of the horizontal scale (for example, 100,000:1) to the vertical scale (for example, 500:1) in an illustration.

Vesicle: A cavity in an igneous rock that was formerly occupied by a bubble of escaping gas.

Viscosity: A measure of resistance to flow in a liquid.

Volatiles: Gaseous materials that are readily lost from a system if not confined; also, substances such as water and carbon dioxide, which are loosely bound into a mineral structure and can escape from a rock if the mineral breaks down during metamorphism.

Volcanic ash: A volcanic sediment of rock fragments, usually glass, less than 4 millimeters in diameter that is formed when escaping gases force out a fine spray of *magma.*

Volcanic ash fall: A deposit of volcanic ash resting where it was dropped by eruptions and winds.

Volcanic ash flow: A mixture of volcanic ash and gases that moves downhill as a *density current* in the atmosphere.

Volcanic block: A pyroclastic rock fragment ranging from about fist- to car-sized.

Volcanic bomb: A pyroclastic rock fragment that shows the effects of cooling in flight in its streamlined or "bread-crust" surface.

Volcanic breccia: A pyroclastic rock in which all fragments are more than 2 millimeters in diameter.

Volcanic cone: The deposit of lava and pyroclastic materials that has settled close to the volcano's central vent.

Volcanic dome: A rounded accumulation around a volcanic vent of congealed lava too viscous to flow away quickly; hence usually *rhyolite* lava.

Volcanic dust: See *Volcanic ash*.

Volcanic ejecta blanket: A collective term for all the *pyroclastic* rocks deposited around a volcano, especially by a volcanic explosion.

Volcanic emanations: Gases, especially steam, emitted from a vent or released from *lava*.

Volcanic pipe: The vertical chamber along which magma and gas ascend to the surface; also, a formation of igneous rock that cooled in a pipe and remains after the erosion of the volcano.

Volcano: Any opening through the crust that has allowed *magma* to reach the surface, including the deposits immediately surrounding this vent.

V-shaped valley: A valley whose walls have a more-or-less uniform slope from top to bottom, usually formed by stream erosion.

Wadi: A steep-sided valley containing an intermittent stream in an arid region.

Warping: In *tectonics,* refers to the gentle, regional bending of the crust, which occurs in epeirogenic movements.

Water mass: A mass of water that fills part of an ocean or lake and is distinguished by its uniform physical and chemical properties, such as temperature and salinity.

Water table: A gently-curved surface below the ground at which the *vadose zone* ends and the *phreatic zone* begins; the level to which a well would fill with water.

Wave-cut terrace: A level surface formed by wave erosion of coastal bedrock to the bottom of the turbulent *breaker* zone. May appear above sea level if uplifted.

Wavelength: The distance between two successive peaks, or between troughs, of a cyclic propagating disturbance.

Wave steepness: The maximum height or amplitude of a wave divided by its wavelength.

Weathering: The set of all processes that decay and break up bedrock, by a combination of physical fracturing or chemical decomposition.

Welded tuff: See *Tuff; Ignimbrite*.

Xenolith: A piece of *country rock* found engulfed in an intrusion.

X-ray diffraction: In mineralogy, the process of identifying mineral structures by exposing crystals to X-rays and studying the resulting diffraction pattern.

Youth (geomorphology): A stage in the *geomorphic* cycle in which a landscape has just been uplifted and is beginning to be dissected by canyons cut by young streams.

Zeolite: A class of silicates containing H_2O in cavities within the crystal structure. Formed by alteration at low temperature and pressure of other silicates, often volcanic glass.

Zoned crystal: A single crystal of one mineral that has a different chemical composition in its inner and outer parts. Formed from minerals belonging to a *solid-solution series,* and caused by the changing concentration of elements in a cooling magma that results from crystals settling out or by crystallization so rapid that the composition of the mineral cannot adjust fast enough so that all parts of the mineral achieve the *equilibrium* composition for each temperature.

Zone of accumulation (soil): See *B-horizon*.

Zone of aeration: See *Vadose zone*.

Index

Page numbers in **boldface** refer to a definition. Page numbers followed by an asterisk indicate an illustration. The Appendixes and Glossary are not covered by this Index.

The Plates of Earth's Lithosphere

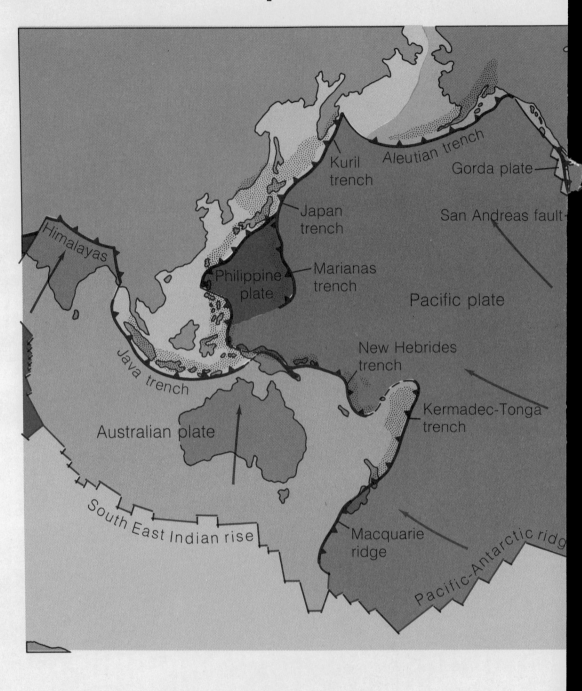

Kuril
trench

Aleutian trench

Gorda plate

San Andreas fault

Japan
trench

Marianas
trench

Philippine
plate

Pacific plate

Himalayas

New Hebrides
trench

Java trench

Kermadec-Tonga
trench

Australian plate

South East Indian rise

Macquarie
ridge

Pacific-Antarctic ridge

 Subduction zone

Transform

Ridge axis

 Uncertain plate boundary

Direction of plate motion

Areas of deep-focus earthquakes

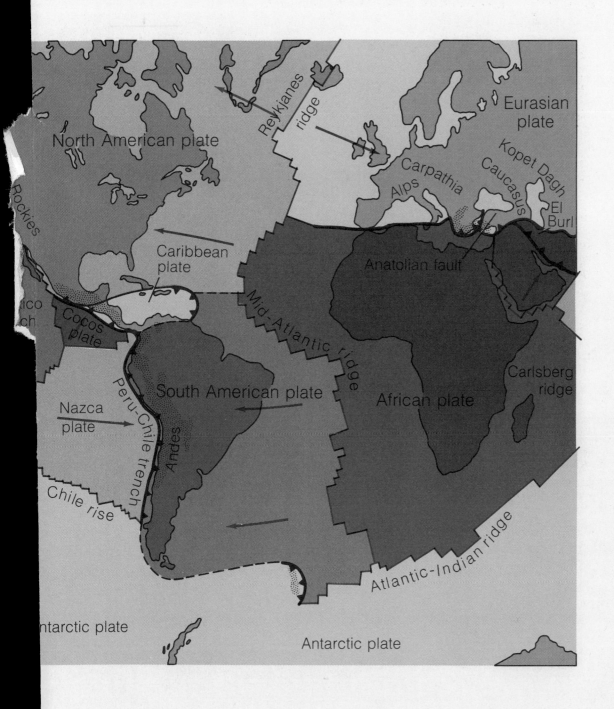

North American plate

Rockies

Reykjanes ridge

Eurasian plate

Kopet Dagh

Carpathia

Caucasus

Alps

El Burl

Anatolian fault

Caribbean plate

Mid-Atlantic ridge

Cocos plate

xico nch

Peru-Chile trench

South American plate

African plate

Carlsberg ridge

Nazca plate

Andes

Chile rise

Atlantic-Indian ridge

ntarctic plate

Antarctic plate